RESOURCES AND INDUSTRIES
OF THE UNITED STATES

RESOURCES
AND
INDUSTRIES
OF THE UNITED STATES

OLIN T. MOUZON
University of North Carolina

NEW YORK
APPLETON-CENTURY-CROFTS
Division of Meredith Publishing Company

Excerpts from INTERNATIONAL RESOURCES AND NATIONAL
POLICY by Olin T. Mouzon. Copyright © 1959 by Olin T. Mouzon.
Reprinted by permission of Harper & Row, Publishers.

To
K. B. M.

PREFACE

Resources and Industries of the United States is a study of a group of industries which constitute the energy base of the economy and a selected group of major metal industries which are required to harness and apply the energy.

Instead of an extensive survey of many industries, the purpose of this book is to give an intensive understanding of the resource base, nature, and structure of the industry, and its function in the national economy.

In addition, for each industry selected problems which require policy decisions are studied in depth. The experience of the author is that study of specific problems brings alive the factual knowledge of the industry and permits the student to share in the understanding of the major problem and policy issues involved. Further, as the selected problems and policies are always changing and new problems are developing, each student can be given the opportunity to supplement his textual material by current problem studies. To encourage and facilitate further study, selected references appear at the end of each chapter following the problems.

This book was written over a 2-year period at the mid-point of the 1960's. Many sources have been used. The basic books and monographs are cited in the selected readings. However, the writer is indebted to many other sources which have been absorbed as background material during his thirty years of work in the field of resources and industries. Every effort has been made to keep the data as current as possible under the limitations of the inevitable lags which occur in their collection and presentation. Sources of the data are cited by reference to the continuations in which they occur and following the tables as they are presented. This should facilitate updating the data when required.

Special thanks are due to many persons, associations, and government agencies who furnished special and detailed information and advice. In addition, the writer is most grateful to say that excerpts from *International*

Resources and National Policy by Olin T. Mouzon, copyright 1959 by Olin T. Mouzon, are reprinted by permission of Harper & Row, Publishers.

The dedication of the above book was OTM/kbm. This partnership grows stronger each year, but the dedication of *Resources and Industries of the United States* is to KBM since the writer is exclusively responsible for the mechanics of typing, as well as for the contents of the book.

O. T. M.

CONTENTS

RESOURCES AND INDUSTRIES
OF THE UNITED STATES

1

RESOURCES AND PRODUCTION

Our interest in United States resources and industries stems from the part they play in solving the economic problem of increasing production. By production is meant the creation of any good or service (utility-want satisfaction) for which people are willing to pay. Economics is the study of man's activities in using scarce resources in order to satisfy a wide variety of wants. A basic objective of any economic system is to organize its resources for the maximum production of goods and services and to build a bigger economic pie with larger slices for each person. Economics is thus concerned with the production, consumption, and distribution of goods and services.

THE IMPORTANCE OF PRODUCTION

The resources, processes, and techniques of production used by industry are of great significance, for they determine the total amount of goods that can be provided by a nation. A nation's production potential as measured by the total amount of goods and services produced is an important factor in determining its standing in the world economy and as a world power. In addition, the total amount of goods and services produced by a nation along with their distribution determines the people's standard of living.

The United States rose to the place of world leadership when it surpassed Great Britain in industrial might. Perhaps what Nikita Khrushchev had in mind when he told the United States, "We shall bury you," was that the U.S.S.R. intended to overtake the United States and to forge to the head of world leadership by building up its economic production potential.

The size of the total economic pie produced is called the *gross national product*, which is the total market value of goods and services pro-

1

duced by an economy during a specific period of time. This concept goes back to the definition of production. Production is what people will pay for, and what they pay is an economic evaluation of the worth of the products and services. Gross national product (GNP) includes the total economic product in a given time, usually one year. One way the GNP is estimated each year is by totalling all expenditures on *final* products sold to consumers or to business for final use as producer's goods. Another way to get a cross-check on GNP is to use the *value-added* method.[1] This method computes the value of total production by counting the value added to commodities in the process of production, and the value of services. The method of computation is to compare the cost of materials with the market price of the finished product. The difference is the value added by the producer. It represents the amount he must pay for wages, rent, and interest, and the profit he will receive on the product. Since he adds utility he is a producer. Thus the summation of the total value added to the products by the various procedures, plus the value of services rendered by others, will be equal to the total production of the economy. While the U.S. total GNP is not actually measured by the value-added method this cross-check does point up the contribution of individual industries to the GNP.

Building a bigger economic pie the economist calls *growth,* by which is meant an increase in the total GNP. Or the economist may mean growth in output per capita, that is, growth in the ratio: total output/total population. Although both concepts are important, the second gives a more direct measure of the economic standard of living of individuals in the nation. For if total output grows but population grows faster, the average individual's standard of living is falling, not rising.

Figure 1.1 gives the past and projected *real* GNP (that is, expressed in constant dollars) in the United States for the period 1900 through 1975. Over the past century our growth rate in real GNP has been about 3 percent per annum; in per capita output about 2 percent. Since World War II this growth rate has been accelerated. Since history provides the main basis for predicting the future, rates of growth for the decades ahead are estimated at 3 or 4 percent. Some economists believe that the

---

[1] In measuring GNP there must not be double-counting of intermediate products. A simple illustration will show the relationship between final products and values added and show the result of double-counting intermediate products. A farmer produces wheat at zero money costs and sells it to a miller for 6¢; the miller works the wheat into flour, which he sells to a baker for 10¢; the baker uses the flour to produce bread, which is sold for 16¢. The value of the *final* product, which is the sum of all the *values added* by the respective producers and is measured by the consumer's expenditure, is 16¢; also, 16¢ is the total of the incomes earned by the value-adders; the farmer receives income of 6¢, the miller receives $10 - 6¢ = 4¢$, the baker receives $16 - 10¢ = 6¢$. While expenditure on the final product is 16¢, expenditures in *all* transactions including the buying and selling of *intermediate* products in interfirm transactions, is $6 + 10 + 16 = 32¢$. This latter is the double-counting that must be eliminated in measuring GNP.

target should be 5 percent. But the size of the per capita growth rate will also be determined by the rate of population growth. Per capita output was greater than $3,000 a year in the United States in the early 1960's. This was about twice that of Great Britain and almost four times that of the U.S.S.R. The steady increase in our GNP has given rise to a bigger share of the GNP pie for each person, and a resultant higher standard of living for the United States than for any of the other major powers of the world.

Figure 1.1: Past and Projected Real Gross National Product, 1900–1975.

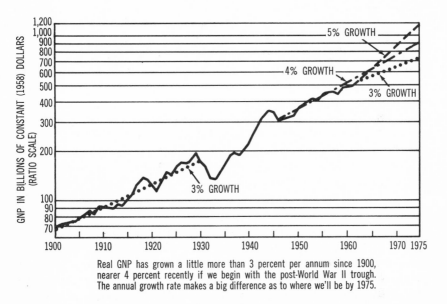

Real GNP has grown a little more than 3 percent per annum since 1900, nearer 4 percent recently if we begin with the post-World War II trough. The annual growth rate makes a big difference as to where we'll be by 1975.

SOURCE: George Leland Bach, *Economics: An Introduction to Analysis and Policy*, Fourth Edition, © 1963. Reprinted by permission of Prentice-Hall, Inc., Englewood Cliffs, New Jersey.

THE DETERMINANTS OF PRODUCTION AND GROWTH

The goods and services that satisfy wants are produced by what the economists refer to as *factors of production:* land (natural resources); labor (human resources); and capital (man-made resources, that is, producers' goods, which are machines and buildings used for the production of other goods). These resources as factors of production are the real foundations of economic progress and growth.

Natural Resources

Natural resources include all the non-man-made aspects of our environment, on the surface of the earth, in the ground, and in the air. In addition to all the natural materials, these resources include all the spatial or area aspects of our environment. Modern economists use this concept of natural resources to describe land as a factor of production, whereas earlier economists thought of land as soil. A simple classification of natural resources would include spatial resources, agricultural resources, and energy-and-material resources.

The earlier concept of natural resources as a two-dimensional area led to the notion that natural resources were substantially fixed in amount and that all or part of them might be used, but their quantity could not be increased. Working within the framework of this concept, Malthus in his *Essay on the Principles of Population* (1798) predicted that population growth would outrun the food supply. Ricardo provided further justification of Malthus' fears with his statement of the *law of diminishing returns.* Loosely stated this law says that if the number of workers applied to any fixed supply of land is increased, the crops obtained from the land will rise, but eventually the output will increase at a slower rate than the rate at which the workers are added. Thus, output per man will decline. The implication of this "law" for the living standard of a growing population is clear. Instead of growth through a bigger slice of the GNP the slices per capita will become smaller and smaller. What a dismal science is economics! Neo-Malthusians are still with us today, and Ricardo's "law" is still operative.

In addition, today we still have the fundamental problem of using scarce resources to satisfy a growing variety of wants. But increased demand for natural resources has led to accelerated technological developments which have in part overcome the limitations and resistances of scarce resources, and, as a result, available natural resources have been expanded tremendously. This dynamic process of expanding the resource base can be illustrated by a simple diagram which shows man attempting to solve his basic economic problem (Figure 1.2).

Man does face his natural environment, which offers many resistances to be overcome. When these resistances are overcome and man begins to use his environment, the portion of his environment that is used becomes available to function as a natural resource. Man's cultural wants expand and go beyond his basic wants, putting further pressures on the natural environment. However, fortunately man uses his technology in the form of his knowledge, tools, and machinery, and is able to overcome the resistances so that it is technically and economically possible to use more and more of his environment which functions as resources to satisfy his ever-expanding wants. Thus, this resource concept is a functional one corresponding to a standard dictionary definition: "an available means of support." And since availability depends in part on expanding wants and technology, the static concept of resources becomes instead a dynamic one. Indeed there appears to exist a reciprocal relationship between the resources base and economic growth. Resources actually lead to more

Figure 1.2: The Dynamic Interrelationship Between Man and His Environment.

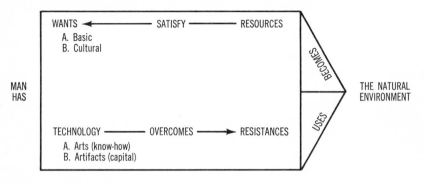

SOURCE: Adapted from *World Resources and Industries* by Erich W. Zimmermann (Harper & Row, 1951).

cultural wants, and more wants result in more technology and more resources. This fact may well be one of the principal contributing factors to the United States' remarkable growth.

In spatial natural resources the United States has been called "an experiment in transportation." Spatial distances were serious resistances that had to be overcome, but the development of water, rail, automotive, and air transport have made the entire United States accessible so that all its land is considered *coreland* (that is, usable by the population). Today we are exploring the ocean floor and outer space.

In agricultural natural resources the United States has expanded its productivity so that its per capita diet is one of the best in the world, while at the same time it remains the world's leading exporter of agricultural products. United States farm output has run ahead of population not only because of restraints on population but also and more importantly because of increased farm productivity. Improvements in cultivation, increased use of fertilizer, and improvements of plants have had dramatic effects. From 1950 to 1962 alone, crop production per acre in the United States increased 39 percent. In 1820 one farm worker was required to supply farm products to 4.12 persons. In 1900 this number stood at 6.95, but as early as 1962, 28.52 persons were supplied by only one farm worker. United States farm production assets per farm worker rose from less than $10,000 in 1950 to over $25,000 per worker in the early 1960's. On the other hand, during the same period, cropland used for crops declined 11 percent. Thus, the story of U.S. agricultural natural resources is one of ever-expanding agricultural productivity. Instead of running out of land the United States is using less.

Energy-and-material natural resources coupled with agricultural products that have been made available have been the real basis of industrial growth in the United States. This country has been blessed with a wide variety in its energy mix—wood, coal, petroleum, natural gas, water power, and now nuclear power. It will be our purpose to study the energy resources and industries in detail. Similarly the availability of mineral materials in the form of iron and steel, copper and aluminum, and other nonferrous metals to harness and apply the energy has contributed to the United States' strength in ways which will be developed in our study. Time and time again when we have heard cries of distress that the country was running out of one or more of these resources, our expanding wants have led us to overcome the resistances of our environment and to find new sources. Indeed, technology has been said to be "the indispensable finder, developer, and multiplier of natural resources." Especially is this true in the case of energy-and-material resources.

One final word about this functional, dynamic concept of resources; resources can be destroyed as well as created through expanding wants and technology, and Ricardo's law of diminishing returns is still at work. In the course of our study of the energy-and-material resources of industry we will find many problems that are generated through this process of creation and destruction.

Human Resources

We have seen that the primary objective of economics is to raise the people's standard of living through economic growth in the total GNP and increased per capita output. Some evidence has already been cited, but the 1964 *Economic Report of the President* shows that the nation's real total output measured in constant 1963 dollars rose 760 percent from 68 billion dollars in 1900 to 585 billion dollars in 1963. This represents an increasing annual growth rate of 3½ percent over the whole period. With population rising from 76.1 million to 189.3 million over this period, real output per person climbed from $890 at the turn of the century to $3,091 in 1963. Although many benefits are not captured in GNP measures, the *Report* thought that this was perhaps the single best summary index of the increased material well-being of the American people. Revised GNP data developed in 1965 showed a slightly increased long-term growth rate, and using these data the 1966 *Economic Report of the President* concluded that real growth in product when measured from 1960 through 1965 was further accelerated to 4.5 percent per year.

In this section we are interested in the contribution of human resources to increased productivity and growth. Students of productivity trends in the United States consider economic growth to be a product of:

1. Technological change, by which is meant the introduction of new arrangements in the process of production and distribution that enable us either to produce new products or to produce existing products and distribute both more efficiently and cheaply, using fewer resources.

2. Increases in the available quantities of labor and capital used in the productive process.

3. Improvements in the quality of labor as a result of the better health, education, training, or motivation of the labor force.

In a 1961 study, *Productivity Trends in the United States,* John W. Kendrick came to the same conclusion with respect to the growth rate of 3½ percent per year since the turn of the century, and he concluded that one half of this growth was due to increases in quantities of labor and capital, while the other half of this increase in productivity was due to a step-up in the efficiency with which the resources are converted into products. This expanded productivity accounted for almost all the increase in output per capita. Education, and research and development were determined to be the strategic factors of growing importance in the stimulation of productivity. Probably one of the most challenging conclusions drawn by Kendrick was that in the private economy, real average hourly earnings of labor have grown slightly faster than output per man-hour, marking labor as the almost exclusive beneficiary of productivity gains, whereas the rate of return on capital has remained relatively stable.

One often expressed fear is that technological progress may benefit property incomes proportionately more than incomes of labor. Kendrick's conclusion certainly tends to refute this past worry. In commenting on this same problem the 1964 *Economic Report* shows arithmetically that, when prices are constant, labor's share in total income will remain unchanged if total labor compensation rises in the same proportion as labor productivity. Although there is no immutable law of either economics or ethics that requires this result, the conclusion drawn by the *Economic Report* was that historically the rise in real earnings of workers has been closely linked with the advance in labor productivity.

So far we have seen that labor has received at least, if not more than, its share of productivity. Now we need to examine briefly labor's role in contributing to productivity through the size and efficiency of the labor force.

Labor Force and the Population. The amount of human resources available to be used in the productive process is a function of the population and its age distribution in a country. United States population passed the 190 million mark early in 1964 and estimates were that the total would approximate 219 million by 1970. During the first half of the 1800's U.S. population grew at around 35 percent per decade. By the decade of the 1930's the rate was down to less than 8 percent for the entire 10 years and predictions were that the U.S. population would begin to level off. But due to the post World War II baby-boom, the rate was back up to around 20 percent between 1950 and 1960; and this meant about 30 million more people in the short span of 10 years.

This changing rate of population growth brought about important shifts in the age composition of the population in the United States between 1950 and 1962 as shown in Table 1.1.

TABLE 1.1

Changes in the Population, by Age: 1950 to 1962

(Numbers in thousands. Total resident population, including

Alaska and Hawaii)

Age	July 1, 1962		April 1, 1950		Change, 1950 to 1962	
	Popula-tion	Per-cent	Popula-tion	Per-cent	Number	Per-cent change
All ages	185,822	100.0	151,326	100.0	+34,496	+22.8
Under 5 years	20,746	11.2	16,243	10.7	+4,503	+27.7
5 to 13 years	33,888	18.2	22,281	14.7	+11,607	+52.1
14 to 17 years	12,743	6.9	8,443	5.6	+4,300	+50.9
18 to 24 years	17,172	9.2	15,926	10.5	+1,246	+7.8
25 to 34 years	22,241	12.0	23,878	15.8	−1,637	−6.9
35 to 44 years	24,425	13.1	21,535	14.2	+2,890	+13.4
45 to 64 years	37,299	20.1	30,724	20.3	+6,574	+21.4
65 years and over	17,308	9.3	12,295	8.1	+5,013	+40.8

SOURCE: Data from U.S. Bureau of the Census.

The net effect of these shifts was a dramatic increase in the number of younger people below 14 and between 14 and 17, and in the older age group of above 65 years. This has important implications for the economy, but here we are interested in the effect of this change upon the labor force. In the United States the labor force is defined to include all persons 14 years of age and over who hold or are looking for paid jobs, or who are self-employed. This includes most of the men between 14 and 65 except those who are in school, and about one-third of all the women.

Over the past century the proportion of the population in the U.S. labor force has averaged about 40 percent. The increasing number of women who work has steadily pushed the percentage up, but longer education and earlier retirement have just about offset the rise. While the percentage has remained fairly constant the occupational trends have changed dramatically. During the period from 1950 to 1960 alone, professional and technical workers as a group increased by 47 percent—a rate of increase more than three times the average for all occupational groups. Second only to this growth was the increase in employment of clerical workers by 34 percent. At the same time employment declined by nearly 10 percent for industrial laborers and by over 40 percent for farmers and farm laborers.

Figure 1.3: Growth in Total Labor Force, 1940–1975.

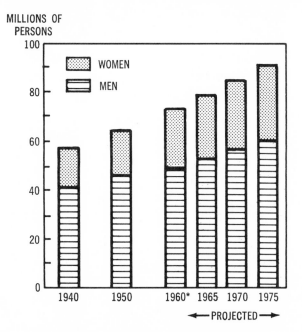

MILLIONS OF
PERSONS

*Alaska and Hawaii included beginning 1960.

SOURCE: U.S. Departments of Commerce and Labor.

In forecasting the labor force requirements for the period 1960–1975, Figure 1.3 and Table 1.2 are most revealing. During this 15-year period the U.S. labor force will increase by 20 million, reaching 93 million in 1975. Because of past demographic trends—a low birth rate during the 1930's and a post World War II baby-boom—the greatest growth in the work force in the 1960's will be in the number of younger workers, with a relative decline in the number of workers in the prime age group from 25 to 44. Also, it is anticipated that women will participate increasingly in the labor force. This has been true since the end of World War II, and since that time women have accounted for about three-fifths of the entire labor force increase. By 1970, half the women between the ages 25 to 54 are expected to be in the labor market, some for the first time, and others after a long absence.

Thus, we can conclude that from the standpoint of size of the labor force as a contributing factor to labor productivity, the United States is in a most favorable position.

The Efficiency of the Labor Force. The productivity of any labor force depends on its quality as well as its size. In view of the conclusion that the increased per capita return to labor has been in large measure

TABLE 1.2
Employment by Major Occupational Group, 1960 to 1975

Major occupational group	Actual, 1960		Projected, 1970		Projected, 1975		Percent change		
	Number (in millions)	Per-cent	Number (in millions)	Per-cent	Number (in millions)	Per-cent	1960–70	1970–75	1960–75
Total	66.7	100.0	80.5	100.0	87.6	100.0	21	9	31
Professional, technical, and kindred workers	7.5	11.2	10.7	13.3	12.4	14.2	43	16	65
Managers, officials, and proprietors, except farm	7.1	10.6	8.6	10.7	9.4	10.7	21	9	32
Clerical and kindred workers	9.8	14.7	12.8	15.9	14.2	16.2	31	11	45
Sales workers	4.4	6.6	5.4	6.7	5.9	6.7	23	9	34
Craftsmen, foremen, and kindred workers	8.6	12.8	10.3	12.8	11.2	12.8	20	9	30
Operatives and kindred workers	12.0	18.0	13.6	16.9	14.2	16.3	13	4	18
Service workers	8.3	12.5	11.1	13.8	12.5	14.3	34	13	51
Laborers, except farm and mine	3.7	5.5	3.7	4.6	3.7	4.3			
Farmers, farm managers, laborers, and foremen	5.4	8.1	4.2	5.3	3.9	4.5	-22	-7	-28

SOURCE: Data from U.S. Department of Health, Education and Welfare.

10

brought about by increased efficiency of the labor force, this factor deserves careful attention.

The efficiency of U.S. human resources, that is, workers and managers, reflects their high levels of health, education, and technical know-how. Several studies have indicated that health, better education, and training on the job have accounted for more than 25 percent of economic growth in recent years. About 30 percent of the population is involved in the educational effort, and the real challenge of the future is clearly pointed up in the number of new workers coming into the labor force and in the changing occupational requirements. Altogether some 26 million new young workers will enter the labor market in the 1960's—the largest number that the nation has had to educate, train, and absorb in any 10-year period. Many of the increasing number of women moving into the labor force will also need training or retraining.

The outlook for the future is for a continuation and an intensification of the occupational trends of the 1950–1960 period. Table 1.2 shows that between 1960 and 1975 professional, technical, and related employment is expected to grow at a rate more than twice the average rate for all fields of work. The increasing complexity of modern technology has created a need for technical workers who have some basic scientific and mathematical knowledge and also specialized training in some aspects of technology. Most interesting is the estimated increase of 45 percent in the number of clerical workers. There is some evidence here that the ever-mounting volume of paper work characteristic of our economy is likely to more than offset the labor-saving effects of automatic data processing and other new office equipment. On the other hand, little change is expected in the number of industrial workers required, and fewer and fewer individuals will be required in agricultural employment.

All these facts point up the massive effort that will be required to train and retrain workers, and the skill requirements of automation are clear. Rather than fear the results of automation, the answer is that the quality of our labor force must be upgraded to improve its efficiency, and there is evidence that labor shares the product of its improved efficiency.

The Role of the Entrepreneur. One special breed among our human resources must be singled out for a word of praise as a contributor to economic growth—the *entrepreneur,* a business man who is prepared to undertake the production of goods and services when there appears to be a potential profit in doing so. So important is the role of management as an organizer of land, labor, and capital that many economists contend that he should be treated as a separate factor of production. Indeed, what most command economies lack is the driving force of the entrepreneur with his ingenuity, energy, organizational ability, and initiative to start and keep the wheels of production moving.

Our data show that 32 percent more managers, officers, and proprietors will be needed between 1960 and 1975. Many observers are concerned that with the shift in form of business organization these new managers will lack the spirit of enterprise that has been so important to economic growth in the past. There is still no evidence, however, that the competitive spirit will not prevail as long as we have the free enterprise system.

Capital Resources

The dictionary defines capital as "An aggregation of economic goods used to promote the production of other goods, instead of being valuable solely for immediate enjoyment." Thus, *capital* is produced goods used in further production, and may be referred to as *producer goods* as distinguished from *consumer goods*. Producer goods are sometimes called investment goods or capital goods. One type of these goods should be emphasized, man-made capital facilities. These include buildings, plants, machinery and equipment, electrical and transmission facilities, etc. In addition to capital facilities, capital includes a tremendous amount of raw materials and semifinished and finished material that fill the industrial "pipelines."

The building of capital facilities is known as *investment*. Investment is capital accumulation. In order to accumulate capital, a portion of national income from current production must be saved. About the only way an agricultural civilization relying on the effects of day-to-day solar radiation can save is to tighten the belt so that something will be left over for investment. On the other hand, a nation, which in addition to agricultural resources, has stored-up natural resources of energy and materials is able to build up net products from its past accumulations. As a result, capital accumulation can be accomplished at a much greater rate, and production potential is increased. Blessed with the dual availability of both kinds of resources, the United States has been and continues to be in a most advantageous position with respect to capital resources.

In addition, the United States has been able to use its capital effectively. Three aspects of this effective use will be examined: (1) capital as an equalizing agent, (2) the relationship between investment, GNP, and income and, (3) the importance of capital, investment, and growth.

Capital As An Equalizing Agent. The capital that the United States has been able to accumulate because of the advantageous natural resources has been put to most effective use to overcome the shortage of labor. Numerous examples can be cited of U.S. capital labor-saving machines, such as the cotton gin and the combine, that have increased output per worker and have thus increased total and per capita income.

In Western Europe where labor has been the long factor, or agent of production, and natural resources have been the short factor, capital has been used to improve the productivity of the land. A particular case in point is the strategy of invention that led to the development of the basic

Bessemer process that made possible the use of the phosphorus-bearing iron reserves of Lorraine. However, with poorer natural resources, the western European countries have had less opportunity to accumulate capital than has the United States.

In many Asiatic countries such as India, labor is so abundant and so cheap that it is not profitable to use capital to the extent that it is used in the United States. There is no incentive to use a harvester for food crops. Some capital accumulation does occur, but only at a slow rate because production barely covers consumption. Thus both the incentive and the capacity to accumulate capital are lacking.

Therefore, in countries rich in natural resources but deficient in manpower, capital made with the aid of natural resources, especially inanimate energy, replaces or supplements manpower. In countries poor in natural resources but rich in manpower, capital made by man through hard work and abstention is used to increase productivity. Capital thus should be used as an equalizing agent that replaces and supplements the short factor of production in order to increase productivity.

The important point to be learned from this discussion is that the efficient use of capital demands its proper use as an equalizing agent. The United States has benefited from this policy in the past, but resource patterns change and it must be prepared to use capital efficiently as a means of replacing short factors whether they be human or natural resources. Where changes in technology result in structural unemployment of resources, mobility of these resources must be facilitated in order to encourage the most efficient use of human, natural, and capital resources.

Investment, GNP, and Income. To maintain the nation's stock of capital facilities, there must be enough investment each year to cover the depreciation of the existing facilities. When investment is greater than the rate of depreciation, the nation's capital facilities are expanded. Thus the most significant function of investment is that it maintains and expands productive capacity.

Investment is also a component of aggregate expenditure, along with personal and government expenditure. Savings out of current national income are put to work by channeling them into investment. Investment expenditure, like the other components of aggregate demand, is a demand for goods. It creates output, employment, and income. Thus investment increases total income and individual income.

The data have been presented showing the rising levels of productivity in the United States. Capital's function in this accomplishment is that it has facilitated the most effective use of resources and has created a rising plane of living by contributing to the growth of the economy, increased output per worker, and higher income. A further conclusion can be drawn that these factors working together, especially capital working efficiently through technology, have set up a reciprocal relationship between an expanding resource base and greater want satisfaction, interacting upon one another to generate an ever-increasing productivity and a higher plane of living.

Capital, Investment, and Growth. During the 1960's the United States became increasingly concerned with growth. How fast was the nation growing absolutely and relatively to other nations? A cult of "growthmanship" grew up in the country. The general consensus was reached that the United States needed to grow and that U.S. policy should facilitate growth. In the process of this self-analysis there arose a real recognition of the primary function of capital, that in the form of investment it is necessary for growth and leads to rising living standards by increasing output and income per worker.

The question was how to stimulate sustained growth through increased investment in the United States. Without going into this complicated problem in detail, clear thinking may be aided by suggesting that there are two parts of the problem: (1) investment opportunities and (2) sources of investment funds.

Investment spending is determined by many different things at different times. Fundamentally, however, the chief determinant is the expectation of profits. A business man will invest, for example, in a new machine when he thinks that he can get back over the life of the machine what it cost, plus operating costs, interest on his money, and some extra return or profit. In addition, an important factor determining investment spending is what is referred to as a favorable climate. This many times includes not only the economic factors but also the businessman's feeling with respect to how political actions will affect the business community. Thus, during the administration of President Dwight D. Eisenhower, attempts were even made to compute the positive force of the "Eisenhower factor." President John F. Kennedy, on the other hand, was thought of as not being favorable to business and this was amplified in the minds of the business community after his action in publicly reprimanding the steel industry for price increases that the industry thought were necessary to cover increasing costs in order to make profits. After the steel episode, President Kennedy set about to show that his administration recognized the value of business investment and began to suggest tax policies favorable to investment decisions. These tax policies will be considered in a subsequent paragraph. President Lyndon B. Johnson was considered to be more favorable to business interests, but the business community insisted on a "show me" attitude in terms of policies favorable to investment opportunities.

Investment funds come from two sources, business savings and personal savings. In turn, business savings come from two sources: profits not paid out to owners (undistributed earnings), and depreciation reserves (amounts set aside to replace wearing-out equipment). Since World War II, such business savings have made up over half the economy's total saving. For example, in 1965 gross retained business earnings (business savings) were 82.8 billion dollars, while personal savings were only 25.1 billion dollars. Further, in recent years businesses' own savings have financed about two-thirds of their total investments.

What meaning does this have for policy? First, it is important that tax policies be such that they do not deter personal savings—and this means that the rates of income tax applicable to the middle and higher income brackets (the savers) should possibly be lowered. Second, business saving is the principal source of investment funds; businesses almost always prefer to use their own savings before going out to secure personal savings. One way to generate increased funds internally is to grant accelerated depreciation allowances, and this was the avowed policy of the early 1960's during the Kennedy administration. A second way is to reduce corporate income taxes. A third way to generate additional funds internally is to decrease the proportion of profits paid out as dividends. This has been a corporate policy that has been practiced, and that has appealed to stockholders who are interested in growth rather than current income. More fundamentally, business net savings depend on how big profits are. Eastman Kodak, DuPont, and the A & P Tea Co. are examples of companies which have grown rapidly almost entirely through reinvested, retained earnings. But there are a great many other businesses that need to obtain additional inside and outside funds to finance new investment for growth.

Thus the conclusion can be drawn that investment is fundamental to economic growth, and that if the nation's growth rate is to be maintained in the future, national and business policy should be such that they not only encourage business investment, but also make possible a sustained flow of savings both from inside business and from outside personal savings. Fundamental to all this are policies that will recognize the necessity of business profits, for these are the principal sources of business investment funds, and they are the principal attraction that draws outside personal savings to business investment.

SUMMARY

Production is the creation of utilities which satisfy human wants and are in the form of goods and services for which man is willing to pay. Production takes place by the utilization of natural, human, and capital resources. A major objective of an economic system is growth by which is meant an increase in the total gross national product (GNP), which is the dollar value of all the goods and services produced in an economy during a given period of time. A more appropriate measure of growth is an increase in the ratio, total output/total population.

The United States has experienced both a sustained total and per capita growth. Principal factors contributing to this growth have been the available natural, human, and capital resources. First, natural resources have been expanded under the dynamic pressure of increasing wants and developing technology to overcome the resistances offered by the environment. Second, human resources have increased in productivity and have been rewarded by an increase in income equivalent to or greater than their contribution. Finally, capital has been generated out of the abundant natural resources to be invested efficiently in man-made productive facilities.

In summary, this chapter has established the importance of production and has examined in detail the contributions of natural, human, and capital resources to economic growth in the United States.

SELECTED REFERENCES

Bach, George Leland, *Economics, An Introduction to Analysis and Policy*, Englewood Cliffs, N.J., Prentice Hall, 1963.

Barnett, Harold J., and Chandler Morse, *Scarcity and Growth, The Economics of Natural Resource Availability*, Baltimore, Johns Hopkins, 1963.

"Choosing a Career—The Economic Framework," *Occupational Outlook Handbook*, Bulletin No. 1375, U.S. Department of Labor, Washington, D.C., 1964, p. 1055 ff.

Dewhurst, J. Frederick, *America's Needs and Resources, A New Survey*, New York, Twentieth Century Fund, 1955.

Economic Report of the President, Washington, D.C., 1964, and later issues.

Hunker, Henry L., Ed., *Erich W. Zimmermann's Introduction to World Resources*, New York, Harper & Row, 1964.

Kendrick, John W., *Productivity Trends in the United States*, Princeton, Princeton University Press, 1961.

Landsberg, Hans H., *Natural Resources For U.S. Growth*, Baltimore, Johns Hopkins, 1964.

Landsberg, Hans H., Leonard L. Fischman, and Joseph L. Fisher, *Resources in America's Future*, Baltimore, Johns Hopkins, 1963.

Mouzon, Olin T., *International Resources and National Policy*, New York, Harper & Row, 1959.

"Population Estimates," *Current Population Reports*, U.S. Department of Commerce, Bureau of the Census, Washington, D.C., July, 1964, and later issues.

Resources for Freedom, a report by the President's Materials Policy Commission, Vol. I, *Foundations for Growth and Security;* Vol. II, *The Outlook for Key Commodities;* Vol. III, *The Outlook for Energy Sources;* Vol. IV, *The Promise of Technology;* Vol. V, *Selected Reports to the Commission*, Washington, D.C., 1952.

Spengler, Joseph L., Ed., *Natural Resources and Economic Growth*, Washington, D.C., Resources for the Future, Inc., 1961.

Zimmermann, Erich W., *World Resources and Industries*, New York, Harper & Row, 1951.

2

ENERGY RESOURCES

ENERGY is the capacity to do work. Obviously the availability of energy and the efficiency with which it is used is fundamental to productivity and economic progress. Fairgrieve tells us, ". . . it may be said that in the widest sense on its material side history is the story of man's increasing ability to control energy."[1] Zimmermann elaborates: "One could almost concentrate the whole history of economic development into the simple transition: man power to animal power to machine power."[2] Thus economic growth has been accelerated as man has successively enlarged his own capacity to do work.

Almost all the energy that man uses is of nuclear origin. Figure 2.1 shows the various ways in which the earth receives solar energy and the manifestations of this energy. In the past the nuclear (atomic) energy used by man has been stellar, chiefly solar in origin, and has been derived from current receipts (flow) and stored-up supplies (fund). The most significant advance in economic productivity was achieved when the shift was made from the principal reliance on flows of energy to the utilization of funds of fossil fuels—coal, petroleum, and natural gas. This shift, accompanied by the harnessing of these fuels by heavy metals, we have called the Industrial Revolution. Students of energy and material have told us that this phase of history was rapidly drawing to a close; and that we were entering upon a stage which would be characterized by continuous energy sources, principally water power converted into electricity and direct solar power harnessed by light metals. Yet even as this stage was dawning a new era exploded. Now nuclear (atomic) energy funds are used directly by man-induced chain reactions in certain fission-

[1] James Fairgrieve, *Geography and World Power*, 2nd ed., New York, Dutton, 1921, p. 3.
[2] Erich W. Zimmermann, *World Resources and Industries*, rev. ed., New York, Harper & Row, 1951, p. 58.

17

Figure 2.1: Energies—Their Origins and Manifestations.

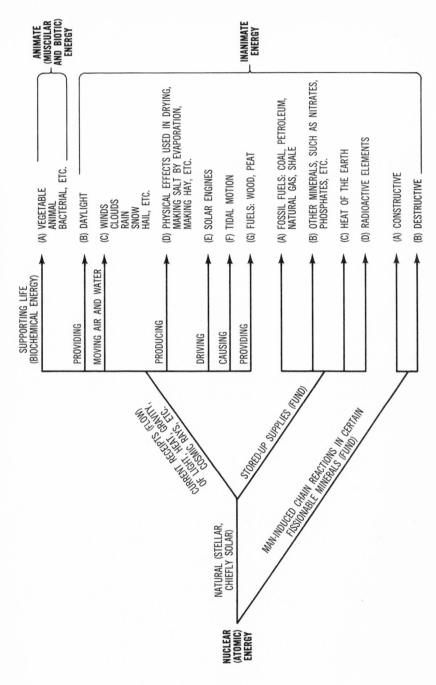

SOURCE: From *World Resources and Industries* by Erich W. Zimmermann (Harper & Row, 1951).

18

able materials. Technology is developing with such rapidity that there are no longer distinct phases of energy history. Future energy resources and potential must be appraised with extreme caution, but with the certainty that the combination of sources (energy mix) will be important in determining the future rate of economic growth.

ECONOMIC GROWTH AND ENERGY

Economic growth goes hand in hand with energy availability and energy consumption. In general, it is true that to increase consumption, production must be increased, and production involves energy expenditure. Since economic growth is closely tied to the output of goods, and since 40 percent of current energy use is devoted to general industrial purposes, it is clear that higher economic growth rates in the United States are made possible by energy, and they in turn raise energy consumption.

Figure 2.2: Real National Output and Energy Consumption.

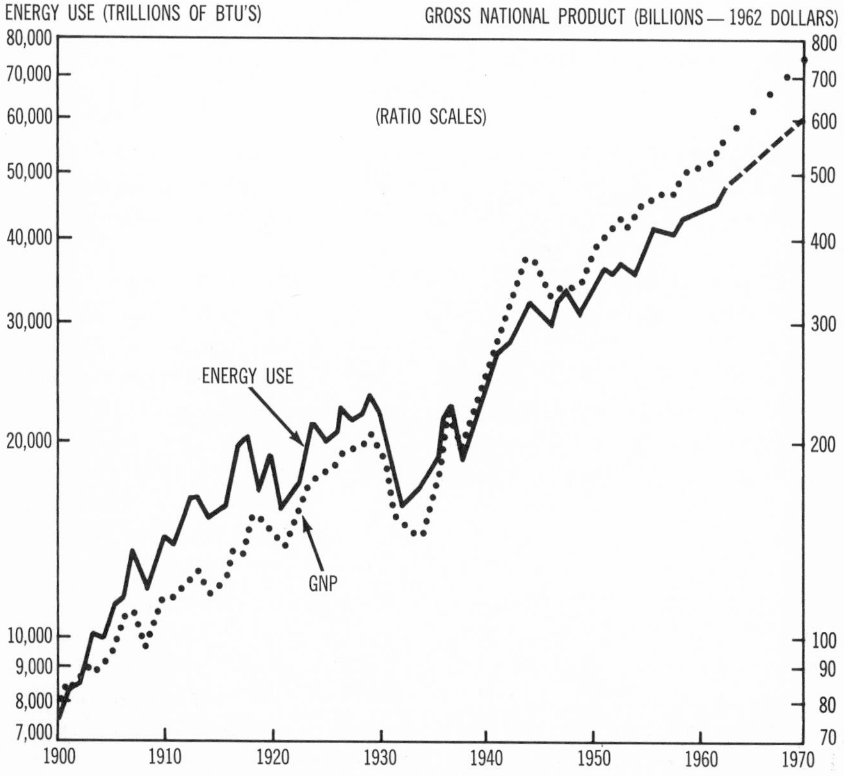

SOURCE: *Energy and Economic Growth,* New York, American Petroleum Institute, 1965.

From about 1910 to 1940 there was a fairly close relationship between real national product and energy inputs (Figure 2.2). However, from 1940 to 1960 real national output rose more rapidly than energy inputs.

By 1900 the United States was undergoing the full impact of the Industrial Revolution and a rapid development of fossil fuels was needed to supply the energy required for industrial expansion. After 1900 U.S. production of goods was shifting away from products consumed at or near their raw material state to products requiring more intensive processing; synthetic fibers rather than cotton or wool; plastics rather than wood; alloys in contrast to base metals. Expanding and upgrading the available products usually results in additional processing steps, and as a very general rule, further processing steps require additional energy. An additional factor contributing to increased energy inputs was the development of the transportation system in the United States, particularly the growing requirements for liquid fuels by automobiles.

Factors at work which have retarded the rise of energy consumption especially after 1940, have been the increased efficiency of capital equipment, and shifts in composition of the national output.

First, improvements in thermal efficiency act to reduce energy consumption even though the technology of production is such that more energy is needed to produce more complex products. More efficient insulation, machines, and heat exchange devices have all tended to reduce the quantity of energy input per unit of output. Examples of this improved efficiency are to be found in the diesel engine, in the generation of thermal electric power, and in the manufacture of pig iron. Diesel locomotives are five times more efficient in the use of fuels than are steam locomotives. A kilowatt-hour (kwh) of electricity was produced in 1960 with 25 percent less heat than in 1950. About 20 percent less coke was required to produce a ton of pig iron in the early 1960's than in 1950. Translated into savings in energy consumption, the consumption of bituminous coal by electric utilities in 1960 was 174 million tons as compared with the 234 million tons that would have been required by 1950 standards of efficiency, a difference of 60 million tons. In the case of the production of pig iron in 1960, about 16 million tons less coal were consumed than had the improvement in efficiency not occurred. Obviously, efficiency in its many aspects has had an important effect in reducing energy consumption.

Second, the changing composition of national output has also acted to retard the growth of energy consumption. The United States is devoting larger shares of national income to the purchase of noncommodities such as professional services, education, and rental, and interest payments. Generally these expenditures do not require either directly or indirectly large amounts of inanimate energy. Thus as disposable income is spent on large shares of services, rather than products, less energy is required per unit of GNP.

Nevertheless, the conclusion can be drawn that even though there are factors at work to retard energy consumption, higher economic growth in the United States has required higher energy consumption. In addition, economic growth has been made possible by the availability of the energy resources in the United States, and any prediction of the future energy requirements must take into account the trends in energy use and the resources available.

ENERGY AVAILABILITY AND USE

The logical expectation is that the types of energy used would be determined by the resources available. But energy use is also a function of the technology of use, the competitive ability of the producers to deliver the energy to the consumers, and the preference of the consumers.

The United States has been blessed with a wide variety of energy sources. When wood was on hand it was used and the technology was adapted to the characteristics of wood. But when coal deposits were discovered and developed, technology was modified, the steam engine was developed, and this in turn induced additional coal production. Coal became vital when processed into coke for the iron and steel industry, and the growth of the coal and steel industry went hand in hand. Oil and gasoline are of greatest advantage when used in mobile units, and the development of petroleum and automotive transportation went forward together. Petroleum brought natural gas with it, but its use had to wait for long-distance natural gas pipelines to be developed. With gas, consumer preferences were and are of particular importance. A combination of all these factors appears to be at work with the development of electric power from nuclear energy for consumers prefer electricity in its many technical applications, and we shall learn that the generation of nuclear-fuel electric power is contingent upon the competitive ability of the electric power industry to deliver the energy to the consumers.

Figure 2.3 shows the changing patterns of energy use in the United States. Noteworthy is the small percentage of hydropower since 1900. So drastic are the changes in coal, natural gas, and petroleum that the reader's attention hardly need be called to them. Coal, which reached a peak of about 70 percent of energy consumption in 1900, declined to less than 25 percent in 1960. Oil and natural gas liquids constituted about 40 percent of energy use in 1960. The growth of natural gas use has been truly dynamic in the last 30 years and accounted for about 30 percent of energy use in 1960. Quantitatively, coal was less important in 1960 than it was in 1915, while during the same period petroleum and natural gas became much more important. Thus the energy mix in the United States has undergone drastic changes which point up the necessity of detailed examination of specific energy sources. At the same time they emphasize the fact that any estimates of future energy requirements by source of energy is subject to innumerable variables.

Figure 2.3: Energy Consumption in the United States, Past, Present, and Future.

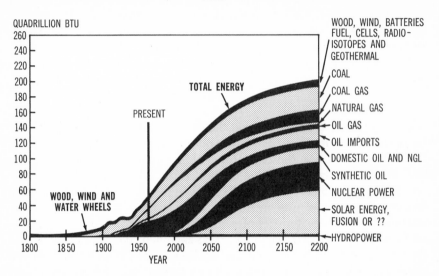

Source: Reprinted from The Texaco Star.

ENERGY REQUIREMENTS AND POLICY

The growing interfuel competition for U.S. energy requirements was responsible in large measure for the most complete research overview of the energy industries and markets ever to be undertaken in this country. The *Report of the National Fuels and Energy Study Group*[3] published in 1962 resulted primarily from the demands of the coal industry which was worried about the sharp inroads that had been made into the coal markets, notably by oil and natural gas. The industry had previously pressed for the establishment of a national fuels policy that would regulate end-uses of various fuels. This proposal was opposed bitterly by other fuel groups, who later agreed to participate in a study of the situation.

The coal industry was joined by the coal-carrying railroads, the United Mine Workers, and the domestic petroleum industry in pressing for special legislation to tighten the regulation of the energy industry and its markets. The growing pressure coaxed the 87th Congress into authorizing Senator Clinton P. Anderson's Committee on Interior and Insular Affairs to assess the U.S. fuel and energy resources and requirements and to recommend changes in fuel policy.

The report of the committee study group found that there was a reasonable consensus among experts that the U.S. projected energy re-

[3] *Report of the National Fuels and Energy Study Group*, Washington, D.C., 1962, 502 pp.

quirements would almost double by 1980 to 82 quadrillion Btu's (British thermal units), that generation of electricity would multiply by some 3½ times to about 2,700 billion kwh, and that consumption of oil will increase about two-thirds to approximately 5.7 billion barrels. The consensus for coal, gas, and nuclear fuel was not so clear, but the following deductions were accepted as usable for policy determination: coal consumption should roughly double by 1980 to 800 million tons or more; gas should almost double to 20 trillion cubic feet or more; hydropower generation should drop from a share equal to 4 percent of energy consumption to one equal to about 2½ percent of energy consumption; and nuclear energy should increase to a level equal to hydropower.

Further, the *Report* found that the U.S. resource base, in terms of each fuel, was adequate to meet projected requirements for the period covered by the study, that is, to 1980. The *Report* did not underestimate the problems in meeting these requirements, but it did not qualify its answer as clearly as the President's Materials Policy Commission, which concluded that the United States could meet its energy requirements "only if" the nation: (1) looks at its energy resources as a whole, (2) exploits fully the shifting interrelationships among various sources of energy, (3) takes fullest economic and technical advantages of the flexibilities in end-use by drawing on each energy resource, and (4) judges and acts upon the energy needs and resources of other free nations.[4]

In the area of policy, however, it is crystal clear that the National Fuels and Energy Study Group is in agreement with the President's Materials Policy Commission that the United States must maintain a policy of flexibility in the end-uses and sources of energy. The real issue at stake in the Study Group's report was whether competition or controls should prevail in the energy market. After a careful and factual study, the conclusion was drawn that U.S. national fuels policy should emphasize free enterprise and that end-use control of fuel resources is not feasible.

The conclusion is drawn that competition has been the keynote of U.S. energy policy to date, and that it has served the public well. End-use controls would result in misuse of natural resources. The Study Group concluded that the continued practice of no end-use controls should accomplish the following results: (1) It would stimulate the use of especially suitable fuels, (2) It would generate a search for and production of more reserves for fuels in greater demand, and (3) It would provide a form of natural regulation of prices because of the threat of competitive fuels.

Finally, the *Report of the National Fuels and Energy Study Group*, once again, confirms the correlation between U.S. economic growth, in terms of real national output and energy consumption. Clearly economic

[4] *Resources for Freedom*, Vol. III, *The Outlook for Energy Sources*, Washington, D.C., June 1952, p. 1.

growth requires an abundance of dependable and relatively inexpensive energy, and the best way to achieve this is through a policy that insures the maximum competitive conditions between the various energy sources.

SUMMARY

Energy is the capacity to do work. Higher economic growth rates in the United States have been made possible by the energy mix available. The United States has been blessed with a wide variety of energy sources which have been selected for use by consumer preference, the technology of use, and the competitive ability of the producers to deliver the energy.

From time to time efforts have been made to recommend a national policy that would control the end-uses of energy. One of the more recent efforts on the part of the coal industry resulted in the *Report of the National Fuels and Energy Study Group*. The conclusions drawn were that consumer preference should remain the dominant factor in determining the type of energy used and that the best way to secure dependable sources of energy is through a policy that insures the maximum competitive conditions between the various energy sources.

SELECTED REFERENCES

Fairgrieve, James, *Geography and World Power*, 2nd ed., New York, Dutton, 1921.

Herfindahl, Orris C., *Mineral Import and Stabilization Policies*, Washington, D.C., Resources for the Future, 1962.

Mason, Edward S., *Energy Requirements and Economic Growth*, Washington, D.C., National Planning Association, 1955.

Morrison, Warren E., and Edward E. Johnson, "Review of the Mineral Fuel Industries," Preprint for U.S. Bureau of Mines *Minerals Yearbook*, Washington, D.C., 1963.

Report of the National Fuels and Energy Study Group to the Committee on Interior and Insular Affairs, United States Senate, 87th Congress, 2nd Session, Washington, D.C., September 21, 1962.

Report on Energy Supplies and Resources Policy, Washington, D.C., Executive Office of the President, February 26, 1955.

Resources for Freedom, a report to the President by the President's Materials Policy Commission, Vol. III, *The Outlook for Energy Sources*, Washington, D.C., 1952.

Schurr, Sam H., Bruce C. Netschert, Vera F. Eliasberg, Joseph Lerner, and Hans H. Landsberg, *Energy in the American Economy, 1850–1975*, Baltimore, Johns Hopkins, 1960.

Sporn, Philip, *Energy; Its Production, Conversion, and Use in the Service of Man*, New York, Macmillan, 1963.

Teitelbaum, Perry D., *Energy Production and Consumption in the United States*, Washington, D.C., United States Department of Interior, 1961.

3

COAL

Coal remains the "power behind the nation" in spite of the fact that petroleum and natural gas have made increasing gains as U.S. energy sources. Coal as an energy source and iron ore have been the bases of modern industrialization. No modern nation has made sustained economic progress without continuous availability of coal. Today, the U.S. economy is still importantly based on coal, for it is an indispensable element in large-scale production of steel and many chemicals. In addition, coal is the principal energy source used in the generation of the enormous quantities of electric power so necessary to sustain industrial production. Upon its production, distribution, and utilization rest the prosperity of many millions of people and the economic growth of the country. Of all fossil-fuel sources of energy, coal is most abundant.

TYPES OF COAL

Coal has come into existence gradually over millions of years, as decaying plant matter in swampy areas was transformed into various ranks of coal. These ranks of coal are not sharply divided, but overlap, because the starting material is similar for all of them. In order of increasing ranks, coals are classified as lignite, subbituminous, bituminous, and anthracite. The rank of coal becomes higher as the amount of fixed carbon increases and as the amount of moisture and volatile matter decreases.

Lignite

Lignite, often called brown coal, has the lowest carbon content and the highest water content, which ranges from 30 to 40 percent in the United States. When it is exposed to air, it shrinks and crumbles to slack. Although there are large deposits of lignite in the United States, its production is not yet important nationally, partly because it is so far from the major markets and the shipment of unprocessed lignite for long distances is uneconomic.

Subbituminous

Subbituminous is black and looks very much like the bituminous coal commonly seen in coal yards. It contains 15 to 30 percent moisture. Like lignite, it weathers when exposed to air, is more difficult to store than higher ranked coals, and is used principally in the areas where it is mined.

Bituminous

Bituminous coal is the most abundant and widespread rank of coal used in the United States. Bituminous coal contains a higher percentage of pure carbon, less water and oxygen than lower ranks, and a considerable amount of gas. Commercially, bituminous coal is rated as metallurgical and steam grades. Metallurgical coal will produce coke when heated in a sealed oven. In this process the volatile elements are driven off and in the carbonization a porous mass called coke is formed. Steam grade is noncoking coal which burns freely without pronounced agglomeration. Noncoking and coking coals may be used interchangeably as fuel for power plants, railroads, heating, and cooking. But only coking coal can be used to manufacture coke for use in smelting iron ore in the blast furnace.

Anthracite

Anthracite, or hard coal, is high in pure carbon content (92 to 95 percent) and so low in volatile matter (oxygen and hydrogen) that it burns with almost no smoke. Most anthracite has somewhat lower heating value than the highest grades of bituminous coals, but its lack of soot, and the fact that it will burn longer without attention, make it a more desirable domestic fuel than bituminous coal. For many years anthracite was the preferred fuel in the United States, but today it comprises only a small percentage of the total amount of coal used in this country.

RESERVES AND LOCATION

Reserves

The approximation has been made that one out of every ten acres of land in the continental United States is underlaid with coal. The United States Geological Survey has prepared Figure 3.1 to show the widespread

Figure 3.1: Coal Fields of the United States.

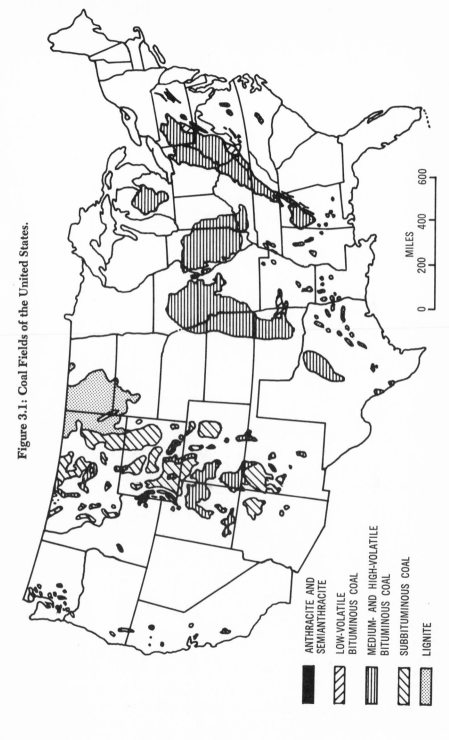

ANTHRACITE AND
SEMIANTHRACITE

LOW-VOLATILE
BITUMINOUS COAL

MEDIUM- AND HIGH-VOLATILE
BITUMINOUS COAL

SUBBITUMINOUS COAL

LIGNITE

MILES

0   200   400   600

SOURCE: United States Geological Survey Bulletin 1136.

distribution of coal. In its report, *Coal Reserves of the United States,* the Survey states that although coal is abundant and widespread in the United States, reserves also have limits. In the extensively mined eastern coal fields it is becoming increasingly difficult to locate new areas containing thick beds of high-rank and high-quality coal. This is particularly true of metallurgical bituminous coal. Furthermore, quantitative reserves of coal must be modified as will be noted below.

TABLE 3.1

Coal Reserves of the World by Region[1]

(In millions of metric tons)

Country	Anthracite; bituminous and sub- bituminous coal	Lignite and brown coal	Total	Percent Region total	Percent World total
Asia					
U.S.S.R.[2]	998,000	202,000	1,200,000	52.4	25.9
China	1,011,000	600	1,011,600	44.1	21.8
India	62,427	508[3]	62,935	2.8	1.4
Japan	9,897	258	10,155	.4	.2
Others[4]	4,711	3,808	8,519	.3	.1
Total	2,086,035	207,174	2,293,209	100.0	49.4
North America					
United States[5]	1,099,906	405,970	1,505,876	94.1	32.4
Canada[6]	62,472	24,450	86,926	5.6	1.9
Mexico[7]	4,306	–	4,306	.3	.1
Total	1,166,684	430,420	1,597,104	100.0	34.4
Europe					
Germany	224,300	62,000[3]	286,300	47.5	6.2
United Kingdom	170,686	([8])	170,686	28.3	3.7
Poland	80,000	18	80,018	13.3	1.7
Czechoslovakia	6,450	12,500	18,950	3.1	.4
France	12,288	430	12,718	2.1	.3
Belgium	5,988	([8])	5,988	1.0	.1
Netherlands	3,400[9]	([8])	3,400	.6	.1
Others[10]	2,622	22,154	24,776	4.1	.5
Total	505,734	97,102	602,836	100.0	13.0

TABLE 3.1 (Continued)

Country	Anthracite; bituminous and sub-bituminous coal	Lignite and brown coal	Total	Percent	
				Region total	World total
Africa					
Union of South Africa	68,000	(^{8})	68,000	97.4	1.5
Others[11]	1,650	200	1,850	2.6	(^{8})
Total	69,650	200	69,850	100.0	1.5
Australasia					
Australia	16,800	41,000	57,800	98.5	1.3
Others[12]	99	785	884	1.5	(^{8})
Total	16,899	41,785	58,684	100.0	1.3
South and Central America					
Colombia	12,000	—	12,000	63.6	0.3
Venezuela	3,068	0	3,068	16.2	(^{8})
Others[13]	3,556	254	3,810	20.2	(^{8})
Total	18,624	254	18,878	100.0	0.4
World total	3,863,626	776,935	4,640,561	—	100.0

1 Brown, Frederick, 1948, 1950, 1952, 1954, 1956, Statistical Yearbooks of the World Power Conference. nos. 4, 5, 6, 7, and 8: Central Office World Power Conference, London. United Nations, 1952, Coal and iron ore resources of Asia and the Far East: Economic Commission for Asia and the Far East, Mineral resources development ser. 1, p. 18. United Nations, 1953, Development of mineral resources in Asia and the Far East: Economic Commission for Asia and the Far East, p. 143–199. United Nations, 1956, Lignite resources of Asia and the Far East, their exploration, and utilization: Economic Commission for Asia and the Far East, Mineral resources development ser. 7, p. 2–9. United Nations, 1957, Energy in Latin America: Economic Commission for Latin America, p. 220–228.
2 Total for European U.S.S.R. included with Asiatic U.S.S.R.
3 Proved reserves only.
4 Includes Burma, Indochina, Indonesia, Korea, Malaya, Manchuria, North Borneo, Pakistan, Philippines, Sarawak, Thailand, and Turkey.
5 Estimates of remaining reserves in tables 1 and 2 converted to metric tons.
6 Includes only minable reserves.
7 Mexico Departmento de Estudios Tecnicos y Economicos, written communication, 1959.
8 Negligible.
9 Beds not less than 50 cm thick.
10 Includes Austria, Bulgaria, Denmark, Greece, Hungary, Ireland, Italy, Norway, Portugal, Roumania, Sweden, and Yugoslavia.
11 Includes Algeria, Belgian Congo, French Morocco, Madagascar, Nigeria, and Tanganyika.
12 Includes New Caledonia and New Zealand.
13 Includes Argentina, Brazil, Chile, Honduras, and Peru.
SOURCE: *Report of the National Fuels and Energy Study Group*, Washington, D.C., 1962.

Total coal reserves of the United States including Alaska were estimated by the Geological Survey at 1,660 billion short tons as of January, 1960. According to the authoritative information contained in Table 3.1

the United States may be said to have approximately one-third of the estimated world coal reserves.

However, quantitative figures for coal need to be modified by two factors. First, investigations by the U.S. Bureau of Mines have shown that, on the average, only about 50 percent of the coal is recovered in underground mining. Losses include coal left in pillars, in areas around oil and gas wells, and under towns, railroads, rivers and streams, in thin impure beds, and in isolated areas not accessible to mining. A second factor to be taken into consideration is that different ranks of coal have different Btu content. Table 3.2 shows the potential recoverable coal reserves in the United States and adjusts them for their Btu volatile bituminous coal value. On this basis, bituminous coal is seen to account for 64 percent of U.S. total recoverable reserves, which are estimated at 807 billion tons.

TABLE 3.2

United States

Potential Recoverable Reserves of Various Ranks of Coal

Rank of coal	Billion net tons	Bituminous coal of 13,000 B.t.u. per pound calorific value, equivalent billion net tons	Total coal reserves on B.t.u. basis, percent	Heating values used in conversion, B.t.u.
	(1)	(2)	(3)	(4)
Anthracite	7	7	1	12,700
Bituminous	525	545	64	13,500
Subbituminous	186	136	15	9,500
Lignitic	232	119	20	6,700
Total	950	807	100	

SOURCE: *Mineral Facts and Problems*, Washington, D.C., 1960.

Location

The location of coal falls into the following coal provinces in the United States: the Eastern including the Anthracite and Appalachian; the Interior; and the Northern Great Plains, Rocky Mountain, Gulf, and Pacific provinces. Table 3.3 shows the percentage distribution of the recoverable coal reserves by rank and by province based on the equivalent heating value. According to this method of evaluation, about 54 percent of the minable coal reserve is in the Eastern and Interior provinces, and 46 percent in the Northern Great Plains, Rocky Mountain, Gulf and Pacific provinces. The coals of the different provinces differ greatly in rank.

TABLE 3.3
United States
Distribution of Recoverable Coal Reserves in Terms of Btu Value,
by Ranks and Provinces
(Percentage)

Rank of coal	Anthracite	Bituminous	Subbituminous	Lignitic	Total
Eastern	1	27			28
Interior		26			26
Northern Great Plains, Rocky Mountain, Gulf and Pacific		14	17	15	46
Total	1	67	17	15	100

SOURCE: *Mineral Facts and Problems*, Washington, D.C., 1960.

The *Eastern* province includes coal of the Anthracite basins in eastern Pennsylvania and the Appalachian bed. Anthracite occurs in five small basins in eastern Pennsylvania extending over 480 square miles, and accounts for less than one percent of the nation's total energy consumption. Cost of mining is increasing due to thin, broken, incline seams and the virtually obsolete methods of extraction. Consequently, anthracite is being replaced in the domestic fuel market by petroleum and natural gas. On the other hand, the Appalachian bed of the Eastern province contains principally bituminous coal, extends from Pennsylvania to Alabama, and possesses 25 percent of the nation's known reserves. The Appalachian mines furnish about 75 percent of the coal mined in the United States. The quality of the coal is high and the deposits are accessible to major markets. Structural conditions are favorable for low-cost mining because the beds are flat-lying, or gently inclined, and are continuous over relatively large areas. Streams have cut narrow valleys so that coal beds are exposed, and mining and transportation by water and rail are facilitated. Almost all the mines are mechanized so that a large output per man-hour is possible.

The *Interior* province includes four fields: the Eastern Interior in Illinois, Indiana, and Kentucky; the Western Interior in Iowa, Missouri, Kansas, and Oklahoma; the Southwestern Interior in Texas; and the Northern Interior in Michigan. The Eastern Interior, containing bituminous coal, is the most important in quantity and quality. While most of the coal is suitable for coking, it is less desirable because of higher ash and sulfur content. Nevertheless, it is very satisfactory for steam and domestic purposes. The coal beds lie deeply buried in the center but are near the surface on the edges. The Western and Southwestern fields have coal of inferior quality, and the relatively small amount mined is for local consumption. The Northern Interior field is of little importance because of the low quality, and even the local requirements are supplied by the Appalachian and Eastern Interior fields.

In the *Northern Great Plains, Rocky Mountain, Gulf,* and *Pacific* provinces 70 percent of the coals are subbituminous and lignite, and neither of these coals is suitable for coking purposes. Relatively small reserves of good coking coal occur in the Trinidad-Raton field of southern Colorado and northern New Mexico. This coal has been used for years to make metallurgical coke. Another good coking-coal reserve of greater extent, but poorer coking qualities, occurs in eastern Utah and western Colorado. The Sunnyside beds in Utah are supplying the coke ovens at Provo and Geneva, Utah; and Fontana, California. Most of the coals in these provinces are useful because of their local availability and great distances from the better grades of coal. But in the Pacific province the coals are unimportant even for local use because they are of poor quality and they cannot compete with other available energy sources of oil and natural gas, and hydroelectric power.

In summary, the United States does have abundant coal reserves, although their life cannot be estimated because of the many variable factors involved. Most importantly, such estimates as are made by competent scientists show that the coal reserves are far more abundant than the reserves of any other mineral fuel, and that they should last well over 2,000 years.

TYPES OF MINING AND TECHNOLOGY

Types of Mines

Types of mines are underground mines, including slope, drift, and shaft mines; surface mines; and auger mines. The type of mining followed depends on the terrain and geography of the area. Slope and drift mines are common in hill and valley terrain, such as is characteristic of the Appalachian area. Shaft and surface (strip mines) are found mostly in plains or on divides. Much coal in the Interior province is strip-mined.

Underground. The underground mines are accessible by vertical shafts and by slope or drift. The terms are derived from the manner of entry and moving coal to the surface as shown in Figure 3.2

Figure 3.2: Types of Underground Mining.

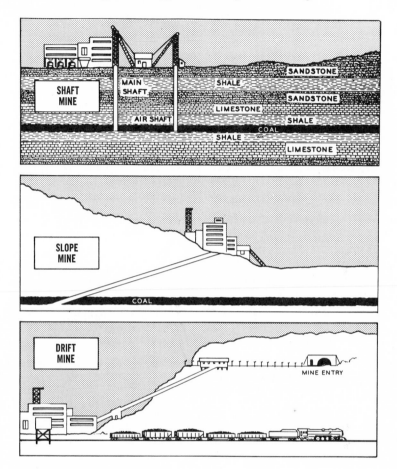

SOURCE: National Coal Association.

Mining methods include the room-and-pillar and long-wall methods. A description of the room-and-pillar method follows since this is the prevailing mining system used in underground mines in the United States.

In general, the entries into the coal mines serve as haulage ways and fan out into the coal bed with side or cross entries by which the coal is removed from the rooms. Up to about 50 percent of the coal is left as pillars to support the roof, which is usually slate or some other rock. To conserve resources, pillars are sometimes removed on the retreat. In the past coal was drilled, blasted, and then manually loaded into cars for transportation to the tipple at the surface. Later, cutting machines were introduced for undercutting, overcutting, or making vertical cuts. In recent years coal mining has become highly mechanized, and loading and conveying are no longer manual. In fact, continuous mining machines have been developed that cut, load, and convey the coal to belt conveyors for transport of the coal to the outside. One type of continuous miner, mounted on rubber tires or crawler treads, has multiple cutters that make vertical cuts from floor to roof. Coal is mechanically swept to a chain conveyor and passed to the rear of the machine onto a shuttle car or a continuous conveyor. Another type of continuous miner has several circular cutters that revolve vertically. The cuttings are thrown by appropriate opposed directions of rotation of the cutters to the center of the machine front, and carried back to the rear of the machine on an integral conveyor to be loaded onto a shuttle car or a continuous conveyor. Developments such as these have reduced the use of explosives and greatly increased the output of coal per man-hour. Even though mechanization is moving ahead at a rapid rate, continuous mining machines accounted for only about 20 percent of the coal mechanically loaded underground in the early 1960's, but over 85 percent of all the coal was mechanically loaded.

Surface. The strip-mining process is of growing importance where the coal is near the surface, for after the overburden is removed from the underlying mineral reserves there are many advantages: (1) From 80 to 100 percent of the coal is recoverable, (2) Strip mines use larger units of machinery than underground mines and the output per man is more than double that in underground mines, and (3) Strip mines can utilize coals that would not be commercially feasible to mine from underground mines. The phenomenal growth in strip-mining has been made possible by developing large capacity shovels, trucks, and new explosives, such as ammonium nitrate, which is now widely used for breaking up the overburden. Strip-mining, however, is not without its disadvantages due to its disruption of the landscape.

Auger. Auger is the newest form of coal mining. Many strip mines, particularly in the rough terrain of the Appalachian area, encounter overburden so thick that strip-mining is uneconomical. Auger mining employs a large auger as a cutting head and a tube and screw for transporting the coal. The labor force is small and recoveries of coal range upward to 65 percent. Just before 1960, auger mining in soft-coal mines in the United States averaged 28 tons per man-day as compared with 22 at strip mines and 9 at underground mines. Under favorable conditions production of 50 tons per man-day has been achieved.

Technology

Improved technology has dramatically affected the coal industry. In the ten-year period 1946–1956 technology and improved labor conditions resulted in a nearly doubled output per man-day of more than 10 tons in the bituminous coal industry. This was to be compared with an output of less than 2 tons per man-day in Poland, West Germany, Great Britain, and France. Improved output per man-day continues to be the rule in the United States, and as early as 1963 output had already surpassed 15 tons per man-day. By 1966 production had reached 17 tons per man-day.

Technological developments such as those discussed in connection with the types of mines, and changes in the use of coal, have led to additional technological developments in the preparation of coal for the market.

Over 60 percent of the bituminous coal is mechanically cleaned in the United States today, as compared with less than 5 percent in the 1920's. The introduction of mechanized mining, which does not differentiate between coal and impurities has given great impetus to coal preparation. Cleaning consists of removing high ash bands, rock, ash-forming material, and sulfur-bearing components of coal. In addition to cleaning, the changing market for coal has brought about crushing and sizing of coal to meet the demand for smaller sizes in stokers. It is also common practice now to treat coal for dust. Such treatment tends to prevent the hazard of explosion by spontaneous combustion, improves burning performances at times, and reduces air slacking and disintegration. The coal industry is finding it increasingly necessary to prepare coal for the consumer market so that it can compete on more favorable terms with oil and natural gas.

COAL COSTS

The cost of producing coal varies from mine to mine depending upon whether the type of mining is underground, surface, or auger. It varies also in response to such items as hardness of the coal, seam thickness, depth of operations, roof conditions, output per man, capital investment, and degree of cleaning required for particular market outlets.

Information on the cost of mining coal is proprietary information and is rarely published. Faced with these difficulties, the National Fuels and Energy Study Group attempted to make some observations and calculations about coal costs. What follows is a report of the Study Group's findings.[1]

Mining engineers have information on coal costs, but otherwise the subject must be approached obliquely. Individual lots of coal may be sold at a loss and a single company may operate at a loss for a period of time, indeed, as we will see, the whole industry did. The Study Group, however, concluded that no company can lose money indefinitely and that therefore the cost of production is, on the average, equal to or less than the sales price.

Table 3.4 and the accompanying chart, Figure 3.3 show the tonnages

[1] *Report of the National Fuels and Energy Study Group*, Washington, D.C., 1962, pp. 252–255.

Figure 3.3: Tonnages of Coal Sold at Various Prices.

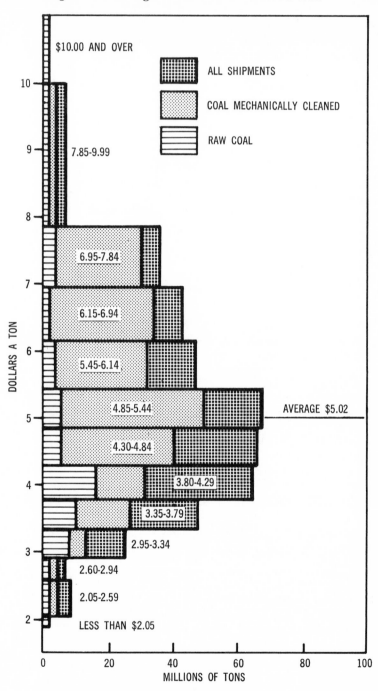

SOURCE: *Report of the National Fuels and Energy Study Group,* to the Committee on Interior and Insular Affairs, United States Senate, 87th Congress, Second Session, Washington, D.C., September 21, 1962.

of coal shipped at various prices in 1958 as disclosed by the 1958 *Census of Mineral Industries*. Shown separately on the chart are the total coal shipped, shipments of coal mechanically cleaned, and shipments of raw coal.

The average sale price according to these figures was $5.02 a ton; the U.S. Bureau of Mines, reporting on a slightly different basis, calculates the average sale price as $4.68 a ton. About half the coal mined was sold at $3.80 to $5.45 a ton. On the basis that cost will not usually exceed the selling price, the average cost of production was around $4.90 a ton, or less by some unknown amount, and about half of the total output was produced and sold at a cost between $3.80 and $5.45 a ton, again less some unknown amount.

TABLE 3.4
Tonnages of Coal Sold at Various Prices
(Rounded figures)

Price range per ton	Tons (thousands)	Cumulative tonnages	Price range per ton	Tons (thousands)	Cumulative tonnages
Less than $2.05	1,400	1,400	$4.85 to $5.44	67,800	283,400
$2.05 to $2.59	7,900	9,300	$5.45 to $6.14	44,700	330,100
$2.60 to $2.94	6,000	15,300	$6.15 to $6.94	42,700	372,800
$2.95 to $3.34	24,200	39,500	$6.95 to $7.84	35,300	408,100
$3.35 to $3.79	47,200	86,700	$7.85 to $9.99	6,300	414,400
$3.80 to $4.29	65,600	152,300	$10 and over	1,700	416,100
$4.30 to $4.84	65,300	217,600			

SOURCE: *Report of the National Fuels and Energy Study Group*, Washington, D.C., 1962.

Since labor accounts for half or more of the total cost, as indicated below, it may be presumed also that cost is inverse to tons per man-day produced, and looking at the sale figures in that light it would appear that cost at auger mines is perhaps $2.00 to $2.40 a ton or less, at the efficient strip mines perhaps $2.40 to $3.50 a ton or less, and at the least efficient strip mines and at the most efficient underground mines perhaps $3.80 or less. The relatively lower costs at nonunion mines are involved in this speculation, but the Study Group could not segregate their influence.

Most of the coal mechanically cleaned was produced at $4.30 to $6.95 a ton or less, and most was produced in the range from $4.85 to $5.45 or less a ton than in any other equivalent, or nearly equivalent, price range. The selling price of raw coal suggests something about mining costs themselves since such costs do not include cleaning costs. More coal was sold at $3.80 to $4.40 a ton than in any other equivalent or near equivalent price bracket, and most was sold in the range from $2.95 to $4.30 a ton. Costs would then be, in general, equal to or something less than that.

The Study Group obtained some verification of the above estimates of strip-mining costs on studies of actual operations in North Dakota, and additional verification by professional opinion was given the Group regarding costs of mining coal by underground methods as follows:

Conventional mining: $3.45–$3.75

Mechanized mining: $3.10–$3.65

The range derives from the thickness of the coal seam. Opinions on cleaning costs ranged from 30¢ a ton to 60¢ or more, depending on the amount of cleaning and the amount of reject coal.

Based on the evidence on coal costs available to the National Fuels and Energy Study Group the conclusion was drawn that the average selling price of $5.02 a ton quoted above would appear to break down the costs per ton shown in Table 3.5. The Study Group felt that this was as

TABLE 3.5

Cost of Coal Production Based on Average Selling Price of $5.02 a Ton

	Dollars per ton	Percent of total cost
Wages and salaries	2.19	–
Fringe benefits	.43	–
Subtotal	2.62	53
Supplies and contract operations	1.26	25
Subtotal	3.88	78
Depreciation and depletion as reported for income tax purposes	.44	–
Taxes, insurance, royalties and miscellaneous cost	.63	–
Subtotal	1.07	22
Total costs	4.95	100
Balance	.07	–
Sales price	5.02	–

SOURCE: *Report of the National Fuels and Energy Study Group*, Washington, D.C., 1962.

far as they could go in estimating the costs of coal in the light of the data available. It is clear from this study that on the average labor costs are more than 50 percent of the total costs of producing coal.

TRANSPORTATION

Transportation has always been a big factor in increasing the cost of coal to coal users. Rising transportation costs are of great concern to the coal industry in its fight with substitute fuels for markets. Almost 80 percent of all coal leaves bituminous mines via railroads, at rates that add about 70 percent to the cost of coal at the mines. Shipments by water amount to only about 10 percent of mine output. A substantial portion of the coal is transferred to barges and other vessels before it reaches the final consumer. Barge tows carrying up to 25,000 tons of coal ply the inland waterway along the Monongahela, Allegheny, Kanawaha, Ohio, and Mississippi Rivers. In addition, substantial tonnages are shipped over the Great Lakes and coastwise along the Atlantic seaboard. Approximately another 10 percent of mine output is carried by trucks, particularly from strip and auger mines. Truck transport, however, is most useful for short hauls to consumers although it is also used to haul coal from mines to rail sidings and river docks for further shipment.

The conclusion can be drawn that mines closest to market have a decided advantage, and since water rates are cheaper, mines with water transportation have lower delivered costs. Three developments have been taking place to alleviate the transportation problem: coal pipelines, integral trains, and location of generating plants near the coal mines for the transmission of electric power from coal over long distances.

A spectacular development in the transportation of coal began in 1956 with the construction of a coal pipeline from Cadiz, Ohio, to Cleveland, a distance of 110 miles. This was the first long-distance pipeline in the world for transporting coal. This pipeline was designed to carry 1,200,000 tons of coal a year at an estimated saving of one million dollars per year over conventional shipping methods. Specially-prepared coal was crushed and mixed with water to form a slurry (a thin watery mixture) to be transported through a 10¾-inch pipeline. At the delivery end the coal was taken from the water, heated, and dried for use. More recent advances in boiler design have made it economically feasible to use coal slurry without a prior drying out process. This pipeline raised the possibility that a network of coal pipelines might one day be built between the mines in West Virginia, Ohio, Pennsylvania, and other coal-producing states, and between coal customers in the Great Lakes, East Coast, and Middle West regions. Indeed, a second and much larger pipeline was planned to run 350 miles from West Pennsylvania mines to East Coast utilities. But this project aroused considerable objections from railroads, which blocked bills introduced in state legislatures giving pipelines the right to condemn property for the right of way. Indeed the threat of pipelines probably caused the railroads to put on their thinking caps and come up with the integral train.

The integral train is a new concept made up of freight cars owned by a utility or a coal company and devoted solely to a shuttle run between a coal mine and the power plant and avoiding yarding and switching. One of the first such services initiated in Pennsylvania allowed rate reductions of over 30 percent. Integral trains are regarded by the railroads as the answer to the coal pipeline and indeed did lead to the closing of the first coal pipeline.

Power plants have been accelerating a trend to move closer to the coal mines, sometimes even so close that only short conveyor belts are used to transport the coal. The electric energy produced from burning the coal in the coal fields is transmitted to points of consumption in industrialized areas. Power losses are a problem, but technical improvements in extra-high-voltage lines are making sizable savings possible.

A recent survey by the U.S. Department of Interior concluded that each of the three methods above was cheaper for moving coal energy eastward than present rail cars. A study of the cost of moving coal from West Virginia mines to markets in New York, Philadelphia, and Baltimore concluded that rail transport averaged $4.59 per ton. Pipeline transport was estimated from $2.26 to $3.25 per ton, while direct mine to market shuttle trains would cost from $2.56 to $3.67. If coal was converted into electricity in West Virginia and moved eastward by transmission lines, the cost would average between $2.50 and $3.51. The report noted that these alternative methods of moving coal to market would be a blow to railroad revenues and to labor. However, even though the report may be looked upon as tentative estimates, it does point up the fact that alternative means of cheaper coal transportation are possible, and they may be necessary if coal is to compete favorably in the competitive fuel markets.

COAL USES

Figure 2.3 demonstrates that during a period of growing total energy use in the United States, coal was losing its share of the energy market, having reached its peak of 70 percent of energy consumption in 1900 and having declined to less than 25 percent in 1960. Coal's decline has been absolute as well as relative, for the yearly production of coal during the early 1960's was less than the average yearly production during the period 1910–1920.

Through the 1900's coal's principal uses have been for generation of electric power by utilities, railroads, steel mills, and for other industrial markets, for retail use, and for export. Dramatic changes have taken place in the use of coal, and the sustained decline in the market has masked some favorable trends. Some estimates indicate that by 1975, domestic production of coal could approach or exceed the record 631 million tons produced in 1947.

Electric Utilities

From Table 3.6 it is clear that coal has been losing ground in all domestic markets except in that purchased by electric utilities for the generation of electric power. This has been a fast-growing market which used about 223 million tons of bituminous coal in 1964, or 50 percent of the total domestic consumption. Utility demand increased more than 80 percent in the previous ten-year period while total domestic usage declined. Utility consumption reached 242 million tons in 1965 and was expected to increase to 257 million tons in 1966.

In our study of the electric power industry we will see that the Federal Power Commission has estimated that the output of electricity in 1980 will be 3½ times that in 1960. Coal will share in the expanded market. While the generation of hydroelectric power is cheaper, low cost water-power sites are hard to find, and coal has a more favorable price trend than the competing steam power fuels of oil and natural gas. In addition to lower transportation costs, another important factor contributing to lower costs per kwh is the improved efficiency of steam boilers which in 1963 used 0.86 pounds of coal to generate one kwh in contrast to 1.24 pounds in 1949 and 2 pounds in 1925. New generating plants often require less than 0.7 pounds per kwh.

While consumption of coal by electric utilities due to increases in efficiency, will not expand as rapidly as the increased demands for electric power, the growing utility demand is the great hope of the industry.

Railroads

Before and during World War II, railroads accounted for over 20 percent of total domestic coal consumption. As a result of the rapid dieselization of railroads after World War II, coal accounts for less than 3 percent of total fuel requirements. Coal used by railroads fell 99 percent from 1945 to 1965, or from 22 percent of domestic consumption to less than 1 percent. This dramatic loss of a major market for coal has been a tough blow for the industry to absorb because railroads had previously had a vital interest in coal. Railroads still transport about three-fourths of all the bituminous coal shipped in the United States. Revenues from coal traffic still amount to about 30 percent of total railroad freight revenue from the major coal-carrying railroads. In spite of the railroads' interest in coal, this market appears to have been lost to the industry. However, railroads are

TABLE 3.6
United States Consumption of Bituminous Coal and Lignite
(In millions of short tons)

Year	Coal consumed per kilowatt hr. (in lbs.)	Electric power utilities	Bunker, foreign and lake	Railroads (class I)	Coke plants Beehive	Coke plants Ovens	Steel and rolling mills	Coal-gas retorts	Cement mills	Other industrials	Retail deliveries[3]	Total of classes shown
1952	1.10	103.3	1.8	38.0	6.9	90.7	9.6	[1]	7.9	93.6	66.9	418.8
1953	1.06	112.3	1.8	27.7	8.2	104.6	8.8	[1]	8.2	95.2	60.0	426.8
1954	.99	115.2	1.2	17.4	1.0	84.4	7.0	[1]	7.9	77.1	51.8	363.1
1955	.95	140.6	1.5	15.5	2.9	104.5	7.4	[1]	8.5	89.6	53.0	423.4
1956	.94	155.0	1.5	12.3	4.0	101.9	7.2	[1]	9.0	93.3	48.7	432.9
1957	.93	157.4	1.4	8.4	3.5	104.5	6.9	[1]	8.6	87.2	35.7	413.7
1958	.90	152.9	1.0	3.7	1.0	75.6	7.3	[1]	8.3	81.4	35.6	366.7
1959	.89	165.8	1.0	2.6	1.8	77.4	6.7	[1]	8.5	73.4	29.1	366.3
1960	.88	173.9	.9	2.1	1.6	79.4	7.4	[1]	8.2	76.5	30.4	380.4
1961	.86	179.6	.8	[1]	1.5	72.4	7.5	[1]	7.6	77.3	27.7	374.4
1962	.86	190.8	.7	[1]	1.3	72.9	7.3	[1]	7.7	78.8	28.2	387.8
1963	.86	209.0	.7	[1]	1.6	76.0	7.4	[1]	8.1	82.8	23.5	409.2
1964[2]	.86	223.0	.7	[1]	2.0	86.7	7.4	[1]	8.7	82.9	19.6	431.0

1 Included in "Other Industrials."
2 Preliminary.
3 To other consumers.
SOURCE: Data from U.S. Bureau of Mines, *Commodity Year Book*, New York, Commodity Research Bureau, Inc., 1965.

making a major effort to help the coal industry through the introduction of integral trains.

Steel Industry

Steel producers are the second largest market for coal and consume about 90 percent of the coking coal, excluding exports. Under present technology, coal is essential for large-scale economic production of most grades of steel, but gains in blast furnace efficiency and improvements in the quality of both coke and coking coal have reduced the amounts of coal required in the steelmaking process.

In producing one ton of pig iron in a blast furnace, about 1,400 pounds of coke are used, which is equivalent to about 2,000 pounds of coking coal. Coal is also used by steel companies for heat and power, but this usage accounts for less than one tenth of the industry's consumption. Overall coke usage per ton of pig iron has declined by one third since 1939 and some industry experts believe further reductions are the order of the day. Factors contributing to these reductions are increased availability of concentrated iron ores which require less fuel in reduction, and further increases in blast furnace efficiency. On a longer range basis, direct reduction of iron ore may become economically feasible. This would further curtail the steel industry's consumption of coking coal, although additional quantities of steam grade might be needed for the large power requirements of the direct reduction process.

Other Industrial Uses

Other industrial uses of coal include manufacture by merchant (nonsteel) coke producers and demand by other industrial users for steam coal. Although use of coal in these areas has been on the decline since World War II, more recently this consumption appears to have stabilized. Some improvement is on the horizon due to the expansion of cement and aluminum production.

Retail Deliveries

Retail deliveries of coal have been used almost entirely for space heating. Before and during World War II retail consumers accounted for over 20 percent of total domestic consumption. From 1945 to 1965 total retail deliveries declined by over 80 percent or from 22 percent of total consumption to less than 5 percent. The technology of coal furnaces was unable to keep abreast of oil and natural gas technology. These fuels were cleaner, more convenient, more efficient, and led to automatic space heating while coal was still striving to break away from hand-firing to semiautomatic and automatic stokers. As a result, the tremendous postwar building boom passed coal by as a source of fuel for space heating.

Export Markets

Before World War II the U.S. industry was not directly concerned about international trade in coal, but it should have been because of the vital issues involved. Nations with coal deficiencies are dependent on coal imports. On the other hand, not only was Great Britain's economy powered by coal, but her industrial might was strengthened and supported by her coal exports. International interdependence on coal was strongest in Europe and Japan. The drive for coal to achieve productivity and power was a motivating factor in economic, political, and military aims. Great Britain's and Germany's strength was in their export position, and France was vulnerable in her coal import position. Japan's drive into Manchuria and China was to overcome her weak import position. The United States confined its export interests to Canada, which has a coal deficiency.

Since World War II Great Britain has been faced with declining coal production and a completely deteriorated export position, while Western Europe and Japan have been short of coal and dependent on the United States and the Soviet bloc as the principal sources of supply. Canada still remains dependent upon imports of coal. During the postwar years U.S. exports have ranged from 5 percent of U.S. production in 1950 to 13 percent in 1957, and have accounted for about 10 percent of output in 1963. Canada, the countries of the European Common Market, and Japan are the United States' principal export markets.

Canada. Canada has historically been the largest single foreign market for U.S. coal and is expected to remain in this position for some time. Table 3.7 indicates that U.S. exports to Canada hit a high of 20,654,000 tons of coal in 1956, only to decline sharply in the years following. Although exports were up to almost 14 million in 1963, U.S. coal exports to Canada had declined by 30 percent in the last 10 years. With the increasing development of oil and natural gas resources and transportation facilities in Canada, its dependence on coal imports was lessening. The outlook thus is one that requires a sustained competitive effort if the United States is to hold the Canadian export market.

Japan. After World War II Japan turned from the Asiatic mainland to the United States for its coal requirements. The postwar policy of the United States was to supply Japan's import needs. Table 3.7 shows how these exports have been sustained and increased. These sharp increases reflect largely the rapid growth in Japanese steel production following the destruction of the war. However, prospects for further expansion of export markets to Japan are not as bright, as the growth rate of the Japanese steel industry will probably be much lower in coming years, and lower transportation costs have made coal from Australia more desirable.

TABLE 3.7
U. S. Exports of Bituminous Coal
(In thousands of net tons)

	1955	1956	1957	1958	1959	1960	1961	1962	1963
No. and Central America	17,289	20,714	18,532	12,306	12,476	11,703	11,239	11,476	13,820
Canada	17,185	20,654	18,445	12,238	12,407	11,625	11,169	11,410	13,762
South America	1,447	2,281	2,268	1,452	1,499	2,178	1,786	2,159	1,933
Brazil	1,115	969	1,060	978	881	1,049	979	1,316	1,156
Europe	28,677	41,156	49,701	32,889	19,129	16,900	15,269	18,284	25,218
Germany (West)	6,678	10,243	15,570	9,708	4,463	4,566	4,216	4,812	5,508
Italy	6,056	7,557	8,762	6,989	5,200	4,846	4,733	5,837	7,612
Netherlands	4,642	6,594	8,063	5,515	3,288	2,785	2,425	3,187	4,170
Asia	3,726·	3,509	5,673	3,550	4,077	5,654	6,617	6,467	6,064
Japan	2,760	3,178	4,873	3,299	4,020	5,617	6,610	6,465	6,053
Africa	139	313	271	95	73	57	63	28	43
Total	51,277	68,546	76,446	50,293	37,253	36,419	34,974	38,413	47,078

Source: Data from U.S. Bureau of Mines and U.S. Bureau of the Census.

European Common Market. The economy of Western Europe, including the United Kingdom, is predominantly based on coal. The U.S. Materials Policy Commission reported that in 1950, 75 percent of the total energy supply of Western Europe was derived from coal, 14 percent from petroleum, and 11 percent from hydroelectric power. Europe has been unable to meet rapid rises in demand for energy in recent years and has had to import coal and petroleum for an increasing proportion of its requirements. With few oil reserves available, Western Europe must supply her liquid fuel needs from imported petroleum and synthetic fuels. Coal costs at the mine head in Europe are increasing, which led the Materials Policy Commission to conclude that by 1975 one-third of Western Europe's energy requirements would come from petroleum, and to suggest the possibility of increased imports of coal.

European coal mines have low productivity—generally less than 2 tons per man-day as compared with more than 17 tons per man-day in the United States. As a result, U.S. coal often competes with domestic coal in Europe. However, to protect their producers from the competition of imported coal and oil, most European nations enacted fuel import quotas that restricted this market for U.S. coal.

In the first decade after World War II, U.S. exports of coal to Europe were very erratic. This feast to famine export business was brought about by the initial need for large exports of coal to the economically crippled nations of Europe. As the European economy recovered, however, coal imports from the United States were curtailed. The National Coal Association was optimistic enough in 1956 to conclude: "In recent years, however, the stability of the European industrial system, which is primarily based on coal, has shown a strength and vigor which would seem to indicate a more stable and continuous export market."

One of the most forward steps in the solution of the coal and steel problem of western continental Europe was taken in July, 1952, with the establishment of the European Coal and Steel Community (the "Schuman Plan"). The European Coal and Steel Community is an unprecedented supranational organization with jurisdiction over the production and distribution of coal, iron, scrap, and steel within its six member countries—France, Belgium, Luxembourg, Italy, the Netherlands, and Western Germany. Under the plan a common market has been created for coal, iron ore, scrap iron, and steel. In order to achieve this goal, the member countries agreed to eliminate all import and export duties and other restrictions on the movement of coal and steel among the six countries.

The real need for the Community lies within the interdependence among the participating countries for coal and iron ore. Luxembourg produces no coal but is an important producer of steel, which requires coal. Belgium and the Netherlands lack the iron ore for their steel industries. Italy needs both raw materials and must depend on imports. France and Germany are dependent on each other; France needs coal (especially coking coal) which Germany has, while Germany needs iron ore which France has. No country in the Community can produce the necessary steel without sizable imports of one or both raw materials. This interdependence of the basic heavy industry is the most convincing argument for the economic unification of Western Europe.

Exports of U.S. coal to the European Community as shown in Table 3.5 have continued to have great variations, but on the average the European Community has taken about 50 percent of U.S. coal exports. Just how stable and continuous the Western European market will be depends upon the requirements of the European Coal and Steel Community and the Community policy toward imports. The High Authority of the Community stated as policy in the middle 1950's that: "The objective of the Community is not the maintenance and development of coal production at any price, but the best possible utilization of its energy resources with a view of making coal an economic source of energy." However, one of the threefold objectives of this policy was that "coal produced within the Community must under normal circumstances successfully compete with the imported coal." Taken together, this has two implications for U.S. coal exported to the Community. First, imports will be admitted to the Community when necessary and therefore, because of their marginal nature, will be especially sensitive to cyclical changes in economic activity. Second, U.S. imports will be admitted on a nonrestrictive, competitive basis.

More recently the European Community and the Common Market have restated the energy policy as one of using the cheapest source of energy consistent with safety of supply. While this may improve export prospects for U.S. coal, the U.S. producers must compete for part of the market with cheap Venezuelan and Middle-East oil as well as with natural gas in Europe and with nuclear energy. While most U.S. coal shipped to Europe is for metallurgical use, some steam coal is shipped, and a fairly sizable portion of the metallurgical coal is gasified by gas utilities before the resultant coke is sold to steel makers.

Market Summary

As early as 1956 *The New York Times* summarized the export outlook for coal: "Talk of overseas shipments brings smiles to the faces of industry leaders." No doubt these smiles were generated by the thought that there was a possible solution to coal's declining share of the domestic energy market. Indeed, leading export coal producers, convinced of the long-range stability of the export market, along with major railroads hauling coal to tidewater and the miners' union, organized the American Coal Shipping, Incorporated in 1956 to "promote the export coal trade on the broadest possible basis." In spite of this optimistic outlook for exports, the market remains very uncertain and is growing more and more competitive.

As a result, the conclusion must be drawn that U.S. coal's best future hope lies in a sustained increase in use by domestic electric utilities.

STRUCTURE OF THE INDUSTRY

The bituminous coal mining industry has been characterized by a large number of small mines, although "captive" mines owned by steel companies, utilities, and other large coal users have been an important factor in the industry and in recent years have accounted for about 15 percent of production. The history of the structure of the industry is presented in detail in Table 3.8. These data not only show a long-term increase in the large number of mines in the industry but also tend to show the ease of entry into the business which is characteristic of a competitive situation.

A brief look at the changing number of mines will indicate, for example, that the number of mines increased from 7,333 in 1946 to 8,700 in 1947, which is an increase of over 18 percent. There was a similar increase in production. Many other examples of increases and decreases in the number of mines can be cited. Much of this flexibility represents the reopening and temporary closing of mines.

However, the ease of entry indicated by the above must be modified. First, most of the entries are of mines previously opened. To open a new mine of more than 500,000 tons annual capacity usually requires about 4 years for a strip mine and from 5 to 6 years for an underground mine. Second, exit from the industry is even less flexible, for once a mine has been opened and is in operation there are strong pressures to maintain production. Production continues even in the face of falling demand and falling prices because the cost of maintaining idle mines is very heavy. Mines must be kept dry, well ventilated, and structurally sound, for after a 2-year period corrosion and water damage will generally force the abandonment of an installation. These factors coupled with the usual fixed costs tend to keep mines operating.

Competition in the industry is modified by the number of captive mines in it. The owners of these mines are parent companies and major consumers of coal who find it advantageous to own their coal supplies in order to reduce fuel costs, insure continuous production, and avoid delays. Captive mines have exerted a twofold influence on the commercial mines by absorbing some of their market and by undermining their position vis-à-vis labor. In the first place, integrated firms producing their own coal simply deny the market to commercial coal operators. In the second place, operators of captive mines have been more willing to come to agreement in labor disputes because of unwillingness to shut down any part of their integrated operation. Independents with less at stake have been more willing to resist the demands of the unions.

The Report of the National Fuels and Energy Study Group presented evidence to show the concentration of company ownership in coal mining.

The ranking five companies, out of a total of 7,500 (0.07 percent), produced almost an even 25 percent of the 1960 coal output. The top ten companies produced 33 percent and the top twenty-five produced 50 percent of the output, while the remaining 50 percent was produced by approximately 7,450 companies.

Table 3.8 indicates the long-run trend has been an increasing number of mines from 5,818 in 1910 to 7,865 in 1960. However, in spite of the increasing number of mines, the concentration of company ownership of mines is paralleled by concentration in the number of mines. A study comparing the situation in 1960 with that in 1910 when coal production was on the way up and output was the same as it was in 1940—416 million tons—shows that although there were a third fewer mines in 1910, they were more uniform in size. Thus while 10 percent of the mines yielded 44 percent of the year's output in 1910, in 1960 this output was provided by only 4 percent of the mines. Or while 10 percent of the mines in 1910 yielded 44 percent of the output, 10 percent in 1960 yielded fully 80 percent of the output. However, if the coal operations of the captive mines are excluded this concentration is less acute.

More recent trends indicate that the number of mines is declining from a high of 9,429 in 1950 to 7,740 in 1962. Contributing to this decline have been increased capital need for opening mechanized mines plus rising wages which have resulted in a trend toward consolidation. With the disbanding of family companies, the seeking of additional reserves by large operators, and the consolidation and closing of marginal mines, further concentration is likely. But despite the degree of mining concentration, small companies operating only one or two mines are still typical of the industry.

Even though there is growing concentration in the industry, the numerous studies that have been made of the industry do not indicate that the existing degree of concentration has led to price leadership or other types of imperfectly competitive market behavior. The widespread distribution of coal, the typical small mine, and growing interfuel competition have effectively prevented any restrictions of competition.

PROBLEMS AND POLICY

"Coal is a sick industry." This evaluation of the "power behind the nation" has been one of the most often repeated descriptions of U.S. industry. If the statement is true, then it is a problem of tremendous concern to the United States.

Problem

Except during World War II and immediate postwar years, the coal industry was concerned with the problem of inadequate net revenue and

TABLE 3.8
The Bituminous Coal and Lignite Mining Industry in the United States

Year	Production (net tons)	Value of production Total	Value of production Average per ton	Number of mines	Capacity at 280 days (million tons)	Foreign trade Exports (net tons)	Foreign trade Imports (net tons)
1910	417,111,142	469,281,719	1.12	5,818	538	11,663,052	1,819,766
1911	405,907,059	451,375,819	1.11	5,887	538	13,259,791	1,972,555
1912	450,104,982	517,983,445	1.15	5,747	566	16,475,029	1,456,333
1913	478,435,297	565,234,952	1.18	5,776	577	18,013,073	1,767,656
1914	422,703,970	493,309,244	1.17	5,592	608	17,589,562	1,520,962
1915	442,624,426	502,037,688	1.13	5,502	610	18,776,640	1,703,785
1916	502,519,682	665,116,077	1.32	5,726	613	21,254,627	1,713,837
1917	551,790,563	1,249,272,837	2.26	6,939	636	23,839,558	1,448,453
1918	579,385,820	1,491,809,940	2.58	8,319	650	22,350,730	1,457,073
1919	465,860,058	1,160,616,013	2.49	8,994	669	20,113,536	1,011,550
1920	568,666,683	2,129,933,000	3.75	8,921	725	38,517,084	1,244,990
1921	415,921,950	1,199,983,600	2.89	8,038	781	23,181,166	1,257,589
1922	422,268,099	1,274,820,000	3.02	9,299	832	12,413,085	5,059,999
1923	564,564,662	1,514,621,000	2.68	9,331	885	21,453,579	1,882,306
1924	483,686,538	1,062,626,000	2.20	7,586	792	17,100,347	417,226
1925	520,052,741	1,060,402,000	2.04	7,144	748	17,461,560	601,737
1926	573,366,985	1,183,412,000	2.06	7,177	747	35,271,937	485,666
1927	517,763,352	1,029,657,000	1.99	7,011	759	18,011,744	549,843
1928	500,744,970	933,774,000	1.86	6,450	691	16,164,485	546,526
1929	534,988,593	952,781,000	1.78	6,057	679	17,429,298	495,219
1930	467,526,299	795,483,000	1.70	5,891	700	15,877,407	240,886
1931	382,089,396	588,895,000	1.54	5,642	669	12,126,299	206,303
1932	309,709,872	406,677,000	1.31	5,427	594	8,814,047	186,909
1933	333,630,533	445,788,000	1.34	5,555	559	9,086,947	197,429
			1.75	6,958	565	10,968,552	179,661

Year							
1935	372,373,122	658,063,000	1.77	6,315	582	9,742,430	201,871
1936	439,087,903	770,955,000	1.76	6,875	618	10,654,959	271,798
1937	445,531,449	864,042,000	1.94	6,548	646	13,144,678	257,996
1938	348,544,764	678,653,000	1.95	5,777	602	10,490,269	241,305
1939	394,855,325	728,348,366	1.84	5,820	621	11,590,478	355,115
1940	460,771,500	879,327,227	1.91	6,324	639	16,465,928	371,571
1941	514,149,245	1,125,362,836	2.19	6,822	666	20,740,471	390,049
1942	582,692,937	1,373,990,608	2.36	6,972	663	22,943,305	498,103
1943	590,177,069	1,584,644,477	2.69	6,620	626	25,836,208	757,634
1944	619,576,240	1,810,900,542	2.92	6,928	624	26,032,348	633,689
1945	577,617,327	1,768,204,320	3.06	7,083	620	27,956,192	467,473
1946	533,922,068	1,835,539,476	3.44	7,333	699	41,197,378	434,680
1947	630,623,722	2,622,634,946	4.16	8,700	755	68,666,963	290,141
1948	599,518,229	2,993,267,021	4.99	9,079	774	45,990,183	291,337
1949	437,868,036	2,136,870,571	4.88	8,559	781	27,842,056	314,980
1950	516,311,053	2,500,373,779	4.84	9,429	790	25,468,403	346,706
1951	533,664,782	2,626,030,137	4.92	8,009	736	56,721,547	292,378
1952	466,840,782	2,289,180,401	4.90	7,275	703	47,643,150	262,268
1953	457,290,449	2,247,943,799	4.92	6,671	670	33,760,263	226,900
1954	391,706,300	1,769,619,723	4.52	6,130	603	31,040,564	198,799
1955	464,633,408	2,092,382,737	4.50	7,856	620	51,277,256	387,145
1956	500,874,077	2,412,004,151	4.82	8,520	655	68,552,629	355,701
1957	492,703,916	2,504,406,042	5.08	8,539	680	76,445,529	366,506
1958	410,445,547	1,996,281,274	4.86	8,264	625	50,293,382	306,940
1959	412,027,502	1,965,606,901	4.77	7,719	614	37,253,431	374,713
1960	415,512,347	1,950,425,049	4.69	7,865	609	36,541,075	260,495
1961	402,976,802	1,844,562,662	4.58	7,648	585	34,969,825	164,259
1962	422,149,325	1,891,554,474	4.48	7,740	594	38,413,424	232,424

SOURCE: U.S. Bureau of Mines, *Minerals Year Book*, Washington, D.C., 1963.

loss of markets to petroleum and natural gas. The prospects throughout the 1950's were that for the next few years the coal industry was likely to sustain further losses of markets. Industry analysts believed, however, that with economic progress in the United States the future would see a much improved coal position, unless unforeseen developments in energy revolutionized the whole fuel industry. These analysts saw the problem as one of keeping "the industry from wasting away during the lean period immediately ahead."

The President's Materials Policy Commission laid the foundation for the optimistic long-run view with the conclusion that: "While coal's percentage share of the 1975 energy total is likely to be less than now, actual volume of coal at that date may be 60 percent above present (1950) levels. Sometime after that date—whenever the cost relationship shifts and domestic oil and gas production become too high in cost or too low in volume—coal is expected gradually to take over the energy burden in the United States. Reserves are more than ample."[2]

The Commission saw that more than a preventive "wasting away" program was required, as indicated by the further conclusion: "The extent and timing of coal's upturn will depend importantly on technologic' de-

Figure 3.4: Trends of Bituminous Coal and Lignite Production, Realization, Mine Capacity, and Net Income or Deficit in the United States.

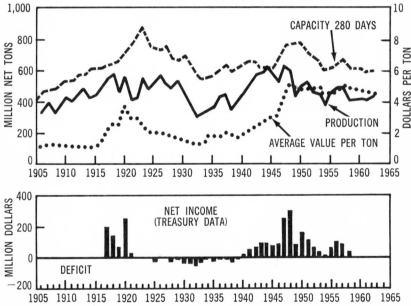

SOURCE: U.S. Bureau of Mines.

[2] *Resources for Freedom,* a report to the President by the President's Materials Policy Commission, Vol. III, *The Outlook for Energy Sources,* Washington, D.C., 1952, p. 24.

velopment—better mining and processing methods, cheaper transportation methods, more efficient utilization. Advances in manufacture of liquid fuels from coal, as well as chemicals, could increase consumption."[3]

In spite of the long-run optimism, coal's short-run problem was the same as the long-run of the past, inadequate income and loss of markets.

Facts Bearing on the Problem

The information revealed in Figure 3.4 is most pertinent to the facts bearing on the problem. Most significant is that within the span of years 1922–1939 the bituminous and lignite mining industry did not make money. These years covered the prosperous twenties and the depression and recovery of the thirties. A comparison of the lower half of the chart with the upper half reveals that this deficit condition occurred at a time when the gap between capacity and production was greatest. When production increased and reached toward capacity during and after World War II, net income soared.

Many studies have been made of the U.S. bituminous coal industry. The results of an analysis of the National Coal Association are helpful because they contain a precise summarization of the 60-year economic history of the industry preceding the Korean War. There follows an outline of the detailed summary of the three periods: pre-World War I (1890–1918), World War I to World War II (1918–1939), and World War II to Korean War (1940–1949).

1. Mechanical improvements have been made. Man hours required to produce a ton of coal have declined for nearly half a century.

2. The decline has not been enough to offset increasing labor costs since 1917, although intervening ups and downs have taken place.

3. While the use of capital equipment has been extended, technical progress since World War I has slowed down. As indicated by data for the more important and typical machine, output per machine has not greatly increased. It was, of course, easier to make technological progress in the earlier period because it largely represented shift from hand operations to machine operations. As time passed, further technological progress required radical improvements in machinery, which are more difficult to accomplish.

4. Labor costs per ton have increased because labor saving has not been enough to offset rising wages.

5. Prices have risen in order to cover the increased costs of labor.

6. Profits have been meager, irregular, and not general throughout the industry. This has clearly been an influence retarding capital improvements. The profits of World War I brought about many mechanical improvements in the 1920's. Continued losses for more than a decade before World War II seriously retarded progress in extending and improving mechanization. The lack of profits had three effects:

[3] *Ibid.*

(a) Earnings were insufficient for reinvestment in plant and equipment.
(b) No attraction existed for new risk capital investment through capital stock flotations and the like.
(c) Impaired credit in many cases made it difficult to borrow for capital improvements.[4]

Just prior to the Korean War, when coal production declined 30 percent from a post-World War II peak in 1947 to a low in 1949, the coal industry began to worry about its economic position. This situation was alleviated temporarily during the first part of the war, but returned in an aggravated form at the close of the war. This economic position of the industry was again relieved temporarily, but returned once more in the late 1950's. Obviously no simple presentation can be made of the facts that bear on the problem, but pointing up some of the more important issues may shed some light on the position of this basic industry. To simplify presentation, the previously mentioned idea of the gap between capacity and production will be pursued.

Capacity. Part of the United States' coal industry's problem is overcapacity. There have been factors at work on the overcapacity problem, that first gave rise to a rapid increase, and then additional factors which maintained this capacity in the face of declining production.

The rapid expansion of the capacity of the coal mining industry was made possible by the availability of coal under such large areas of land, and exploration and development of coal was facilitated by the Anglo-Saxon mineral law which gave mineral rights to the property owners rather than to the state as is the case under the Roman mineral law. The facts are clear from Figure 3.4 that from 1905 capacity rose from 417 million tons to an all-time peak of 885 million tons in 1923. Peak production was reached in 1918. Thereafter the gap between capacity and production continued until World War II. In addition to the factors of availability and incentives, the rapid rise in coal capacity was facilitated by railroads which made transportation available for coal because of the importance of coal as a source of revenue to them. Railroads and iron and steel industries which purchased captive coal mines to supply their own energy needs also facilitated the rise in coal capacity.

After 1923 capacity was decreased, but many things worked against more rapid adjustments that would have helped close the gap between capacity and production. The nature of mining is such that once a mine is opened, the practice is to keep it in operation because of the rapid deterioration that sets in when it is closed, and because mines have no abandonment value since they cannot be put to an alternative use. These characteristics of mining, together with the facts that labor is such a large part of the cost of mining coal and that coal is the principal source of revenue in mining communities are among the economic and social pressures at

[4] Donald R. G. Cowan, *More Capital Equipment, Coal's Foremost Economic Need*, Washington, D.C., National Coal Association, July, 1948, p. 18.

work to keep mines open over a long period of time even when it is not economically profitable.

Other economic factors that have maintained capacity are the nature of mine ownership and competition within the industry. As already noted, about 15 percent of U.S. coal is produced by captive mines, or those in which coal is produced for a parent company, principally the steel companies. The operation of these mines is determined by the position of the parent companies. The other mines are highly competitive. This is a characteristic which is not typical of mining in general. The large number of mines and mining companies has worked against rational adjustments of capacity to production which are often achieved in other segments of industry where ownership is more concentrated.

Thus there have been fundamental characteristics of the bituminous coal mining industry which have expanded capacity, worked against downward capacity adjustment, and led to intense competition. These have been contributing factors to the sustained financial losses of the industry.

Consumption. Production of coal is determined directly by consumption. Coal companies do not stockpile because coal moves directly into railroad cars, barges, and trucks, and stockpiles would entail additional handling costs. So coal is left in the ground until needed. Consumer stockpiles tend to even out over the years. However, they are normally not large— 30–40 days prewar and 50–60 days postwar. During the early 1950's John L. Lewis, long-time chief of the United Mine Workers, manipulated labor to keep these stockpiles down in order to improve labor's bargaining position. Consequently the production line of Figure 3.4 is a direct function of consumption.

The absolute decline in production of coal before and after World War II and its relative decline in importance as an energy source are a direct result of factors that affect the consumption of coal. Although improved coal fuel efficiency has been a contributing factor to the loss of markets, coal's primary problem has arisen from increased competition from petroleum and natural gas. In an expanding energy economy coal has not even kept its market. Petroleum and natural gas have been the evil demons that have helped make coal sick while other segments of U.S. industry were healthy and growing into robust giants.

Consumption of U.S. bituminous coal by users has been studied in detail. Two significant trends have changed the pattern of coal consumption: (1) Petroleum and natural gas have cut into coal's old major markets of the railroads and domestic and industrial space heating. (2) The rapidly expanding electric power utilities have increased their consumption of coal over the pre-World War II years.

Coal's loss of the railroad market has been due to the shift to diesel- and electric-powered locomotives. Greater convenience of use, transportation, and cleanliness have sold petroleum and natural gas to the public.

In addition, heating equipment for these fuels was far ahead in design to meet the needs of the modern home. These are long-run unfavorable trends for coal that continue into the present.

Thus consumption and production of coal have lagged behind and helped create the gap between capacity and production.

World War II demands for coal brought about increased production, which temporarily closed the gap and enabled the coal industry to show net profits. But more fundamentally, the productive achievements of the war gave positive proof of the industrial potentials of the United States. On the positive and favorable side, they set in motion a tremendous growth of the electric power industry which increased its consumption of coal. This growth in consumption of coal by the electric power industry as previously noted, has been sustained and accelerated. It is this optimism over the use of coal in the generation of electric power that leads industry analysts to predict a favorable solution to coal's problem of a declining market.

Policy

Conditions that have existed in the coal industry have strongly influenced labor policy through the National Industrial Recovery Act (NIRA), the Wagner Act, the Taft-Hartley Act, and coal price and production policy through the NIRA and the Bituminous Coal Acts. In addition, the coal problem has led to restrictive public policy against competing industries such as petroleum and natural gas. Both public and private policy have in recent years encouraged research.

Price and Production Policies. Under the National Industrial Recovery Act of 1933 minimum coal prices were set by regional code authorities. Government authority granted industry the right to set prices. Intercompany and inter-regional rivalry led to the sale of coal under minimum prices, and code enforcement collapsed before the NIRA was declared unconstitutional in 1935. Section 7a of the NIRA gave labor the right to bargain collectively.

Coal operators and the union sponsored and obtained the passage of the Bituminous Coal Conservation Act of 1935 to replace the NIRA. The Supreme Court declared this act unconstitutional before it became operative on the grounds that regulation of labor was an intrastate problem.

In 1937 the Bituminous Coal Act was passed. It omitted the labor provisions of the 1935 act. This new act provided that minimum and maximum coal prices could be fixed by a Bituminous Coal Commission. Noncooperating producers were taxed 19½ percent of the mine price of coal. The coal fields were divided into districts and the districts were grouped into ten price areas.

Individual district boards, made up of operators plus one representative of the union, were supposed to initiate the price-fixing process. However, in 1937 the Commission set prices without following this procedure, and a period of litigation ensued until October, 1940, when the prices prescribed by the Commission went into effect. The defense boom soon swept coal prices above the minimum, and when the Bituminous Coal Act expired in 1943, it was not renewed. The OPA (Office of Price Administration) set maximum prices for coal in 1942.

The short period of operation of the acts does not permit careful analysis of what the long-run effects would have been on the industry. Since there were no controls on production and entry of new firms, there is ample reason to believe that unwarranted increased production would have resulted from higher prices. The most significant result of the acts was government recognition of the problems of the industry and the establishment of a government regulation policy that the industry approved.

Beginning in 1949, there were renewed discussions of the need for government legislation to assist the coal industry. However, no proposals of price and production controls were actively sponsored, perhaps because it was clear that any proposal for higher coal prices would hardly be a solution to the problem of recapturing lost markets from competitive energy sources.

Restrictive Policy. In the areas of restrictive policy, both operator and industry groups have lobbied against programs that would lead to the development of other competitive energy sources. Examples of such policy programs are the attempt to prevent the use of the Big Inch and Little Big Inch emergency-built pipelines for transportation of petroleum or natural gas after World War II, and very vigorous action to put preventive tariffs and import quotas on petroleum supplies. This latter policy is an issue that will be discussed in the subsequent chapter on petroleum. Although policies of prevention and protection have many strong supporters, particularly in the area of tariffs and quotas where foreign competition is involved, they are difficult to defend in pursuance of an overall objective of economic progress. Economic progress is not to be achieved by checking and penalizing the growth of other energy sources.

The most serious attempt at restrictive policy was begun in the late 1950's with a concerted effort to obtain a national fuels policy that would advocate end-use controls. Senate Resolution 105 of the first session of the 87th Congress resulted in the formation of a National Fuels and Energy Study Group which reported in September, 1962, to the Committee on Interior and Insular Affairs of the United States Senate. Controlled end-use was one of the principal policy issues with which the Study Group was concerned.

The issue of controlled end-use is legislative or regulatory control of the use to which a fuel may be put. The controlled end-use doctrine has its roots in the *wasting asset theory*, that is, since fossil fuels are exhaustible, the consumption of each fuel should be channeled to its best use.

Controlled end-use was most recently involved in the Transco case (F.P.C. v. Transcontinental Gas Pipe Line Corporation; National Coal Association v. Transcontinental Gas Pipe Line Corporation 365, U.S. 1, 1961). In this case the Supreme Court held that the Federal Power Commission had authority to consider conservation and the use for which a supply of gas was intended as factors in authorizing or denying the construction of facilities to transport gas.

Thus, the coal industry argues that policies should be adopted restricting the uses of other fuels because they are wasting assets that should be conserved, while coal is more abundant. Indeed one phrase in the Supreme Court's opinion on the Transco case was: "One apparent method of preventing waste of gas is to limit the use to which it may be put, uses for which another, more abundant fuel may serve equally well." The coal industry argued that current policy favored other fuels and that legislation should be enacted by Congress in ten needed areas.[5]

The National Fuels and Energy Study Group examined the policy directions indicated by control end-use, that is, complete adherence to the controlled end-use concept, no end-use controls, and some middle ground position. The Study Group concluded that the fundamental cost of strict acceptance of the doctrine of controlled end-use would seem to be a broad range of cumbersome policies that would perhaps economically misallocate resources.

The Study Group found that the principal cost of the rejection of end-use controls would be to those industries that would gain through their imposition. The complete rejection of end-use controls would stimulate the use of especially suitable fuels at a faster rate than otherwise, and the use of less suitable fuels at a slower rate. The conclusion was drawn, however, for a fast rate of use to be a cost factor requires the assumption that the supply is limited. The assumption is valid, but if the limited supply is greater than the need for it then the "wasting asset" feature becomes irrelevant. In the case of gas, the Study Group found the supply well beyond requirements. Most importantly, the Study Group found that no end-use controls would retard price increases that might otherwise come forth with controls.

Finally, the Study Group found that a middle ground position on controlled end-use would represent administration by episode, where decisions are influenced partly by fact, but also in terms of the cliches of the day, the eloquence of its advocates, and the influences of other objectives.

In short, the Study Group completely rejected the demand of the coal industry for end-use controls in favor of the free market. Finally, the conclusion was that the continued practice of no end-use controls should

[5] "Statement of the National Coal Policy Conference and the National Coal Association," *Report of the National Fuels and Energy Study Group*, Washington, D.C., 1962, p. 427.

accomplish the following results: it would stimulate the use of especially suitable fuels, it would generate a search for and production of more reserves for fuels in greater demand, and it would provide a form of natural regulation of prices because of the threat of competitive fuels.

Research Policy. A much sounder policy than either of the two previously discussed is that of sponsoring research to achieve better mining and processing methods, cheaper transportation, more effective marketing methods, and more efficient utilization. Most important are investigations to promote advances in the manufacture of gas, liquid fuels, and chemicals from coal.

The small size of most coal companies and their low rates of return on capital have prevented them from actively sponsoring research programs. Attempts have been made by the industry and government to correct this situation. The coal industry is promoting joint research, the government is sponsoring research, and the coal and petroleum industries have combined programs. In addition, railroads and the electric power companies are cooperating in the research program,

To overcome the handicap of small-scale enterprise, the coal industry organized a cooperative research agency at the end of World War II, called Bituminous Coal Research, Incorporated. It was supported by more than 300 coal, railroad, and equipment companies. One of the major projects was the designing of a coal-fired gas turbine locomotive—a direct attack to recapture this market from diesel fuel. Railroads operating in the coal regions were actively interested in the project. Nine railroads joined with four large coal operators to form the Locomotive Development Committee of Bituminous Coal Research, Incorporated, and in 1952 the American Locomotive Company began work under a contract to develop the turbine for commercial application, and to design a chassis for locomotive use. The U.S. Bureau of Mines reported that by 1962 the Union Pacific Railroad had started tests of its experimental direct-fired, coal-burning gas turbine for driving electric locomotives.

The Mining Development Committee of Bituminous Coal Research, is attempting to find ways to produce coal more cheaply and faster with minimum manpower through practical continuous mining. Other research projects are sponsored by Bituminous Coal Research to develop more efficient utilization of bituminous coal by householders, electric utilities, and industrial plants.

The U.S. Bureau of Mines has had a coal research program for about thirty years. Research is actively sponsored in the area of coal mining methods and coal preparation. One of the major projects of the Bureau has been the development of synthetic fuels from coal, lignite, and oil shale. At the end of World War II, upon the recommendation of the Fuels and Lubricants Division of the Army Service Forces, a surplus ordnance plant at Louisiana, Missouri, was turned over to the Bureau of Mines for research purposes. At this plant extensive research is being carried on to lower production costs of synthetic oils and gasoline from coal by the hydrogenation and the Fischer-Tropsch processes.

In this latter connection the most desirable research program is one in which large companies such as Standard Oil (New Jersey), Pittsburgh Consolidation Coal Company, Gulf Oil, and Koppers join together to improve coal-to-oil synthesis. Individual oil companies have been actively at work in this endeavor, which is already technically and economically feasible.

There is a sustained research interest in the gasification of coal to synthesis gas which can be used as fuel, and as a source of coal chemicals. Near Gorgas, Alabama, the U.S. Bureau of Mines and the Alabama Power Company have been conducting tests on gasifying coal in the ground. The purpose is to burn the unmined coal so as to produce usable gas which then can be burned for power, used to make chemicals derived from gas, or perhaps even synthesized into gasoline.

In the area of transportation, significant progress has been made in reducing costs. As we have already noted, because of the demonstrated feasibility of moving coal in a water slurry through pipelines, legislation was introduced in Congress for the right of eminent domain for construction of interstate coal pipelines. To meet this competition, the railroads introduced the concept of the integral train for moving coal from the producer to the consumer. The integral train included the design of new cars and rapid loading and unloading facilities. With this new idea of bulk transportation, greater efficiency was achieved and resulted in substantially reduced railroad freight rates. Another promising technological innovation was the development of methods of transmitting electricity at extra-high voltages—as much as 500,000 volts or more—from mine-mouth generating plants. As a result, the Bonneville Power Administration, and The Tennessee Valley Authority in cooperation with a group of surrounding utilities began the planning or construction of 500,000-volt circuits.

Research to promote more efficient utilization of coal is being carried on intensively by the U.S. Bureau of Mines and by private industry. This type of research works two ways. On the one hand, less coal input is required per unit of output. On the other hand, more efficient use results in a lower consumer cost and thus improves coal's competitive position. Nowhere is this improved efficiency more important than in the generation of electric power. Steam units continue to grow in size and efficiency. In 1962 the largest generator was designed to deliver 6,500,000 pounds of steam per hour to the turbine at a pressure of 2,400 pounds per square inch. The turbine had a capability of generating over a million kilowatts of electricity. But the important contributing factor to lower costs of electricity per kwh has been the improved efficiency of steam boilers, which in 1963 used 0.86 pounds of coal to generate one kwh in contrast to 1.24

pounds in 1949 and 2 pounds in 1925. New generating plants often require less than 0.7 pounds per kwh and the overall rate is expected to decline further as new units are built and older units are replaced.

Due to the structure of the coal industry and its need for research, a fairly strong case can be made for government-sponsored research in cooperation with and in addition to independently generated private research. As late as 1957, a House committee found that the "amount of coal research conducted in the United States has been wholly inadequate" and that the "coal mining industry is not in position to undertake a coal research program of the magnitude required to meet its short-term needs . . ." The same report noted that of the $17,382,000 expended in 1955 for coal research, only $4,863,000 was contributed by the federal government.[6]

Perhaps one result of this emphasis on the need for coal research was the establishment of the Office of Coal Research (OCR) within the U.S. Department of the Interior. But the coal industry is quick to point out that for the fiscal year 1962, the Congress appropriated for coal research purposes only 1 million dollars to the OCR and approximately $7,300,000 to the U.S. Bureau of Mines. For the fiscal year 1963, the Bureau of the Budget recommended 2 million dollars for the OCR and approximately $7,600,000 for Bureau of Mines Research purposes. Thus, even with the creation of the OCR, annual governmental expenditures for coal research increased less than 5 million dollars since 1955, the year studied by the House committee. In contrast, the coal industry emphasizes that the United States government spent about 500 million dollars during the same 3-year period on a nuclear reactor construction program to produce civilian power competitive to coal.[7]

Although this last comparison may not be exactly valid, a case can be made that the recommendation of the coal industry should be followed: "Legislation should be enacted which will provide adequate Federal funds for coal research within the U.S. Department of Interior."[8]

This legislation proposal is designed to carry forward the 1957 finding of the House subcommittee that:

Since the welfare of the coal industry is highly important to the economy and security of the United States and since the public would derive substantial and lasting benefits from research which could be expected to result in the more economic and effective utilization of the Nation's fuel resources, the subcommittee concludes that it would be in the national interest for the Federal Government to support a greatly expanded coal research and development program over a period of 12 or more years.[9]

[6] House Report No. 1263, 85th Congress, 1st Session, pp. 60, 61, 90.
[7] *Report of the National Fuels and Energy Study Group, op. cit.*, p. 463.
[8] *Ibid.*
[9] House Report No. 1263, *op. cit.*, p. 82.

SUMMARY

The conclusion can be drawn that the coal industry has not shared in the growth of energy use in the United States, but its long-run future lies in the steady growth of energy use in the United States and especially in the development of the electric power industry. In the policy area, government and industry regulation and restrictive measures are rejected in favor of a free market to encourage the most efficient use and allocation of energy resources. Research programs indicate that industry and government are working together to solve short- and long-run energy problems of the U.S. coal industry. This is the progressive and active type of solution that has made the United States productive and will abet economic progress in the future. Where private industry and public objectives are closely allied there is adequate reason for optimism that the objectives will be achieved. However, an ever-present problem is that policies will be adopted to correct short-run problems which will work against the achievement of long-run objectives.

SELECTED REFERENCES

Averitt, Paul, *Coal Reserves of the United States—A Progress Report*, January 1, 1960, Geological Survey Bulletin 1136, Washington, D.C., 1961.

"Bituminous Coal," in *Mineral Facts and Problems*, Bureau of Mines Bulletin 585, Washington, D.C., 1960, pp. 111–140.

Coal—Basic Analysis, Standard & Poor's Industry Surveys, New York, Standard & Poor, 1963 and later editions.

"Coal Turns the Corner—The Question Is: How Soon?," *Business Week*, July 9, 1955, pp. 81 ff.

Cowan, Donald R. G., *More Capital Equipment, Coal's Foremost Economic Need*, Washington, D.C., National Coal Association, July, 1948.

The European Coal and Steel Community, Studies in Business and Economics, Bureau of Business and Economic Research, Parts 1 and 2, University of Maryland, December, 1955, and June, 1956.

Moyer, Forrest T., and James A. Vaughan, "Anthracite," in *Mineral Facts and Problems*, Bureau of Mines Bulletin 585, Washington, D.C., 1960, pp. 43–60.

Resources for Freedom, a report to the President by the President's Materials Policy Commission, Vol. III, *The Outlook for Energy Sources*, Washington, D.C., 1952.

"Statement of the National Coal Policy Conference and the National Coal Association," *Report of the National Fuels and Energy Study Group*, Washington, D.C., 1962, pp. 427–459.

Young, W. H., and R. L. Anderson, "Coal—Bituminous and Lignite," Preprint for U.S. Bureau of Mines *Minerals Yearbook*, Washington, D.C., 1963.

4

PETROLEUM

PETROLEUM is vital to victory in war just as it is the growing source of power in peacetime. The importance of petroleum to the security of the United States was clearly established during World War II, when more than 50 percent of all the shipments of supplies to our military forces were petroleum products. Petroleum furnishes more than a third of the energy used in the United States, but even this figure does not give a true picture of its significance as a liquid fuel. As a fuel petroleum is absolutely essential in most forms of transportation.

Four functional groups describe the U.S. petroleum industry: (1) exploration, drilling and production; (2) refining and processing; (3) transportation; and (4) marketing.

NATURE AND OCCURRENCE

Most crude petroleum appears as an oil that upon treatment under heat, pressure, or other means yields different products ranging from gas, through liquids to solids. Even though crude oil differs widely in characteristics and properties, it is all composed of hydrocarbon molecules made up of varying numbers of hydrogen and carbon atoms. The nature of the crude determines the products which can be obtained from it by simple refining methods.

Petroleum is organic in origin, and it is assumed that whatever the organic material from which petroleum developed, it was first deposited in clays and sands along seacoasts, in swamps and lakes, and that its rapid destruction by oxidation was prevented by a covering of beds of other material. It is believed that when oil was formed in the buried sediments of ancient seas, it existed first in the form of droplets widely dispersed in rock layers. With oil in the rock, there was also salt water. Along with the oil, gas had been formed from the same organic matter. Because oil is lighter than water and gas is lighter than both, the three may be said to sort themselves out. Much of the oil and gas came to the surface of the earth years ago. But not all escaped; much was caught in subterranean *traps* formed by the buckling and folding of the earth in early geologic time. Four types of these traps are shown in Figure 4.1.

In the case of oil trapped by a *fault*, a break in layers of rock may have occurred. The rock on one side of such a break slips up or down so that the uptilted end of a porous layer is thrust against a nonporous layer and is thereby sealed.

A second kind of trap is formed when porous rock is folded upward, producing a subterranean formation something like an upside-down bowl. Oil and gas may collect at the top of such a bowl and be prevented from escaping by an overlying nonporous layer. This kind of trap is called an *anticline.*

In a third type of trap, buried sandstone that may once have been a beach tapers off like a wedge, ending between layers of rock that are nonporous. Here the oil moves through the sandstone until it can go no farther and collects to form an oil field. This type of formation is called a *stratigraphic trap.*

Under great pressure salt becomes plastic and acts somewhat like putty. Thick layers of it, deep underground, sometimes were forced upward to form a *salt dome*, against which migrating oil might accumulate. Oil has often been found by drilling along the flanks of salt domes, especially along the Gulf Coast of the United States.

Before turning to the question of the United States reserves, let us discuss exploration, drilling, and production upon which knowledge of reserves depends.

EXPLORATION, DRILLING AND PRODUCTION

Exploration

Exploration is now conducted with the scientific knowledge of the petroleum geologists. Oil is no longer looked for by guess or directly; today the search for oil begins by a search for traps. Today we have a science of geophysics at work in the search. And the scientists have such instruments as the gravity meter, the magnetometer, and the seismograph to aid them in their search. But in spite of all the advances made in the science of exploration, the only way to prove that there is oil in the ground is to drill and find it.

Drilling

Drilling a well is accomplished by two methods: cable tool and rotary drilling. In each case a derrick, a tapering tower, is erected as a means of hoisting the many pieces of equipment that must be lowered into the

Figure 4.1: Four Types of Oil Traps.

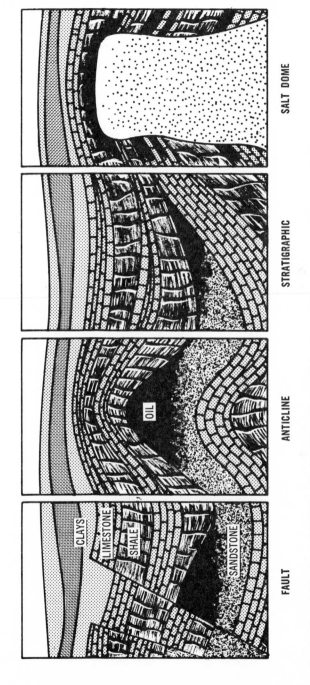

FAULT

ANTICLINE

STRATIGRAPHIC

SALT DOME

CLAYS

LIMESTONE

SHALE

SANDSTONE

OIL

SOURCE: Stewart Schackne and N. D'Arcy Drake, *Oil For The World* (Harper & Row), Copyright © 1950, 1955, 1960 by Standard Oil Company (New Jersey), p. 41.

well. Cable tool drilling is an old method originally used by the Chinese to dig water wells. A hole in the ground is punched by repeatedly lifting and dropping a heavy cutting tool hung from the cable and called a bit.

About 85 percent of all wells today are drilled by the rotary method. Rotary drilling bores a hole into the earth by means of a steel turntable in the middle of the derrick floor. The rotary table turns a pipe at the lower end of which is located a bit. During the drilling a mixture of water, special clays and chemicals, known as drilling mud, is pumped down through the hollow pipe and is forced back to the surface in the space between the outside of the pipe and the walls of the hole.

As the hole becomes deeper it is lined with steel pipe called a casing. Each length of casing is called a stringer, and additional stringers are added as the well becomes deeper. During the course of drilling, information is obtained about the strata being penetrated. This is brought up either by the mud or by special cylindrical sections cut out of the rock. This material is analyzed, and a fairly accurate picture can be obtained of the inside of the well.

If oil-bearing rock is reached, the drill is removed while the mud holds back the flow. A final string of casing is set, and a small pipe called tubing is lowered into the well through which the oil flows out. At the surface end of the tubing, a system of valves known as a *Christmas tree* is fastened. These valves control the flow of oil up through the tubing and into surface pipes leading to storage tanks.

Drilling in the United States is risky and expensive. Only one wildcat, or exploratory, well in nine finds any oil, and only one in forty-four finds a field that is commercially profitable. Of about 50,000 exploratory and development well (wells in existing fields) drilled each year in this country, about 50 percent find oil, 10 percent find natural gas, and the remaining 40 percent are dry.

The expense of drilling a well is great and is increasing. This latter is true because wells are being drilled to greater depths and because of the increased cost of offshore drilling in the Gulf Coast area. It costs very much more to drill a deep well than a shallow one as the cost per incremental foot goes up at a rapid rate. For example, the following costs per foot would apply at these depths: 0-1,250 = $6.63; 2,500-3,750 = $10.62; 5,000-7,500 = $18.27; 10,000-12,500 = $41.80; and over 15,000 feet = $105.91 per foot. The newer discoveries are deep, averaging 10 to 12 thousand feet, three to four times the depth at which the lucrative discoveries in the Texas-Kansas-Oklahoma area usually have been found. In these three states a well costs about $60,000, but offshore Louisiana, where really significant discoveries have been made since the middle 1950's the cost per well approaches $400,000. In addition, the offshore areas require elaborate and expensive geophysical surveys before the first exploratory well can go down.

Finally, one point which was emphasized in testimony before the National Fuels and Energy Study Group was that historically there has been a close relationship between the number of wells drilled and petroleum reserves developed. Although more advanced technology and improved recovery techniques may tend to alter this relationship somewhat, the conclusion was that this basic relationship would continue to exist, and thus the future of the United States reserve position depended upon sustained exploration and drilling.

Production

Production of crude petroleum comes from deposits which are referred to as *pools*. As we have seen, the oil occurs in the pores of underground rock; and the forces that push the oil through the rocks are known as *drives*. There are three major types; dissolved-gas drive, gas-cap drive, and water drive.

1. *Dissolved-gas drive.* This type of drive occurs where there is no gas above the oil or water below it, but there is gas dissolved in it. Expansion of the gas moves the oil through the rocks to the wells. Oil recovery with this type of drive is low.

2. *Gas-cap drive.* In this instance there is a large amount of gas above the oil as well as in it. This gas cap expands into the oil sand and pushes the oil before it.

3. *Water drive.* With this type of drive a large quantity of water below the oil and gas moves into the oil-bearing rock and flushes the oil ahead of it.

There was a time when oil wells were allowed to flow freely so as to get the oil out of the ground as quickly as possible and wells were drilled in close proximity to one another to accomplish this recovery. Today the nature of the oil drive and the geological structure of the field is carefully studied. Flow from each well is regulated so that the proper oil-gas ratio is maintained, and wells are properly spaced in order to maintain the maximum efficiency of recovery (the MER).

Many modern fields have only one well for each 40 acres, which means wells spaced about one quarter of a mile apart as compared with the early Spindletop field in Texas where wells were drilled so close together that a man could walk a mile stepping from one derrick floor to the next. When withdrawal from a field continues underground pressure declines; now it is much slower because it is controlled at an anticipated rate. When pressure drops to a point where natural forces are no longer sufficient to bring up the oil, pumps are installed.

Many new petroleum reserves are added each year in existing fields due to new developments that make possible additional recovery of oil. Two methods that have greatly increased secondary recovery are waterflooding to flush oil ahead of it, and pumping natural gas back into the producing formation. In many instances this latter method is used from the very beginning to obtain maximum recovery. But even with all the new advances in recovery methods only about one-third of the oil in the ground reaches the surface.

The oil and the gas from a well reach the surface in a frothy mixture which is routed through valves of the *Christmas tree* to vessels where the gas is separated from the liquid and the oil is sent to storage. Any petroleum liquids remaining as vapors in the gas are removed in natural gasoline plants, and the dry gas is used in various ways. Some is used in the field and is pumped back into the reservoir to maintain pressure. There was a time when most of the gas was burned away, but now most of it is sold for transmission to the market, and about one-third of all natural gas used in the United States comes from oil wells.

The next functional operation is refining, but we are now in a position to look at petroleum reserves. These reserves are a function of exploration, drilling, and production recovery, and additions to them come from the finding of new fields and new developments in old fields.

PETROLEUM RESERVES

Petroleum reserves are stated as *proved reserves*. Proved reserves are defined as: "The volumes of crude oil which geological and engineering information indicate beyond reasonable doubt to be recoverable in the future from an oil reservoir under existing economic and operating conditions." Thus proved reserves tell us what is in the ground and can be recovered but they do not indicate future possibilities or deposits in the ground that can not be obtained.

A common, but misleading practice, has been to express petroleum reserves in terms of the ratio between the reserves figure and the current rate of production. For example, "reported oil reserves are equivalent to about 13 years of production." Thus, the general public has been led to believe that the United States will run out of oil in 13 years. Actually as one looks at this ratio as plotted in Figure 4.2 it appears that the U. S. industry has maintained a working inventory of proven reserves of about 12 or 13 years. Thus, proved reserves have increased as production has increased. The true measures of the U. S. petroleum productive capacity should be potential production measured against anticipated demand.

The American Petroleum Institute, based on studies of individual pools, maintains an annual record of *proved reserves* in the United States. There are two separate ways by which new crude oil supplies are made available: (1) new developments increasing the recovery of oil in known deposits, and (2) new discoveries of deposits. Thus, to proved reserves at the beginning of the year are added new proved reserves, which result from new developments and new discoveries, and from this figure must be subtracted production for the year. Thus, the figure for crude oil reserves (not including natural gas liquids) at the beginning of 1960 was 31,719,347,000 barrels. This figure was arrived at by taking the proved reserves at the beginning of 1959 of 30,535,917,000 barrels, adding 3,666,-745,000 barrels of new reserves during the year, and subtracting 2,483,-315,000 barrels of crude production during 1959. Figure 4.3 gives a graphic distribution of these 1960 petroleum reserves by states and by districts.

Figure 4.2: Petroleum Reserves, Annual Production, and Ratio of Reserves to Annual Production.

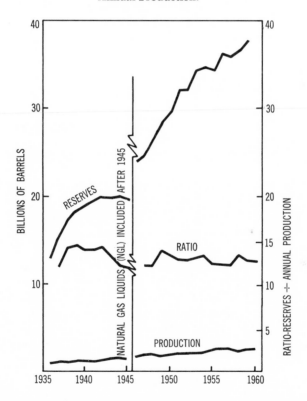

SOURCE: *Report of the National Fuels and Energy Study Group,* to the Committee on Interior and Insular Affairs, United States Senate, 87th Congress, Second Session, Washington, D.C., September 21, 1962.

The important point in the above discussion is to note that in the United States, new reserves are being added to proved reserves each year and that these additions must be continued at an annual rate greater than anticipated demand if the customary inventory is to be maintained. One

TABLE 4.1
Proved Crude Oil Reserves in the United States January 1, 1965
(Thousands of barrels of 42 U.S. gallons)

	Proved reserves as of December 31, 1963 (1)	Changes in proved reserves due to extensions and revisions during 1964 (2)	Proved reserves discovered in new fields and in new pools in old fields in 1964 (3)	Production during 1964 (4)	Proved reserves as of December 31, 1964 (columns 1 + 2 + 3 less column 4) (5)	Changes in reserves during 1964 (column 5 less column 1) (6)
Alaska	74,920	19,000	–	11,054	82,866	7,946
Alabama	45,069	13,537	–	8,710	49,896	4,827
Arkansas	225,291	5,191	615	25,937	205,160	(–) 20,131
California [a]	3,599,735	785,347	39,275	298,876	4,125,481	525,746
Colorado	368,375	9,775	2,585	34,401	346,334	(–) 22,041
Illinois	416,612	44,859	890	70,825	391,536	(–) 25,076
Indiana	63,432	8,185	164	11,102	60,629	(–) 2,803
Kansas	841,349	51,024	10,034	105,866	796,541	(–) 44,808
Kentucky	100,456	32,737	5,005	20,337	117,861	17,405
Louisiana [a]	5,088,605	385,777	166,564	478,458	5,162,488	73,883

Michigan	68,543	5,068	185	15,497	58,299	(−) 10,244
Mississippi	384,909	22,011	5,451	55,804	356,567	(−) 28,342
Montana	271,253	4,745	6,290	30,668	251,620	(−) 19,633
Nebraska	83,583	2,816	3,450	18,748	71,101	(−) 12,482
New Mexico	1,010,729	48,251	6,148	108,336	956,792	(−) 53,937
New York	18,435	(−) 3,000	–	1,874	13,561	(−) 4,874
North Dakota	389,158	9,763	3,914	25,599	377,236	(−) 11,922
Ohio	87,814	27,598	–	15,850	99,562	(−) 11,748
Oklahoma	1,628,138	149,925	6,701	198,879	1,585,885	(−) 42,253
Pennsylvania	91,734	–	–	5,113	86,621	(−) 5,113
Texas[a]	14,573,125	585,109	70,309	928,696	14,299,847	(−)273,278
Utah	219,576	25,017	3,315	28,400	219,508	(−) 68
West Virginia	57,303	4,693	–	3,286	58,710	1,407
Wyoming	1,254,306	77,939	12,960	140,669	1,204,536	(−) 49,770
Miscellaneous[b]	7,540	3,157	2,438	1,262	11,873	4,333
Total United States	30,969,990	2,318,474	346,293	2,644,247	30,990,510	20,520

a Includes off-shore reserves.
b Under Miscellaneous are included Arizona, Florida, Missouri, Nevada, South Dakota, Tennessee, and Virginia.
SOURCE: *Proved Reserves of Crude Oil, Natural Gas Liquids, and Natural Gas*, New York, American Petroleum Institute, 1965.

important trend is that additions to proved reserves, as computed by the American Petroleum Institute, declined from a 5-year average of 3.2 billion barrels per year in the early 1950's to 2.6 billion barrels per year for the period 1958–1963. The effect of this decline was to slow the growth of proved reserves of crude oil almost to a halt. Between 1950 and 1956 total year-end reserves increased by 5 billion barrels. In the succeeding 6-year period (1956–1962) reserves increased by less than one billion barrels, and in four of the previous seven years, additions to reserves were less than withdrawals for use. By January 1, 1964, proved crude oil reserves had fallen to slightly less than 31 billion barrels, 30.97 to be exact. At a production rate of 2.59 billion barrels in 1963 this represented a ratio of 11.9 barrels of crude oil proved reserves for each one produced in that year.

Table 4.1, which gives significant data for each of the United States, shows that at the beginning of 1965 crude oil reserves had increased slightly over the previous year-end total to 30.99 billion barrels; but at the 1964 production of 2.64 billion barrels, the ratio of proved crude reserves to production had fallen to 11.7.

One fact bearing on the reduction in proved reserves was the decline in the number of wells drilled from 58,200 in 1956, to 43,600 in 1963, a reduction of 25 percent. In commenting on this deteriorated proved reserve position, the U.S. Department of Interior concluded: "This is no cause for immediate alarm, but it does indicate that what has been done since 1956 to find new supplies of oil, whether through new discoveries or through increasing recovery rates of old deposits, has not been enough to provide a sound basis for future growth."[1]

The limiting factor on how much petroleum reserves can be increased is the amount in the ground waiting for man to find. But the availability of this oil depends, of course, on technology and economics. The National Fuels and Energy Study Group estimated that the total volume of oil and natural gas liquids present in the drilled portions of known reserves was about 270 billion barrels. However, only 70 billion barrels of this was determined to be economically recoverable by present techniques. In addition to these reserves, the Study Group offers the challenge of reserves *on order* (new discoveries). This is the amount of oil in the ground waiting for man to find. In this highly speculative field the Group concluded the estimate of oil recoverable from pools yet to be discovered should range from less than 270 to 370 billion barrels. The National Fuels and Energy Study Group concluded that the above figures on recoverable oil were so large that it was not necessary to pursue further the speculation about the total amount of oil in the ground. To make the potential reserves move into the proved category proper incentives are required.

[1] *An Appraisal of the Petroleum Industry of the United States*, Washington, D.C., United States Department of the Interior, 1965, p. 17.

Figure 4.3: Proved Crude Oil Reserves, By States as of January 1, 1960 (Billions of barrels).

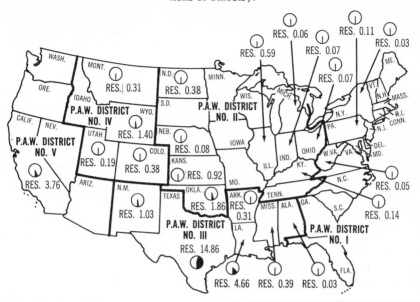

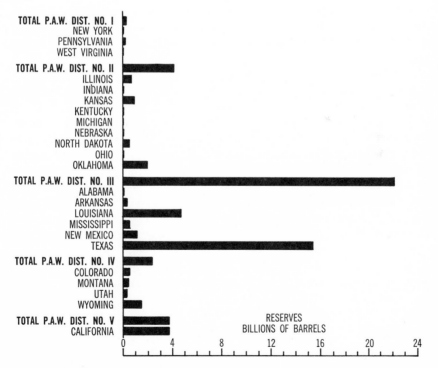

SOURCE: Data from American Petroleum Institute, *Twentieth Century Petroleum Statistics*, Dallas, Texas, DeGolyer and MacNaughton, 1960.

The search for petroleum reserves in the United States arose out of the ever-increasing demands for transportation. The same drive led U. S. oil companies to carry their search abroad in order to insure continued domestic availability of crude petroleum and to be able to supply what they correctly estimated to be a soon growing foreign demand for crude and petroleum products. Six companies operating in the United States, five of them American, were the leaders in undertaking tremendous foreign investments. The five were—Gulf Oil, Socony Mobil, Standard Oil (California), Standard Oil (New Jersey) and the Texas Company—the sixth was the Royal Dutch Shell Group.

These six companies, together with the British Oil Company, through concessions and other agreements with foreign governments undertook a vigorous search for crude, and as a result produced most of the oil in foreign areas. Up to 1960 they produced about 87.5 percent of the foreign crude oil in the free world. The international investments were made principally in the major export areas of the Caribbean and the Middle East. Proved crude oil reserves in the free world in 1961 are given in Table 4.1

TABLE 4.2
Proved Crude Oil Reserves in the Free World

	Billion barrels	Percent of total
Middle East	155.0	66.0
United States	31.8	13.5
Venezuela	17.5	7.4
Far East	11.0	4.7
Africa	8.0	3.4
Canada	4.2	1.8
Mexico	2.0	0.9
Other Countries	5.5	2.3
Total	235.0	100.0

Source: Data from the *Oil and Gas Journal, Petroleum Facts and Figures,* New York, American Petroleum Institute.

In the early part of the 1960's exploratory interest was dominated by developments outside the United States. In addition to the sustained search in the Middle East, which had 66 percent of the proved reserves, there was considerable activity in the Sahara Desert, Libya, Argentina, and Australia. By 1963 Middle East proved reserves had risen from the

155 billion barrels in 1961 shown in Table 4.2 to 204.5 billion barrels, and African reserves had increased from 8 billion barrels to 14 billion barrels in 1963. Total foreign proved reserves in the free world rose from 203.2 billion barrels shown in Table 4.1 to 261.8 billion barrels in 1963. At the same time U.S. proved reserves fell from 31.8 billion barrels to slightly less than 31.0 billion barrels at the end of 1963.

Some evidence of United States' company ownership of the estimated proved reserves for the world can be seen from the following table which gives the approximate conditions that obtained in the early 1960's. The total U.S. control was in the neighborhood of 148.0 billion barrels of crude oil, with the percent of control in each area shown in Table 4.3.

TABLE 4.3
Percent of United States Control of Crude Oil Reserves by Area

Area	Percent
North America	87.5
South America	68.9
Total Western Hemisphere	81.0
Europe (excluding USSR)	25.0
Africa	1.0
Middle East	58.8
Far East and Oceania	53.5
Total Eastern Hemisphere	57.3
World Total (excluding USSR and Communist controlled countries)	63.0

Source: *Twentieth Century Petroleum Statistics,* Dallas, Texas, DeGolyer and MacNaughton, 1960.

One interesting change taking place in the search for crude oil outside the United States was that during the first half of the twentieth century only five American owned companies had undertaken the search either because of the tremendous amount of capital involved or because of the company's own particular need for crude. Just before the 1960's these companies were joined in the search abroad by other American companies. Probably one of the reasons for this is that the U.S. petroleum industry is backed by somewhat thinner proved reserves than other areas, for the United States accounted for about 50 percent of the free world demand for petroleum but held only a little more than 13 percent of the proved reserves. Further, reserves were rising much faster outside the

United States than in the United States; for example, reserves in the Middle East between 1943 and 1964 increased eleven times while those in the United States increased only 56 percent. At the same time, maintenance of the crude reserve position was becoming more difficult as evidenced by data that show the amount of oil found in the United States for each foot drilled has been decreasing. Most importantly, this increased activity abroad, on the part of United States companies, emphasized the fact that increased importation of crude oil into the United States is inevitable.

One possible alternative to crude oil as it is presently used is that oil in some amount or other is found in shale in twenty-nine states, but only the shales in Colorado, Utah, and Wyoming have been considered to have potential commercial significance. The oil shale deposits in these three states are estimated by the U.S. Department of Interior to contain more than 1,000 billion barrels of petroleum-like material that could be converted into products similar to or identical to those obtained from petroleum. The oil-forming material in oil shale is a solid organic substance called kerogen. The three main steps in obtaining saleable liquid products from this substance are: (1) mining the shale and crushing and sizing it; (2) heating or retorting the crushed and sized rock to convert the kerogen to liquid (shale oil); and (3) refining the shale oil.

Experimental work done in early 1960 indicated that oil could be recovered from the shale at a price close to $3.00 a barrel. This would be oil delivered to a refinery on the Pacific coast. The average price in California for domestic crude oil in 1960 was $2.48. At least 50 billion barrels were estimated producible at the $3.00 price.

The conclusions drawn by the National Fuels and Energy Study Group about the availability of shale oil were as follows:

1. The amount of oil in shale in the United States is the same general magnitude as the amount of petroleum in the United States.

2. How much oil is initially available for production and use is a matter of the relation between the competitive market price of crude oil and the beginning costs of producing shale from oil by the new technology.

3. At the price of $3.00 a barrel for crude oil, the initiation of an oil industry is marginal. If the cost-price differential were improved enough to get the industry started by a small sustained rise in price, by a lowering of costs (by a different and cheaper process, for example), or by government subsidy of some sort, reserves would amount to some 50 billion barrels of oil.

4. As efficiency in operation is gained and costs of production are correspondingly cut, additional oil will become commercially recoverable. The limiting total is more than 1,000 billion barrels.[2]

A large share of the oil shale deposits are in 5.1 million acres of land owned by the federal government. Thus a conditioning factor determining

[2] *Report of the National Fuels and Energy Study Group*, Washington, D.C., 1962, p. 85.

development of this land will be U.S. policy. This is a continuing policy problem that should be followed. A Shale Oil Advisory Board was appointed to recommend appropriate policies, but when they reported in 1965, the six Board members disagreed as to how the research necessary to tap the shale oil deposits should be conducted. Part of the Board thought that commercial oil companies should be granted leases on tracts of unspecified size for research and the development of methods for extracting oil. Another part of the Board argued against research and development leases on the ground that it would result only in the transfer of lease rights to private owners who might be more interested in controlling potential oil reserves than in developing them. As an alternative, the suggestion was that the government should contract for the development of shale oil extraction processes, ultimately leasing the lands when an adequate knowledge of extraction costs made it possible to determine their true value.

In view of the availability of a cheaper source of crude oil abroad and the existence of excess domestic crude capacity, which will be discussed next in connection with imports, it is highly unlikely that shale oil would be exploited if a feasible extraction process were now available. Therefore it is appropriate to view the shale oil lands as potential oil reserves.

PRODUCTION OF CRUDE, CAPACITY, AND IMPORTS

Production of Crude and Capacity

The problem has always been whether the United States has sufficient productive capacity to meet its demands. The *Report of the National Fuels and Energy Study Group* shows that since 1950, crude productive capacity has been running far ahead of crude production. There are two ways of estimating capacity. One method, used by the Petroleum Administration for War in the years 1940–1946, by the U.S. Bureau of Mines in 1948, and by the National Petroleum Council in other years since the war, is based on the definition of capacity as that volume of production possible from existing wells; the implication being that this capacity will not continue unless the necessary drilling is continued. The estimates shown in Figure 4.4, along with crude production from 1940 to 1960, indicate that 100 percent of capacity was being used from 1944 to 1947, but an excess has been accumulating since then, which by January 1, 1960, had reached 3,350,000 barrels a day. The Independent Petroleum Association uses a second method of estimating capacity which assumes no further drilling will take place, and thus comes up with lower figures for capacity and reserve capacity.

These estimates of capacity refer to capacity at the maximum efficient rate of output (MER). Engineers estimate that these capacity figures could be increased by as much as 25 percent if concern over efficiency and ultimate recovery were neglected, provided this became necessary during a war.

Figure 4.4: Estimates of United States Crude Oil Production and Capacity.

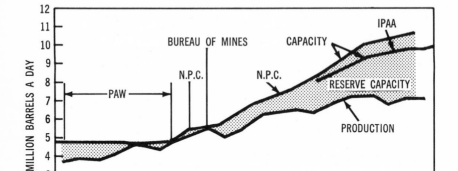

Source: *Report of the National Fuels and Energy Study Group*, to the Committee on Interior and Insular Affairs, United States Senate, 87th Congress, Second Session, Washington, D.C., September 21, 1962.

One point of major interest is that most of the nation's reserve capacity is located in Kansas, Mississippi, Arkansas, Louisiana, Oklahoma and Texas which contain almost 75 percent of the nation's productive capacity, but 93 percent of the reserve capacity. Most of this is in Texas and Louisiana. This is brought about by restriction of production (proration), which is the first problem that we will set aside for special study under the heading of conservation.

It is quite evident from the above that capacity was in excess of production. However, a crude reserve capacity representing the difference between the MER and actual production is required by the petroleum industry in order to provide sufficient flexibility for normal operations. As a result of conservation and regulatory measures a reserve capacity of 1,000,000 barrels a day was available before World War II that was the reservoir of strength out of which victory was achieved. Similarly, the reserve capacity shown on our chart for 1950, which was declared a sign of "ill health" and a result of imports, was helpful in meeting the increased demands of 1951 and 1952 brought about by the Korean War. The Petroleum Administration for Defense set up a program for a reserve productive capacity as a cushion against an emergency, and in October, 1952, a reserve of 1,000,000 barrels a day was a fundamental part of this nation's security program. However, this reserve should not be a set figure, but should be a function of anticipated emergency requirements and normal requirements.

Certainly, our data show that more than an adequate reserve had been achieved by January 1, 1960, with an estimated capacity of 10,585,-000 barrels a day, and production of 7,035,000 barrels a day. The question that many domestic producers were raising was why more of the capacity was not being used to supply the U.S. consumption of 9,797,000 barrels a day. Instead crude oil and an additional quantity of refined products, principally residual fuel oil, were being imported to satisfy the domestic demand.

Petroleum Imports

From 1923 until 1947 the United States was a net exporter of petroleum supplies. Imports of petroleum consisted of crude petroleum, residual fuel oil, and a small quantity of refined petroleum products. The Western Hemisphere, principally Venezuela, furnished the United States with all imports up until 1947, when crude oil and some refined products began to be imported from the Eastern Hemisphere.

After 1947 the United States became a net importer of petroleum in rising volumes. In 1958, just before mandatory import controls were initiated in March, 1959, total imports of crude oil, residual fuel oil and refined products reached a high of 25.3 percent of domestic crude oil production. The increased importation of crude oil in the United States undoubtedly was a result of higher costs of finding and developing crude in the United States. These costs were estimated at $1.73 a barrel in the United States, and much lower costs existed outside the country.

This relationship between production of crude, capacity, and imports is a matter of major concern in the United States. Therefore, the economic impact of the increased imports will be one of the special problems that will demand our thorough study in the problems and policy section of this chapter.

REFINING

Refining Processes

All crude oils, domestic and foreign, vary widely in physical properties. Petroleum is made up principally of molecules containing hydrogen and carbon. The molecules in crude oil contain different numbers of hydrogen and carbon atoms arranged in a great variety of patterns. Those molecules with many carbon atoms make up the thicker and heavier components, like asphalt. Those with relatively few carbon atoms make up the lighter and more volatile components, like gasoline. The conversion of the raw crude into the many finished petroleum products requires that the crude be put through a manufacturing process known as refining.

The first process in refining is distillation (Figure 4.5). Indeed the first refineries used only the process of distillation which is a physical rather than chemical operation. In distillation, crude oil is run through coils of pipe lining a large brick furnace, the interior of which is hot with flame. After being heated to about 800 degrees Farenheit, the crude enters the bottom of a tall steel cylinder known as a fractionating tower. When the crude is released into this tower all but the heaviest portions flash into vapor.

Since the various components of the crude oil have different boiling points, it is possible to separate the oil into different fractions or cuts. The various components change from liquid to vapor or condense back from vapor to liquid at different temperatures. The fractionating tower contains a number of perforated horizontal trays set one above the other. Those near the bottom, where the heated oil is introduced, are the hottest, while those above are successively cooler. As petroleum vapors rise in the tower, they condense on the trays according to the temperature at which each becomes a liquid again. Gasoline begins to collect in the top trays at a temperature of about 100 degrees. Kerosene begins to condense a little lower down at a temperature of about 300 degrees. Heating oil begins to condense at about 450 degrees. Residual oils collect at the very bottom of the tower. Each component of the crude thus can be drawn off from the tower at a different level, and sent separately for further refining.

Thus distillation can separate crude into its various fractions. But this, the earliest method of refining used (straight-run), cannot get more out of a particular fraction of crude than was put in it by nature. For example, distillation usually can yield only about 20 percent gasoline.

As the demand for gasoline began to increase, a process called "cracking" was discovered for creating gasoline out of the heavier fractions. Under heat and pressure the heavier molecules are literally cracked open. In this process, known as thermal cracking, gas oil, the cut just under kerosene, is fed into cracking stills where, under heat and pressure, it is broken down and then fed into the regular fractionating towers to yield the same products as the original crude. As a result it was possible to raise the yield from a regular straight-run refinery, which might have yielded a maximum of 28 percent in 1921, to 42 percent in 1930 and 43 percent in 1939. With the beginning of World War II, the need for less gasoline for the civilian market, the need for more fuel oil, and the need for aviation gasoline so changed the product demand that 45 percent was the maximum need for gasoline; but the principal result was the proven need for greater flexibility in refinery runs.

One problem with thermal cracked gasoline was that it could not be

Figure 4.5: Petroleum Refining.

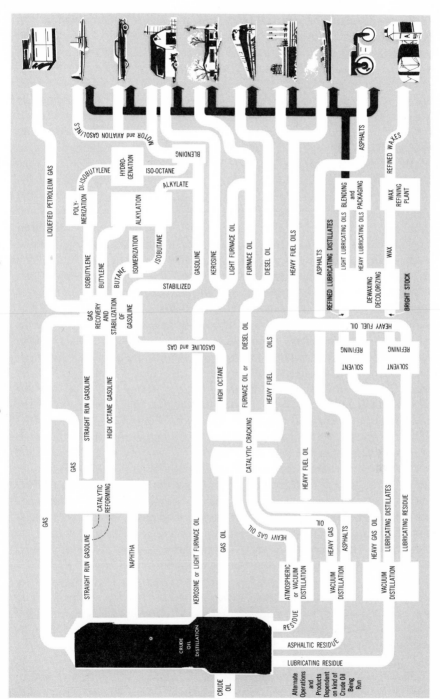

SOURCE: American Petroleum Institute.

used for high compression aviation motors and higher octane gasoline was needed for a standard military fuel and for aviation gasoline. The thermal cracked molecules had a tendency to recombine once they were subjected to compression again in motors, and scientists had been working on a solution to this problem by the use of a catalyst in the cracking process. A catalyst is a substance that helps other substances to change chemically without becoming a part of the final product. Fortunately, Eugene Houdry had just developed a fixed-bed catalytic principal that went into operation in 1936, and which solved the problem of the recombining of the thermal cracked molecules.

Although Houdry's process suffered from grave limitations in that the catalyst coked up so that the plant had to be shut down every ten minutes, and the catalyst regenerated, it led the way to Thermfor Catalytic Cracking (TCC) and the fluid *cat cracker,* which were both continuous processes. The improved Houdri-flow process followed. These processes enabled the refinery to control the product-mix and to improve the octane yields of the gas without adding lead.

The TCC process, first used in 1943, employed bucket conveyors to shuttle the catalyst between reaction and regeneration vessels. In the fluid process the catalyst is so fine that when agitated it flows and can be controlled just like a fluid. After being used for a while, the fine grains of catalyst become coated with carbon removed from the oil and are rendered inactive. However, in this process the catalyst is reactivated by being whirled into a regenerator where the carbon is burned off, and can be used over and over again. Thus, fluid cracking achieves one of the main goals of industrial technology, namely, continuous processing. A fluid cat cracker may operate for three years or longer after which it is shut down for inspection and overhaul.

Petroleum refining employs many processes for taking molecules apart, putting them together and rearranging their atoms. *Polymerization* is the linking of similar molecules to make larger molecules. *Alkylation* does the same for dissimilar molecules. *Isomerization* is the alteration of a molecule so that the atoms though unchanged in number, are arranged differently. These processes are used in the conversion of gaseous and light liquid components into high-octane gasoline.

In addition to all the processes that separate and rearrange hydrocarbon molecules, many others are used to make the finished products as perfectly suited as possible for the intended uses. Products are blended or are mixed with additives. Premium automotive fuel may, for example, contain as many as 25 ingredients.

An important and recent refining development is catalytic reforming. During World War II, a persistent demand developed for aromatic hydrocarbons, mainly benzene and toluene, as well as cumen (isopropyl benzene), styrene (phenyl ethylene), and other compounds. Coking coal, the traditional source of these compounds was inadequate, and the petroleum industry was asked to supply a large share of the demand. Catalytic reforming, a cracking procedure in which straight-run or other naphthas are processed, was developed to provide the bulk of the aromatics needed. This method converts non-aromatic constituents of the refinery streams into a product that contains aromatics either as separate compounds or in admixture. Mixtures of aromatics are separated into pure compounds by means of a selective solvent process.

Following World War II, catalytic reforming grew in use, not only as a means of production of aromatic compounds, but also as a source of higher octane gasoline than could be produced by conventional catalytic cracking. Catalytic reforming began to play an important role as one of the refiner's tools for meeting the demand for premium gasolines. In addition catalytic reforming became important because much hydrogen is made available as a by-product of the chemical reactions that occur. This relatively low-cost hydrogen was instrumental in the rapid development of *hydrogenation* processes much used in the modern refinery to upgrade products such as diesel fuel and distillate fuel oils, particularly in regard to storage stability and burning characteristics.

There was some evidence by the mid-1960's that catalytic reforming as a means of raising octane ratings without the use of tetraethyl lead was abating as the reforming capacity held static. On the other hand, there was some evidence that the hydrogenation process, developed before World War II, which added more hydrogen atoms to a hydrocarbon, was beginning to be used more since there was an increase in hydrogenation capacity in the early 1960's. Before catalytic cracking and other chemical processes were developed, it appeared at one time as if petroleum hydrogenation would become as important in the United States as coal hydrogenation was in Germany before World War II.

TABLE 4.4

Petroleum Yield by Major Products

Year	Gasoline	Kerosene	Gas oil and distillate	Residual fuel oil	Jet fuel	Lubricants
1962	44.8	5.0	23.2	9.6	3.3	2.0
1952	43.0	5.4	21.3	18.6	0.0	2.3

Source: *Petroleum Facts and Figures,* New York, American Petroleum Institute, 1963.

Table 4.4 shows a comparison of the change in yield of the major products during a 10-year period.

The table points up a general upgrading of the product and a move away from residual fuel oil. This is just one example of the results of an industry that is continually endeavoring to develop more efficient processes to obtain an increased yield of more valuable products and a better utilization of by-products. Although commercial catalytic cracking as practiced today is a comparatively recent development which requires a larger capital investment, catalytic cracking has the advantage of affording greater refining flexibility, and larger yields of higher quality products.

One major problem of the refinery is to balance the yield of different products with respect to demand. We have noted changes in yield such as the substantial increase in gasoline which required increasing the gasoline yield from crude oil to around 45 percent just before World War II. Since then, residual yields have declined substantially, and the output of distillates has increased, with gasoline varying from year to year within a narrow range.

As a rule, any large refinery must undergo almost constant modernization to keep it on a highly competitive basis. Thus large amounts of money will continue to be put into refining facilities so that these refineries will become more efficient and more flexible to meet the ever-changing demand for petroleum products.

Refinery Location

Table 4.5 gives the number and capacity of refineries by refinery districts and the location of refining areas in the United States. The more than 300 refineries are fairly widely distributed in the United States. Generally speaking there are three types of refineries classified in accordance with location: field, market, and seaboard.

Field refineries are situated at or very near the source of crude, and supply products to their own area and elsewhere. Field refineries tend to be small, though several large ones have been established in the mid-continent refining districts. Usually field refineries lack pipeline and tanker facilities for efficient transport of petroleum and, therefore, must locate close to oil fields in order to obtain continuous supplies for operation. In many instances these refineries have a short life span of operation, after which they are shut down and dismantled.

Seaboard refineries are large refineries located on navigable water and served by pipelines, tanker facilities, and barges. In many instances seaboard refinery locations are at intermediate trans-shipment points between crude oil supplies and markets. The most important location of seaboard refineries in the United States is the Gulf Coast area, especially the Louisiana Gulf Coast as shown in Table 4.5. From this high concentration of refinery capacity, products move to domestic markets along the Gulf

TABLE 4.5

Number and Capacity of Refineries, by Refinery Districts, as of January 1, 1963

Refinery district	Number of refineries			Capacity (barrels per day)				
	Operating	Shutdown	Total	Operating	Shutdown	Total operating and shutdown	Building	Total operating, shutdown, and building
East Coast	23	3	26	1,387,700	72,000	1,459,700	0	1,459,700
Appalachian No. 1	13	0	13	119,440	3,000	122,440	0	122,440
Appalachian No. 2	3	1	4	117,000	6,000	123,000	0	123,000
Indiana, Illinois, Kentucky	50	5	55	1,743,339	33,080	1,776,419	2,500	1,778,919
Minnesota, Wisconsin, North and South Dakota	8	0	8	149,200	5,000	154,200	20,000	174,200
Oklahoma, Kansas, Missouri	29	1	30	824,130	25,500	849,630	1,500	851,130
Texas Inland	29	3	32	370,100	46,500	416,600	0	416,600
Texas Gulf Coast	26	2	28	2,235,850	82,800	2,318,650	28,000	2,341,650
Louisiana Gulf Coast	9	1	10	801,250	8,500	809,750	100,000	909,750
Arkansas, Louisiana Inland	17	0	17	149,650	0	149,650	0	149,650
New Mexico	6	2	8	31,675	5,000	36,675	0	36,675
Rocky Mountain	31	3	34	361,705	4,850	366,555	1,000	367,555
West Coast	43	0	43	1,523,752	11,300	1,535,052	30,300	1,565,352
U.S. total	287	21	308	9,814,791	303,530	10,118,321	178,300	10,296,621

1 Includes Alaska and Hawaii. NOTE: Figures shown under "Building" represent additional capacity under construction at existing refineries, as well as new plants being built.
SOURCE: *Petroleum Facts and Figures*, New York, American Petroleum Institute, 1963.

and East Coasts, and along the Mississippi waterway and by tanker to foreign markets. On the West Coast there is another important concentration of refineries in the metropolitan Los Angeles and San Francisco Bay areas. Los Angeles is an example of an area where an important oil-producing region, a large refined-products market, and an ocean and rail transport point all merge. The San Francisco Bay area receives Central Valley crude petroleum by pipeline, and some California coastal oil and imports from Venezuela by tanker. In the East Coast area the largest concentration of refineries is between Philadelphia and New York. Here both domestic and foreign crudes are received for refining into products, principally for the domestic market.

Market refineries are market oriented and are usually large. They may or may not have significant oil reserves nearby, and the refined products are primarily for local and nearby markets. Market refineries are so located in order to reduce transport costs between the producing fields and the markets for petroleum products. The refineries are located as close to the markets as possible or where water transportation can be utilized to marketing centers. Sometimes refineries of this type perform the functions of both the seaboard and market types as they may be at seaboard locations near large cities and industrial complexes, or at inland points. Refineries at Philadelphia and on San Francisco Bay are of the seaboard type, while Chicago is a prime example of an inland location. The Indiana, Illinois, Kentucky refining district has the second largest capacity in the United States, and Chicago is the largest petroleum marketing and transportation center in this area.

The major trend in refinery location has been a shift to consuming areas for petroleum products. This has been true both within the United States and in the world at large. In the United States, the East Coast and West Coast areas are the preferred sites for new construction, while outside this country the greatest expansion in refining capacity has occurred in Western Europe. As a result of the expansion of refining capacity in consuming centers outside of the United States, this country's share of the world refining capacity has declined from over 70 percent before World War II to only about 33 percent, even though during this period domestic refining capacity doubled.

Several factors have combined to bring about the growth of refining at points of consumption. Technical improvements, which we have noted, have reduced the waste in refining, thus decreasing the pull of areas close to the site of crude production, transportation has become more efficient, and increased demand has enabled consuming areas to construct large, economic refineries. Outside the United States, especially in Western Europe, the demand for petroleum products has been growing at a rapid rate, and the shift has been from import of refined products to import of cheaper crudes from the Middle East. In part this has been a move to conserve foreign exchange, but new refineries also act as a general stimulus to the economy, and permit the development of ancillary industries such as petrochemicals.

The effect of increased refinery capacity outside the United States and a shift by these importing countries to foreign sources of crude has also had an effect on refinery location in the United States. Before World War II the Gulf Coast possessed the greatest concentration of refining capacity in the world and exported tremendous quantities of refined products. Today this latter is no longer the case. As a result, even though the Gulf Coast still has the largest concentration of refining capacity, its rate of growth has been retarded because of the loss of export markets for refined products. On the other hand, East and West Coast refineries have had an accelerated growth both because they are domestic market oriented and because their seaboard location permits importation of foreign crude into the United States.

Thus, refinery location has become more market oriented in the United States in inland areas and on the seaboard, and outside the United States, especially in Western Europe. Part of this shift, as we have seen, is a result of new sources of foreign crude, but more importantly it has been caused by the great growth in demand for petroleum.

USES OF PETROLEUM

The two principal uses of petroleum are to produce power and heat. All major forms of transportation are powered by petroleum: automobiles, busses trucks, trains, airplanes, and ships. Here the principal fuels used are gasoline, kerosene, diesel fuel, jet fuel and other distillate oils. Distillate fuel oils are widely used for all kinds of space heating, especially for homes and small commercial establishments; and the residual grades of fuel oil are used generally in the larger heating units and for generating steam in industrial plants. Petroleum coke can be used in large heating installations, and in the form of briquets, it is an excellent fuel for picnic cooking and fireplaces. Liquefied petroleum gas, which is used in the same manner as natural gas for heating and cooking, is both a refinery product and manufactured from natural gas. Liquefied petroleum gas finds its market principally where natural gas is not available because of the absence of pipelines. It is available in all large cities and suburban areas, and in most rural areas.

Few industries can claim the sustained increase in demand that has characterized the oil industry. Table 4.6 shows these increases in demand as well as the sources of the supply. Primarily responsible for this outstanding growth in demand has been the consumption of gasoline that has increased along with motor population. The major use for gasoline is in spark-ignited, internal combustion engines, principally in passenger

TABLE 4.6
United States Petroleum Supply and Demand 1940 to 1962
(Thousands of barrels)

New Supply	1962[1]	1961	1960[2]	1955	1950	1945	1940
Domestic production:							
Crude oil	2,676,185	2,621,758	2,574,933	2,484,428	1,973,574	1,713,655	1,353,214
Daily average	7,332	7,183	7,035	6,807	5,407	4,695	3,697
Natural gas liquids	370,989	361,689	340,157	281,371	181,961	112,004	55,700
Benzol	91	169	275	526	158	2,880	3,167
Total production	3,047,265	2,983,616	2,915,365	2,766,325	2,155,693	1,828,539	1,412,081
Imports:							
Crude oil	411,039	381,548	371,575	285,421	177,714	74,337	42,662
Refined products	347,953	318,118	292,536	170,143	132,547	39,282	41,089
Total new supply, all oils	3,806,257	3,683,282	3,579,476	3,221,889	2,465,954	1,942,158	1,495,832
Daily average	10,428	10,091	9,780	8,827	6,756	5,321	4,087
Change in stocks, all oils	+11,795	+40,516	−30,235	−74	−20,409	−13,510	+38,746
Demand							
Total demand	3,794,462	3,642,766	3,609,711	3,221,963	2,486,363	1,955,668	1,457,086
Daily average	10,396	9,980	9,863	8,827	6,812	5,358	3,981
Exports:							
Crude oil	1,786	3,227	3,087	11,571	34,823	32,998	51,496
Refined products	59,511	60,336	70,819	122,617	76,483	149,985	78,970

Domestic demand:							
Motor fuel	1,583,404	1,533,173	1,511,670	1,329,788	994,290	696,333	589,490
Kerosene	164,020	144,435	132,499	116,808	117,844	75,573	68,776
Distillate fuel oil	732,085	694,356	685,268	581,128	394,885	226,084	160,851
Residual fuel oil	545,382	548,678	559,439	557,057	553,793	523,423	340,163
Jet fuel	112,401	104,436	102,803	60,703			
Lubricating oil	43,606	41,534	42,676	42,477	38,853	24,690	35,334
Wax	3,965	4,390	4,438	4,056	3,238	1,274	2,403
Coke	70,706	67,184	54,472	24,403	15,021	7,035	9,214
Asphalt	114,085	107,753	104,696	84,286	58,677	28,182	38,350
Road oil	6,965	5,802	5,880	8,356	6,897	7,849	2,505
Still gas	130,829	127,537	129,480	116,506	83,743	75,950	103,458
Liquefied gases	255,041	233,908	227,291	147,572	85,505		28,688
Miscellaneous	31,112	28,144	25,208	13,062	4,394	2,411	9,169
Losses	60,436	62,077	50,015	1,573	17,917	19,949	22,151
Total domestic demand	3,733,165	3,579,203	3,535,805	3,087,775	2,375,057	1,326,620	1,772,685
Daily average	10,228	9,806	9,661	8,460	6,507	3,625	4,857
Stocks (End of Year)							
Crude oil	252,011	244,664	239,800	265,610	248,463	276,615	223,259
Natural gas liquids	31,385	37,067	28,931	13,564	7,355	5,704	4,322
Refined products[1]	553,473	543,343	515,827	435,685	326,892	282,265	235,998
Total, all oils[3]	836,869	825,074	784,558	714,859	582,710	564,584	463,579

1 Preliminary. Data for other years are final.
2 Includes Alaska beginning in 1959 and Hawaii beginning in 1960.
3 Revised. Beginning in 1960 includes pipeline stocks of jet fuel, bulk terminal stocks of lubricants, asphalt, and miscellaneous oils.
SOURCE: *Petroleum Facts and Figures*, New York, American Petroleum Institute, 1963. Data from U.S. Bureau of Mines.

automobiles, trucks and aircraft. Some stationary engines require gasoline, as do some watercraft engines, tractors and construction equipment engines. Gasoline accounts for over 40 percent of the demand for petroleum products, and since gasoline is still by far the most important source of revenue for oil companies, efforts are concentrated on obtaining more of this high-value product from a barrel of crude.

Kerosene is used principally for heating and cooking (about 60 percent). Some 3 percent is consumed as tractor fuel, and the remainder is used as commercial jet fuel, lamp fuel, orchard heating fuel, and in other minor ways. Military jet fuel also contains kerosene, but jet fuel has been shown as a separate use category since 1952.

Distillate fuel oils have had their greatest increases in use in domestic heating oils and diesel fuel. The tremendous increase in domestic oil burners was brought about by the many convenience advantages of oil over coal, and the correlation between the increase use of distillate fuel and oil burners has been close. About two-thirds of all distillates are used for space heating. One disadvantage of the space heating demand is that it is seasonal, and storage capacity at retail and secondary levels in consuming areas is small. Railroads are large users of diesel oil and account for about 13 percent of all the distillate fuel use. Here again, in this category coal has been hard hit with the dieselization of the railroads. Smelters, mines, manufacturing industries, electric power plants and watercraft, including diesel tankers, are other important users of smaller quantities of distillates.

Residual fuel oil is principally in demand for space heating. But earlier gains on the part of residual at the expense of coal are being slowed by increasing competition from natural gas, but some of these losses may be offset by shifts from coal to oil on the part of operators of large hotels and apartment houses. On a heating unit per dollar basis, coal and residual fuel oil are not far apart and considerable interfuel competition will persist. About 20 percent of residual fuel oil is consumed by tankers and other vessels.

The jet fuel shown represents that principally used in military aircraft and in testing military engines. Most of the jet fuel used by commercial aircraft is kerosene and is shown in that category. The components of blended jet fuels are gasoline, kerosene, and to a small extent distillate fuel oil.

Lubricants compose less than 2 percent of refinery output, yet these vital products are essential for the operation of our mechanized civilization.

Petrochemicals (organic chemicals produced from petroleum hydrocarbons) constitute over 50 percent of U.S. output of organic chemicals and are profitable products for the oil industry. Production requires only about 2 percent of refinery yields, and the drain on petroleum supplies will never be great for these important products.

Figure 4.6: The Petroleum Tree of Products.

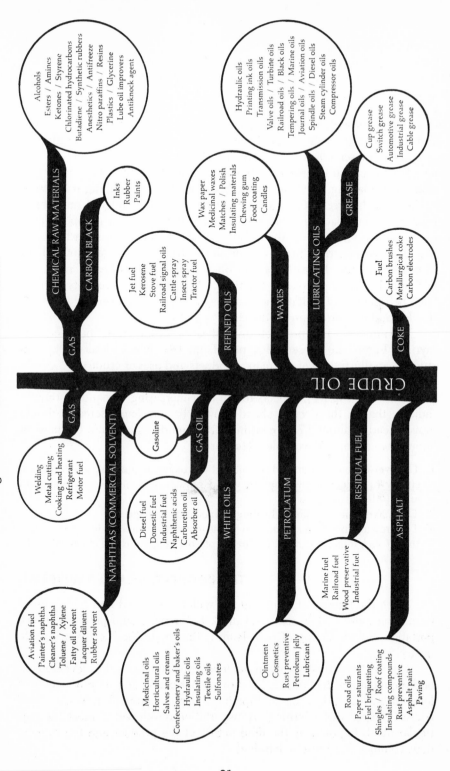

SOURCE: Stewart Schackne and N. D'Arcy Drake, *Oil For The World* (Harper & Row), Copyright © 1950, 1955, 1960 by Standard Oil Company (New Jersey), p. 89.

91

By-products of petroleum are unlimited since petroleum contains the basic compounds for the production of any organic compound. One outstanding product derived from petroleum is synthetic rubber. In World War II the United States lost its access to natural rubber sources in the Far East and we found that we had a transportation system with nothing to roll on. Through the outstanding cooperation between the U.S. government and the rubber and the petroleum industries we were able to develop from scratch a synthetic rubber industry with production sufficient to successfully prosecute the war. Synthetic rubber has made possible longer lasting tires and tubes, has placed a price ceiling on natural rubber, and has freed this nation from complete dependence on natural rubber. Carbon black, another product of both natural gas and petroleum fractions, is a vital part in the finished synthetic rubber used in the tires. For many years carbon black was produced from natural gas; now, about 57 percent of the domestic carbon black is made from heavy, relatively undesirable liquid petroleum fractions. Thus, we have products derived from petroleum to facilitate motor transportation, which further increases the demand for petroleum products.

In summary, the product diversification from crude petroleum is myriad. Figure 4.6 presented a petroleum tree which deserves careful study as an illustration of the many products and uses of crude oil.

Looking into the future, possibly the brightest outlook for the petroleum industry is in its prospects for an ever-increasing demand. Estimates indicate that in the decade ahead growth in petroleum demand should move ahead at about 2.7 percent in North America and about 5.7 percent annually in Europe. Favorable factors are:

1. The ever-increasing demand for oil and petroleum liquids to provide mobile energy to a decentralized industry and growth of population in nonurban areas ("the urban sprawl").
2. The convenience of efficient heating by means of oil or gas.
3. The growing use of oil and natural gas as major raw materials in the manufacture of such items as textiles, fertilizers, plastics, and industrial chemicals.

TRANSPORTATION AND MARKETING

Since the sources of crude oil are widely dispersed and far removed from even more widely scattered markets for petroleum products, transportation and marketing of petroleum is the key to the success of the industry.

One of the industry's main achievements has been the development of equipment and techniques for moving petroleum and its products over long distances at low costs. Pipelines, barges, railroad tank-cars, and trucks are specialized forms of transportation developed to meet the particular needs imposed by the fluid nature of the product and the tremendous volumes that must be handled.

The first task is the gathering of the crude and the movement to the refineries. *Flow lines* connect individual wells to field storage tanks where oil is collected before being taken by *gathering lines* to a pump station for shipment in long-distance *trunk lines*. The trunk lines carry the crude directly to refineries, or to waterside terminals where it is transferred to tankers or barges.

Some idea of the magnitude of the job can be obtained from the fact that in 1960 the United States had about 560,000 producing wells in 31 states, and nearly 350 refineries in 37 states. Of the total receipts of domestic crude oil at these refineries about 75 percent is delivered by pipeline, and the balance is carried to waterside refineries by tankers and barges. The United States has about 160,000 miles of crude oil gathering and trunk lines.

The distribution of petroleum products from the refineries involves the utilization of pipelines, railroads, boats and barges, and trucks to carry products to some 20,000 terminal and bulk plants. From these central points, tank trucks supply the thousands of filling stations and final consumers.

Petroleum pipelines include a separate system for petroleum products which extended for about 40,000 miles in 1960, with many new product lines scheduled to be built in the 1960's. Perhaps the greatest concentration of product pipelines in the country is found in the Midwestern states. Some product lines move only liquefied petroleum gases (LPG), but many other lines move a wide variety of products including LPG. One great advantage of the product line is that various products can be moved simultaneously without mixing.

Although pipelines are the vital artery for moving domestic petroleum, the shipment of crude in international trade depends upon the tanker. The standard tanker during and after World War II was the T2, a vessel of 16,600 tons holding around 135,000 barrels of oil. Today, ships of 26,000, 38,000, and 54,000 tons are common. Many larger tankers of more than 100,000 tons have been, or are being built. These tankers can hold 1,000,000 or more barrels of oil, enough to fill 4,000 railroad tank-cars and make a train 30 miles long.

Oil companies own only about one-third of the tankers they need to move oil to the refiners and to the consumers. The balance are rented, or chartered from independent tanker owners. In 1960 oil companies and independent operators owned about 2,700 tankers. The role of the tanker was vital to victory in World War II. More than half of all the supplies shipped from the United States were petroleum products; and about three-fourths of all the petroleum the Allies used was produced and refined and sent abroad from the United States.

Three other forms of transportation are used to move oil in bulk: barges on inland waterways, railroad tank-cars, and tank trucks. Oil barges carry up to 2,000,000 barrels of crude oil and products on inland waterways in the United States daily. Railroad tank-cars seldom carry oil for long distances any more, but some oil products move to industrial consumers and to bulk terminals by railroad tank-cars. The last few miles of petroleum's journey to service stations, or to the consumer's home, or place of business, are usually made by tank truck. In size these trucks range from a small tank strapped to a truck body, to huge truck and tanker combinations with a capacity of 12,500 gallons.

The petroleum industry has indeed perfected the means of transportation of its products. But of all the means, pipeline movement is generally the most economical method of transporting oil over land. Tariffs published by the Texas and Eastern Transportation Company for refined product movement through the Little Big Inch pipeline are in the range of 0.04 to 0.05¢ per mile per barrel. A new pipeline being engineered (the Colonial Pipeline) is expected to have a cost of no more than 0.02¢ per barrel per mile.

Another big advantage of the pipeline, which really captured the public fancy, was the speed of construction of the World War II emergency-built Big Inch (24 inches in diameter) and Little Big Inch (20 inches in diameter) pipelines. For example, the construction of the Big Inch pipeline, 1,254 miles of main line during World War II required about two years; one year for preliminary work, and one year for construction. This line replaced 60 to 75 tankers, or 30,000 tank-cars. Construction is even faster today with better equipment and without the delays of wartime shortages.

The economic reasons for development of the petroleum transportation system in its present form are quite clear. Cost factors greatly favor the tanker and the pipeline over the railroad tank-car. But cost factors have been changing. Whereas several years ago pipeline and rail rates were three and eight times tanker rates, respectively, pipeline and average tanker charges now are not far apart, with rail costs well above both and rising.

Marketing of petroleum products is achieved by distribution principally through company-owned or independent service stations, dealers, and jobbers. The latter are of two kinds: those selling under their own brand names, and those distributing advertised brands. Lesser known brands are usually marketed on a price basis as a competitive factor. Of the approximately 205,000 service stations in the 50 states, about 95 percent are owned or operated by local individuals.

ORGANIZATION OF THE INDUSTRY

One feature of the organization of the petroleum industry in the United States is the coexistence of thousands of so called *independents* and a relatively few *majors*. In the early 1960's about twenty oil companies were referred to as majors, but the U.S. Bureau of Mines gives summary statistics on thirty-two companies to show the degree of concentration in the industry. There is no fixed definition of a major, but it is thought of as a relatively large company that is integrated, that is, engaged in all the functions of the industry from exploration and producing to marketing. The vast majority of the independents are engaged in the search and production of petroleum, and even though some of the small or medium sized companies are partly integrated, they usually are engaged in only one branch of the industry.

Concentration of ownership was the rule in the early days of the industry. By 1900 the Standard Oil Trust owned all or part of many large companies in the United States and in many countries abroad. In 1911, however, the U.S. Supreme Court declared the trust a monopoly and ordered it separated into thirty-four independent companies.

While the Standard Oil Trust was expanding its markets in Europe, Africa, South America, and the Far East, a number of European companies were taking an active interest in the international oil business. Three great companies grew from their efforts: Royal Dutch-Shell, Anglo-Iranian (now British Petroleum), and Compagnie Francaise des Pétroles.

The U.S. companies that emerged in the international field (and once referred to as the international majors) were Standard Oil Company (New Jersey), Standard Oil Company of California, Socony Mobil Oil Company, and Texaco. Up until 1954 only ten of the major companies imported petroleum in addition to producing and purchasing domestic crude. Six of these companies, including the five above and Royal Dutch-Shell, had undertaken tremendous foreign investments. These six companies, together with the British Oil Company, produced 87.5 percent of the foreign crude oil in the free world. In recent years a large number of relatively small companies have entered the foreign oil business. The number reached about 150 by 1960, or more than three times the number that were active ten years before in exploring for oil abroad.

Among the various functions of the industry (producing, refining, transporting, and marketing), it is in refining that the large companies have the greatest percentage of total capacity, because refining is primarily a mass production operation that requires vast capital investment. The twenty majors referred to in the first paragraph of this section have about 75 percent of the refining capacity in the United States, and the remaining 25 percent is owned by 150 companies. Not one of the twenty majors has more than 20 percent of the refining capacity.

In the United States, as contrasted with the rest of the world (with the exception of Canada), the free enterprise system allows individuals, small companies, and large companies to compete in all phases of the petroleum industry. State ownership of land in most of the rest of the world precludes any but the large companies from engaging in the industry, and in many countries the exploration and production of oil requires a company to set up its own private exclave of an economy within the foreign country.

In the United States there are over 18,000 distinct entities engaged in the exploration, drilling and production phase. These include individuals, partnerships, corporations, and subsidiary companies of large oil companies. In total there are over 200,000 oil businesses in the country, including more than 175,000 filling station operators and 270 refineries. But 32 large companies account for 62 percent of the domestic crude oil production, and 58 percent of that in the free world. These same 32 companies refined 66 percent of the crude oil processed in the United States and 62 percent of that in the free world. These companies as a group also control a major share of the transportation and marketing at home and abroad.

The National Fuels and Energy Study Group reports further on the concentration of ownership. In crude oil production the five ranking companies were reported to have produced 25 percent of the output, and the fifteen top companies 44 percent. In refining 40 percent of the output was determined to be owned by the first five companies, and 60 percent by the fifteen leading companies.

But, in spite of this concentration, competition is intense in every function of the industry. There is intense competition for private leases, and agreements with government for producing properties. There is competition in refining to lower the cost per gallon of manufacturing, and to produce superior products. In marketing there is constant competition for sales, which involves product quality, and location of outlets, as well as price. Even in the pricing of crude in the field to independents there is always the fear that if the posted price is not a fair one the source of supply will be lost. There are those who see in the stability of crude oil prices and even in retail prices a lack of competition, but the industry sees it another way. They must pay the highest price and sell for the lowest price if their company is to maintain its position in the petroleum business.

There is no question about the fact that there is concentration in the petroleum industry, but what has resulted is a competition among giants. However, most amazing is the sustained role of the independent, who coexists with the giants. The independent with his willingness and ability to take risks has played a real part in the development of the U.S. petroleum industry for it is he who has had "oil in the back of his head" and has looked for and found the crude petroleum reserves that have supplied the petroleum industry. He has trod where the giants feared to tread.

PROBLEMS AND POLICY

In view of the fact that petroleum is an indispensable ingredient of economic growth and is essential to national security, a basic objective of national policy must be the assurance that the United States shall have adequate and available supplies of oil for all peacetime and emergency requirements. The discussion which follows will single out three specific issues which are of primary concern in the exploration, development, and production of petroleum. The problems which will be studied are conservation, import policy, and tax policy. As a background to these problems the outstanding facts are that consumption of petroleum in the United States was less than production before World War II, that this situation was reversed in 1947, and that evidence points to a continuation and possible growth of this excess of domestic consumption over production.

Conservation

The petroleum conservation problem has its origin in the fugacious nature of oil and the subsequent application of the *rule of capture*. The legal right to ownership of mineral reserves on one's property has been fundamental as an incentive to discovery. However, the rule of capture, which was applied in the case of oil, had additional effects, as the petroleum under the land of many owners became the property of the person first able to produce the oil from wells drilled on his property. Adopted in the erroneous belief that oil and gas were in constant unpredictable movement, and therefore not susceptible to regulation by law, the rule of capture gave the landowner the right to do as he pleased, and thereby destroyed another kind of property right. This rule of capture led to the drilling of many wells and the production of oil in order to get possession of it, and without consideration of the damage to the producing pool. In addition, there was very little relationship between production and market demand. With large discoveries, such as the East Texas field, the price of crude fell to as little as ten cents a barrel in the early 1930's, Thus the rule of capture resulted in wasteful inefficient practices in the production of oil. In addition, refiners had little incentive to use efficient methods in the production of petroleum products.

Facts Bearing on the Problem. To cope with the conservation problem, several of the states began in the thirties to limit production of oil per well (proration), and attempted to regulate the spacing of wells and to have each oil reservoir operated as a unit (unit pool operation). State authorities have since extended regulation to include limitations on the oil-gas ratio to prevent excessive impairment of the gas pressure and to reduce the waste of natural gas. Regulations have also been used to preserve the driving force of underground water pressure.

State governments were slow to act in respect to oil and gas conservation, even though the state of Oklahoma had passed a constructive conservation law as early as 1915. In the late 1920's there were extensive investigations on the part of committees of Congress, the American Bar

Association, and oil associations and producers. The remedies suggested covered many approaches to the problem. The Federal Conservation Board, created in 1924, rendered the last of five reports in 1932 and pointed to the advisability of having the states assume responsibility for the conservation of petroleum in spite of the fact that some thought conditions had reached a point where regulation by the federal government was necessary. Secretary of the Interior Ray Wilbur suggested in 1929 the formation of a compact of states to bring about petroleum conservation. The Oil States Advisory Committee, sometimes known as the "Governors' Committee," organized in 1931, recommended the passage of effective conservation statutes and the formation of an Interstate Oil and Gas Compact Commission. The Cole Committee, after its very thorough investigation of the oil and gas industry, recommended the formation of a compact among the states in its preliminary report to Congress in January, 1935.

From all the thought and study that was given, three general conclusions emerged: (1) Waste prevention could be effectively accomplished only by regulation under proper law; (2) State rather than federal regulation was a course consistent with the rights and obligations of the several states expressed in the Federal Constitution; (3) A compact among the oil-producing states would be a means of effectively carrying a sound conservation program to the national level.

As a result of the need for interstate coöperation in conservation, the Interstate Oil Compact Commission was formed and sanctioned by Congress in 1935. The Compact has twenty-two member states and six associate members. The purpose of the Compact has been to assist the various states in the formulation of sound oil and gas conservation programs. All the member states have enacted conservation laws. Many of the states have adopted almost all of the provisions of the suggested conservation act prepared by the Interstate Oil Compact Commission.

Every state, with the exception of Texas, Kansas, and certain older producing states, has a general well-spacing statute. Texas requires specifically 20-acre spacing of wells unless an exception is granted, and Kansas achieves a form of spacing by limiting production in proportion to acreage.

Limiting of oil by well (proration) is the second form of conservation laws in operation. This production regulation has as part of its background, the fact that oil does not appear on the surface under its own power. As we have learned, the energy required to force the oil to move through the rock and ultimately to the surface of the earth is usually supplied by the expansion of the gas dissolved in the oil, or from the influx of water into the reservoir. Unrestricted or wide-open production of either oil or gas would cause premature dissipation and inefficient utilization of these forces, and would make a large volume of the original oil unrecoverable in places. Almost all of the oil-producing states except the older ones (Illinois, Indiana, Kentucky, Ohio, Pennsylvania, Tennessee, Virginia and

West Virginia) and California limit production of both oil and gas for the purpose of conserving reservoir energy. In California a cooperative group, with no powers of the state behind it, attempts to determine the MER of withdrawal for each field. Compliance is voluntary.

A third area of conservation relates to above ground waste. In the past, when oil was produced at a rate faster than could be absorbed by the market, the excess was often stored on the surface in open pits, and in dammed creeks where it was subject to fire and evaporation, and the gas produced from such oil was flared or vented to the atmosphere. Several states have attempted to eliminate such waste by limiting current production to market demand. Kansas, Louisiana, New Mexico, North Dakota, Oklahoma, and Texas issue allocations under the market demand provisions of their waste prevention statutes. Alabama, Arizona, Michigan, and Washington have authority to limit production to market demand, but do not do so. Alaska and Nevada define excess above ground storage as being wasteful but do nothing about it; Arkansas restricts production. The states of Colorado, Mississippi, Montana, Nebraska, Nevada, South Dakota, Utah, and Wyoming are prevented by state law from limiting production to market demand; and in another group of states (California, Illinois, Indiana, Kentucky, Ohio, Pennsylvania, Tennessee, Virginia and West Virginia) the commissions are not authorized to limit production for any reason.

In summary, the typical oil conservation statute prohibits the waste of oil gas and defines *waste* to mean not only physical waste but also: (1) the inefficient, excessive, or improper use or unnecessary dissipation of reservoir energy, (2) the locating, spacing, drilling, operating, or producing of any oil or gas well or wells in a manner which causes, or tends to cause, reduction in the quantity of oil or gas ultimately recoverable from a reservoir under prudent and proper operations, and (3) the production of oil and gas in excess of transportation or storage facilities, or in excess of reasonable market demands. The statute empowers an administrative agency of the state to determine at regular intervals the quantity that will be required to meet the demand for oil produced in the state. The quantity so determined must then be allocated among all the pools in the state on an equitable basis, the quantity allocated to a particular pool is its *allowable* production. When there is demand for all the oil that can be produced (as was the case during and for a few years after World War II) the administrative agency determines for each pool its *MER of production* (that is, the maximum quantity that can be produced without unnecessary injury to the reservoir); and that amount becomes the allowable production for the pool. By whichever method determined, the allowable production for a pool must be prorated among all the wells in the pool in such manner that each producer will be allowed to produce his fair and equitable share of the allowable production.

The Connally Act, enacted by the Congress in 1935, has served to support state limitations on production of oil by prohibiting shipment in interstate commerce of petroleum produced in excess of quotas set by state agencies.

The first achievement of state regulation of petroleum production was the adjustment of output to market demand, which has led to greater market stability. There is little doubt that this is one of the reasons that oil producers, who are rugged individualists, do not consider conservation statutes control of business. As a result of regulation, study, and cooperation, however, there is no question about the fact that much has been accomplished in the maximum efficient recovery and conservation of petroleum. An estimate has been made that 50 percent more oil has been recovered since 1932 than would have been recovered in the absence of state regulation.

One major area in conservation of petroleum production which needs strengthening is the achievement of a unified program of operations for each oil reservoir best fitted to the particular characteristics of the reservoir. Engineers have solved the technical problems of unit pool operation. The principal obstacle to a unified operation is the inevitable holdout, the leaseholder or royalty owner who thinks he can do better without unit operation, even though the pool as a whole will do much better with unit operation. In some states unit pool operation can be made compulsory when the specified majority of the acreage agree. However, few common sources of supply have been placed under unit operations, except where special conditions make unit operations imperative as in condensate reservoirs or in secondary recovery.

The advantages of unit pool operation have been clearly established. The petroleum industry knows how to operate a pool and has achieved the benefits of such operation where ownership is common in the United States and in overseas areas. The problems involved in multiple ownership can and should be worked out by industry and state legislative and control agencies so that each leaseholder will receive his fair share of the petroleum and maximum recovery can be achieved.

The problems involved in conservation in the more efficient use of petroleum products have also been solved in so far as technology is involved. Refining has been developed to such an extent that with the use of a modern catalytic cracker almost 100 percent of the crude oil can be converted into petroleum products in the proportion in which they are demanded. Improved gasoline mileage must be co-engineered with automobiles. However, the additional possibilities of improving mileage are rather limited unless the public will accept smaller cars or less powerful engines. This appears to be a remote contingency. The President's Materials Policy Commission presented an estimate that a high compression ratio and a fully automatic transmission or suitable overdrive might double automotive efficiency from the usual fifteen or twenty miles per gallon to thirty or forty without any loss in performance characteristics. This accomplishment has already been approximated under good open road conditions and by drivers who are economy minded and trained. However, most of our driving is not under such conditions. Drastic increases in gasoline prices and/or an emergency might bring about great conservation in use.

Conclusions. The conclusion is that conservation has developed out of a pre-World War II background when domestic production was in excess of consumption for reasons of market stabilization and waste elimination, and has been continued into the present for similar reasons. Most importantly the conservation practices affect the economics of the petroleum industry. The National Fuels and Energy Study Group came to the following conclusions. Well-spacing statutes tend to reduce costs, and therefore prices, by reducing the number of wells drilled. On the other hand, the output restrictions tend to increase prices during some periods by restricting supply. In any event, conservation prevents the wild swings of production and in prices that unsupervised operation would invite. The result is a stabilizing influence. Of course the most important effect is the oil and gas saved for eventual production and use; and state conservation officials believe that this will result in lower prices over the long-run period. However, for a devastating critique of conservation practices the reader's attention is called to the analysis of Gilbert Bruck which is cited among the selected references at the end of this chapter.

Import Policies

The petroleum problem that has been consistently in the news since the end of World War II is the matter of petroleum imports. The United States has been an importer of petroleum since 1918, but 1947 became a major turning point in the U.S. petroleum industry because for the first time since the discovery of the East Texas oil field in the early 1930's, the United States became a net importer of petroleum. Prior to 1947 the United States had produced more petroleum than it consumed, and had a surplus available for export.

Most U.S. exports have been refined products to Europe, which is the principal deficiency area in the Eastern Hemisphere. Before World War II, Europe's deficiency was met by these exports from the United States and by supplies from the Caribbean and some imports from the Middle East. Some U.S. exports went to Japan and China, but most of the oil in the Far East was supplied by the Netherlands East Indies. Since World War II these interregional movements have undergone tremendous change. United States exports to Europe have in large part been replaced by imports of crude oil from the Middle East, which also has supplied most of the oil for the Far East. The Caribbean continued to supply part of the European deficiency and has been the principal source of U.S. increased imports.

United States imports of crude petroleum and residual fuel increased steadily between 1933 and the early 1960's, with the exception of the war years 1942–1944. Total petroleum imports, principally crude and residual fuel oil, averaged 147,000 barrels a day for the period 1933–1939. Imports in barrels a day increased from 377,000 in 1946 to 952,000 in 1952 to 2,090,000 in 1962. The total in 1962 as shown by Table 4.7. consisted of 1,110,000 barrels of crude oil; 770,000 barrels of residual fuel oil; and 210,000 barrels of finished and unrefined products.

Of the U.S. imports of 1,016,000 barrels of crude oil daily in 1960, approximately 60 percent came from the Western Hemisphere, 30 percent from the Middle East, and less than 10 percent from the Far East. Venezuela accounted for over two-thirds of the imports from the Western Hemisphere, Canada for 113,000 barrels daily, and Mexico for 3,000 barrels daily.

As we have already seen one of the basic questions that independent domestic producers were raising was why more of the United States productive capacity was not being used instead of importing crude oil and an additional quantity of residual fuel oil to satisfy domestic demand. In truth, the domestic producers knew the answer to this question. What they were demanding was restrictions on petroleum imports.

The Independent Petroleum Association of America made it quite clear in its report to the National Fuels and Energy Study Group that the basic cause of accelerated petroleum imports into the United States is the increasing availability of relative low cost foreign oil.

Increasing availability was found in the growth of proved reserves in the free world outside the United States to a level in excess of 240 billion barrels. This constituted a fourfold increase in the previous ten-year period in supply, at a time when consumption in the free world outside the United States only doubled.

Lower costs outside the United States were cited in a Chase Manhattan Bank report, *The Petroleum Industry,* which listed the following total expenditures for exploration and development per barrel of crude oil production for the period 1951–1960:

Canada	$3.10
United States	1.73
Far East	.82
Venezuela	.51
Middle East	.16

These exploration and development costs in Venezuela and the Middle East are strikingly low on a production basis, but, as the *Report* points out, the costs in the foreign areas, particularly in Venezuela and the Middle East, would be substantially lower than is indicated by the comparative figures based on expenditures per unit of production if they took into

TABLE 4.7

United States Petroleum Imports Versus Crude Oil Production, 1946–1962

| | Crude oil production | Imports | | | | | | |
		Crude oil	Finished and unfinished products	Total (except residual)	Ratio to production	Residual fuel oil imports	Total imports	Ratio to production
	Thousand barrels per day	*Thousand barrels per day*	*Thousand barrels per day*	*Thousand barrels per day*	*Percent*	*Thousand barrels per day*	*Thousand barrels per day*	*Percent*
1946	4,751	236	19	255	5.4	122	377	7.9
1947	5,088	266	21	287	5.6	149	436	8.6
1948	5,520	353	15	368	6.7	146	514	9.3
1949	5,047	421	18	439	8.7	206	645	12.8
1950	5,407	487	35	522	9.7	328	850	15.7
1951	6,158	491	27	518	8.4	326	844	13.7
1952	6,256	573	28	601	9.6	351	952	15.2
1953	6,458	648	26	674	10.4	360	1,034	16.0
1954	6,342	656	42	698	10.1	354	1,052	16.6
1955	6,807	782	49	831	12.2	417	1,248	18.3
1956	7,151	934	57	991	13.9	445	1,436	20.1
1957	7,170	1,022	77	1,099	15.3	475	1,574	22.0
1958	6,710	953	248	1,201	17.9	499	1,700	25.3
1959	7,054	965	205	1,170	16.6	610	1,780	25.2
1960	7,035	1,016	162	1,178	16.7	637	1,815	25.8
1961	7,183	1,046	199	1,245	17.3	644	1,889	26.3
1962, 1st 6 months	7,350	1,110	210	1,320	18.2	770	2,090	28.4

Source: *Report of the National Fuels and Energy Study Group. Washington, D.C., 1962.*

account the volume of new reserves found and developed as a result of these expenditures.

These data, together with information on rates of production and volume of proved reserves per producing well in foreign areas versus the United States, are indicative of the relatively low cost in the principal foreign producing areas as compared with average costs in the United States. As an illustration, crude oil production in 1961 averaged 12 barrels per day per well in the United States as compared with 295 in Venezuela, 4,400 in Kuwait, and 6,400 barrels per day in Saudi Arabia. Finally, the point is made that the variations in costs are due primarily to the wide differences between proved new reserves and total expenditures for exploration.

Thus the Independent Petroleum Association of America sees increasing availability of lower cost foreign oil as the basic cause for the growth in U.S. oil imports as shown in Table 4.7. The Association is of the emphatic opinion that growth of these petroleum imports is detrimental to the discovery and development of domestic petroleum resources.

On the other hand, the major international petroleum companies argue just as emphatically that petroleum imports are necessary to supplement domestic production and will be necessary for national security purposes. The military agree with this latter point. Some consumer representatives believe that imports should result in lower prices.

The effect of the increased volume of petroleum imports upon the domestic industry and the security of the United States has been the subject of many discussions and legislative and executive hearings. It gives rise to the basic problem: the establishment and implementation of a petroleum import policy that will maintain a strong domestic industry integrated with international sources of supply.

Facts Bearing on the Problem. Our problem must be studied in the light of the necessity for oil imports and United States policy toward imports.

Various estimates have been made of the future import requirements of the United States. Of course all of these estimates depend on many variables. Thus, at the beginning of the 1950's the Independent Petroleum Association of America contended that it would be possible to produce all the petroleum that would be required in the United States by 1955. On the other hand, the President's Materials Policy Commission concluded that, regardless of the level of domestic production, imports of petroleum by 1975 might be 2,500,000 barrels a day, as compared with 540,000 barrels a day in 1950. This was based on peacetime needs.

The National Fuels and Energy Study Group had available to it all previous petroleum studies and it found it necessary to conclude, before making certain required comments, that the nation's ability to meet its oil requirements could not be conclusively assessed because of the lack of definite data.

Based on a thorough study, the report of the Group estimated that by 1980 consumption would be 5.7 billion barrels as compared with 3.5 billion barrels in 1960. The total required over the 20-year period was estimated to be about 90 billion barrels.

The Study Group took as a beginning inventory figure the proved reserves of both crude oil and natural gas liquids at the end of 1960, which were rounded out to 40 billion barrels. Since production experience had settled into a pattern that called for about 12 barrels of proved reserves for each barrel of annual production, and even though this figure was not immutable, the Group chose to stay with this ratio; and thus proved reserves in 1980 would have to be about 70 billion barrels.

The report estimated that no less than 3 billion barrels, and as much as 4 billion barrels, are expected to be added to reserves each year through revisions of estimates and extensions to fields, as the fields become known over the years. Over the span of 20 years the total would be 70 billion barrels.

Thus, one approach to look at requirements would be as follows:

	Billion barrels
Requirements:	
Consumption over the 20-year period	90
Reserves in 1980	70
Total Requirements	160
Supply:	
1960 reserves	40
From extensions and revisions	70
Total Supply	110
Additional reserves necessary to be developed	50

Another approach to look at required discoveries follows from the knowledge that one barrel of proved reserves has eight barrels behind it:

	Billion barrels
Requirements:	
Consumption over the 20-year period	90
In the ground, as representing 70 billion barrels of proved reserves in 1980	560
Total Requirements	650
Supply:	
Recoverable from oil already discovered under present technology from proved parts of known reserves	70
Additional in the ground at present	205
Total Supply	275
Required to be discovered over the 20-year period	375

But the report found that the assumptions as to the future ratio of reserves to production, and as to what the rate of recovery might be in 1980 were too rickety to have much value beyond helping to indicate the ramifications of the problem. Consequently the Report felt that it must conclude that to supply the nation's needs for oil until 1980 will require that:

1. There be some imports;
2. or, the ratio of reserve to rate of output, normally not less than 12, be established at some significantly lower figure;
3. or, much more attention be given to secondary recovery than is now the rule;
4. or, the rate of drilling be stepped up significantly;
5. or, interest in the production of oil from shale be intensified;
6. or, a combination of these steps be taken.[3]

Thus, the conclusion is drawn that petroleum imports into the United States are going to be necessary to fill the peacetime requirements. The military make the case for imports during an emergency even stronger. The Department of Defense recognized the importance of foreign oil in its unpublished policy statement submitted to the President's Commission on Foreign Economic Policy in which it stated:

1. The Department of Defense considers it impractical to plan for the wartime supply of petroleum on a purely national basis, inasmuch as our plans recognize the necessity of considering allied military and essential civilian requirements, in evaluating petroleum policies and plans.

2. In these plans it is recognized that the most reliable source of supply in an emergency would be the United States domestic production followed closely by the production from Western Hemisphere sources, notably Canada and Venezuela.

3. In view of the expanding demand . . . and the fact that approximately two-thirds of the presently known petroleum reserves are located in the Middle East, it is probable that as time goes on, increased reliance will have to be placed upon this source of supply to meet emergency requirements.

The National Fuels and Energy Study Group also reviewed the U.S. emergency petroleum requirements. After appraising requirements in the event of a nuclear attack, a general war without nuclear attack, limited war, and mobilization short of war, the conclusion was drawn that in any one of these circumstances the availability of foreign oil would be necessary.

Actually even the independents agree that under some circumstances petroleum imports are necessary, but they are willing to permit them only if they supplement not supplant domestic production. However, they see no security in foreign oil. On the other hand the majors insist that imports

---

[3] *Report of the National Fuels and Energy Study Group, op. cit.,* p. 304.

are required and that availability of foreign oil is vital to the security of the United States.

Finally, one of the fundamental facts that must be considered in evaluating the necessity of petroleum imports is that it is absolutely essential to consider crude oil and residual fuel oil as separate parts of the problem.

In the case of crude oil it should be pointed out that the oil import situation is substantially different on the two sides of the Rockies. The west coast is a deficit area which cannot produce enough crude oil to satisfy the local demand. The area east of the Rockies has a reserve productive capacity and is, in fact, operating at only about two-thirds capacity, although the East Coast itself is a deficit area like the West Coast. During 1960, for example, approximately one-fourth of all imported crude oil moved to the West Coast area, while the balance moved to refineries on the East Coast.

Residual fuel oil is that part of the barrel of crude remaining after the higher priced products have been removed in refining. Generally it is sold at a price necessary to capture a competitive energy market. Residual is unique among petroleum fuels in that it is sold on a Btu basis in direct competition with both coal and gas. As we have seen, it is primarily used for space heating, but about 20 percent is consumed by tankers and other vessels. Thus, residual fuel oil competes with coal as a boiler fuel, and as we have seen in the chapter on coal, it is the coal industry which protests most vigorously against residual fuel oil imports. The facts are that the use of residual fuel oil remained fairly uniform in the decade before the early 1960's at about 550 million to 560 million barrels a year. While this was happening, domestic production declined as refineries shifted to more valuable products, and net imports rose, increasing from 104 million barrels in 1950 to 215 million barrels in 1960. Forty-five percent of the imports came from Venezuela, 40 percent from the Netherlands West Indies, and 2 percent from the Eastern Hemisphere.

The issue of imported residual fuel oil arises mainly with respect to the East Coast where most of this imported fuel is consumed. Residual fuel oil moves from the port of entry or, if it is domestic, from the refinery to its point of use by water transportation and then overland the short distance permitted by the cost of movement. It moves inland until its delivery cost becomes equal to that of some other fuel, allowance being made for consumer preference, availability of equipment using it, and fuel efficiency. On the average, residual oil moves inland about 125 miles from the coastline, and perhaps 20 miles each side of the riverways, until it comes in competition with coal moving by rail and gas coming north by pipeline.

Total residual imports on the East Coast in 1960 were about 208 million barrels. The National Fuels and Energy Study Group estimated that the nonbonded portion of the 1960 volume was equivalent to 40 million tons of coal. To the extent that imports of residual fuel are kept out, or are permitted to enter, any coal involved would come from mines in Pennsylvania, Virginia, and West Virginia, or would be lost by those mines, as the case may be. Economists in the coal, oil, and gas industries disagree as to how the affected market would be distributed among coal, gas and domestic residual fuel oil. The fact is then that residual fuel oil is imported because of consumer preference, and the question is should imports be restricted to protect domestic producer interests.

Import Policy. Having looked at some of the facts bearing on the need and purpose of crude oil and residual fuel oil imports, we turn our attention now to the facts bearing on United States import policy.

The Independent Petroleum Association of America was organized in 1929 "for reason that imports of oil at that time were threatening destruction of the domestic petroleum industry." The Association states that: "The problem was solved by an act of Congress in establishing in 1932 an excise tax on the importation of oil. This provides the first policy guide because it constitutes the expressed policy of Congress." The 1932 excise tax of 21¢ a barrel on crude was an important deterrent to imports of crude when the price of crude was less than one dollar per barrel.

The one-dollar price for crude was a result of the discovery of the East Texas oil field in 1930, increasing domestic production and the depression-lowered consumption. The Independent Petroleum Association continued to appeal for import restrictions. And from 1933 to 1935, when the National Industrial Recovery Act was found unconstitutional, the National Recovery Administration Petroleum Code empowered the President to restrict oil imports by quotas.

The depression of the 1930's brought on round after round of retaliatory import restrictions by the industrialized nations of the world. During the years 1929 to 1934 world trade fell by 66 percent and U.S. foreign trade fell by 76 percent. Out of this period came the recognition that foreign trade was a two-way street, and the Trade Agreements Act of 1934, which has been extended to the present by periods of not more than three years at a time. By this agreement and its later amendments, the President of the United States has been given the power to enter into reciprocal trade agreements without the approval of Congress, with provisions, however, that these agreements could be terminated at the end of not more than three years, and that tariff reductions were to be limited to 50 percent of the existing duties.

Under the Venezuelan Trade Agreement in 1939, crude and fuel oil duties were reduced to 10½¢ per barrel in amounts up to 5 percent of domestic refinery runs of the previous year. The tax remained at 21¢ a barrel on volumes exceeding this quota.

During World War II, on January 30, 1943, the quota provisions of the above agreement were eliminated under the Mexican Trade Agreement, and under the most-favored-nation clause this provision was extended to the Venezuelan Agreement. Thus, the 10½¢ per barrel remained without limitation on amount. This rate remained until the end of 1950 when the cancellation of the Mexican Trade Agreement resulted in the reinstatement of the quota amounts that could be brought in at reduced rates, that is, reverted to the terms of the 1939 Venezuelan Trade Agreement.

Prior to the abrogation of the Mexican Trade Agreement in 1947, the United States entered into a multilateral agreement with some twenty nations covering all oil products not included in the Mexican and Venezuelan Agreements. In the following year the General Agreement on Tariffs and Trade (GATT) was established whereby the individual agreements made with other countries, together with similar agreements they negotiated among themselves, were brought together and formalized. One result of this action was to reduce the import tax on gasoline from 2½¢ to 1¼¢ per gallon. Thus as a result of the Venezuelan Trade Agreement (1939), The Mexican Trade Agreement (1943) and GATT (1947), the excise duties on crude and all petroleum products established by Congress in 1932 were reduced by 50 percent.

As we have noted above, when the 1950 Mexican Trade Agreement was abrogated, the duties and quota system that had been in force from 1939 to 1943 were temporarily reinstated. Temporarily, because in October, 1952, the United States entered into a Supplementary Agreement with Venezuela under which excise taxes on imports were further reduced and quotas were removed on the amounts that could be brought in at reduced rates. Crude and fuel oil of less than 25 degrees API gravity (a scale expressing density) were taxed at 5¼¢ a barrel while petroleum of higher gravities were taxed at 10½¢ a barrel, regardless of the amount imported. This is the agreement under which the industry operated in the 1960's.

The tax of 21¢ a barrel was a deterrent to imports when petroleum was selling at one dollar a barrel, but with the subsequent increase in the price of crude and the reduction of the tax to 5¼¢, the tax ceased to have any significance as a deterrent to imports. The industry testified that even at 21¢ a barrel the tax was no deterrent to imports at existing prices although some suggestions have been made that it was restrictive. However, most important to the independents is the fact that the existence of a tax is an expressed policy of the United States that domestic petroleum production is to be given protective priority. This expression of protection to the domestic industry was clearly written into the Trade Agreements Extension Act of 1951 through the provision for *peril point* findings and the inclusion of the *escape clause* in subsequent agreements. (The so-called peril point is that point beyond which tariff concessions cannot be made without threatening injury to a domestic industry.)

In the hearings on the Supplementary Agreement with Venezuela, during which discussion was confined principally to crude and residual fuel oil, three of the Tariff Commissioners found that the peril point was a tax of 10½¢ a barrel on crude oil, topped crude, gas oil (including diesel oil), finished fuel oil, and residual fuel, while the other three Commissioners found that the then existing tax of 10½¢ a barrel and 21¢ a barrel on imports in excess of a quota of 5 percent of the crude petroleum processed in domestic refineries during the preceding calendar year represented the peril point. The peril point findings were based on potential rather than present threats to the industry, although there was no evidence given that the tax would offer a protection against such threats. The findings of all six of the Commissioners were overruled, and the President sent a message to Congress justifying the Supplementary Agreement that went into effect on October 1, 1952.

Hence, the expressed policy through the import-excise tax is that the domestic industry must be protected, that the Tariff Commission is looking into the future for threats, and, in addition, that lighter products should be taxed at higher rates.

The National Petroleum Council, representing the independents and the majors, at the request of the Secretary of the Interior formulated *A National Oil Policy for the United States,* published in 1949. This recommended policy stated the "Aims of a National Oil Policy," developed the "Fundamental Principles" to a sound policy, and spelled out in detail "The Elements of a National Policy" under five headings: "Domestic Oil," "Natural Gas," "Foreign Oil," "Imports," and "National Security."

"Domestic Oil" recommendations include the following:

1. The key industry function of oil exploration and discovery presents extraordinary difficulties and risks. It is best promoted by competitive effort and by the incentive of commensurate reward.

2. Conservation of our petroleum resources will best be furthered by facilitating continued industry efforts to reduce waste and promote maximum recovery of oil through optimum-rate production, unit operation, secondary recovery, and other methods.

3. The economic and efficient development of synthetic fuels to supplement natural petroleum as needed can best be achieved by private industry.

4. The provisions in tax laws which have long recognized the requirements of petroleum operations are essential to the continued development of our oil resources and, in furtherance of the public interest, should be maintained.

5. The petroleum resources of the lands beneath the marginal seas extending to the outer edge of the continental shelf can best be explored and developed under state, rather than federal, control.

"Foreign Oil" recommendations include the following:

1. The participation of U. S. nationals in the development of world oil resources is in the interest of all nations and essential to our national security.

2. An effective oil policy should encourage access by our nationals to world oil resources on equal terms with other nationals, and stable agreements between foreign governments and private industry on a basis which will promote development by free enterprise methods.

3. The federal government should encourage foreign oil development by American nationals by efforts directed through diplomatic channels to reduce political risks involved in such foreign operations and by permitting U. S. citizens to operate abroad in conformity with the laws and customs of other countries.

"Imports" call for a policy that will encourage domestic exploration and development and will make available a maximum supply of domestic oil to meet the needs of the nation "produced under sound conservation practices, together with other pertinent factors." This "provides the means to determine if imports are necessary and the extent to which imports are desirable to *supplement* our oil supplies." It is further recommended that the implementation of the policy "should be *flexible* so that adjustments can be made from time to time."

This policy has been interpreted by some of the independents to mean that no imports will be made if the product can be produced in the United States. However, other international interests have suggested that the "other pertinent factors" phrase includes the necessity of an integrated international petroleum program that will supplement our domestic industry.

"National Security" recommendations are as follows:

1. The maintenance of a vigorous oil industry in time of peace is the best way to assure the reserves and facilities needed in time of war.

2. The government should accumulate such inventories of petroleum products in peacetime as would be needed by the armed services in the early stages of a conflict.

3. Procedures for government-industry consultation should be maintained on a permanent basis so that plans to meet emergencies can be adjusted continually to changing conditions.

The rising level of oil imports during the early 1950's and the problem of their subsequent effect on the domestic industry was one of the primary reasons that caused President Eisenhower to establish the Cabinet Committee on Energy Supplies and Resources in July, 1954. The Committee reported in February, 1955, that imports of crude and residual oils should be kept in balance with domestic production at the proportionate relationship that existed in 1954. The Committee also recommended that the ratios should be reevaluated from time to time.

The Committee did not specifically recommend a course of action limiting imports. Instead the importing companies were requested to cut back imports on a voluntary and individual basis. However, after expressing alarm at the rising trend of imports, the Committee noted that ". . . if in the future imports of crude and residual fuels exceed significantly the respective proportions . . . appropriate action should be taken." The term "appropriate action" was not defined, but it clearly hinted that mandatory limitations would be imposed if the voluntary recommendations failed.

Later, as a result of growing debate in Congress over the subject of petroleum imports, the following paragraph (Section 7) was included in the Trade Agreements Extension Act of 1955:

(b) In order to further the policy and purpose of this section, whenever the Director of the Office of Defense Mobilization has reason to believe that any article is being imported into the United States in such quantities as to threaten to impair the national security, he shall so advise the President, and if the President agrees that there is a reason for such belief, the President shall cause an immediate investigation to be made to determine the facts. If on the basis of such investigation, and the report to him of the findings and recommendations made in connection therewith, the President finds that the article is being imported into the United States in such quantities as to threaten to impair the national security, he shall take such action as he deems necessary to adjust the imports of such article to a level that will not threaten to impair the national security.

It is through this *security clause* that the President has the right to set trade limitations by his own authority whenever he feels that our national security is threatened.

In May, 1956, the Office of Defense Mobilization (ODM) reevaluated the limitations on petroleum imports, and excluded from imports review all crude coming from Canada and all crude being imported into the West Coast. Venezuela was also exempted from imports review because it was conforming to ODM standards. But because imports into the United States, excluding the West Coast, continued to exceed the 1954 relationships, the ODM requested Middle East importers to take steps that would effect a reduction in their future programs.

Most major companies, fearing government regulation, restricted their imports under the voluntary program as recommended. However, the Independent Petroleum Association of America, dissatisfied with the informal voluntary restrictions, filed a petition on August 7, 1956, requesting action under Section 7 of the Trade Agreements Extension Act of 1955.

At the hearings held in October and in early December, 1956, the Director of Defense Mobilization announced that he was suspending action because of the changed conditions due to the Suez crisis. But subsequently when the importing companies submitted their plans for 1957, the President was advised on April 23, 1957, pursuant to Section 7 of the Trade Agreement Act, that the estimates constituted a threat to national security. As a result, on June 26, 1957, the President established the Special Committee to Investigate Crude Oil Imports.

The Special Committee made its recommendations on July 29, 1957. The Committee, using the five petroleum districts set up as PAW districts by the Petroleum Administration for War, made a distinction between the Pacific Coast or District V and the rest of the country, Districts I–IV. According to the committee report, petroleum production in District V, which was represented almost entirely by California oil fields, was not controlled by regulatory bodies, was at its maximum capacity, and was insufficient to meet the requirements of the District. As a result increased imports were necessary to meet domestic demand.

According to the Special Committee, this condition was not true of Districts I–IV, which were found to have a substantial productive capacity in excess of actual production. Even though the volume of production was controlled by regulatory commissions, stocks were in excess of normal demand. As a result the Committee concluded that the increasing volume of crude oil imports into Districts I–IV constituted a threat to national security and that for this reason a limitation on imports was necessary.

The plan which was devised was to be voluntary; but, if after a certain period, the companies were found to be lax in their compliance, the President would be requested to take action according to the *security clause* of the Trade Agreements Act of 1955. It was hoped that a ratio between imports and domestic production of approximately 12 percent could be achieved in Districts I–IV and that the relationship between imports and domestic demand would be approximately 9.6 percent in these same districts. However, for District V imports were to be restricted, within reasonable limits, to the difference between demand and the domestic crude oil available. Thus, they would be supplementary.

Evidence can be presented to show that the 1957 voluntary program did restrict the level of crude oil imports. More important, though, were the violations of the spirit of the program in a six-fold increase in the level of imports of unfinished oils from 1956 through 1958. Unfinished oils, which only require a small amount of additional processing to bring them up to the standard of finished products, were not counted in the crude oil quotas under the voluntary program. The increased importation of these unfinished oils, though acceptable according to the letter of the program, threatened to imperil the whole oil import program.

The Trade Agreements and Extension Act of 1958, Section 8 required mandatory controls of oil imports which had been certified by the Office of Civil Defense Mobilization as being "in such quantities as to threaten to impair national security."

In March, 1959, President Eisenhower, through the office of the Secretary of the Interior, imposed mandatory controls on the imports of petroleum. The stated reason for the restrictions was "to encourage development of domestic resources in the interest of national security."

The mandatory oil import program as modified and in operation in

1965 works as follows for crude oil. In Districts I–IV imports of crude oil were initially limited to 9 percent of the U.S. Bureau of Mines' estimate of demand for petroleum products other than residual fuel oil (demand defined as "consumption at current prices"). Effective January 1, 1963, it became necessary to restrict importation of crude oil in District I–IV to 12.2 percent of the estimated domestic production. Imports overland from Canada and Mexico are exempt from licensing requirements, but they are deducted from the total level of licensed offshore imports. When the total quantity of oil to be permitted entry by license has been determined, it is then allocated to refineries. The first basis of allocation was to historical importers. They are permitted to import a percentage of their last quota under the previous Voluntary Oil Import Program. In practice this is a minimum allocation for they also have a choice to use refinery input experience if this gives them a larger allotment. All oil remaining after allocation to the historical importers is divided among other refiners who either had no history of imports or whose historical imports were nominal on a basis of refinery inputs. The amount of oil subject to allocation to historical importers has been constantly reduced. After the company allocations are computed, importing licenses are issued, permitting the companies to import their oil quotas. The import quotas are revised every six months.

In District V imports of crude are determined by subtracting the total of domestic supply and overland imports from estimated demand. The program is thus designed to fill the supply-demand gap that exists in the District. Estimates are made by the U.S. Bureau of Mines prior to January 1 and July 1 each year, and quotas are allocated by the same method as in Districts I–IV.

In the case of residual fuel, the mandatory oil import program works as follows.

District I imports of residual fuel oil are treated differently from those into all other Districts. Due to the industrial and population concentration along the Atlantic Seaboard, the domestic supply of residual fuel oil is insufficient to meet demand. In District I the domestic supply is subtracted from the domestic demand, based on estimates of the U.S. Bureau of Mines. The supply-demand gap which is indicated then becomes the level of importation. The allocation to individual importers is made in much the same fashion as that for crude oil, except any oil which is not allocated on a historical basis of imports is allocated to persons having deepwater terminals on the basis of terminal input.

Imports of residual fuel oil for Districts II–V are considered in the *finished product* category and are restricted as noted below. In these Districts residual fuel is used principally as an industrial fuel and in small amounts for space heating, and residual fuel is generally in oversupply.

Imports of finished products and unfinished oils, including residual fuel oils for Districts II–V, excluding residual fuel oils for District I, are limited to those companies importing these products in 1957 and to the amounts which were imported in that year. Finished products are a minor part of the import program as they constitute only about 5 percent of total imports.

One important provision of the mandatory import regulations is that they enable importers to exchange imported oil for domestic oil. Section 7 of the Federal Code of Regulation specifies that no allocation "may be sold, assigned or transferred." But contrary to this specific statement, this rule does not mean that quotas cannot be used as the basis of crude oil exchanges, in which, just as effectively as by sale, dollar values are transferred for quotas. This device has been used to secure import rights by major international importers from oil firms operating in the mid-continent, which received quotas by refinery thruput allocation and which had never imported oil before. The result is that U.S. firms with overseas supplies but limited foreign markets have had to bid for quota rights from mid-continent refiners, and the latter, in turn, have received windfall gains from the assignment and exchange of import quotas.

Conclusions. It is clear from the foregoing presentation that the United States has moved toward a more restrictive policy in the solution of the basic problem: the establishment and implementation of a petroleum import policy that will maintain a strong domestic industry integrated with international sources of supply.

Perhaps the reason so much interest centers around petroleum imports is that the basic problem breaks down into many separate problems, each of which has numerous implications. Some of these problems that require study are the effect of petroleum imports on: (1) The coal industry; (2) The petroleum industry in relation to; (a) production cutbacks, (b) conservation, (c) the rate of new discoveries; and (3) national security and international relations.

The domestic interest group with the greatest stake in residual oil imports is the coal industry; and in the discussion of the coal industry the problem of petroleum imports was shown to be an area in which the coal industry has taken vigorous action to place preventive tariffs and import quotas on petroleum supplies.

The principal markets for residual fuel are for ship bunkering, steam locomotives, steam power generating installations, industrial plants, and space heating. Many purchasers in steam generating facilities and industrial plants have equipment that enables them to switch from one fuel to another. About 10 percent of residual fuel imports have been bonded free for ship's bunkers, but in this use residual is not very competitive with coal because vessels have progressively shifted to more convenient and efficient residual and diesel fuel and all the new ships burn oil only. Residual fuel and coal have both been losing the market to diesel fuel for use in the more efficient diesel locomotive engine. In electric power generation, residual has been losing the market to coal. But the competition between coal and residual fuel has been keen in the area of industrial use and space heating.

The case for restriction of residual fuel to help coal in District I is an extremely poor one, for in this district the use of residual fuel is of critical importance to heat hospitals, apartments, office buildings and other large spaces, and New England requires an adequate supply of residual fuel which is effectively used in that area because of savings in transportation costs compared with coal due to the all-water shipment of residual.

The mandatory restrictive program does treat residual fuel oil as a separate commodity and it further recognizes that the demand for domestic fuel oil is greater than domestic supply. District I is set apart from all other districts because of its distinguishing characteristic as the prime deficiency area, while the remaining districts have an oversupply.

Finally, it should be noted that no significant increases of domestic supplies of residuals can be expected and there is a rising demand for residuals outside the United States, accompanied by declining yields.

One concludes that we have in residuals a case in which they fall short of meeting demand and are more economical for certain specific uses. Thus, imports of residual fuel supplement domestic production. But what of coal's case for restricting residual imports? There is no question about the fact that residual fuel is competitive with coal; but the national interest requires residual imports, for the way to economic progress and productive strength is not through restrictions to competition. In spite of these conclusions the U.S. government has seen fit, even while recognizing the market for residual, to restrict residual imports. Why did it do so? One government official gave the answer: "This restriction was necessary because of the interplay of economic forces in the oil industry and in order to control all phases of oil imports."

The case for or against the restriction of imports in relation to the petroleum industry rests on the complicated interrelationship of the impact of crude oil imports upon production cutbacks, conservation, and the rate of new discoveries.

Imports of petroleum have a direct and immediate effect on crude production because many state conservation and regulatory agencies restrict production to *market demand* (total domestic and export demand minus imports). Thus, the producer sees imports as a subtraction from the amount of allowable production. What the independent producers would like is to produce at the MER and import just enough petroleum to supplement this amount to satisfy total domestic and export demand. From previous analysis it is clear that this objective would have to be modified to provide for the required reserved productive capacity within the MER. Thus the maximum allowable that national policy would permit would be at the MER minus reserves. Petroleum would be imported to the extent necessary to supplement domestic production so that total domestic and export demand would be met. Under this policy imports become the residual figure in place of production. This simplified suggestion treats a barrel of petroleum supplies as a barrel of crude. The independent producers would approve of this method, but the majors would be quick to point out that separate consideration must be given to crude oil and residual fuel oil.

One argument advanced for imports is that they conserve domestic reserves of petroleum. At first this may seem to be a truism. However, enough has been said to prove that what is needed is an active productive domestic industry. The industry will accept a policy that imports should *supplement* domestic production but rejects a policy that imports should *supplant* domestic production. Another significant conservation issue is involved in the intra-industry arguments for federal legislation to limit petroleum imports. This is the issue that there is too much danger to state regulation of conservation in this approach. The fear is that if the federal government enters the field of limiting imports in order that imports and domestic production shall not exceed demand, it is only one more step to say that limitation of supply to *market demand* cannot be effectively brought about by federal action unless the federal government at the same time has control over domestic production.

Another principal argument advanced for the limitation of petroleum imports is that they are likely to retard new discoveries and development of petroleum by reducing the incentives of the independents. Since the independents have found about 75 percent of domestic reserves, this is a problem that deserves careful consideration. The basic problem is that imports should be maintained at a rate that will supplement and not interfere with the development of an adequate crude capacity. We have seen that in District V crude oil imports supplement domestic production. Further, we can conclude that the impact of imports will come primarily through adjustments of production and resultant changes in total income rather than through price, although a strong case may be made that with more importers, prices will be more competitive. Because of a decline in income, from whatever cause, the independent will be discouraged from looking for new sources of oil because: (1) Reduced income may prevent the independent from setting aside the sums of money needed for domestic development, and (2) The independent will be unwilling to spend his reduced income for oil that he cannot market.

There is evidence that production of domestic crude is not only less than the MER minus an emergency reserve, but that production was stabilized within narrow limits after 1955. The net effect was of course reduced income to producers. What effect did this have on petroleum reserves? From Figure 4.2 it was determined that total proved reserves were increasing, although they had decreased in some years. In addition, it was noted that the U.S. industry had maintained a working inventory of

proved reserves of about twelve to thirteen years which seemed to be set-
tling around a figure of 12. One might conclude that there was no cause
for alarm. But one should remember the further conclusion that the true
measure of the U.S. petroleum productive capacity should be potential
production measured against anticipated demand which is rising, and, in
addition, more recent reserve figures show declining trends.

Further, the Independent Petroleum Association is always alert to
point out that there are advanced indicators of additions to reserves. Geophysical and core drilling activity is seen as a reliable indicator of the
future of the producing industry since it is the forerunner of exploratory
drilling and development programs. Decline in the number of exploratory
crews eventually is reflected in decreased drilling, and historically there
has been a close relationship between the number of wells drilled and
petroleum reserves developed.

The Independent Petroleum Association submitted Figure 4.7, which
shows the relationship between exploratory activity and new field discoveries, to the National Fuels and Energy Study as an illustration of the
dangerous consequences of the downward trend beginning in the early
1950's. The Independent Petroleum Association of America was careful to
note that although advanced technology and improved recovery operations may tend to alter this relationship somewhat, the basic fact is: "A
prolonged decline in drilling, therefore, provides the warning as to our
future reserve position."

Evidence of the type presented above led to the conclusion by the
government that import controls were necessary. However, the Independent Petroleum Association of America was not satisfied with the level of
controls and continued to press its historic position for more restrictive import controls. The Association pointed out in its report to the National
Fuels and Energy Study Group that since the mid-1950's, along with a
lower rate of growth of consumption, there had been a marked decline in
every principal indicator used to measure the vigor and health of the industry. A comparison of 1961 with 1956 showed the following:

1. Geophysical and core drilling crews active in exploration is more than 30
percent below 1956.

2. Wells drilled in 1961 were 19 percent below 1956. Exploratory drilling
dropped 30 percent in this period.

3. Rotary rigs active in 1961 were 33 percent below 1956.

4. Employment in the production of oil and gas was 9 percent below 1956.

5. The price of domestic crude oil in 1961 was 20 cents a barrel below 1957,
in the face of steadily increasing costs.

6. The rate of return on invested capital for the domestic petroleum industry
has fallen below the average for manufacturing industries in general.

7. During the last 5 years, there has been an unhealthy trend toward sellouts
and mergers in the producing segment of the domestic oil industry.[4]

[4] *Report of the National Fuels and Energy Study Group, op. cit.,* p. 416.

Figure 4.7: Exploratory Activity and New Field Discoveries, 1950–1960.

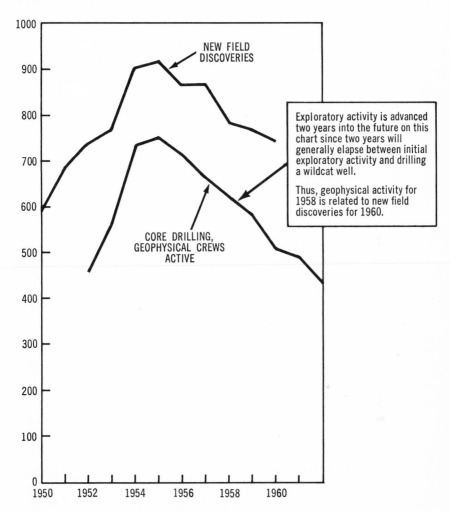

Source: *Report of the National Fuels and Energy Study Group*, to the Committee on Interior and Insular Affairs, United States Senate, 87th Congress, Second Session, Washington, D.C., September 21, 1962.

The National Fuels and Energy Study Group concluded that before the mandatory import controls were imposed the increasing flow of imports was a depressing influence on the domestic industry. While the Study Group, as in other policy matters, did not take a position with respect to the need for more restrictive import policies, it did point out that a relaxation of controls would restore the pressure on the industry, and that drilling might decline even more than it had since 1956.

On the other hand, those who argue for unrestricted imports claim that eventually, a competitive coexistence between imported and domestic oil would be established. The claim is that under the pressure of unrestricted imports the industry could emerge with a smaller basis, a somewhat lower wellhead price, and a considerably higher degree of efficiency. This latter point is made with a great deal of emphasis by many economists who claim that state regulatory authorities discriminate in favor of the least efficient wells, which are permitted to produce at capacity, while the output from the most productive wells is kept considerably below the MER. Finally, it is claimed that with greater efficiency and the resultant competition from imported oil, the lower priced oil would tend to reduce the cost of all energy in the United States. This would clearly be in the public interest because of the great and growing importance of energy in the United States economy. Hence, those who hold the pure economic point of view contend that the general welfare would clearly be enhanced by the abolition of oil import restrictions.

The fact of the matter is that the decision to place restriction on petroleum imports was not made exclusively on economic considerations. It is quite clear that the decision to restrict oil imports was made in the interest of national security.

The third part of our problem, the impact of petroleum imports on national security and international relations has many ramifications.

Standard Oil Company (New Jersey) argues as follows:

Oil supplies outside the United States, developed by Americans, were highly important in both World Wars I and II.

In World War I the availability of large quantities of Mexican crude oils made it possible for the United States to meet the enormous demand for fuel oil for the Allied navies and merchant ships.

In World War II Venezuela was an important supplier of oil for industry and for the Allied armed forces. In later stages of the conflict, oil from the Middle East was a large part of the fuel used for operations in the Pacific. It is estimated that at the height of the war more than a third of the combined oil requirements of the United States and its Allies for military and shipping needs were being met with oil produced outside the United States. Without Caribbean and Middle East sources to draw on, the military requirements of the United States and its Allies for oil could not have been met.

Today, defense production and the requirements of military establishments within our own borders call for strong domestic fuel industries, with reserve capacity for use in case of emergency. But access to oil sources abroad is also essential. The development of such sources depends to considerable degree on keeping markets open to them, and by far the largest single market is the United States. If American defense were limited to fuel sources within our own borders, our ability to conduct military operations on a broad scale, and to keep aggressors at a distance from our shores, would be handicapped severely.[5]

[5] *Facts About Oil Imports,* New York, Standard Oil Company (New Jersey), April 15, 1953, p. 9.

The Independent Petroleum Association of America argues the point briefly and concisely on its letterhead: "There Is No Security in Foreign Oil for the Defense of Our Own Borders."

Ample evidence has been presented to show that petroleum imports will be required in peace as well as war. The truth of the matter is that the future does not present such black and white alternatives but requires continuous defensive efforts to prevent a major war. The military have recommended an expanding oil development first, in the continental United States; second, in the Western Hemisphere; and third, in other world areas. To implement this policy with respect to imports, a recommended petroleum policy would recognize that the economic development and military security of the Western Hemisphere require that petroleum productive capacity must be available throughout the hemisphere, and that these sources should be given first priority for U.S. imports. The Western Hemisphere is rapidly becoming a balanced area of petroleum production and consumption. In the event of a major war all the petroleum productive capacity of the Western Hemisphere would be required and rationing for civilian use would be necessary. Oil for war is a hemispheric problem. Therefore, in order to meet economic and military requirements outside the hemisphere, petroleum productive capacity in the Middle East and other areas of the Free World should be developed to minimize the use of Western Hemisphere sources and transportation facilities and to maximize nonhemispheric productive capacity. This latter poses the additional problem of threats to the Western Hemisphere industry of imports from the Middle East. However, the degree of security involved in this policy is greater than that for some other commodities, because these resources and productive facilities represent the investments of U.S. nationals who place national policy first and have a mutual interest in domestic and foreign operations. If we expect other oil-producing regions to supply our emergency requirements market outlets must be provided.

The problem of market outlets is much broader than that of military security as it is an integral part of our national policy to strengthen our national economy and our international interests. In addition, trade is a two-way street; our purchases of imports provide dollars for the purchase of United States exports. Venezuela is an excellent illustration. Venezuela is not only the United States' principal source of oil imports but, as will be seen, also the number one supplier of iron ore imports. Venezuela's purchases of goods from the United States are so large and varied that every state in the Union exports some kind of product to Venezuela. Thus Venezuela is a primary source of our basic resources and a major purchaser of our exports. The result is a strengthening of both United States and Venezuelan economies. Restrictions on petroleum imports must take into account all these factors. In addition, restrictions invite retaliatory actions.

But in the final analysis there are those who argue petroleum transportation in a major war would be so vulnerable as to be unavailable, and that even in peacetime the availability of foreign oil, even though under American concessions, is subject to the discretion of foreign powers. The National Fuels and Energy Study Group concluded that unlimited imports of petroleum into the United States would increase U.S. dependency on foreign oil in times of emergency, and it would be necessary to adopt measures to offset this condition. One such measure would be to provide military forces to protect the foreign sources of supply and naval forces to protect the transportation. Another measure would be to maintain an adequate emergency reserve between the MER and production, which would have to be financed at the expense of the domestic industry. The third alternative, which the United States has chosen, is to restrict imports at the expense of the international majors in the hope that this will strengthen the domestic industry and reduce the dependence on overseas sources.

Thus, national security constitutes the overriding consideration in the case for a restrictive import policy. In issuing the Presidential Proclamation for mandatory controls the basis of the program was declared to be the "requirements of our national security which make it necessary to preserve to the greatest extent possible a vigorous, healthy petroleum industry in the United States."

Finally, with respect to the mandatory import program it seems important to draw the conclusion that if the basis of the program was national security, there seems little justification in the method of administration of quotas in a manner that interferes with the established marketing patterns. But this is exactly what has been done with the reduction of the quotas to the historical importers.

Under the regulations in effect in 1965, about 36 percent of the crude imports going to the East Coast were brought in with quotas assigned to refiners who never previously purchased foreign oil and who could not economically ship it to their refineries. These inland refiners, unable to use the imports, trade them with East Coast refiners for domestic crude oil at a premium of about one dollar per barrel. This trading of quotas represents a forced transfer of East Coast refiners' profits to inland refiners' profits, and the windfall gain previously mentioned. Dr. Rene P. Manes of Purdue University computed this direct profit transfer at 60 million dollars for 1960 alone.[6] Even though it is true that those refiners which have received the windfall gain have become supporters of the mandatory program, this market interference on the part of the government cannot be justified to implement the policy of import restrictions.

Dr. Manes concluded that the U.S. government found itself in the unenviable position of making decisions which directly redistribute profits between companies, which alienate oil-producing, neighboring nations,

[6] Rene P. Manes, "Import Quotas, Prices and Profits in the Oil Industry," *The Southern Economic Journal*, July, 1963, p. 23.

and which imperil vast U.S. investments in those lands. These decisions have not fully achieved the first objectives of the program since the domestic producers are not satisfied with the results obtained.[7] Here is a case of the government deliberately using a stated need for regulation in one area for security purposes to effect changes in another area which appears to be unrelated. This is a specific illustration of one segment of the petroleum industry's contention that government regulation in one area soon leads to another.

Freedom of enterprise and the possibility of increased competition in the petroleum industry, which might conceivably result in lower consumer prices, have thus been lessened in the hope of providing increased national security by restricting petroleum imports.

Tax Policies

The basic petroleum tax problem that has commanded much public attention during recent years is whether the petroleum depletion allowance should be modified. Industry spokesmen have been ardent in defense of the allowance as essential to the growth of the industry while its opponents have called the depletion allowance: "One of the greatest scandals in the tax system," and "the most inequitable loophole in the tax laws."

In the light of the vigorous conflicting opinions, there is need to understand the nature and the purpose of the depletion allowance. What are the facts?

Facts Bearing on the Problem. The dictionary defines depletion as "impairment" of capital; decline in value caused by the consumption or diminution of an asset. In the case of oil this takes place as each barrel is extracted from the earth. As this occurs, the owner's "capital" is permanently used up.

As the law now stands depletion of petroleum may be calculated on the basis of 27½ percent of the gross income applied separately to the income from each oil-producing property but may not exceed 50 percent of the net income before depletion. The legal basis for the federal income tax is the 16th amendment to the United States Constitution, passed in 1913, which authorizes Congress "to lay and collect taxes on incomes from whatever source derived, without apportionment among the several states and without regard to any census or enumeration." The chief purpose of the amendment was to remove the constitutional requirement that such taxes be in proportion to population. However, it also limited the collection of taxes to income, and thus implicitly disallowed the direct taxation of capital. The law does allow taxation of some increases in capital such as capital gains. But in these circumstances the tax is on the increment in value, and even in these instances special treatment is given.

The Revenue Act of 1913, which levied the first income tax in the

[7] *Ibid.*, p. 24.

United States, set the depletion deduction at 5 percent of the gross value of the oil, to be taken every taxable year until the recovery of the original cost of the property or its market value as of March 1, 1913. This statute established the principle of relating the depletion allowance to a fixed percentage of the taxpayer's gross income, and except for the period 1916–1925, this principle has formed the basis of all federal income tax provisions concerning oil and gas depletion.

The Revenue Act of 1916 amended these provisions, by removing the percentage deduction and substituting a provision permitting oil and gas producers a "reasonable allowance" for depletion not to exceed the actual cost of discovery, except on properties discovered before March, 1913 which could be depleted at fair market value. The cost-of-discovery limitation was an attempt to put depletion on the same accounting basis as depreciation by permitting the recovery of "the capital originally invested." Back of this principle was the concept that the value of an asset reflects only the actual direct costs expended on it, and thus excludes such value determinants as risk and scarcity on which its market price is based. However, for wells or mines discovered before 1913, value was equated with market price.[8]

The Revenue Act of 1918 again changed the cost basis and authorized producers to base the "reasonable allowance" either on the discovery cost or market value of the property. Subsequent revenue acts have adhered to this formula. However, in 1921 it was provided that the deduction for depletion could not exceed 100 percent of a producer's profit from each property. In 1924 this limit was reduced further to 50 percent, and is still in effect.

The practical implication of the 1918 Revenue Act choice between cost or market was that depletion of most oil properties was computed on a market-value basis because it generally exceeds actual direct cost, due to the high risk factor in oil drilling plus the great demand for oil. The Congressional hearings which preceded the passage of the 1918 Act revealed three major influences that apparently prompted the shift of the depletion allowance base from discovery cost to discovery value: (1) the recognition that discovery cost depletion might not be sufficient to enable mineral producers to replace their exhausted properties, (2) the desire to encourage oil prospecting activities, and (3) the awareness of the strategic importance of oil.[9]

---

[8] The coexistence of these two different concepts of value in the same law are thought by Lichtblau and Spriggs to be a reflection of the great debate on the nature of value carried on by the world's leading economists during the late 19th and early 20th centuries. John H. Litchblau and Dillard P. Spriggs, *The Oil Depletion Issue,* New York, The Petroleum Industry Research Foundation, 1959.

[9] Based on testimony found in *Legislative History of the Depletion Allowance,* Staff data prepared by the Staff of the Joint Committee on Internal Revenue Taxation for use of the Committee on Ways and Means, Washington, D.C., March, 1950.

The determination of market-value of properties was a complex proposition because under discovery-value depletion, valuations of the worth
of the property had to be made in the case of each discovery well. Frequently these valuations were subject to dispute between oil producers
and Federal tax authorities. As a result, in 1925 the United States Senate
appointed a special committee to investigate the difficulties encountered
in administering the depletion deduction for oil and gas properties based
on their discovery value. A year later, the Senate Finance Committee, acting on the special committee's findings, recommended that depletion in
the petroleum industry be based on a percentage of gross sales.

The Finance Committee proposed that the actual rate be set at 25
percent. However on the floor of the Senate strong efforts were made to
increase the percentage, and after debate, a rate of 30 percent was
adopted. After a conference with the House of Representatives, percentage depletion was lowered to 27½ percent, and enacted into law.

The Revenue Act of 1926, which is still in effect, thus provided that
percentage depletion for oil be at a rate of 27½ percent of gross sales; but
it also limited percentage depletion to 50 percent of the taxpayer's taxable
income. In addition to percentage depletion, the law also provides for cost
depletion which is based on the actual discovery cost or purchase price of
the property. Under the law, the taxpayer is required to take whichever
allowance is larger, and reduce the remaining depletable basis of his
property by that amount. Cost depletion ceases when full cost recovery
has been effected while percentage depletion continues throughout the
productive life of the property. Since percentage depletion allowance is
the object of the public attack, how does it work?

The following two examples illustrate percentage depletion. The first
where that statutory limit of 50 percent of net income does not apply, and
the second where it does.

Gross Income	$10,000
Costs	4,000
Net Income before Depletion and before Income Tax	$ 6,000
Depletion Deduction	2,750
Taxable Income	$ 3,250
Gross Income	$10,000
Costs	6,000
Net Income before Depletion and before Income Tax	$ 4,000
Depletion Deduction (limited to 50 percent of net income)	2,000
Taxable Income	$ 2,000

In the first illustration if an individual or a company owned an oil or
gas property from which gross sales amounted to $10,000 and the costs of

operation amounted to $4,000, net income from the property would be $6,000. Thus, the percentage depletion (27.5 percent of gross income) would amount to $2,750. This is less than the statutory limit of 50 percent of net income (50 percent of $6,000, or $3,000) so the 27.5 percent could be deducted in full in calculating the income tax liability of the property.

In the second illustration if the cost of operating this same property were $6,000, taxable income would amount to $4,000. In this example the 50 percent of net income (50 percent of $4,000, or $2,000) would prevent the operator from using the full percentage depletion deduction ($2,750) because it would exceed the statutory limit. Thus, the actual deduction in computing the income tax could not be greater than $2,000.

The second example applies in quite a few instances in the oil industry. As a result, the effective depletion rate for the industry as a whole has been less than the maximum rate. Just how much less is a matter of contention—but depletions range from an industry estimate of an applicable rate of 23 percent to a United States Treasury estimate of 24.5 percent.

Percentage depletion for oil and gas properties has been a controversial issue. It has frequently been the subject of public criticism, both in and out of Congress. Much of the debate stems from the fact that it is a unique tax deduction, available only to producers of depletive resources, among which oil and gas operators have the highest rate.

One of the main arguments advanced against percentage depletion is that it results in an unneutral tax and that it makes the oil industry an unusually profitable industry.

When one compares the average percent of net income paid as a tax by all U.S. corporations it will be found to be a multiple of that paid by most oil companies. Indeed, critics are fond of citing examples of individual oil producers who pay no income taxes. The industry contends that when income is correctly defined, the tax paid on petroleum is fair relative to other industries. The industry position is that the figure referred to as "income" from producing operations includes a complex mixture of capital values that cannot be taken out of the business or taxed as income without impairing the capital assets needed to continue in business.

As to the claim that the percentage depletion contributes additional profits to an already excessively profitable industry, oil operators claim that the notion that the oil business is excessively profitable is a myth. As proof of this claim, they show that the earnings of the 90 largest oil companies over a period of 20 years have been 11.8 percent after taxes, as compared with 12.4 percent for all manufacturing companies. However, one should note that this 11.8 percent covers companies operating in all phases of petroleum, not just production.

Actually, the petroleum industry might be in a sounder position if it would spend less time arguing that percentage depletion is not an unneutral tax, and would base its position on the purpose of the tax allowance. Since most of the obvious criticism stems from the unneutral tax treatment, the point should be emphasized that most taxes have purposes other than that of raising revenue. Percentage depletion is thus not to be evaluated as a means of revenue, but as an instrument to facilitate growth in petroleum reserves.

Another main line of argument accepts percentage depletion as sound in principle but argues that the rate is too high. During the early 1960's most opponents to the existing rate advocated a reduction to 15 percent, although there still was a group that wanted to abolish the exemption altogether. There appeared to be no justification for the 15 percent figure other than it was an accepted target. The petroleum industry argues that the 27½ percent is not only not too high, but that this rate is necessary to accomplish the objectives of depletion.

One argument cited to show 27½ percent is not too high is that studies of oil-producing companies indicated that discovery value depletion as practiced prior to the Revenue Act of 1926 had represented a slightly higher percentage of gross income than 27½ percent. During 1926 a study of this question by the Joint Committee on Internal Revenue Taxation of the Congress concluded that for 117 oil-producing companies the percentage depletion to gross income was 28.4 percent for the year 1924. Further samples in the same year of twenty-one producing companies and two major producing companies placed the figure at 28.3 percent and 31.1 percent respectively.[10]

The fundamental argument advanced for the depletion allowance is that the rate of 27½ percent is necessary because of the risk involved to find new reserves to replace the "capital" reserves that are being used up through production. The contention is that percentage depletion has its principal effect on exploration and drilling which have actually declined sharply in recent years. The industry's contention is that the real test of the adequacy of current incentives lies in the rate of development of new reserves and in the relation of proved reserves to future demands for petroleum. Figure 4.2 showed that the ratio of reserves to current production has been declining. Some of this change has been due to improved technology making it possible to produce reserves more rapidly. Such developments raise the supply immediately available, but they also hasten the exhaustion of resources unless exploration efforts are maintained at levels needed to meet long-range future requirements.

The claim is that oil is the only major industry in which at least three-fifths of every dollar of sales must be reinvested to find and develop new capital assets to replace assets depleted. Oil exploration requires funds that are difficult to obtain through the credit processes, since the risk of discovery is so great. The funds for exploration and development must come from venture capital and from the overall difference between cash

[10] *Legislative History of the Depletion Allowance, op. cit.,* pp. 11–12.

income and cash outgo. The contention is that the removal of any of the percentage depletion would be a serious blow. With the chances of finding oil being long chances, indeed the odds would stack even higher against the explorer if the government took the bulk of his capital assets when he should find such assets. It is further contended that it is true that once the independent operator finds oil and possesses a capital asset, he can arrange his financing in part through commercial banks and other commercial sources, assigning oil runs as security. But here again, the 27½ percent depletion allowance is a major factor in credit financing. The industry concludes that if the depletion allowance is taken away, the operator would find further financing very difficult, to say nothing of the great burden of meeting outstanding loans and continuing in business.

Opponents of percentage depletion contend that the domestic petroleum industry doesn't need capital. As a matter of fact there is evidence to support the charge that percentage depletion has attracted too much capital into petroleum production and brought on the substantial restriction on the output of some domestic wells, particularly in Texas. For example, at the beginning of the 1960's the domestic industry was estimated to have a total productive capacity of about 10,000,000 barrels daily and a shut-in capacity of about 3,000,000 at an average producing rate of about 7,000,-000 barrels. As a result, critics conclude that too much capital has been invested in the industry. The industry concludes that the operating rates are certainly less than desirable, but points out that this is only one of the facts to be considered in judging adequacy of current investment and capacity.

One contention is that excess capacity is mainly due to a combination of production controls and imports. As we have seen, the industry's position is that production controls are necessary for conservation. In addition, we have seen that a reserve in domestic production capacity is necessary for emergencies, and that a level of 1,000,000 to 2,000,000 barrels is probably desirable. Further, the industry sees no discrepancy between importing foreign oil which eats into the domestic market, while limiting production to market demand. When one accepts these premises, then one can follow the argument for depletion with production controls. Since production controls cut down the amount of oil that can be produced, they cut down income. The depletion allowance helps the producer to survive this reduced income. Further, the depletion allowance in itself does not encourage the holding of discovered oil in reserve since depletion only comes with production. However, it does make it possible for investors to tolerate and maintain a larger capacity. This argument is valid only if one accepts the need for extra capacity and conservation. However, many economists contend that the effect of depletion allowances on conservation is questionable as they claim that depletion allowances result in a lower price for petroleum and thus increase consumption.

Another contention is that excess capacity in the petroleum industry is not a result of depletion allowances but reflects a lag in adjustment to the rapid increase which has occurred in imports and to the slowing down in the rate of growth of domestic demand. But more importantly, the point is made that current productive capacity is only a short-term measure of the adequacy of capital input. A better measure for the long-run is the behavior of proved reserves. Proved reserves have shown only a small increase or a slight decrease even though demand continues to advance at a long-term rate of about 3 percent a year. This development reflects the decline in exploration and drilling as an adjustment to the rise in imports, the increase in shut-in capacity, and the decrease in the growth of demand due to intensive competition from gas. The industry concludes that the ratio of domestic reserves to demand was somewhat lower in the early 1960's than had traditionally existed in the past, indicating that investment in petroleum has not been excessive.

Finally, the industry concludes that not only is investment not excessive in petroleum, but percentage depletion is necessary to sustain the industry to protect the security of the United States. Cited is the fact that the Director of the Office of Civilian and Defense Mobilization and a Special Cabinet Committee concluded that petroleum imports should be restricted because they constitute a threat to the level of exploration and drilling considered desirable for national security. Thus, in view of these considerations, percentage depletion cannot be said to have encouraged excessive development of domestic resources. On the contrary, one of the best reasons for maintaining percentage depletion at existing rates is that the system has worked well to encourage new resources at about the rate required to meet the needs of the United States' expanding economy.

But in spite of all these persuasive arguments in favor of percentage depletion, critics still claim that the requirements for petroleum could be met if percentage depletion were done away with, and if not that, then, at least lowered.

Conclusions. The preceding presentation has merely given some of the facts involved in the differential tax treatment of petroleum. There are many other issues involved which make the problem even more complex. One tentative conclusion seems warranted. The percentage depletion provisions have been on the statute books for a long period of time and investments in this essential industry have been encouraged by these differential tax provisions. Any change in the system will necessarily create adverse consequences for the industry, and will quite likely lead to higher petroleum prices for consumers. Impartial analysis of this problem by Congressional committees in the past and by special governmental agencies such as the President's Materials Policy Commission and the Special Cabinet Committee on Energy Resources and Supplies, has led to the conclusion that percentage depletion should be continued at existing rates because such action best serves the public interest.

Our tax system functions not only to provide revenue, but also to serve many other purposes. One of these purposes is to provide growth, and has received renewed attention. The big problem of determining the equity of the tax advantages for petroleum as with the so-called loopholes for many other taxpayers is that Congress has really no accurate yardsticks to measure what tax treatments are necessary to secure the right social result or the correct amount of investment for growth. As a result the achievement of the proper function of a tax is hard to obtain. Even more difficult, as we have seen in the case of petroleum, is to clarify what the true purpose of a tax is. In view of the uncertainties involved, we may conclude that the long-established system of percentage depletion will continue to be in effect without change. Certainly the United States, which has established a policy to restrict petroleum imports to protect and encourage the domestic industry, should not adopt a tax policy which runs counter to this objective.

SUMMARY

Petroleum has been seen to be vital to victory in war and a growing power source in peacetime. Its importance as an energy source is even greater than indicated by the fact that it supplies more than a third of the United States' energy requirements since it is absolutely essential as a fuel in all forms of transportation. Adequacy of petroleum reserves to meet projected demands has been seen to depend upon continued discovery and development of proved reserves. The organization of the industry is such that both independent and major companies have actively contributed to the growth of both a domestic and international industry. There has been a steady increase in U.S. companies' development and ownership of crude reserves outside the country in order to benefit from these low cost supplies at a time when crude costs were increasing in the United States. These foreign sources of supply have thus become available as imports to supplement domestic crude and to supply the growing foreign markets for petroleum products.

Government policies affecting the industry have centered around state conservation laws, the attempt to regulate imports, and tax depletion policies to stimulate the exploration and development of domestic reserves. In general the policy pattern has been the avoidance of federal regulation if possible, and a preference for state regulation where necessary.

SELECTED REFERENCES

An Appraisal of the Petroleum Industry of the United States, Washington, D.C., United States Department of the Interior, 1965.
Annual Analysis of the Petroleum Industry, New York, The Chase Manhattan Bank, 1960 and later issues.

Bennett, Elmer F., ". . . *the facts behind the decision to control oil imports!*," address presented by Under Secretary, Department of Interior before the American Bar Association, Tulsa, Independent Petroleum Association of America, 1960.

Burck, Gilbert, "U.S. Oil: A Giant Caught in Its Own Web." *Fortune*, April, 1965, pp. 113 ff.

Facts About Oil Imports, New York, Standard Oil Company (New Jersey), April 15, 1953.

Gonzales, Richard J., *Percentage Depletion*, Presented to the Committee on Ways and Means House of Representatives, Houston, Humble Oil & Refining Company, December 1, 1959.

Litchblau, John H., and Dillard P. Spriggs, *The Oil Depletion Issue*, New York, The Petroleum Industry Research Foundation, 1959.

Manes, Rene P., "Import Quotas, Prices and Profits in the Oil Industry," *The Southern Economic Journal*, July, 1963, pp. 13–24.

Moore, J. Cordell, *Remarks of J. Cordell Moore, Administrator, Oil Import Administration*, Washington, D.C., United States Department of the Interior, May 16, 1964.

Mouzon, Olin T., *U.S. Petroleum Import Policy*, Trade Policy Study, a report for the Public Advisory Board for Mutual Security, Washington, D.C., Executive Office of the President, December 19, 1952.

A National Oil Policy for the United States, Washington, D.C., National Petroleum Council, January, 1949.

Oil—Basic Analysis, Standard & Poor's Industry Surveys, New York, Standard & Poor, 1963 and later editions.

"Oil Shale," Bureau of Mines Bulletin 585, Washington, D.C., 1960, pp. 573–580.

Petroleum Facts and Figures, New York, American Petroleum Institute, Centennial Edition, 1959 and later editions.

Raciti, Sebastian, *The Oil Import Problem*, New York, Fordham University Press, 1958.

Report on Energy Supplies and Resources Policy, Washington, D.C. Executive Office of the President, February 26, 1955.

Schackne, Stewart, and N. D'Arcy Drake, *Oil for the World*, New York, Harper & Row, 1960.

Smith, Arthur A., *The Vital Need for Percentage Depletion*, New York, American Petroleum Institute, 1963.

"Statement of the American Petroleum Institute," *Report of the National Fuels and Energy Study Group*, Washington, D.C., 1962, pp. 407–427.

"Statement of the Independent Petroleum Association of America," *Report of the National Fuels and Energy Study Group*, Washington, D.C., 1962, pp. 407–427.

Teitelbaum, Perry D., *Energy Production and Consumption in the United States*, analytical study based on 1954 data, Washington, D.C., U.S. Bureau of Mines, 1961.

Twentieth Century Petroleum Statistics, Dallas, DeGolyer and MacNaughton, 1960.

Williamson, Harold F., and Arnold R. Daum, *The American Petroleum Indus-*

try, 1859–1899, The Age of Illumination, Evanston, Northwestern University Press, 1959.

Williamson, Harold F., Ralph L. Andreano, Arnold R. Daum, and Gilbert C. Klose, *The American Petroleum Industry, 1899–1959, The Age of Energy,* Evanston, Northwestern University Press, 1963.

5

NATURAL GAS

THE natural gas industry has risen rapidly to a position of major importance as a supplier of energy in the United States and now contributes more than a third of the nation's total energy requirements. Fifty years earlier the infant industry supplied 3 percent. Yet it was only three decades ago when the industry began to grow, and not until after World War II did it reach the take-off period in its growth that has led to its present position of importance.

The natural gas industry is divided into three major parts: production, transmission by interstate pipelines, and distribution to consumers by local distribution companies. All of these segments have contributed to growth, but real progress was not made until the three parts began to work together as a whole. The gas industry started out with the distributing companies using gas manufactured from coal, coke, and later oil. The natural-gas-producing branch, on the other hand, sprang up as a by-product of the petroleum business, where the industry had limited operation because there was no means of moving the natural gas from oil and gas fields of the Southwest to the populous areas served by the distributors. The gap was in transportation where the mechanical means were limited. The earliest pipelines were less than an inch in diameter, but today the pipelines are so big that a small boy can stand upright inside. This technological development has meant that gas can be transmitted with speed and volume under pressure.

The big changes in transportation that have come about since World War II are those that have linked the producing fields to the consumer. In 1930, two out of every three gas customers depended on manufactured or mixed gas supply. By 1950 only 41 percent were receiving either manufactured, mixed, or liquefied petroleum gas service through utility mains. Since 1950, however, such tremendous growth has taken place that today 94 percent of residential and 93 percent of industrial gas users are served by natural gas.

PRODUCTION

Production, the first branch of the industry, deals with a commodity which is a fund natural resource. The other two branches of the industry deal with a service, either transporting a product through interstate pipelines, or distributing the product to consumers. The term *natural gas producer* includes several functions: exploring for, finding, developing, gathering, processing, and selling natural gas. Some pipeline companies and, to a lesser extent, some distributing companies also own gas-producing properties and explore for gas to meet part of their requirements. However, the great majority of producers are independent of the other two branches.

Exploration

Exploration for natural gas is very similar to that for petroleum. Like petroleum, natural gas is generally believed to be derived from plant and animal organisms deposited at the bottom of ancient seas and buried under layers of sediment. With passing ages, pressure and temperature acted to decompose these organisms and to transform them into hydrocarbons. The simplest forms of hydrocarbons are gaseous like natural gas. Where they occur with increased molecular weight they become liquid (crude oil) and finally solid (coal). As we have noted in our study of petroleum, the gaseous and liquid forms are frequently found in the same deposits. These deposits occur in porous rock formations, and they accumulate in traps created when the porous formations are sealed off by the nonporous formations. A trap may result from a structural deformation, or from the squeezing, or pinching out of the reservoir rock by the impermeable layers. In either case the porous rock layer is surrounded by impervious formations which the natural gas cannot penetrate.

It is in these traps that the natural gas producer looks for reserves using methods similar to those employed to look for petroleum. As we have seen, all oil in nature has gas dissolved in it, and some oil fields have distinct reservoirs of gas called "gas caps" above the pools of oil. In addition, there are gas fields unassociated with oil. Up to now, about 70 percent of the gas found in the United States has been in reservoirs without oil or in which the production of gas is not significantly affected by the production of oil.

The only way to discover gas or petroleum is to complete a well. An operator who undertakes to drill for gas in an unproven area is called a "wildcatter." This same terminology is used in the oil business. In each business a "wildcatter" must use all the scientific knowledge at his command and have tremendous initiative. His risks are high, for only one wildcat well in 9 has been completed as a gas or oil-producing well. But even these figures paint an overly optimistic picture because according to statistics developed by the American Association of Petroleum Geologists, only one "wildcat" in every 37 drilled opens a profitable commercial field.

Reserves

Reserves of natural gas like those of petroleum are expressed as proved reserves. As of January 1, 1965, proved reserves totalled 281,251,-454 million cubic feet distributed among the United States as shown in Table 5.1. This table also shows the factors involved in the changes of reserves from one year to the next. The high degree of concentration of 42.3 percent of the reserves in Texas and 28.1 percent in Louisiana is the most noteworthy feature of the natural gas distribution between the states.

The ratio of reserves to production has been falling ever since World War II. But just as in the case of petroleum, this "life index" has limited usefulness, for what really counts is how much gas can be produced in the future in response to a changing demand. Yet some significant points about this index should be developed. While the "life index" for oil has reached a point of stability which the industry tries to achieve, the gas industry still has to reach this point. In the early days of the petroleum and gas industry when there was no market for gas, the "life index" was high, derived by dividing a large figure for reserves by a small figure for production. As markets have developed and rates of production increased, the "life index" progressively dropped as shown in Figure 5.1 prepared by the National Fuels and Energy Study Group.[1] The projection of this trend would show that the index fell below 20 for the first time at the beginning of 1963, and reached a low of a little less than 18⅓ years at the beginning of 1965. Where the index should stabilize is not yet known. But one factor influencing the life index of natural gas that does not affect petroleum is that the FPC in the past has normally issued a "certificate of public convenience and necessity" for the construction of a gas pipeline only if enough gas is assured to supply the project for twenty years. Similarly, the banking community will not finance a pipeline unless a field has proven itself to the extent of a 20-year reserve.

The National Fuels and Energy Study Group attempted to make some sort of tentative estimates as to what volume of future reserves might be added to the proved reserves of natural gas. What follows are tentative conclusions which in large measure are dependent on how much money and effort the industry spends looking for reserves, and this, in turn, may be greatly dependent on environmental and public policy factors affecting the industry.

In the past, exploration and production of natural gas have been prin-

[1] *Report of the National Fuels and Energy Study Group*, Washington, D.C., 1962, p. 304.

TABLE 5.1

Estimated Proved Recoverable Reserves of Natural Gas in the United States
(Millions of cubic feet—14.73 psia, at 60° F)

	Reserves as of December 31, 1963[b] (1)	Changes in Reserves During 1964					Reserves[b] as of December 31, 1964			
		Extensions and revisions [b] (2)	Discoveries of new fields and new pools in old fields [b] (3)	Net change in underground storage[c] (4)	Net production[d] (5)	Total (columns 7+8+9+10 also columns 1+2+3+4 less column 5) (6)	Non-Associated[e] (7)	Associated[f] (8)	Dissolved[g] (9)	Underground storage[h] (10)
Alaska	1,690,724	146,058	1,000	0	6,417	1,881,365	1,748,527	0	82,838	0
Arkansas	1,792,644	286,586	97,780	7,165	84,083	2,100,092	1,569,426	317,722	189,191	23,753
California[i]	8,865,726	672,499	141,808	11,598	637,924	9,053,707	3,354,184	1,647,953	3,849,350	202,220
Colorado	1,876,057	(−) 64,438	18,050	1,313	101,724	1,729,258	1,399,949	79,323	244,421	5,565
Illinois	168,595	(−) 128	80	17,301	6,347	179,501	72	0	35,047	144,382
Indiana	60,180	2,264	16	12,048	3,270	71,268	607	597	16,883	53,181
Kansas	17,994,235	42,157	57,134	2,579	817,963	17,278,142	16,578,324	428,220	178,777	92,821
Kentucky	1,085,236	5,217	68,776	9,578	74,452	1,094,355	982,153	0	66,978	45,224

Louisiana[i]	75,364,992	4,915,365	2,950,060	121	4,154,229	79,076,309	65,012,415	9,175,211	4,887,971	712
Michigan	722,812	44,293	14,309	23,566	30,704	774,276	151,853	73,709	53,663	495,051
Mississippi	2,481,627	58,306	10,250	581	195,000	2,355,764	1,907,408	179,547	262,256	6,553
Montana	598,131	6,660	2,176	11,397	28,095	590,269	384,278	21,122	78,165	106,704
Nebraska	100,042	(-) 534	2,771	3,035	11,931	93,383	56,484	8,169	15,352	13,378
New Mexico	15,037,822	1,116,604	85,800	598	886,389	15,354,435	11,463,976	2,114,892	1,749,048	26,519
New York	132,285	(-) 1,147	1,360	3,785	2,794	138,489	38,288	0	31	95,170
North Dakota	1,119,575	19,420	7,884	0	36,234	1,110,645	6,372	328,340	775,933	0
Ohio	748,187	(-) 22,378	6,000	15,325	37,713	709,421	228,818	0	89,278	391,325
Oklahoma	19,138,820	1,586,206	239,688	149	1,207,628	19,757,235	14,963,987	2,700,233	1,959,732	133,283
Pennsylvania	1,214,498	69,555	14,560	30,284	85,322	1,243,575	703,957	0	18,104	521,514
Texas[i]	117,809,376	4,403,407	3,074,409	4,112	6,436,249	118,855,055	80,457,781	25,010,649	13,309,782	76,843
Utah	1,638,324	(-) 65,955	12,058	64	65,088	1,519,403	882,146	382,106	254,299	852
Virginia	31,303	0	2,800	0	1,923	32,180	32,180	0	0	0
West Virginia	2,311,164	175,859	27,353	30,022	196,453	2,347,945	1,936,618	0	61,202	350,125
Wyoming	3,988,546	(-) 53,775	70,062	(-) 880	235,393	3,768,560	3,223,793	151,545	372,687	20,535
Miscellaneous[a]	180,332	736	3,087	11,370	3,703	191,822	38,764	0	19,005	134,053
Total	276,151,233	13,342,837	6,909,301	195,111	15,347,028	281,251,454	207,122,360	42,619,338	28,569,993	2,939,763

a Includes Alabama, Florida, Iowa, Maryland, Missouri, Tennessee and Washington.
b Excludes gas loss due to natural gas liquids recovery.
c The net difference between gas stored in and gas withdrawn from underground storage reservoirs, inclusive of adjustments and native gas transferred from other reserve categories.
d Net production equals gross withdrawals less gas injected into producing reservoirs. Changes in underground storage and gas loss due to natural gas liquids recovery are excluded. Fourth quarter production estimated in some instances.
e Non-associated gas is free gas not in contact with crude oil in the reservoir; and free gas in contact with oil where the production of such gas is not significantly affected by the production of crude oil.
f Associated gas is free gas in contact with crude oil in the reservoir where the production of such gas is significantly affected by the production of crude oil.
g Dissolved gas is gas in solution with crude oil in the reservoir.
h Gas held in underground reservoirs (including native and net injected gas) for storage purposes.
i Includes off-shore reserves.
SOURCE: Proved Reserves of Crude Oil, Natural Gas Liquids, and Natural Gas, New York, American Gas Association, American Petroleum Institute, 1965.

Figure 5.1: Natural Gas Reserves, Annual Production, and Ratio of Reserves to Annual Production.

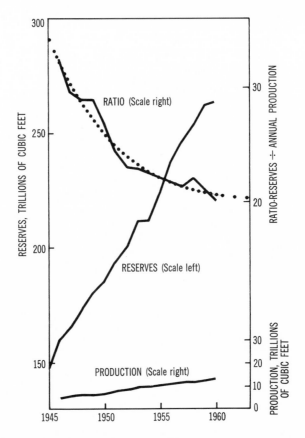

Source: *Report of the National Fuels and Energy Study Group*, to the Committee on Interior and Insular Affairs, United States Senate, 87th Congress, Second Session, Washington, D.C., September 21, 1962.

cipally a result of looking for oil; gas discoveries and production were incidental. During the 1950's a gradual shift took place toward the search for gas as a primary objective. Since 1947 when data are available the record has been favorable with respect to new discoveries, and the Study Group predicted that beginning with a total of 270 trillion cubic feet a total of some 35 to 40 trillion cubic feet of recoverable gas could be expected to be found in new reservoirs by 1965. This is an annual average rate of increase of from 7.5 to 8 trillion cubic feet. Adding to this the gas that might be developed in known reserves beyond the present totals, the estimate was that from 85 trillion to more than 100 trillion cubic feet of new gas would be available by 1965.

If the growth rate of discovery is still upward by 1980, some 225 trillion cubic feet of recoverable gas can be expected to be found in new reservoirs, and the annual rate at that time could be around 15 trillion cubic feet. If the rate should flatten off to 11 trillion cubic feet a year, perhaps by 1980, 175 trillion cubic feet will be discovered. The Group went on to conclude that from all the studies by geologists, engineers, and statisticians it might be possible to surmise that if all the natural gas were discovered, it would mean approximately an additional 1,000 trillion cubic feet made available for use in the United States over some indefinite period of time. But these figures were very tenuous.

Production

Production of gas by states is given in Table 5.1 in which reserves are also shown; and most noteworthy is the extremely close correlation between the percentage of gas produced and reserves held in the states of Texas and Louisiana. Gas is either produced from gas wells or along with crude oil. The amount of gas that can be taken from each well is limited by physical and economic conditions which will be described in the following paragraphs.

There are two types of gas wells. Gas produced from so-called "dry gas" wells is accompanied by only relatively small amounts of liquid hydrocarbons when it is reduced to atmospheric pressure and temperature. The other type of gas well is the gas condensate well. Gas from condensate reservoirs is accompanied by larger amounts of liquid hydrocarbons which may be in the gaseous state under reservoir conditions but liquefied in the production and processing operation. This type of well has come into prominence in recent years because it is the type most likely to be found at the greater depths at which most exploration is now being carried on. In a gas-condensate reservoir the hydrocarbons originally are considered to be in a single gaseous phase. On reduction of pressure, condensation of some of the hydrocarbons will result. The liquid so obtained is termed "condensate." Gas-condensate reservoirs contain, in addition to condensate, natural gasoline and lighter hydrocarbons similar to those found in gas associated with oil. The extractable constituents fall into the broad classification of natural gas liquids; the amount ranges from 10 to 75 barrels per million cubic feet of gas. Often, these liquids will be stripped out of the gas at the surface, and the dry gas recompressed and returned to the reservoir in a cycling project. The object is to increase the recovery of the liquid hydrocarbons. The ultimate sale of the dry gas is deferred until liquid recovery has been largely completed.

Another type of well from which gas is produced is the crude oil well from which about one third of the nation's natural gas supply is produced. Both gas and oil are brought to the surface and the gas, known as "casinghead gas," is separated from the oil. Casinghead gas is limited in production to the petroleum associated with it, and the quantity produced is determined by the proration of oil. Gas also occurs as "gas cap" gas when it exists as a "cap" above an oil accumulation. For that reason it cannot be produced until the recoverable oil has been taken out. To take the gas out would limit the amount of oil that could be recovered as the pressure of the gas-cap is necessary to recover the oil. Sometimes, casinghead gas and gas-cap gas can be recompressed at the surface and injected back into the reservoir. This process substantially increases oil recovery, but the gas is not available for sale until the oil recovery is substantially complete.

One significant economic factor affecting the production and sale of natural gas is the previously mentioned liquid hydrocarbons that are extracted from both natural gas and oil at the wellhead. These hydrocarbons were formerly wasted, but they became increasingly important after the mid 1930's as major petroleum companies began to recover them partly for blending purposes. Today these hydrocarbons are also recovered and sold in the form of liquefied petroleum gases, such as butane, propane, and the like.

Methods of extracting hydrocarbon liquids from natural gas are the results of three stages of development as described by the U.S. Bureau of Mines. In the early years of the industry, extraction was accomplished by compressing and cooling. The crude natural gasoline recovered by this method contained a considerable amount of butane and propane which made the gasoline unstable at atmospheric pressure and temperature. As the more volatile constituents vaporized, some of the desirable heavier components were carried with them. Because of the inefficiency of this method, the number of compression plants has declined, and they have been replaced by larger and more efficient absorption type units. The absorption process involves passing the produced gas through an absorber countercurrent to the absorption oil from which the liquid hydrocarbons are removed by distillation. The process gives high extraction efficiency and is capable of close operational control.

During the 1930's the charcoal-absorption process came into limited use. This consisted of passing the produced gas through absorber towers containing activated charcoal to absorb liquid hydrocarbons from the gas. These liquid hydrocarbons were then recovered by passing live steam through the charcoal.

Today there are well over 600 natural gasoline and cycling plants in the United States, with a capacity to produce natural gas liquids in excess of one million barrels a day. About 75 percent of this capacity is represented by the absorption process. As early as 1962 production of natural gas liquids had already exceeded one million barrels a day, which was an increase of over 60 percent in a decade. Of these natural gas liquids, about two-thirds was used in the form of liquefied petroleum gas (LPG), mainly for home heating, and to a lesser extent for chemicals, motor fuels, and other miscellaneous purposes.

The importance of these liquefied petroleum gases in the production of natural gas is that they are becoming more and more the controlling factors, and this is likely to continue if there are no significant increases in gas prices. It is noteworthy that some companies are extracting more and more liquefied hydrocarbons, and using the natural gas or gas found in the association with petroleum for repressuring oil pools rather than selling at current prices. To cite another trend of the same type, some companies are using increasing amounts of natural gas reserves in chemical operations. Prices realized from natural gas on that basis may reach four or five times the amount realizable from direct sales to pipelines.

Subject to the physical and economic limitations mentioned above, the gas produced in the field is available for market and the gas producer has three principal ways in which he can sell it. First, he may be able to sell it himself or use it himself in or near the producing field. Considerable amounts are required for use in the field by the equipment; it may be used in the production of carbon black, or it can be sold to near-by industrial users or local gas distributing companies. A second method of sale is that the producer may transport his own gas to large industrial users or electric utilities some distance from the field. Some industrial lines of this type may extend several hundred miles. The third method is to sell the gas to a pipe-line company (the second branch of the industry) which in turn transports it to the ultimate points of consumption. Some pipeline companies operate only within one state and concern themselves with gas produced only within the state. Other pipeline companies transport gas across state lines, sometimes more than 2,000 miles. These pipelines are the interstate pipelines, the so-called "long lines." About 55 percent of the net gas production in the United States moves in interstate commerce by way of the long lines.

The importance of the type of sale has grown significantly since June 7, 1954; for on that date for all practical purposes the regulation of sales in interstate commerce by producers to pipelines for resale came into being. This was sixteen years after the original enactment by Congress of the Natural Gas Act, which set up the regulatory authority of the Federal Power Commission over natural gas. During those years it was widely believed throughout the industry and by the Federal Power Commission itself, that the Act was *not* intended to regulate field sales of natural gas producers. On June 7, 1954, however, the United States Supreme Court ruled otherwise in a 5–4 decision in a very far reaching case involving the Phillips Petroleum Company. The precedent thus established brought all other independent producers under the regulatory control of the Federal Power Commission. So important is this case and the problems generated that it will be given special study in the problem and policy section.

For the moment this problem of price as related to production needs to be emphasized. Since World War II the producer has been in a sustained price-cost squeeze. The producer received very little more for each million Btu's produced in 1961 (33¢) than he got over a decade before that (an average of 29¢ in the years 1947–1949). This trend is in contrast to an increase of 52 percent in drilling and completion cost per foot drilled and to the increase of 123 percent in drilling costs per unit of reserves added.

The effects of increased costs combined with stable unit realization from hydrocarbon production have already contributed to a decline in the profit ratios of domestic producers. (The *profit ratio* is the ratio of profit to equity investment.) In recent years producers' profit ratios have fallen to near the levels received by pipeline companies, gas distributors, and manufacturing enterprises, each of which faces substantially smaller risks than gas production.

A declining profit ratio is of serious import for future exploratory activity. Not only do producers rely heavily on revenues from operations to finance the search for new reserves, but new venture capital is not likely to go where the returns are not sufficient. Alternative investments may look better. For example the return on net assets for all U.S. manufacturing was 10.1 percent on the average in 1961, as compared with 10.4 percent in petroleum production and refining, where the risk is much greater.

There is some real evidence that the impact of the declining profit ratio had already affected exploration in the United States as illustrated by Figure 5.2. The chart shows that geophysical and core drilling operations reached their peak in 1953, and have declined ever since. Wildcat and development drilling peaked in 1956—three years later than geophysical work, and then a steady downward trend started. This three-year gap between the peaks of geophysical activity and drilling reflects the time lag between the start of an exploration program and its culmination in wildcat drilling. The results of geological and geophysical activity are not generally apparent until three or four years later.

Large numbers of wells do not automatically mean large reserves, but we do know that the only way to find the gas in the future estimates of U.S. reserves is to drill for it. Whether these estimates actually show up as proved reserves depends on whether the natural gas producers are able to operate in an atmosphere conducive to continuing exploration and development. And in addition, we have seen that pricing policies may determine whether the natural gas, when found, is produced and sold as gas or is used in some more profitable manner.

PIPELINES

The pipeline companies are the middle branch of the natural gas industry. They are the connecting link that purchases the supply of gas

Figure 5.2: Oil and Gas Exploration and Well Drilling Activity.

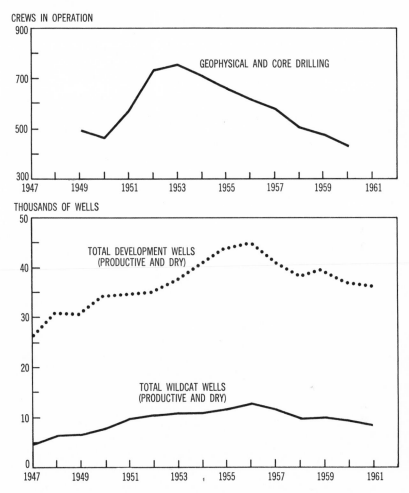

Source: *Natural Gas, A Study in Industry Pioneering*, American Gas Association.

in one area and transports it to be distributed in the distant consuming markets. The network of pipelines is so large that it covers almost every state in the United States. Of the mainland states only Maine and Vermont are not yet served with natural gas.

The main purpose of the pipeline is to provide the essential link of transportation of natural gas from the producers to the distributing company. We have noted the function of the producer includes that of gathering. That is, the gas from each well is gathered by a piping system and delivered to some central point adjacent to the producing area. Most of these gathering systems are owned and operated by the particular producer whose gas is being transported. Others are owned by independent organizations and some few by the long-line transmission company. The point at which a gathering line jurisdictionally becomes a transmission line is sometimes vague. Lines that originate at individual wells are true field or gathering lines, but after a number of these come together into a larger pipe and before they reach the long-line transmission system, the character of the line is difficult to identify.

The exact point at which the pipeline does become the long-line transmission line is important because it is at this point that the middle branch of the industry takes over operation and the FPC takes over jurisdiction. Normally at this point the first long-line compression station would be located; whereas, prior to this point only field booster pumps would have been required.

Under the Natural Gas Act of 1938, the supervision and regulatory control of interstate natural gas transmission lines was vested in the Federal Power Commission, a regulatory agency which had been in existence since 1920. The jurisdiction of the FPC includes routing, construction, the allocation of gas to markets, valuation of utility plants, and determination of the rates or the amounts the transmission companies can charge to move the gas. At one time the courts construed the Natural Gas Act to give the FPC jurisdiction of certain local distributions of natural gas which had been purchased for resale, but this interpretation of the law has changed with the passage of the Hinshaw amendment by Congress in 1954. As a result it is clear now that the jurisdiction of the FPC ends at the same time as does the function of the interstate pipelines. When the local distributing companies, the third branch of the industry, take over, they are regulated by state commissions and/or municipal authorities.

Thus, the role and the function of the pipeline companies is clear: they provide the transportation of natural gas from the producer to the distributing company. The American Gas Association describes the job as follows: "The typical pipeline company must: (1) obtain a steady, reliable supply of gas from numerous producers under different conditions as to price, location, and volume; and (2) sell and deliver it to numerous distributing companies and other customers under different conditions as to price, location, and volume." And of course all this must be done to the satisfaction and profitability of all three branches of the industry.

It may be an oversimplification to say that the actual construction of the pipeline is no longer a problem, but certainly this statement is relatively true because of the technological improvements. In the 1930's, for example, the average pipe was 20 to 22 inches in diameter and operated at a pressure of 500 to 600 pounds per square inch. Today, pipes 36 inches in diameter and operating at pressure of 1,000 pounds per square inch are common. The possibility of 40 to 54 inch pipe is being developed. Mechanization is well advanced as the pipe is mechanically handled at the construction site, mechanically wrapped, and mechanically laid in the ditch and backfilled. One big improvement in operational procedures is improved gas turbine compressers to move the gas along with horsepowers now as much as 30,000 as compared with 5,000 only a few years ago.

The result of these improvements is that a modern large-diameter pipeline powered with a modern compressor could be built in the 1960's for about two-thirds of the cost of a line in the late 1940's. And it is certainly well that this is true for one of the distinguishing criteria of pipeline companies is their large capital requirements. On the average, it takes almost three dollars in plant investment to produce a dollar in revenue for the pipeline companies. In comparison, for other forms of U.S. industry to produce one dollar of revenue it takes only 13¢ in retail trade and for manufacturing industries it takes 49¢. This means that the fixed investment costs of depreciation, return (including interest), and taxes are high.

These high fixed costs must be recovered regardless of the quantity of gas transported. As is the case in all instances where fixed costs are high, it is most advantageous to obtain a high capacity factor, or in other words, to obtain the greatest utilization of plant, or in this case, pipeline capacity.[2] For fixed unit costs are smallest when these total annual fixed costs can be spread over the greatest number of units.

The gas industry uses the rule of thumb of 1.5 to 2¢ a thousand cubic feet (Mcf) per 100 miles as the cost of moving gas through modern, large-diameter, long-distance pipelines operating at high capacity factors of 85 percent or more of full capacity. At high capacity factors about four-fifths of the 1.5 to 2¢ represents fixed costs. The other fifth represents the variable costs of physically moving the gas through the pipeline.

Assuming an average cost of 2¢ per Mcf per hundred miles at maximum capacity factor, Table 5.2 shows the effect of reduced capacity factors on costs.

What makes this high fixed cost problem of particular importance to the pipeline is the great seasonal variation in the demand for natural gas. There are great peaks in the domestic heating markets during the winter months only to be followed by valleys. In order to overcome this problem and lower the unit fixed costs for moving gas, the pipeline companies use two techniques: storage, and interruptible sales to industrial consumers.

Pipeline companies have developed storage areas, preferably near the main transmission line at the delivery end of the system. Depleted gas and oil fields and other suitable underground formations are used. These reservoirs are filled during the summer and other slack periods of pipeline

---

[2] The extent to which installed capacity is being utilized is measured in terms of capacity factor and load factor. *Capacity factor* is the ratio of the average load on the machine, equipment, or plant for a certain period of time to the rating of the machine, equipment, or plant. *Load factor* is the ratio of the average load over a designated period of time to the peak load in that period.

operations, so there is a supplementary supply available during peak demand, and the pipeline is used in offpeak demand. There is a growing number of these fields located in seventeen states; and the President's Advisory Committee on Energy Supplies and Resource Policy recommended in 1955 that: "The power of eminent domain for the acquisition of surface and mineral rights for the development of underground storage reservoirs for natural gas should be granted subject to appropriate safeguards to protect the public safety, including the mining industry."

TABLE 5.2

Effect of Capacity Factors on Transportation Costs

(in ¢)

Capacity factor	Variable costs	Fixed costs	Total costs
100 percent	0.4	1.6	2.0
75 percent	0.4	2.1	2.5
50 percent	0.4	3.2	3.6

SOURCE: *Report of the National Fuels and Energy Study Group*, Washington, D.C., 1962.

Interruptible sales of gas for industrials is the second method used to raise the capacity factor. The pipelines use this method and also help the distributing companies to sell gases for such purposes. Such industrial customers buy gas in large and fairly even quantities all during the spring, summer and fall. Many of the companies suspend their use during very cold days. This is facilitated by a policy of low price gas during offpeak periods; and there is no question that these interruptible sales play a vital part in the economical operations of pipeline and distributing companies and thus enable the domestic consumer to have gas available at lower costs. However, there are those who argue that interruptible sales do not make the highest possible use for natural gas, and furthermore the coal industry is most unhappy about this practice. So much has been said about this practice that it will be studied separately in the section on problems and policy.

Pipelines and the Federal Power Commission

The role of the FPC in regulating pipelines falls into two broad categories: the control of physical construction, and the control of rates paid for service.

In the first category of control, the interstate pipeline companies are required to obtain prior approval for the construction of new facilities and the expansion of old facilities. Among the items considered are the adequacy of gas supply, the design of facilities, the estimated cost of construction, the economic feasibility, the rates at which the gas will be sold, and, in general, whether such new projects are required by the "public convenience and necessity." Every new project or addition by a pipeline company must be spelled out in great detail in an application. No approvals are given by the FPC until after extensive public hearings are held.

The second category of rate regulation is very complex. For every change in rate involving a sale of natural gas for resale through interstate transportation, the pipeline companies must file rate schedules with the FPC, accompanied by detailed supporting data specified under Commission rules. This is followed by an investigation of the Commission's staff, including extended field investigations and hearings. In addition to rate changes which the pipeline companies file, the state commission and other interested parties may make complaints against the rates already in existence; or the FPC may do so. These activities result in proceedings which look toward rate reduction.

But most important in the area of rate regulation are the guiding principles of rate determination. In the famous 1944 pipeline case, FPC v. Hope Natural Gas Company, the United States Supreme Court said that in fixing rates under the Natural Gas Act, it is important that there should be enough revenue not only for operating expenses but also for the capital costs of the business. This includes interest on debt and dividends on stock. This case stated further that such rates should provide for the equity owners (shareholders) a return commensurate with returns on investments in other enterprises having similar risks. The court added that the rate ". . . should be sufficient to insure confidence in the financial integrity of the enterprise so as to maintain its credit and to attract capital."

This is certainly a clear statement of policy, but its method of implementation by the FPC has not been without problems for the pipelines. In the first instance, the Commission has refused to deviate from its original cost method in fixing rates. This is the old problem of what is a "fair value" of assets. This original cost method in fixing rates means that the pipeline company's earnings are locked to a past dollar investment which has lost its meaning due to the continual rising cost of pipeline facilities today. The estimate was that pipeline construction in 1960 was twice as expensive as in 1950.

What constitutes a "fair rate of return" on a "fair value" is another problem. During the early part of the 1940's the FPC established a practice of approving rates which would yield up to 6½ percent a year on the overall investment (minus accrued depreciation) of pipeline companies. At that time pipeline companies could successfully issue bonds paying as little as 2½ percent annual interest. This meant that the rest of the company's net earnings might be devoted to increasing the benefits of the stockholders either through dividends or increased equity investment. This led to a very good return to stockholders under what is called "leverage benefits." It means in this case, that shareholders receive a higher percentage on their investment than the 6½ percent return allowed to the company.

In the late 1940's the Commission cut the rate of return by adopting a general uniform rate policy of fixing rates which would yield 6 percent on pipeline company investment. During this period bond purchasers were requiring more interest and the cost of capital was rising rapidly. But even with the reduced leverage that resulted, pipeline companies were still able to earn considerably more than 6 percent on their common equity.

However, recently, the Commission has used a new approach that eliminates the leverage on the equity. While this method gives apparent recognition to the cost of debt capital, which was averaging about 5 percent, the Commission concurrently penalized the pipeline companies by reducing the return on equity significantly below the historical level of pipeline earnings.

Summary

Thus, in summary we have seen that the pipeline companies have really brought together the two other branches of the natural gas industry, and through their great expansion of the pipeline network have opened vast new markets for natural gas. They are regulated as a public service enterprise by the FPC and their future success is going to be determined to a large extent by the policies of the regulatory commissions and of Congress. The pipeline companies have a sustained interest in developing new and unique uses for gas and in providing improved services for the delivery of natural gas to the distributing companies.

THE DISTRIBUTION COMPANIES

Of the three branches of the natural gas industry, the gas distribution company is usually the only one that comes in direct contact with the consuming public. We have seen that some pipeline companies sell gas directly to large industrial consumers as do some of the producers. But the typical user of gas, whether residential, commercial, or industrial, does business with the distributing company.

The distributing companies are the oldest branch of the industry, which goes back before natural gas was distributed, to the period when the distribution companies manufactured their own gas supplies from bituminous coal. By 1850 there were about 300 local distributing companies in the United States, principally in the larger cities. As the use of gas for household purposes gained acceptance, hard coal, coke, and oil were used to make gas of high heating value. Still later liquefied petroleum, gas, and oil were used to manufacture gas with even higher heating value. Today, with the growth of pipelines, natural gas has taken over all but a small fraction of the load served by the distribution companies throughout the United States. The 1,400 gas utility distribution systems are almost entirely converted from manufactured, or mixed, to straight natural gas. Natural gas now goes to about 94 percent of all gas customers in the United States, and 99 percent of the industrial gas sold is natural gas.

Today, the industry has over 34 million residential customers who purchase about 35 percent of all the gas sold by distributors and pipeline companies to ultimate consumers. The rest of the gas sales are made to the industry's 3 million commercial and industrial customers. The residential class is composed of household consumers. The commercial class includes a wide range of users from corner grocery store, and small restaurants to large hospitals, office buildings, and other establishments not engaged in manufacturing. The industrial class consists of customers that use gas in a manufacturing process, whether as a source of energy or as a petrochemical feed stock.

In 1965 in the residential class there were over 94 million appliances installed in homes for space heating and cooling, water heating, refrigeration, laundry drying, incineration, and outdoor lighting. Commercial use is principally for cooking and space heating. In industry, as noted, gas is used both as an energy source and as a raw material. Natural gas is used to forge, cut, harden, galvanize, dry, purify, and to perform many other processing and fabricating chores. It has played an ever-increasing role in the manufacture of steel, textiles, plastics, paints, tile cement, glass, salt, chemicals, clay, pipes, and paper. As a raw material, natural gas and valuable liquid hydrocarbons extracted from it are combined with other substances to create plastics, synthetic rubber and fibers, insecticides, medicines, detergents, solvents, and many other synthetic materials.

The role of the natural gas distributor in making available the gas begins with the construction of the service pipelines from the "city gate," where the gas is received from the interstate lines, to homes and places of business of the hundreds of customers served. In addition to the service pipeline, other durable plant items include regulators and meters, and service equipment to maintain the fixed investment. Once in business the distributor has two principal functions to perform: (1) The purchase of natural gas so as to insure an adequate gas supply at stable and predictable prices, and (2) The sale of natural gas under increasingly competitive conditions.

The Purchase of Natural Gas

One unique feature of the natural gas distributor is the necessity of purchasing gas from one source of supply. Very few of the gas distributors produce or transport any of the natural gas they deliver to their customers and they must rely on the pipeline companies and producers for the gas. Most gas distributors buy their gas from only one pipeline and some few from two. The reason for this is that the FPC has limited the number of long-lines that service any one area in order to eliminate duplication of facilities.

As a result of this unique arrangement the supply contracts between the pipeline companies and the gas distributing companies are for long-term periods. However, with few exceptions, these contracts do not attempt to specify definite or stated prices. With the establishment of federal regulatory control in 1938, these contracts have usually contained provisions that rates to be charged at the "city gate" or other point of delivery will be those determined by the FPC. One purpose for this reliance on more flexible rate regulation was that the pipeline companies, themselves, do not know in advance what the total costs will be.

A result of this method of purchase is that the distributing companies must keep informed about *all* costs that are covered by the rates charged by pipeline companies. Sometimes they attempt to and do affect the field prices paid by their supplier to producers. For this purpose, intervention by distribution companies is permitted in cases before the FPC.

Over a long period of time there has been some confusion and uncertainty about the price of gas to the distributing company. Before and since the United States Supreme Court decision in 1954 producer prices increased; but after the decision some 8,000 gas producers, many very small, found themselves subject to the price-fixing regulatory authority of the FPC under the Natural Gas Act. So many rate filing cases have been created that several years have elapsed between the filing of a rate case and a final determination by the Commission. During this period neither the buyer nor the seller knew what would be allowed, even for gas already sold and consumed. A good deal of effort has been made to clear this up, but as long as it lasts the uncertainty about price will continue.

The Sale of Natural Gas

Figure 5.3 gives the rising consumption of natural gas and projected demand until 1970. Much of this increase has been due to certain inherent advantages of natural gas. It is clean and convenient, available instantly on demand, and readily sensitive to precise thermostatic control. It needs neither handling nor storage by the customer, and leaves neither smoke nor ash. It comes ready to burn and its flame, easily ignited and controlled, develops its maximum heating capacity at once. Nevertheless, gas distributors must compete with other fuels and the price relationships are going to be important.

On the basis that the same price relationship between fuels that ex-

Figure 5.3: Consumption of Natural Gas in the United States and Projected Demand for Gas to 1970.

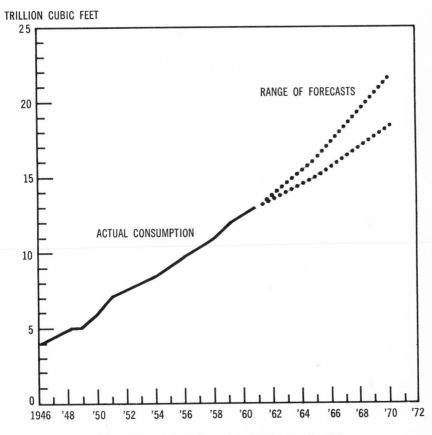

TRILLION CUBIC FEET

RANGE OF FORECASTS

ACTUAL CONSUMPTION

SOURCE: *Natural Gas, A Study in Industry Pioneering,* American Gas Association.

isted in 1961 continues, the American Gas Association has estimated that gas sales by distributors will reach nearly 14.2 trillion cubic feet by 1970 as compared with 9.2 trillion cubic feet in 1961. This estimate, of course, does not take into account the increased consumption due to greater field use and direct industrial sales which are shown in Figure 5.3. But the important question is whether the distributors will be able to meet the competition of other fuels. In some parts of the industrial markets, gas has already approached, reached, or passed a point of price parity with other fuels. And even in the house-heating market—a field of strong preference for gas—this same situation is developing in communities distant from the natural gas fields. As the gas price becomes higher, competition will become greater. Even electric heating is becoming competitive in some areas. Clearly then local competition places a ceiling on the price that consumers are willing to pay for gas, and the job of selling natural gas by distributing companies is likely to become more competitive.

The Distribution Branch as a Public Utility Under Regulation

When the early natural gas companies first came into existence they were regarded as a private business and there was nothing to prevent distributing companies from competing with each other, even in the same area. It soon became apparent, however, that duplication of distributive facilities was uneconomic and that gas distribution companies should be given an exclusive franchise to operate in an area. As a result there developed what we now call utility regulation—although it was then only on a limited local basis. This regulation which began as a local matter, gradually shifted to the state level, although in some few states regulation by municipalities continues to be an important part of the pattern.

Most, but not all state commissions also regulate other utilities as well as gas distributing companies. The list of regulated utilities varies from state to state and includes electric power and telephone, water supply, urban transit, and other forms of intrastate transportation. Regulation includes operating areas of the gas distributing companies, and rates, but in most states it also includes continuous supervision over accounting and financing of security issues, consolidations, mergers, and sales.

The regulation which grants an exclusive franchise to a gas distributing company and guarantees a fair rate of return on a fair value imposes the following obligations on the gas distributing company: (1) Service must be extended on comparable terms to all qualified customers who apply within the designated service area, (2) Service must be safe and adequate, and must cover the minimum and maximum requirements of each customer, subject to regulation or special contract, (3) Rates must be reasonable for each class of service rendered, and (4) There must be no unjust discrimination among customers either as to service or rates.

The Three Branches—Distribution, Pipelines, and Producers

In common with the pipelines, the distribution companies have high fixed costs—$1.90 of investment is required to produce $1.00 in revenue. Also in common with pipelines, the distribution companies are faced with a fluctuating seasonal demand and the need to increase the capacity factor in order to lower the unit fixed costs. As the distributor is close to the customer he is particularly interested in lower prices. From Table 5.3 it can be seen that the transportation and distribution costs are the most important cost items subject to reduction.

TABLE 5.3

Transportation-Distribution and Wellhead Costs as a Percentage of Average
Price of Gas at the Point of Consumption

	1945	1950	1955	1960
Transportation-distribution costs	76	76	74	72
Wellhead costs	24	24	26	28
Total	100	100	100	100

SOURCE: Data from the U.S. Bureau of Mines.

In an attempt to lower costs of transportation and distribution and even out the seasonal variation, the distribution companies, like the pipelines, are utilizing underground storage and interruptible sales. This seasonal variation in consumption is usually measured by what is termed "load factor" which compares the sales on an average day to sales on a peak day. Because of seasonal variations in use, a distributor serving only residential and commercial customers may operate at a sales load factor as low as 30 percent, while the average distributor who also has industrial customers operates at about 50 percent load factor. Sales are made on a "firm" basis and on an "interruptible" basis. Residential service is always firm; commercial service is usually firm but may be subject to interruption. Industrial service is both firm and interruptible. The interruptible sales are offered only for off-peak or seasonal service, generally between the months of April and October. The users of this service include mainly the chemical industry, processors of agricultural products, cement mills, and oil refineries.

Interruptible consumers are generally required to maintain facilities for alternative fuels. Interruptible consumers are not necessarily large users. Many are small users who are in a position to use other fuels during the expected period of interruption. About two-thirds of interruptible sales are made by distributing companies and one-third by the pipeline companies. Thus the distributing companies along with the pipeline companies defend the use of interruptible sales as a means of lowering the price for the consumer.

The relation between the distributing companies and the producers with respect to the federal regulation of price of natural gas sold by producers is interesting. Distributors are interested in low prices of natural gas for their customers, yet at the same time they recognize that natural gas production does not lend itself to orthodox forms of public utility regulation, for the business of exploring and developing natural gas in the field is not really a public utility function. Hence the distribution companies favor some form of control over gas field prices but they are sympathetic with the problems of the producers which have been created by the role of the FPC since 1954. The uncertainty arising from the delay in arriving at some fair and sensible method of fixing field prices for natural gas is shared with the producer by both the distributing companies and the pipelines.

In summary, the conclusion can be drawn that the distribution companies share both in the progress of the growth of the natural gas industry with the other two branches of the industry, but they also share in some of the special problems of the industry. Thus we turn our attention now to examine in detail two problems and related policy.

PROBLEMS AND POLICY

Two of the major natural gas problems which have commanded industry and public attention during recent years are interruptible sales of natural gas, and federal control of prices of natural gas. While both of these problems involve national policy issues, the second has been the subject of a raging national debate and therefore will be studied at length.

Interruptible Sales of Natural Gas

The problem is whether the sale of natural gas to industrial consumers under interruptible rate schedules should be permitted. From our previous study we have learned that an interruptible sale is one made by a pipeline company or distributor to an industrial or large commercial customer, at a rate usually less than for firm service. The supplier reserves the right, or is required by regulatory authorities, to curtail or stop delivery when the gas or pipeline capacity is needed for higher priority uses. The customer usually must provide equipment that can burn other fuel during periods when service is interrupted.

The case against interruptible sales is argued thus by the coal industry: (1) The natural gas industry sells gas below cost under interruptible sales contracts. (2) Natural gas sold under interruptible sales contracts is being put to "inferior" uses and such practice hastens the exhaustion of an irreplaceable commodity. To correct these practices the coal industry concludes that there is no practical or logical reason for excluding direct sale of natural gas for industrial use from FPC jurisdiction, and that Congress should enact legislation to correct this. The coal industry also concludes that Congress should enact legislation that will require the FPC to establish rates for gas companies under its jurisdiction in such a manner that all types of gas users carry their full share of costs of doing business, including a proper apportionment of fixed costs.

The natural gas industry answers the first argument by saying that interruptible gas is not sold below cost, and that such sales actually lower the cost of natural gas to firm customers. The point is made that the fixed costs of the pipeline must be met whether or not there is one cubic foot of gas moving through the pipeline. The rates which are allowed by regulatory bodies are based on the total cost of service, one element of which is a reasonable return on fixed capital. Consequently, during the slack period between peaks of firm demand, any gas sold to interruptible customers which helps to pay off some of the fixed charges also helps the firm customers (household, commercial and industrial) by keeping their prices down. The minimum price necessary to achieve this is anything exceeding the average field cost of the gas, plus the out-of-pocket costs of transporting it. Anything more absorbs a portion of the fixed costs of the system. Indeed, it is argued that the FPC through the Atlantic Seaboard formula requires that a certain amount of fixed charges be assigned to that part of the pipeline rate associated with the cost of gas as a commodity as well as to that part of the pipeline rate associated with the capacity of the pipeline. Thus the natural gas industry concludes that "it is difficult, then, to see how coal's charge of selling below cost can be supported." Studies presented show that interruptible sales contributed 394 million dollars to fixed costs in 1960.

The natural gas industry answers the second argument by stating that there is no "inferiority" of gas use; "only waste would be inferior" and "only release to atmosphere or flaring would be waste." The contention is that interruptible sale of gas benefits people and thus is of use to society. The point is made that 67 percent of interruptible sales is for boiler fuel, and that about 63 percent of this generates power. The contention is that this is just as much a "superior" use of fuel as domestic home heating. The natural gas industry simply does not agree with the coal industry that industrial interruptible uses are of a lower value on some scale of value to society than other uses.

Facts Bearing on the Problem. The National Fuels and Energy Study Group studied the charges of the coal industry with respect to interruptible sales of natural gas and presented the following facts bearing on the problem:

1. Residential and commercial uses of gas are concentrated in the winter, so that facilities constructed to meet the maximum heating needs of customers have unused delivery potential during the warmer months.

2. The higher the capacity factor at which gas facilities are operated, the lower is the average unit transportation or distribution cost. The average pipeline operates at 75 percent capacity factor, the average distributor at about 50 percent capacity factor.

3. Interruptible sales directly to industrial users are not subject to the rate-making authority of the FPC, but the FPC does have authority over certification

of facilities to serve the interruptible customer. Two considerations of such certification are a demonstrated supply of gas and that the price charged be not so low as to burden remaining customers.

4. A part of the fixed costs associated with service to residential and commercial customers is allocated to the interruptible gas sold by pipelines. This allocation of nonassociated (fixed charges) plus the cost of gas itself and the cost of moving it constitute a cost floor against which the revenue from interruptible sales must be measured. Under the Atlantic Seaboard formula the fixed-charge allocation (taxes, depreciation, and return) is 50 percent of the entire system's fixed charges per unit of sales.

5. About 2.1 billion Mcf of gas was sold to interruptible users in 1960. The revenue from these sales was approximately 650 million dollars of which 250 was for out-of-pocket costs and 400 was allocated to fixed charges. If interruptible sales were prohibited the 250 million dollars would be lost revenue, but the 400 million dollars fixed charges would be wholly or in great part reassigned to existing firm customers. This assignment of a possible added 400 million dollars to the bills of the remaining customers certainly would have a detrimental effect on the sale of natural gas in the long run and might possibly have an immediate effect.

Conclusions and Recommendations. The conclusions drawn by the National Fuels and Energy Study Group were:

1. Interruptible sales absorb a part of fixed costs, and the prohibition of such sales would have the effect of raising rates to the remaining customers, since part of the system's fixed costs would simply be shifted to them.

2. Inasmuch as natural gas is used in electric power plants it is competitive for one reason or another, or it would not be used. The elimination of interruptible service to power plants would thus require the substitution of a less economic or less convenient fuel, and the higher costs of a substitute fuel would have to be passed on to the consumers in increased electric rates.

3. The elimination of interruptible sales would mean about a 5 percent increase in coal output, but not a corresponding increase in man-hours employment. The estimated 22 million-ton gain in coal production would add 100 million dollars in coal revenue at 1960 prices.

4. If the opposite policy of the elimination of interruptible sales were followed, *i.e.,* complete freedom in making interruptible sales with respect to cost allocation were followed, the result would be greater capacity factors and lower prices. Increased sales would add about 180 million dollars in revenue to the natural gas industry.

5. On the other hand complete freedom in making interruptible sales would probably cost the coal industry 25 million tons of output and 120 million dollars of revenue at 1960 prices.

The general conclusion can be drawn that interruptible sales play a vital part in the economical operations of pipeline and distributing companies and thus enable the consumers of natural gas to have gas available at lower costs than would be possible if interruptible sales were eliminated. Pipeline rates involve two classes of customers: those whose service is under the jurisdiction of the FPC (those who purchase for resale), and those outside its jurisdiction (customers who are themselves the consumers). Since both classes of customers draw on the same pipeline, rates are designed for each to bear a part of the pipeline system's overall return, depreciation, and taxes. The FPC generally treats one-half of all fixed costs as though they were variable costs. This method of cost allocation which we have referred to as the Atlantic Seaboard formula is explained as follows by the FPC:

> By assigning 50 percent of the constant costs to the volumetric function, all of the gas carried through the line will share in a proportion of such costs. Thus customers that are interrupted during the peak period share in at least half of the constant costs.
>
> Unless such division of the constant costs is made, a customer taking no gas during the peak period (either voluntarily or because of curtailment), would not contribute in the rate he pays toward compensation of the company for any portion of the costs designated as constant.[3]

Whether the Atlantic Seaboard formula for cost allocation is the best method to obtain full year-round use of pipeline capacity is debatable. One point that the National Fuels and Energy Study made was that underground storage was the ideal way to obtain maximum capacity use. Yet paradoxically the transference of fixed costs away from their economic kin to interruptible customers understates capacity costs and minimizes the economic benefits of underground storage.

The recommendation is that the FPC continue to have responsibility for certification of pipeline facilities to serve nonjurisdictional customers (customers who are themselves the customers); and that the FPC continue to insist that a prior condition to such certification is that the rates charged for interruptible gas be no less than the commodity part of the jurisdictional rate charged to customers for resale. Since the FPC through the Atlantic Seaboard formula requires that a certain amount of fixed charges be assigned to that part of the pipeline rate associated with the cost of the commodity, this recommendation would assure that interruptible gas would bear part of the burden of the fixed costs. While a direct sale at the commodity rate to a large industrial customer may not pay a large part of a system's total fixed costs, it still pays the part included in the commodity charge. For example, at an average field cost of 15¢ per Mcf plus out-of-pocket costs of 4¢ for transporting the gas 1,000 miles, a commodity charge of 25¢ per Mcf contributes 6¢ per Mcf toward fixed costs (25¢–19¢). In 1960, as previously reported, this totaled approximately 400 million dollars. The recommended policy would be that the

---

[3] Opinion Number 269, Panhandle Eastern Pipeline Company, Federal Power Commission cited in *Report of the National Fuels and Energy Study Group, op. cit.* p. 237.

FPC continue to certify projects whose economic feasibility depends on high capacity factor operation even when they are predicated on the ability to provide interruptible sales.

Federal Control of Prices of Natural Gas

A simple statement of this basic problem is: Should the federal government (the FPC) control the prices received by producers of natural gas?

Facts Bearing on the Problem. Even prior to the Phillips Petroleum case in 1954 all three parts of the natural gas industry were regulated. The facts of these three parts and their regulation may be summarized as follows:

Producers perform the functions of looking for developing, producing, and gathering the gas. The latter operation consists of taking the gas as it emerges from the wellhead and releasing it into a pipeline which is one of a number forming a "gathering system." The networks of local pipelines come together at a central point, from which the gas is delivered to the second part of the industry, the pipeline companies. These companies transmit the gas to distant points where it is purchased by the third part of the industry, local utilities, which sell it to the consuming public.

Producers (production and gathering) are regulated by state agencies. Mr. Justice Clark explains:

The states have been for over 35 years and are now enforcing regulatory laws covering production and gathering, including *pricing*, proration of gas, retable taking, unitization of fields, processing of casinghead gas including priority over other gases, well spacing, repressuring, abandonment of wells, marginal area development, and other devices. Everyone is fully aware of the direct relationship of price and conservation. And the power of the states to regulate producers' and gatherers' prices has been upheld in this Court (the United States Supreme Court).

Pipeline companies are granted franchises by the FPC for the interstate transmission and resale of natural gas. They operate as public utilities and their transmission rates are regulated by the FPC. Local distributing companies also operate as public utilities. They are granted franchises and their rates are regulated by local and state commissions.

This problem of the federal control of natural gas prices strikes at the heart of the problem of competitive pricing, and thus it is our purpose in the following discussion to develop fully the facts and the policy bearing on the problem.

The Natural Gas Act was passed in 1938. According to the Supreme Court as stated in the Phillips case, 374 U.S. 672: "Protection of consumers against exploitation at the hands of natural gas companies was the primary aim of the Natural Gas Act." Section 1 (b) of the act made the regulatory provisions applicable "to the sale in interstate commerce of natural gas for resale for ultimate public consumption," but it also made them inapplicable "to the production or gathering of natural gas." The Natural Gas Act was a direct result of a Supreme Court decision (Missouri v. Kansas Natural Gas Company, 265 U.S. 298) which held that the state of Missouri was not empowered to prevent an increase in the price of gas sold to Missouri distributors because the gas had moved in interstate commerce. Edward F. Arn, Governor of Kansas, stated in September, 1954, that "Congress recognized this area wherein there was no control and so enacted the Natural Gas Act in 1938. During the extensive Congressional hearings held, many noted authorities made it explicit that the proposed legislation was not intended to regulate the field rates or the ultimate price which would be charged by the independent producers and other gatherers of gas."

In 1940 the FPC ruled in Columbian Fuel Corp., 2 FPC 200, that a company whose only sales of natural gas in interstate commerce were as an incident to production was exempted from the jurisdiction of the Commission.

In 1947 the FPC stated in Order No. 139 of August 7: "The Commission gives its assurances to independent producers and gatherers of natural gas that they can sell at arm's length and deliver such gas to interstate pipelines and can enter into contracts for such sale without apprehension that in so doing they may become subject to assertion of jurisdiction by the Commission under the Natural Gas Act."

But in 1947, while the FPC was denying any jurisdiction over independent producers, the Supreme Court in Interstate Natural Gas Co. v. FPC, 331 U.S. 682, held that the Commission had jurisdiction of the Interstate Company's sales and that the company was a natural gas company. However, the Court had this to say: "Thus, where sales, though technically consummated in Interstate Commerce, are made during the course of production and gathering and are so closely connected with the local incidents of that process . . . the jurisdiction of the FPC does not attach."

This Supreme Court ruling created a feeling of uncertainty in the natural gas industry that resulted in the passage by Congress in 1950 of the Kerr bill, clearly stating that sales of natural gas to interstate pipelines by independent producers would be a part of production and gathering, and exempting the latter from FPC control. The Kerr bill was vetoed by President Truman.

The basis of this controversy is that, in order to protect natural gas consumers, price regulation must be in effect at the local public utility level, in transportation, and all the way back to the wellhead through the production and gathering system, or at least as far back as through the sale of natural gas by producers and gatherers to the interstate pipelines. The Supreme Court on June 7, 1954, in the famous Phillips case (347 U.S. 672) held that the interstate sales by producers and gatherers are subject to regulation under the Natural Gas Act, and thus established a clear legal basis for regulation by the FPC in direct conflict with previous FPC rulings.

Mr. Justice Douglas in dissenting in the Phillips case contended: "There is much to be said from the national point of view for regulating sales at both ends of these interstate pipelines. The power of Congress to do so is unquestioned. Whether it did so by the Natural Gas Act of 1938 is a political and legal controversy that has raged in the Commission and the Courts for some years. The question is not free from some doubts. For while P 1 (b) of the Act makes the regulatory provisions applicable 'to the sale in interstate commerce of natural gas for resale for ultimate public consumption,' it also makes them inapplicable 'to the production or gathering of natural gas.'"

The Phillips decision arose from a dual investigation of the activities of Phillips as an independent producer of natural gas by the FPC. First the Commission was to determine if these activities were within the jurisdiction of the Natural Gas Act. Second, it was to decide whether the rates for natural gas were unfair. The second point was not considered, as after hearings in April and May, 1951, the Commission made a specific finding of fact that Phillips was exempt from the jurisdiction of the act because Phillips transportation and sales constituted a part of or were connected with its gathering process.

The finding of the Commission was appealed to the U.S. Court of Appeals for the District of Columbia by the consuming states and on May 22, 1953, the Court reversed the decision by finding that Phillips was a "natural gas company" and that the Commission should fix the rates for its sales. This decision was carried to the U.S. Supreme Court by Phillips.

The Supreme Court held, with Douglas, Clark, and Burton dissenting, that an independent natural gas producer, which sold gas to interstate pipeline companies for interstate transportation and resale, was a "natural gas company" with the Natural Gas Act, and its sales were not within the section of the act exempting "production or gathering of natural gas."

In delivering the opinion of the Court, Mr. Justice Minton stated: "We are of the opinion . . . that production and gathering in the sense that those terms are used in P 1 (b) end before the sales by Phillips occur." Justice Minton cited directly to the point of the Supreme Court's decision in Interstate Natural Gas Co. v. FPC: "We have held that these sales are in interstate commerce. It cannot be doubted that their regulation is predominantly a matter of national contrasted to local concern. . . . Unreasonable charges exacted at this stage of the interstate movement become perpetuated in large part in fixed items of costs which must be covered by rates charged subsequent purchasers of gas including the ultimate consumer. It was to avoid such situations that the Natural Gas Act was passed." Justice Minton further stated, "Thus we are satisfied that Congress sought to regulate *wholesales* of natural gas occurring at both ends of the interstate transmission."

Mr. Justice Clark, with whom Mr. Burton concurs in dissenting, argued:

That Congress aimed at abuses resulting in the "gap" at the end of the transmission process by integrated and unintegrated pipelines and not at abuses prior to the transmission, is clear from the final report of the Federal Trade Commission to the Senate on malpractices of the natural gas industry. (S. Doc. No. 92, 70th Cong., 1st Sess., 1935) This report was the stimulus for federal intervention in the industry. The Federal Trade Commission outlined the abuses in the industry which the "gap" made the states powerless to prevent; the abuses were by monopolistically situated pipelines which gouged the consumer by charging local distribution companies unreasonable rates. The Federal Trade Commission did not find abusive pricing by independent producers and gatherers; if anything, the independents at the producing end of the pipelines were likewise the victims of monopolistic practices by the pipelines.

Mr. Justice Clark argued further to the impact of the decision on state regulation:

By today's decision, the Court restricts the phrase "production and gathering" to "the physical activities, facilities, and properties" used in production and gathering. Such a gloss strips the words of their substance. If the Congress so intended, then it left for state regulation only a mass of empty pipe, vacant processing plants and thousands of hollow wells with scarecrow derricks, monuments to this new extension of federal power. It was not so understood. . . .

There can be no doubt, as the Commission has found, that federal regulation of production and gathering will collide and substantially interfere with and hinder the enforcement of these state regulatory measures. We cannot square this result with the House Report on this Act which states that the subsequent enacted bill is so drawn as to complement and in no manner usurp State regulatory authority.

If we look to Interstate for guidance, we would do better to focus on the following words of the late Chief Justice:

"Clearly, among the powers thus reserved to the States is the power to regulate the physical production and gathering of natural gas in the interests of conservation or of any other consideration of legitimate local concern. It was the intention of Congress to give the States full freedom in these matters. Thus, where sales, though technically consummated in interstate commerce, are made during the course of production and gathering and are so closely connected with the local incidence of that process as to render rate regulation by the Federal Power Commission inconsistent or a substantial interference with the exercise by the State of its regulatory functions, the jurisdiction of the Federal Power Commission does not attach.

Mr. Justice Douglas, dissenting, presented the most important question as to the impact of the decision on the discovery, development, and production of natural gas:

The fastening of rate regulation on this *independent producer* brings "the production or gathering of natural gas" under effective federal control, in spite of the fact that Congress has made that phase of the natural gas business exempt from regulation. The effect is certain to be profound. The price at which the *independent producer* can sell his gas determines the price he is able or willing to pay for it (if he buys from other wells). The sales price determines his profits. And his profits and the profits of all the other gatherers, whose gas moves into the interstate pipelines, have profound effects on the rate of production, the methods of production, the old wells that are continued in production, and new ones explored, etc. Regulating the price at which the independent producer can sell his gas regulates his business in the most vital way any business can be regulated.

Thus we have in the words of the Supreme Court of the United States some of the principal arguments for and against federal regulation of the price of natural gas charged by the producers and gatherers.

The session of Congress meeting in 1955 offered the first opportunity to modify the Natural Gas Act in light of the Supreme Court decision so as to make it clear that federal control should be limited as it was before the Phillips decision, or to strengthen the act as interpreted by the courts. The arguments for and against less federal regulation have been presented in great detail. The principal advocates for less government control were the producers and gatherers, the interstate pipelines, and the state regulatory agencies. The opposed were representatives of the consumer interests. A summary of the arguments for and against modification of the Supreme Court's ruling follows:

For:

1. The ABC's of free competition versus regulation and controls in the nation's sixth largest industry are:

a. One gas distributor. Because the local gas company has an exclusive franchise for gas in its area, it operates as a *public utility,* and its rates are regulated.

b. One gas transporter. Because the long-distance pipeline which brings gas to the local distributor is a sole supplier, it operates as a *public utility,* and its rates are regulated.

c. Thousands of competing gas producers. Because there are more than 8,000 producers competing to find natural gas and sell it, controls are unnecessary. These freely competing producers have tripled supplies in sixteen years, and the average price of gas to residential users has risen only one-eleventh as much as the cost of living.

2. Such price increases to the consumer as occur should be studied in

the light of where the shares of each dollar of the consumer's gas bill go: 9¢ is received by the gas producer; 21¢ is received by the pipeline transporter; and 70¢ is received by the local gas company distributor.

3. Federal controls are unfair because they single out one competitive industry for such controls. "It is a step without peacetime precedent to price-fix a commodity at its source."

4. Controls are dangerous because they could easily be the first step toward federal price-fixing of coal or oil—or lumber or grain or any business.

5. Price controls are short sighted "because they will stifle the bold and risky exploring that is needed to assure adequate supplies of natural gas for the future."

6. Less natural gas as a result of federal control will lead to increased prices to the consumer.

7. Federal control of gas prices received by the producers of gas will drastically interfere with the functions performed and rightfully delegated to the state regulatory and conservation agencies.

8. The FPC by a vote of 4 to 1 is opposed to controlling gas prices of producers and gatherers. The administrative problem would be difficult. "Reasonable" rates for thousands of producers would have to be calculated and costs vary widely between producing wells. In addition, gas and oil are joint products of many wells and cost allocations would be almost impossible. The Commission also feels that controls will lead to a diminution of gas supplies.

Against:

1. Consumer prices of natural gas cannot be controlled unless control is exercised over prices received by producers and gatherers.

2. Consumer prices will rise rapidly because of the anticipated short supplies of natural gas.

3. Consumer prices will rise because cost of production of natural gas is rising. Although interstate pipelines make long-term twenty-year contracts with producers, these contracts include "escalator clauses" incorporating the "most favored nation principle" so that all producers of natural gas in an area selling gas to a pipeline must be given the benefits of price increases granted under new contracts.

4. Owing to the "most favored nation clauses" prices will rise even though costs of production of natural gas at all wells or from all suppliers do not rise.

Many more arguments and details can be spelled out on each side of the issue. Fundamental to the solution of the problem is the extent to which price should be determined in a free market. Obviously it is not true that federal price regulations are not in effect in other areas of the economy. In most instances—as for example, in agriculture, these controls have been to benefit the producer, not the consumer. There is no question about the fact that, faced with conditions of an increasing demand for natural gas, consumer prices will rise unless production of natural gas is increased. The solution to this problem must be on the basis of the maximum efficient production and utilization of a scarce natural resource. This is *the fundamental economic problem.* The solution should be sought first in the maximum use of the free market. This will facilitate shifts in the most efficient use of alternative energy sources and the maximum efficient production. Where regulation of production is necessary for conservation purposes, it can best be achieved, as already concluded, by state conservation and regulatory agencies.

Those forces advocating Congressional legislation to change the Supreme Court's ruling in the Phillips case by either a new law or modification of the Natural Gas Act received strong support from the President's Advisory Committee on Energy Supplies and Resources Policy which on February 26, 1955, recommended:

We believe the problem of natural gas regulation should be approached from the viewpoint of assuring adequate supplies and the discovery and development of additional reserves to support such supplies, in the interests of national defense, an expanding domestic economy, and reasonable prices to consumers.

To secure these objectives, it is essential to give due consideration to (1) the operations known as the production of natural gas, (2) the transportation of gas in interstate transmission lines, and (3) the distribution of gas in municipalities. Individual companies may engage in more than one of these activities. Each operation of such companies should be treated by like criteria according to its appropriate industry function.

In the production of natural gas it is important that sound conservation practices be continued. This area of conservation management is under the jurisdiction of State conservation commissions. In the interest of a sound fuels policy and the protection of the national defense and consumer interests by assuring such a continued exploration for and development of adequate reserves as to provide an adequate supply of natural gas, we believe the Federal Government should not control the production, gathering, processing or sale of natural gas prior to its entry into an interstate transmission line.

The interstate transmission of natural gas by the interstate transmission lines and the subsequent sale of such gas for resale is a public utility function and should be under the regulation of the Federal Power Commission. In considering the certification of new lines and applications for increased rates based on new or renegotiated purchase contracts, the Commission should consider, in order to provide protection for the consumer, not only the assurance of supply but also whether the contract prices of the natural gas which the applicant has contracted to buy are competitively arrived at and represent the reasonable market field price, giving due consideration, in the interest of competition, to the reasonableness and appropriateness of contract provisions as they relate to existing or future market field prices.

The several states or their political sub-divisions should continue to provide the public utility regulation of distributing companies in accordance with usual utility practices.

Thus the complete cycle of natural gas production, transmission and utilization will be appropriately regulated: The production and conservation of natural gas by the state conservation commissions; the interstate transmission of natural gas by the Federal Power Commission; and the distribution by the local public utility commissions.

After much debate the House passed a natural gas bill by a narrow margin in the closing days of first session of the 84th Congress during the summer of 1955. This bill moved through under the guidance of Speaker Sam Rayburn. Its purpose was to strip the FPC of direct regulatory power over the prices charged for natural gas by producers. The FPC was to continue to have strict regulatory powers over interstate pipeline operators. These powers included the right to veto a pipeline company's contract with a gas producer if the FPC found the contract price was unreasonable. Key words in the bill were "reasonable market price," which the bill sought to guarantee producers for their natural gas.

If Senate Majority Leader Lyndon B. Johnson had not had a heart attack, he probably would have been able to force this bill through the Senate during the last day the Senate was in session during the summer of 1955. If this had been done the bill would have been signed and would have become public law.

Senator Johnson was back on the job by January, 1956, and he made the bill (H.R. 6645) the first subject for debate for the second session of the 84th Congress. During the fall of 1955 the regulation of natural gas was one of the major topics of public discussion, and this debate was carried to the Senate floor. Lobbying by both pro-producer and pro-distributor interests was intense. The latter claimed to be representing the interests of consumers of natural gas. H.R. 6645 was passed by the Senate. Just before the bill was to be voted on, Senator Francis Case of South Dakota announced that he had been offered a $2,500 campaign donation in what a Senate resolution called an "alleged improper attempt" to influence his vote.

Business Week reported on February 11, 1956: "The Senate this week dumped one of the most controversial—and least understood—measures it will have to deal with this session on Pres. Eisenhower's desk. The measure: the so-called natural gas bill. Eisenhower is expected to sign it, even though he has not publicly committed himself on the bill. . . . He is understood to have given ranking Republican Congressional leaders private assurance that he will not veto the bill."

On February 17, 1956, President Eisenhower announced:

I am unable to approve H.R. 6645 "to amend the Natural Gas Act as amended." This I regret because I am in accord with its basic objectives. Since the passage of this bill a body of evidence has accumulated indicating that private persons, apparently representing only a very small segment of a great and vital industry, have been seeking to further their own interests by highly questionable activities. These include efforts I deem to be so arrogant and so much in defiance of acceptable standards of propriety as to risk creating doubt among the American people concerning the integrity of governmental processes.

At the same time, I must make quite clear that legislation conforming to the basic objectives of H.R. 6645 is needed. It is needed because the type of regulation of producers of natural gas which is required under present law will discourage individual initiative and incentive to explore for and develop new sources of supply.

In the long run this will limit supplies of gas, which is contrary not only to the national interest but especially to the interest of consumers.

I feel that any new legislation, in addition to furthering the long-term interest of consumers in plentiful supplies of gas, should include specific language protecting consumers in their right to fair prices.

President Eisenhower's veto was called: (1) "evidence of his integrity"; (2) "an outright political gesture indicative of his intention to announce for a second term." However, one thing was certain: President Eisenhower would not get his "needed legislation conforming to the basic objectives of H.R. 6645" during the election year 1956, and he did not.

In his address to Congress in January, 1957, the President stated:

In returning the Harris-Fulbright Natural Gas Bill to the 84th Congress without my approval, I stated that legislation conforming to the basic objectives of that bill was needed. I am still of that opinion. It is essential that the consumers of natural gas be protected. We must endeavor to make sure that there will be continued exploration and development of adequate field supplies of gas and that producers' sales prices are arrived at fairly and competitively. In this way, and with the authority vested in the Federal Power Commission to regulate interstate pipelines as to the price at which gas may be charged as an item of cost in fixing their rates, the cost to the public will be fair.

Legislation freeing gas producers from public utility-type regulation is essential if the incentives to find and develop new supplies of gas are to be preserved and sales of gas to interstate markets are not to be discouraged to the detriment of both consumers and producers, as well as the national interest.

Even though President Eisenhower had stated that natural gas legislation freeing gas producers from public utility type legislation was essential, no such legislation was passed during the final term of his administration. When President John F. Kennedy came into office there was no longer executive backing for such legislation. With Senator Lyndon B. Johnson as Vice President, and with the untimely deaths of Speaker of the House Sam Rayburn and Senator Robert S. Kerr (of Kerr-McGee Oil Company) the legislative leadership calling for such passage was gone. After President Johnson succeeded to the presidency, he found it necessary, especially during the election year of 1964 to project a national image rather than to be concerned with the problems of the natural gas producers.

With no amending legislation forthcoming the FPC was faced with the reality that field sales of natural gas for transportation and resale had been held by the Supreme Court to be within the regulatory jurisdiction of the Commission.

Following the Phillips decision, the Commission moved forward to carry out the mandate of the highest court. Six weeks after the court had spoken, the Commission issued an order imposing retroactively to June 7, 1954, a price freeze on the field sales of natural gas for resale in interstate commerce. This order was notification that all such sales would be regulated under the Natural Gas Act.

However, from the very beginning, the Commission did not attempt to apply traditional utility rate-making concepts to producer price fixing. But the Commission was prodded by a series of court decisions which, with respect to gas produced by pipelines, insisted on the use of utility regulatory methods, at least as a "point of departure." The result was that a case-by-case, cost-of-service approach of fixing rates based on a return allowance on property investment was introduced into producer regulation.

The Commission in these cases attempted to apply the rate-base method in setting producer prices in certain cases, even though it was still of the opinion that such a method was not proper. After several years of attempting to apply such a formula to producers, the Commission and the entire natural gas industry realized that the utility-type regulation was not a workable solution. After a frustrating experience of six years, during which thousands of producer rate cases continued to pile up on its docket, the Commission finally issued a policy order on September 28, 1960, in which it sought to break out of the bottleneck arising from the attempt to apply cost-of-service in determining producer prices. The Commission stated that it had become convinced that a gas producer's prices cannot realistically or properly be determined on a utility or cost-of-service basis. As an alternative, the FPC announced that it would henceforth apply a system of so-called "area prices."

In the establishment of area prices today and in the future, the Commission must determine what level of field prices will be required in each area to provide adequate supplies of gas. In so far as area prices are based primarily on market prices, the intent of Congress as expressed in the Harris-Fulbright bill, vetoed by President Eisenhower, is being carried out. Preliminary court rulings were favorable to area pricing. Under the Kennedy administration there was a complete turnover of the five members of the FPC, and these five members all were in favor of going forward with area pricing. Thus, even though no new legislation was forthcoming, some progress was being made toward the solution of the industry problems, and the great backlog of rate cases could gradually be disposed.

The method of procedure by the FPC in 1960 was to set interim price ceilings on natural gas for twenty-three producing areas. However, the FPC singled out the Permian Basin in West Texas and a corner of New Mexico as an area on which extensive hearings would be held and pricing policies would be determined. Hearings lasted until September 12, 1963, and on September 17, 1964, FPC examiner, Seymour Wenner, issued an initial decision adopting a two-price system—one price for gas from old gas wells, gas from oil wells and any residue gas derived from either, and another higher price for gas from new gas wells. Then on August 5, 1965 the FPC issued a final opinion that set a ceiling price for gas from new gas wells at 16.5¢ per 1,000 cubic feet for Texas production and 15.5¢ for New Mexico gas, and a ceiling on all other gas at 14.5¢ for 1,000 cubic feet in Texas and 13.5¢ for New Mexico. The difference in prices between the two states is to allow adjustments in state production taxes. At the time of this last action, Commission sources said that the price in the Permian Basin was about 17.5 to 18¢ per 1,000 cubic feet. Producers had argued for a one-price 20¢ ceiling on the ground that gas was the same commodity regardless of source.

The Commission selected the Permian Basin, which accounts for about 11 percent of all gas moving in interstate commerce, as a test case. If the same principles are applied in deciding pending proceedings involving three other major producing areas, it would place production of about 75 percent of the natural gas flowing through interstate pipelines under definitive FPC ceilings.

The FPC argued that the Permian Basin decision takes into consideration the gas industry's ability to find "new gas-well gas as distinguished from finding gas as a by-product in the search for oil." The contention is that based on this skill at "directional exploration," the two-price system "will make use of the economic drive of the industry in order to bring needed gas supplies to consumers at the lowest reasonable price."

In addition, the FPC claims that area pricing provides "a strong incentive . . . to prudence and economy which does not exist in individual company cost-pricing in an industry where individual cost norms are difficult to determine and apply." Another important advantage to the area-rate approach, from the Commission's view, is the ability to determine in a single proceeding rates otherwise requiring hundreds of individual cases.

On the other hand, the Commission pointed out in the Permian decision that a number of producers contend that we are pursuing an inherently illegal method of regulating the field price of natural gas through a system applied to areas rather than individual companies.

Natural gas producers generally expressed indignation over the FPC's decision in the Permian Basin gas-price case, and the prediction was that it would be challenged in the courts and in Congress. Producers were particularly angered about the two-price system and the low ceilings set on wellhead prices of gas.

H. A. True, Jr., President of the Independent Petroleum Association of America, summed up the reactions of the natural gas producers: "If any further evidence is required to establish the urgent need for Congress to stop the interminable administrative orgy indulged in by the Federal Power Commission, it is provided by the Commission's decision in the Permian Basin case."

Conclusion. The conclusion of our problem study of government regulation of producer prices is clear. The attempt to apply utility-type price regulation to the producer segment of the natural gas industry jeopardizes the producer's economic incentive. This is a most important consideration for the consumer because it means that gas supplies may diminish if artificially low prices are imposed which disregard production cost trends. Federal government attempts to control commodity prices have been notoriously unsuccessful. But if field prices of natural gas are to be regulated, which seems to be the accepted fact of the 1960's, area pricing appears to have the best, if not the only, possibility of success. But during the first half of the 1960's the producer was still faced with delay, uncertainty, and legal complications surrounding the applicability of area prices.

The recommendation is that there should be legislative enactment that would establish area pricing as a regulatory program which would provide certainty and stability. Without such legislation the FPC has no authority to assure a gas producer that once his contract and contract prices are approved such contract will be binding and effective.

SUMMARY

The conclusion can be drawn that natural gas is truly a growth industry, the ultimate expansion of which is limited in terms of available supplies. The principal problems of the industry arise out of the basic economic problem of the allocation of scarce resources. The solution should be sought in the maximum use of free market forces in a complicated three-part industry that is regulated by state agencies at two ends and the federal government in the middle. Extension of federal regulation should be checked, but if it must be applied to producer prices, a clear and certain method must be established by Congress which will establish just and reasonable area prices which will provide adequate supplies of natural gas.

SELECTED REFERENCES

"Interruptible Gas," *Report of the National Fuels and Energy Study Group,* Washington, D.C., 1962, pp. 332–341.

Natural Gas—A Study in Industry Pioneering, New York, American Gas Association, 1962.

Parsons, James J., "The Geography of Natural Gas in the United States," *Economic Geography,* July, 1950, pp. 162–178.

"Petroleum and Natural Gas," in *Mineral Facts and Problems,* Bureau of Mines Bulletin 585, Washington, D.C., 1960, pp. 589–630.

"Phillips Petroleum Company v. State of Wisconsin *et al.,* Federal Power Commission v. State of Wisconsin *et al.,* 347 U.S. 672, *Supreme Court Reporter,* Vol. 74, New York, West Publishing Company, 1954, pp. 794–807.

"Producers Await Gas Decision," *Business Week,* May 21, 1955, pp. 129–131.

Report on Energy Supplies and Resources Policy, Washington, D.C., Executive Office of the President, February 26, 1955.

Reports on Proven Reserves of Crude Oil, Natural Gas Liquids, and Natural Gas, New York, American Gas Association, December 31, 1963 and later editions.

"Statement of American Gas Association," *Report of the National Fuels and Energy Study Group,* Washington, D.C., 1962, pp. 370–381.

Utilities—Gas—Basic Analysis, Standard & Poor's Industry Surveys, New York, Standard & Poor, 1963 and later editions.

6

ATOMIC ENERGY

In the introductory chapter on energy resources the point was made that almost all of the energy man uses is of nuclear origin. In the past the nuclear (atomic) energy has been stellar, chiefly solar, in origin and has been derived from current receipts (flow) and stored-up supplies (funds). The most significant advance in economic productivity was achieved when the shift was made from the almost exclusive reliance on flows of energy to the utilization of the funds of fossil fuels—coal, petroleum, and natural gas. This shift, accompanied by the harnessing of these fuels by the heavy metals, we have called the Industrial Revolution. Students of energy and material have told us that before World War II this phase of history was rapidly drawing to a close, and that we were entering upon a stage which would be characterized by continuous energy sources—water power converted into electricity as a carrier and direct solar radiation—harnessed by the light metals. Electricity has indeed been developed as a carrier of water power—both from falling flows of water power (hydro) and expanding water power (steam) produced from funds of fossil fuels. Direct solar radiation is now in its developmental stage. Light metals have become harnessers. Yet even as this stage was dawning a new era has exploded.

Current energy historians tell us that the "Atomic Age" began with the destruction of Hiroshima in 1945. This is a dramatic oversimplification of a complex development of a new energy source—a new source of fuel—which requires new metals and methods for harnessing. This era was thrust upon us with the remarkable discovery that matter may be turned into energy and energy into matter. The evolutionary origin of the new age is beyond the scope of this study; its development is still dawning; its revolutionary effects will be beyond the scope of imagination.

The atom is not new. More than 2,000 years ago in the fifth century B.C. a Greek philosopher called Democritus developed the concept of the "atom"—the smallest, the indivisible particle of matter—describing it from the Greek word "atomos," meaning something which cannot be cut. This atomic theory was rejected by Aristotle (who lived from 384 to 322 B.C.), and so great was his influence that for twenty centuries the idea of atoms was largely ignored. It was brought to life again in the revival of learning in Europe that followed the Renaissance. The concept that matter consists of such indivisible units seemed logical to Galileo and Descartes and other sixteenth and seventeenth century scientists on the Continent, and in England to Francis Bacon, Robert Boyle, and Isaac Newton. In fact the idea became rather generally held, as an abstract philosophical notion.

It remained for another Englishman, John Dalton, a schoolmaster who lived in Manchester, to bring out a fully developed atomic theory in his book, *A New System of Chemical Philosophy*, which was published in 1808. Dalton did not claim originality, but what he did was to articulate that all matter is composed of tiny, indivisible particles called *atoms*. Basic substances in nature, like lead, gold, oxygen, and carbon were called *elements*. Each element was composed of one kind of atom. Dalton came to the important conclusion that *elements combine together in a simple numerical proportion, according to the number of atoms in each*. One atom of sodium would combine with one atom of chlorine to make sodium chloride. He measured the atomic weights of many elements and assigned symbols to them. Today 92 natural elements are known, and others, such as plutonium, have been created.

From the ideas of philosophers like Democritus and the experiments of chemists like John Dalton, and others such as Lavosier and Robert Boyle, who laid some of the foundations for Dalton, mankind was given a picture of how atoms, supposedly the smallest particles of matter, behaved. However, there was still very little known about the atom itself. One of the first clues to the nature of the atom was discovered by accident. In 1896 the French physicist Antoine Henri Becquerel was experimenting with substances which shine in the dark; one of these substances was a compound of uranium. He placed a small bottle of uranium salt in his desk for safe keeping, which accidentally was placed alongside an undeveloped camera plate which he had used to take a photograph of his family. The plate when eventually developed was badly fogged, and Becquerel came to the conclusion that *something* coming from the uranium had fogged the plate. He had discovered radioactivity—the strange property which certain substances have of giving off rays which can fog photographic plates. Marie Sklodowska Curie, a Polish woman scientist who was working with her husband, Pierre, in Becquerel's laboratory, called this strange effect "radioactivity" in 1898.

Pierre and Marie Curie began to study some of these radioactive effects, and were surprised to discover that a piece of pitchblende, the ore from which the uranium was extracted, was even more radioactive than uranium itself. Thus, they set to work to find some other highly radioactive element in the pitchblende. In the search they first discovered one new element to which they gave the name polonium. But even though the polonium was radioactive, it was not sufficiently so to explain the great activity of the pitchblende. Their search ultimately led them to obtain a product 900 times as active as uranium—a hitherto unknown element. To this the Curies gave the name radium, from the Latin word "radius" meaning a ray.

About seventeen years after Becquerel's discovery Lord Rutherford in England and Niels Bohr in Denmark pictured the atom as a miniature solar system composed of (1) a central core or nucleus containing particles held together by strong forces and (2) rings of other particles circling about the nucleus. The particles rotating about the nucleus were identified as electrons. The particles in the nucleus were later identified as protons and neutrons. The stage was set for modern atomic science.

The *atom* is the smallest particle in which any element may exist and yet retain its peculiar chemical characteristics. The atom of one element is differentiated from the atoms of every other element by the number of protons contained in its nucleus. Uranium is the heaviest natural element and contains 92 protons. Hydrogen, the lightest element, contains 1 proton.

There are also differences between the atoms of any given element depending upon the number of neutrons contained in the nucleus. These atoms differ in weight and are called isotopes. The two uranium isotopes found in nature that are most often referred to are U-238, which contains 92 protons plus 146 neutrons, and U-235, which contains 92 protons plus 143 neutrons. More than 99 percent of all the uranium found in nature is U-238; slightly less than 1 percent is U-235.

In January, 1939, a German scientist, Lise Meitner, and her nephew, Otto Frisch, concluded that the Italian Enrico Fermi and two Germans Otto Hahn and Fritz Strassmann, in earlier work, had succeeded in splitting the uranium atom by bombarding it with neutrons. Meitner and Frisch called this process *fission*.

When U-235 is fissioned, the isotope absorbs a neutron, then splits approximately in half. Two new atoms are produced and two or three neutrons are released. The weight of the new isotopes and the neutrons is less than that of the original U-235 atom. The loss in weight appears as energy—the same energy which had formerly bound the protons and neutrons together in the atom's nucleus. This was the new source of atomic or nuclear energy.

By 1940 many scientists had split atoms—one at a time—by bombarding them with neutrons. At that time, however, no way was known of bringing about a self-sustaining process, or chain reaction, that would release more energy than it consumed. Shortly thereafter it was generally known that three kinds of atoms—uranium 235, plutonium 239, and uranium 233—when split, could throw out enough energy and neutrons to strike and "fission" similar atoms and thus cause a chain reaction. This process occurs trillions of times in a fraction of a second and can produce an explosion (the atomic bomb); or the chain reaction can be controlled and directed to yield nuclear energy at a desired rate, in two forms: as heat, which can be harnessed to raise steam and drive a turbine, and as radiation.

The problem in the case of U-235 is that uranium found in nature contains only one part of U-235, the fissionable isotope for every 139 parts of nonfissionable U-238. Thus U-235 must be separated or concentrated. This is done by a method of gaseous diffusion. Plutonium is not a natural element but must be produced as a by-product of a nuclear reactor in which the more abundant nonfissionable U-238 is bombarded with neutrons and transformed into fissionable plutonium. U-233 must be produced from thorium, a metallic element, in the same manner as plutonium. Atoms of thorium are put into a reactor, where they are transmuted by bombardment into U-233. U-235 and plutonium are used as fissionable materials. However, thorium has not been used extensively but is considered to have growing future possibilities.

The second new source of nuclear energy is through the fusion reaction which is the basis of the hydrogen bomb. In this instance, instead of splitting very heavy atoms, very light atoms, such as hydrogen atoms, are heated to a temperature of millions of degrees and fuse together into heavy atoms, giving off tremendous quantities of energy. This process takes place inside the sun, under enormous pressures and with temperatures of the order of 20 million degrees. For the first time, the uranium fission bomb made it possible to achieve such temperatures on earth, and it occurred to some of those working on the Manhattan Project that this might be a way of starting such a "thermonuclear" reaction in hydrogen. That is, an atomic bomb might serve as a fuse for a hydrogen bomb. The thermonuclear process in the sun operates with ordinary hydrogen, but takes millions of years to complete. However, it operates more easily if one starts with deuterium, a heavy hydrogen containing one neutron, or even more readily with tritium, a superheavy hydrogen containing two neutrons. Deuterium is present to the extent of about two percent in natural hydrogen, and can easily be extracted. However, tritium, which is the preferred fuel for atomic fusion reactions, is much more rare, but can be produced by neutron bombardment of lithium in a reactor in much the same manner as plutonium is produced.

RAW MATERIALS AND RESERVES

Uranium as a source of energy is by far the most important raw material of the new energy age. Thorium probably will increase in importance in the future. Lithium is of significance in the fusion process.

However, short-term plans for the development of nuclear power have depended primarily on the use of uranium.

Uranium

Natural uranium, the dominant source material of atomic energy, consists of three radioactive isotopes: about 99.3 percent U-238; about 0.7 percent U-235; and a trace of U-234. The earth's crust is estimated to contain about three grams of uranium per ton of rock; and thus uranium is more abundantly distributed than antimony, bismuth, cadmium, gold, mercury, or silver. More than 150 uranium-bearing minerals are known, but only a few have been found in sufficient concentration to be of economic value. The most important uranium minerals are uraninite or pitchblende, carnotite, tyuyamunite, coffinite, and autunite.

Although uranium was discovered by H. M. Klaproth in 1789, uranium ores remained laboratory curiosities until about 1898 when Mme. Curie discovered that radium was contained in the ores. The first important source of uranium, mined for its radium content, was the pitchblende ore from the Joachimsthal mines in Czechoslovakia. Since these ores were a government monopoly, a world-wide search began for other radium-containing materials. The investigation led to discovery of autunite occurrences in Portugal; pitchblende veins in Cornwall, England, and Schneeberg and Johanngeorgenstadt in Saxony; and pitchblende and carnotite in the United States. Attention finally centered on a relatively small area in southwestern Colorado and southwestern Utah where carnotite was known. The United States became the first major producer of uranium ore and from 1911 to 1923 was the world's principal source. Carnotite from the western states was processed for the recovery of radium at Denver, Colorado, and Pittsburgh, Pennsylvania.

Rich deposits of pitchblende at Katanga, Belgian Congo were discovered in 1913 and in ten years dominated the world market causing the almost complete collapse of the U.S. uranium industry. Extensive high-grade deposits at Great Bear Lake, Canada were discovered in 1930. Deposits of varying extent were found in many other places including the United Kingdom, Portugal, West Germany, U.S.S.R., Madagascar, Union of South Africa, and Australia and many were worked from time to time for recovery of the radium content of the ore.

From 1930 until 1940 the uranium industry was divided principally between Canada and Belgium for recovery of the radium content of the ores. The uranium content was usually neglected, but a minor amount was recovered for use in ceramics and glass products, primarily as a coloring agent, and in photographic films. After the invasion of Belgium by the German army in 1940, the African ores were shipped to the United States and Canada for refining.

In 1942 uranium became a strategic material, but between 1942 and 1948 not one new source of uranium was brought into production. The Shinkolobwe Mine in the Belgian Congo became the mainstay of the U.S. atomic energy program and the world's most important producer of uranium. As late as 1948 the Belgian Congo was almost the sole supplier of uranium to the United States. Canada had a very small production. The United States had almost none with minor production from 15 mines on the Colorado Plateau.

In 1948, the Atomic Energy Commission (AEC) initiated a uranium procurement program that provided guaranteed minimum prices for domestic ore, a bonus for the discovery and production of high-grade domestic ore, a mine development allowance, premiums for higher-than-average grade ore, and a haulage allowance. Gold tailings from mining operations in the Union of South Africa offered a large uranium production potential; therefore arrangements were made by the AEC to purchase South African uranium production which began about 1951. The 1948 program also was designed to stimulate exploration for uranium in Canada, and resulted in discovering significant deposits there.

By 1955, the Belgian Congo and South Africa were the leading producers of uranium, but Canada was making a strong bid for first place in world uraninum production under the direction of the Canadian Atomic Energy Commission. The United States Atomic Energy Commission reported that Canada had several hundred thousand tons of uranium in the moderate-cost class and that the most important deposits from the standpoint of future production would be the then most recent discoveries in the Beaverlodge area of Saskatchewan and the Blind River District of Ontario.

By 1960, the U.S. Bureau of Mines enumerated the major uranium producing areas in the world as:

United States	Colorado Plateau
Canada	Blind River, Ontario
Union of South Africa	Witwatersrand gold reefs
U.S.S.R.	Ferghana field
Australia	Rum Jungle, Radium Hill area
France	Lachaux Province, La Crouzelle Province
Belgian Congo	Shinkolobwe mine
Portugal	Urgeicera mine

In the United States, as previously noted, the Atomic Energy Commission's program to develop domestic sources of uranium was launched in 1948. At that time there were two mills producing uranium from Colorado Plateau ores. These mineral reserves have been explored and exploited since about 1910—first for radium, later for vanadium, and now for uranium, formerly considered an almost worthless by-product. The ores mined in 1947 came from a small area known as the "mineral belt" in southeastern Utah and southwestern Colorado.

By 1951 uranium discoveries had been beyond the narrow limits of the mineral belt in other areas of the Colorado Plateau, which is the high land on both sides of the Colorado River (up to 200 miles) in Utah, Colorado, Arizona, and New Mexico. *Business Week* reported in March, 1951, that each time a new uranium deposit was discovered it was loudly touted as "fabulous" or "enough to free us from dependence on foreign sources." This was considered to be not true and not possible unless sizable quantities of pitchblende were discovered.

All the 1950 discoveries and just about all previous uranium finds in the U.S. are hardly more than enriched rock or dirt. It's classed as rich ore if it contains as much as 1 percent uranium oxide (20 lbs. to the ton). In contrast, pure pitchblende made from Canada or Belgian Congo contains up to 60 percent uranium, and, since the ore is rich in pitchblende, uranium content or a ton of raw ore may run up to 20 percent or more."

So domestic discoveries can never free us completely from dependence on foreign ore. By intensive exploration and major expansion of high-cost milling facilities, we could, if we had to, support a bare minimum war program on our own ores. If the Russians should ever overrun the Belgian Congo mines—where we get about 70 percent of our pitchblende—there would be feverish development of the plateau resources. But we'd still lean strongly on Canadian pitchblende.

Business Week should have known better than to underestimate the temperature set off by the bite of the uranium bug. One source described the 1953 activity in the Colorado Plateau as follows:

The feverish search for uranium ores both on the Colorado Plateau and in Canada has within the last year reached such a pitch as to be comparable to the famed Gold Rush of a hundred years ago. All over Colorado, Utah, Arizona and New Mexico—and in Wyoming and Montana, too—the number one subject of conversation is uranium. One cannot eat breakfast in Grand Junction, Colorado, site of the AEC's main Western office, without hearing about it, nor can one walk through any hotel lobby in Salt Lake City without overhearing a discussion of a claim or a new strike.

This uranium fever has drawn every able-bodied man and woman into the mountains and deserts of the West in search of the yellowish carnotite or its richer relative, pitchblende. Along with the traditional pick and shovel of the prospector goes the Geiger counter which discloses the characteristic radio-activity emitted by uranium ores. In fact, the pick and shovel these days are often left at home.

The only customer for uranium oxide (uranium never occurs as the pure metal) is the Atomic Energy Commission, and the prices, which vary with the concentration, are fixed until 1962. There are now more than 550 mines producing on the Colorado Plateau. The owners and operators of these mines vary from an individual to some of the largest mining firms in the world.

On April 5, 1955, Jesse C. Johnson, director, Division of Raw Materials, AEC, described the United States uranium reserves as follows:

In the United States, most of the uranium is coming from the Colorado Plateau. New production is being developed in Wyoming, North and South Dakota and other western states. Recent discoveries in Texas also may prove important. With few exceptions, these deposits are found in flat-lying sedimentary beds. The uranium content generally ranges from 0.1% to 0.5% U-308 and many of the deposits are small. Early in the present program the bulk of our production came from deposits containing only a few thousand tons. A ten or twenty thousand-ton ore body was considered large. During the last three years numbers of deposits have been found which contain in excess of 100,000 tons and at least one contains several million tons. Probably 80% of our present known ore reserves are in deposits larger than 50,000 tons. These are deposits that can supply uranium at moderate cost.

In spite of the great improvement in ore supply, which has made the United States one of the leading uranium producers, most of the deposits now developed may be mined out in less than ten years. However, if exploration continues as actively as at present, after ten years of full production developed ore reserves may be even greater than today.

There are vast areas throughout our western states that may contain uranium deposits similar to those being mined—but the problem is to find them. Deposits exposed on the surface will be found by surface and airborne surveys using Geiger and scintillation counters which are now standard equipment for every prospector. At present, the buried deposits can be found only by drilling.

Private exploration is now active in all parts of the country where some evidence of uranium has been found. New discoveries are adding uranium reserves faster than they are being mined. This activity will continue, however, only as long as there is a market for the production. At present, there is only a government market which is guaranteed through March 31, 1962 (now 1970). Beyond that it still could be a factor until the commercial market can sustain a production rate of some importance.[1]

In February, 1956, Mr. Johnson brought the public up to date in remarks indicating that approximately 80 percent of the U.S. known reserves had been developed in the last three years. Most of them were discovered during this period. Over 70 percent of our known ore reserves were in three districts: the Big Indian Wash-Lisbon Valley area of Utah, the Laguna Indian Reservation, New Mexico, and the Ambrosia Lake area, New Mexico.

On December 5, 1956, the AEC removed the classified categories of information data on reserves and production subsequent to June 30, 1955. Then in December, 1959 the AEC made public additional statistics on domestic uranium production up until the end of the fiscal year 1959. This information plus subsequent releases permits the presentation of the status of domestic uranium reserves in Table 6.1.

Following a detailed review of uranium ore reserve data, the AEC began in January, 1962 to present what the agency thought was a more accurate accounting of reserves which represented in-place reserves eco-

[1] *Commodity Year Book,* New York, Commodity Research Bureau, Inc., 1955, pp. 350–351.

nomically minable at a price of $8.00 per pound U-308 in concentrate under a mining policy of maximum extraction. (U-308 is the oxide in which uranium content is generally expressed.)

TABLE 6.1
United States Uranium Reserves

	Tons of ore	Percent U-308	Tons U-308
Estimated Reserves Jan. 1, 1963	68,000,000	0.25	167,000
Additions to reserves in 1963	3,800,000	0.23	7,600
Shipments to mills in 1963	5,800,000	0.25	14,600
Estimated Reserves Jan. 1, 1964	66,000,000	0.24	160,000

° Year-end unless otherwise noted.
SOURCE: United States Atomic Energy Commission.

The reserves for 1963 and 1964 reflect this more accurate estimate. The reserves at the beginning of 1964 were estimated to be approximately 66,000,000 tons containing 160,000 tons of U-308. This estimate as indicated in the tabulation below was arrived at by adjusting the previously published estimate for January 1, 1963 to reflect ore mined and new reserves developed during 1963. Additions to reserves resulted largely from further development of operating mines and extensions into contiguous ground.

TABLE 6.1A

Year*	Thousands of tons
1948 (January)	1,000
1949	1,000
1950 (July)	2,000
1951	2,000
1952	3,000
1953	5,000
1954	10,000
1955	27,000
1956	63,000
1957	78,000
1958	82,500
1959 (July)	88,900
1960 (January)	86,100
1961 (January)	82,000
1962 (January)	71,000
1963 (January)	68,000
1964 (January)	66,000

Table 6.2 gives the distribution of uranium ore in the United States by states.

TABLE 6.2
Distribution of Uranium Ore Reserves By States January 1, 1964

	Tons of ore (thousands)	Percent U-308	Tons U-308	Percent total
New Mexico	32,000	0.24	76,800	48
Wyoming	24,100	0.24	57,000	36
Colorado	3,100	0.27	9,300	6
Utah	2,300	0.30	6,700	4
Others*	3,900	0.22	10,200	6
	66,000	0.24	160,000	100

* Includes Alaska, Arizona, California, Idaho, Montana, Nevada, North Dakota, Oregon, South Dakota, Texas and Washington.
SOURCE: United States Atomic Energy Commission.

The AEC estimates that with no further discoveries of uranium the 160,000 tons of U-308 will be reduced by usage to 95,000 to 100,000 tons by the end of 1966 and to about 86,000 tons by the end of 1970. Actual reserves in 1970 will depend on company mining practices, the quantities of ore discovered in the intervening years, and the prevailing U-308 prices at the time.

TABLE 6.3
Free World Reserves of U-308
(Short tons)

Country	Reserves
U.S.A.[1]	160,000
Canada[1]	245,000[3]
Republic of South Africa	150,000[4]
France	40,000[5]
Australia	12,000[6]
Other[2]	25,000
Total	632,000

1 Updated to January 1, 1964. All others as of January 1, 1963.
2 Argentina, Congo, Germany, India, Japan, Mexico, Portugal and Spain.
3 Canadian Department of Mines and Technical Surveys.
4 South African Atomic Energy Board.
5 French Commissariat de l'Energie Atomique.
6 Australian Atomic Energy Commission.
NOTE: In-place reserves except Canada where 25 percent production loss is estimated.
SOURCE: United States Atomic Energy Commission.

The AEC estimates that uranium reserves available at $8.00 per pound from Free World nations are shown in Table 6.3.

In 1963 total U.S. procurement of U-308 was 23,020 tons which came from the following sources: U.S.A. 14,218; Canada 4,651; South Africa 4,134 and Australia 17. The 17 tons were received early in the year from Australia to complete this overseas contract. In 1964 total procurement of U-308 was estimated at 16,900 tons of which 11,900 was domestic and 5,000 tons imports.

The changing sources of uranium ore, U.S. policy, and the outlook for the future, are of such special importance that they will be discussed separately under the problems and policy section of this chapter.

Thorium

Thorium is a grayish-white metal which has long been noted chemically and industrially for its use in giving a brilliant glow to mantles in gas lights, a use that was predominant for decades before World War II. Other nonenergy uses are for alloying with magnesium, for chemical and medicinal purposes, and for electric and radio-tube filaments. Thorium oxide (ThO_2) has a melting point of about 5,000 F.°, and therefore is in demand for refractories. The major importance of thorium now is due to its potentialities in the field of nuclear production. A number of artificial isotopes have been prepared from thorium, the most important being the isotope U-233, which we have seen is fissionable with the release of energy similar to that produced by U-235.

Thorium, like uranium is widely distributed. The major commercial source is monazite, a phosphate of rare-earth metals containing from less than one percent to 18 percent ThO_2. World reserves of thorium are given in Table 6.4 which follows on page 182.

Owing to the small quantity of thorium thus far required for reactor development, little exploration has been made for it compared to that made for other metals. Concentrations of thorium are found chiefly in four geologic environments: (1) placer deposits, which are the sources of most of the production, and which consist of beach, fliviatile, and residual (eluvial) concentrations of heavy thorium-bearing minerals; (2) epignetic deposits, which include vein or lode deposits and contact-metamorphic or replacement bodies; (3) sedimentary rocks, which comprise ancient placers, thorium-bearing dolomite, and deposits in conglomerates; and (4) igneous and metamorphic rocks, which include thorium-rich granite, alkalic rocks, carbonatite, fenite, pegmatite and pegmatitic-migmatite, and thorium-rich zones in metamorphic rock.

Known thorium reserves of the United States are estimated at about 100,000 tons ThO_2. Total potential reserves are probably much larger—possibly 500,000 tons or greater—for additional thorium will no doubt be found in undiscovered districts and at unexplored depths in known districts. The U.S. Geological Survey prepared and published for the Atomic Energy Commission in 1964 *Geologic Distribution and Resources of Thorium* which catalogs the distribution of thorium resources and potential in the United States, and suggests availability in other areas of the world.

TABLE 6.4

Estimated Resources of Thorium in the Free World

Price Range $5–$10 Per Pound of ThO_2 (Short tons ThO_2)

Country	Reasonably assured resources	Possible additional resources
United States	100,000	500,000
India[1]	250,000	250,000
Canada[1,2]	80,000	155,000
Africa[3]	50,000	unevaluated
Australasia[4]	10,000	unevaluated
Brazil	10,000	20,000
Totals	500,000	925,000

1 Estimates are based on information in papers presented by delegates at the Third United Nations International Conference on the Peaceful Uses of Atomic Energy, Geneva, 1964.
2 Thorium occurs in uranium deposits; availability is partially dependent upon uranium market.
3 Includes central and southern Africa and Malagasy Republic.
4 Includes Australia, Burma, Ceylon, Indonesia, Malaysia, South Korea, Taiwan and Thailand.
SOURCE: United States Atomic Energy Commission, August, 1965.

Perhaps best known sources of thorium in the United States have been the monazite-bearing placers which are found in all western states, in the southeastern states and in Alaska. The placer deposits of greatest potential are in Idaho, Montana, North and South Carolina, Georgia, and Florida. Placer deposits near Jacksonville, Florida and at Hollow Creek, S.C. have been mined for heavy minerals, including monazite. However the United States is now known to have at least one major thorium province, which consists of thorium-bearing veins in part of Lemhi County, Idaho, and in neighboring Montana. This area is known as the Lemhi Pass district, and accounts in large part for the AEC's estimate of 100,000 tons of thorium resources in the United States. Indeed, the AEC sees that there is the possibility that Lemhi Pass district might produce several times that amount of thorium at prices comparable to those for uranium.

Recently domestic production of monazite has consisted only of a small tonnage from the Florida beach sands. In the past U.S. ore requirements have been supplied principally by imports from South Africa, but with the closing in 1963 of a monazite mine, which had been one of the world's largest producers since 1954, a realignment of thorium supply can be expected in the next few years. In addition to South Africa, the other major producers, Brazil, India, and Malagasy, have been sources of monazite ore imports; but after the closing of the South African mine in 1964, total U.S. imports dropped sharply to 27.5 percent of the 1963 total with imports coming from Australia, Ceylon, and Malaysia. However, thorium metal and alloys were imported from Canada and England. Since thorium is produced as a by-product of uranium processing in Canada, a conservationist case could be made for relying on Canada for any required imports, because once the waste solutions from uranium milling are discarded, the thorium may be dispersed beyond reclaiming.

Nonenergy consumption of thorium in the United States was averaging about 50 tons a year during the first five years of the 1960's, and it was felt that the use of thorium as a nuclear fuel would continue to be limited. The AEC estimated in 1965 that the energy requirements for thorium would probably be measured only in hundreds of tons, with annual requirements during most of that period of less than 100 tons.

There seemed to be no concern about the immediate future supply of thorium because the AEC's requirements could be readily satisfied from existing stockpiles. Thorium was not only held in the three governmental stockpiles to be discussed, but under the authority of the Atomic Energy Acts of 1946 and 1954 the AEC had an inventory of almost 1,750 tons of thorium at the end of 1964.

The long-run future domestic supply of thorium seems to depend more on demand than reserves because the undefined vital factor in self-sufficiency is the anticipated demand for thorium metal and oxide in nuclear reactors for power generation. This factor cannot be resolved at present; but the AEC has been of the opinion that as long as uranium is cheap and plentiful, "the market for thorium will be slow to develop."

THE URANIUM ROUTE

The uranium route as shown in Figure 6.1 consists of uranium mining, uranium concentration, and uranium refining, which will be described in the following paragraphs.

Uranium Mining

In the early period of the uranium industry, most Colorado Plateau uranium deposits were developed by incline entries driven into a canyon or sloping ground to recover small deposits of carnotite and associated minerals. Development usually consisted of following the ore leads. The discovery of larger and deeper ore bodies made development and mining more complex. Larger mines under development use room-and-pillar methods, and at least one mine uses a caving-panel retreat method enabling almost 100 percent recovery of uranium ore. In Wyoming large open pit mines are being developed.

Figure 6.1: The Uranium Route.

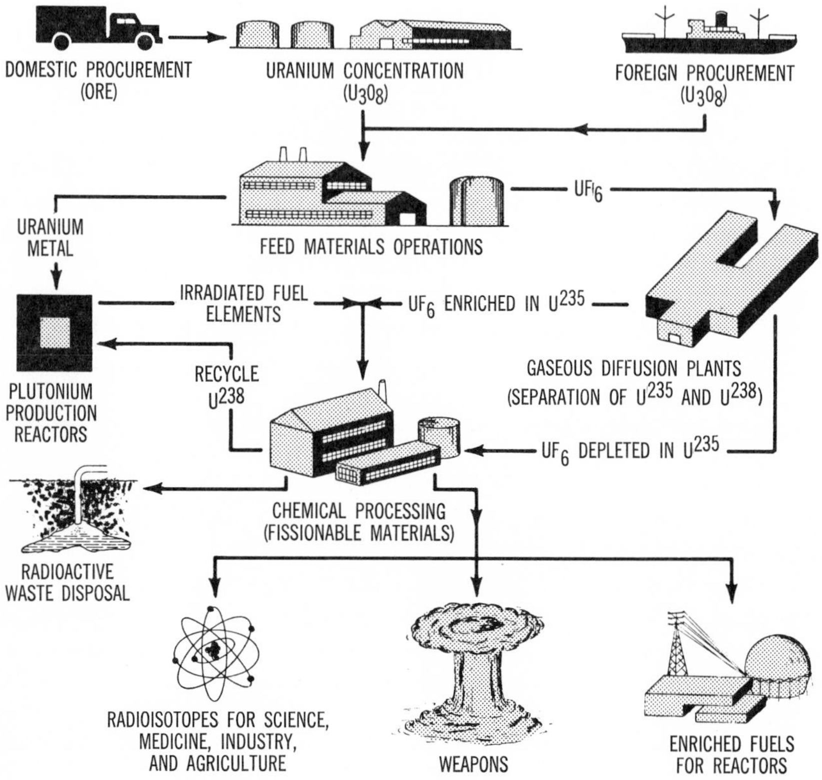

DOMESTIC PROCUREMENT (ORE)   URANIUM CONCENTRATION (U_3O_8)   FOREIGN PROCUREMENT (U_3O_8)

URANIUM METAL   FEED MATERIALS OPERATIONS UF_6

IRRADIATED FUEL ELEMENTS UF_6 ENRICHED IN U^{235}

RECYCLE U^{238} GASEOUS DIFFUSION PLANTS (SEPARATION OF U^{235} AND U^{238})

PLUTONIUM PRODUCTION REACTORS UF_6 DEPLETED IN U^{235}

CHEMICAL PROCESSING (FISSIONABLE MATERIALS)

RADIOACTIVE WASTE DISPOSAL

RADIOISOTOPES FOR SCIENCE, MEDICINE, INDUSTRY, AND AGRICULTURE   WEAPONS   ENRICHED FUELS FOR REACTORS

SOURCE: U.S. Bureau of Mines.

The number of uranium mines in the United States increased from 15 in 1946 to over 1,000 in 1956. Since then the number of operating mines has declined. The trend was toward consolidation of smaller properties for more economic operation, and toward an increase in the percentage of total production by the large producers. At the beginning of the 1960's, 28 mines produced about 60 percent of the annual production.

The income derived from uranium mining is eligible for a 23 percent depletion allowance under the Internal Revenue Code of 1954. To maintain a high rate of exploration, development, and production, the AEC established incentives, including: guaranteed minimum base prices for ores of various grades until 1962; bonuses for the discovery and production of high-grade deposits; bonuses for the initial production from new mines until March 31, 1960; and haulage and development allowances until March 31, 1962.

Thus after April, 1962, the price of domestic ore was not guaranteed, and none was bought by the government. Instead, from that date on, uranium ore has been bought by licensed concentrating mills on the commercial markets.

Uranium Concentration

The average content of U.S. uranium ore is about five pounds per ton or 0.25 per cent U-308. Thus the uranium ore must first be concentrated at mills before further processing. Milling near the mine yields a concentrate averaging about 80 percent U-308. Principal steps in uranium milling include ore preparation by crushing, grinding, and occasionally roasting to improve uranium solubility and ore handling; acid or alkaline leaching for digesting the ore; clarification of leach liquor by decantation and filtration; or sandlime separation to permit subsequent product recovery operations either by chemical precipitation, ion exchange, or solvent extraction.

There were 21 concentrate producing plants in the United States in 1963 as listed in Table 6.5.

As previously noted, after April, 1962 the AEC ceased buying uranium ore, and since then the concentrate mills have bought the ore in the commercial market. Instead of buying the ore, after April 1, 1962 the AEC shifted to buying uranium concentrate U-308 from the mills which were given guaranteed contracts at $8.00 a pound from that date until December 31, 1966. This program of the AEC of converting to a concentrate rather than an ore price was to establish a uniform base for market quotations on the primary produce (U-308) desired by industry, and thus anticipated a transition from a government controlled market to a commercial market.

Thus, initially, December 31, 1966 was the cut-off date, after which the uranium mills would have to sink or swim in the commercial market. However, late in the year 1963 the outlook for uranium after 1966 was brightened by the announcement of a stretch-out of the 1962–1966 program, whereby the concentrate milling companies with contracts through 1966 would be allowed to defer to the period 1967–1968 a portion of the material scheduled for delivery to the AEC prior to 1967. In return, during 1967–1970, the Commission would purchase at fixed formulated prices U-308 concentrates equal to the quantity deferred and delivered in 1967 and 1968. The contractual status of the mills, the amount of the contract, and the expiration date are shown in Table 6.5. As it now stands there will be strictly a commercial market for U-308 concentrate after 1970.

TABLE 6.5
U-308 Concentrate Producing Plants

Company	Location of mill	Contract expiration date	Tons U-308 deliverable under contract from Jan. 1, 1963
American Metal Climax, Inc.	Grand Junction, Colo.	12/31/66	1,907
Anaconda Co.	Grants, N. Mex.	12/31/70	6,046[1]
Atlas Corp.	Moab, Utah	12/31/66	8,964
Atlas Corp.[a]	Mexican Hat, Utah	12/31/66	
Cotter Corp.	Canon City, Colo.	2/28/65	560
Dawn Mining Co.	Ford, Wash.	12/31/66	1,075
El Paso Natural Gas Co.	Tuba City, Ariz.	12/31/66	1,034
Federal-Radorock-Gas Hills Partners[b]	Fremont County, Wyo.	12/31/66	3,156
Globe Mining Co.	Natrona County, Wyo.	12/31/67*	1,358
Homestake-Sapin Partners[c]	Grants, N. Mex.	12/31/66	12,524
Kermac Nuclear Fuels Corp.	Grants, N. Mex.	12/31/66	9,986
Mines Development, Inc.	Edgemont, S. Dak.	12/31/66	1,523
Petrotomics Co.	Carbon County, Wyo.	12/31/66	1,355
Susquehanna-Western, Inc.	Falls City, Tex.	12/31/66	544
Union Carbide Corp., Nuclear Div.	Maybell, Colo.	12/31/66	773
Do	Rifle, Colo.	12/31/67*	5,015
Do	Uravan, Colo.	12/31/67*	
Utah Construction & Mining Co.	Fremont County, Wyo.	12/31/66	3,718
Vanadium Corp. of America[d]	Shiprock, N. Mex.	12/31/66	1,768
Vitro Chemical Co.	Salt Lake City, Utah	12/31/66	940
Western Nuclear, Inc.	Jeffrey City, Wyo.	12/31/67*	3,811

1 Contract extended through 1970.
a Mexican Hat mill acquired by Atlas from Texas-Zinc Corp. in July.
b The Federal-Radorock-Gas Hills Partners mill is currently treating, on a toll basis, ores diverted from the Riverton, Wyo., plant of Susquehanna-Western, Inc., which discontinued operation in June.
c The Homestake-Sapin Partners mill is toll-treating ores formerly tributary to the Phillips Petroleum Co. mill which was acquired by United Nuclear Corp. in March and shut down.
d Shiprock mill acquired by Vanadium Corp. of America from Kerr-McGee Oil Industries, Inc., in February. VCA's Durango, Colo., mill was subsequently shut down and ores formerly tributary to Durango are being treated at Shiprock.
e Previous expiration dates extended provisional stretchout agreements.
SOURCE: *Annual Report to Congress of the Atomic Energy Commission for 1963*, Washington, D.C., 1964.

Uranium Refining

The U-308 concentrate is converted into usable forms through a series of refining processes known as feed materials operations, and these forms are then used for the manufacture of fissionable materials for weapons and fuel for power reactors.

Feed Materials Operations. The uranium chemical concentrates from domestic mills and from foreign sources up until 1962 were treated principally at two feed material centers to remove impurities and to convert the uranium to metal or intermediate chemical products for further processing. The feed material centers were located at Weldon Spring, Missouri and Fernald, Ohio. The principal stages in feed materials processing are: (1) refining the uranium mill concentrates to recover the orange trioxide (UO_3) of uranium; (2) the conversion of UO_3 to green salt (UF_4), and reduction of green salt to uranium metal (U-238); and (3) the balance of the uranium tetrafluoride (UF_4) is converted into uranium hexafluoride (UF_6).

In 1962, the refining section of the government-owned plant operated by the National Lead Company at Fernald, Ohio was placed on standby, and refinery operations were consolidated in the government-owned feed material plant operated by Mallinckodt Works at Weldon Spring, Missouri. The privately owned Allied Chemical plant at Metropolis, Illinois, also produces UF_6 from U-308 concentrates.

Manufacture of Fissionable Materials. The bulk of refined uranium metal and uranium compounds produced at the feed materials plants have been shipped to AEC plants for the manufacture of fissionable materials. The uranium 238 metal fuel elements fabricated at feed materials plants are shipped to the uranium production reactors, and the uranium hexafluoride goes to the gaseous diffusion plants. See Figure 6.1.

There are two plutonium production reactor centers. At the beginning of 1964 there were eight reactors at Hanford, Washington, with one additional reactor under construction; and there were five reactors at Savannah River, Aiken, South Carolina. Fissionable material is produced at both these centers by the conversion of uranium metal by neutron bombardment in nuclear reactors. The Hanford plant was built and operated by the duPont Chemical Co. until 1946; and from that time until 1966 was expanded and operated by the General Electric Co. The Savannah River plant was built in 1951 by the duPont Chemical Co. as a part of the H-bomb project. It was designed so that either tritium can be produced from lithium or plutonium can be produced from U-238. The Savannah River plant is operated for the AEC by duPont.

There are three gaseous diffusion plants located at Oak Ridge, Tennessee, Paducah, Kentucky, and Portsmouth, Ohio. Fissionable U-235 is separated from U-238 by gaseous diffusion. The separating medium in gaseous diffusion is a thin porous material which contains hundreds of millions of submicroscopic openings per square inch. The lighter, fast-moving molecules, U-235 F_6, strike the barrier more often than the slower heavy moving molecules of U-238 F_6 and thus more of them pass through the barrier. The gas must be pumped through a cascade of several thousand barriers to achieve the desired degree of enrichment.

By tapping the line at different places in the gaseous diffusion process, uranium hexafluoride of almost any desired degree of enrichment can be drawn off. Highly enriched UF_6, or 93 percent U-235 is produced principally for military purposes, and slightly enriched UF_6 containing about 3 percent U-235 is produced for fabrication into fuel elements for commercial power reactors. The UF_6 is reduced to metal or oxide for fabrication into fuel elements. Formerly all this processing, including the fabrication of fuel elements was done by the government-owned plants. Now however, the slightly enriched commercial power plant materials are sent to private plants for further processing. The first three of these plants producing natural and enriched fuel materials for commercial power plants were: Davidson Chemical Division, W. R. Grace, Erwin, Tennessee; Malinckodt Chemical Works, Hematite, Missouri; and Nuclear Materials and Equipment Corporation, Apollo, Pennsylvania.

The Shifting Role of Government in the Manufacture of Fissionable Materials. The U.S. government's role in the manufacture of fissionable materials has been a fascinating one. One of the initial problems of the Manhattan project of 1942 was to produce enough fissionable material to build an atomic bomb. Two types of large-scale production were developed: the separation of fissionable U-235 from the larger quantity of nonfissionable U-238, and the conversion of nonfissionable U-238 through neutron bombardment into fissionable plutonium.

Isotope separation of U-235 from U-238 was the function of the Oak Ridge plant. This was accomplished by gaseous diffusion and by an electromagnetic plant. From the beginning in 1945 the gaseous diffusion process was unbelievably successful, and the more expensive and inefficient electromagnetic plant was shut down.

Plutonium production by bombardment of U-238 was the function of the Hanford plant, on which construction was begun in the summer of 1943. This was to be accomplished in three reactors. By the summer of 1945 shipments of highly concentrated fissionable materials were being made from Oak Ridge and Hanford.

For about two and one-half years after the destruction of Hiroshima on August 6, 1945, the atomic energy program stagnated while Congress arrived at a policy, the AEC was created, and the Manhattan District organization was rebuilt. However, in 1947 expansion was begun. At that time, manufacture of plutonium nuclear reactors appeared to be more promising, and the AEC concentrated its expansion plan on plutonium. The General Electric Company took over the Hanford plant, rehabilitated and restored the reactor operation to wartime capacity, and began the construction of two new reactors and a chemical plant to extract plutonium. The expansion continued and eventually eight reactors were in operation at Hanford.

In 1948 the test of a more powerful A-bomb at Eniwetok proving ground seemed to have demonstrated a continuing need for U-235 as well as plutonium. A few months after the test the AEC announced a 60 million dollar expansion at Oak Ridge. In 1949 the Russians exploded an A-bomb, and the AEC began an additional 160 million dollar expansion at Oak Ridge. This appeared to about double the Oak Ridge capacity.

In 1950 came the Korean War and President Harry Truman's decision to develop the H-bomb, and the AEC: (1) began construction of a second gaseous diffusion plant at Paducah, with the same capacity as Oak Ridge, and (2) and started work on three dual purpose reactors at Savannah River: (a) to manufacture tritium from lithium for the super H-bomb and (b) to produce plutonium from U-238.

The expansion following the Korean War continued and a third gaseous diffusion plant was built at Portsmouth, Ohio; and two more reactors were built at Savannah River to bring the total to five. The two reactor installations at Hanford and Savannah River, and the three gaseous diffusion plants at Oak Ridge, Paducah and Portsmouth—five government-owned plants for the manufacture of fissionable materials—are gigantic installations each of which cost more than one billion dollars.

In 1962 the U.S. government through the AEC began a period of consolidation and contraction of operations. Sections of the government-owned gaseous diffusion plants—one at Oak Ridge, Tennessee, operated by Union Carbide Nuclear Company and the other at Portsmouth, Ohio, operated by Goodyear Atomic Corporation—were shut down in 1962. Subsequently, further cutbacks in gaseous diffusion plant operations have been made.

The AEC, as it moved toward less need for military uses and more requirements for peaceful uses, was not only consolidating its operations but also was moving toward private ownership where possible. Mention has already been made of the entry of private enterprise by three firms which took slightly enriched UF_6 containing about 3 percent U-235 and processed it for nuclear materials for private commercial power plants. Formerly all processing of this type was done by government-owned plants.

It should be made clear that the production of materials for private commercial power plants involves two stages: (1) the conversion of slightly enriched UF_6 to forms in which uranium fuel elements could be fabricated, and (2) the fabrication of uranium fuel elements. The AEC reported that by 1964, ten private companies converted UF_6 to forms from which uranium fuel elements could be fabricated, and twenty firms were in the then "highly competitive" fabrication field. Several firms were in both fields.

Another function of government-owned plants has been to process spent fuel from production reactors at Hanford and Savannah River and from test reactors and submarine reactors, while the spent fuel from commercial power reactors has been stored. The latter was true because the AEC had made a decision to attempt to encourage private processing of spent fuel from power reactors. A step of major importance was taken with the licensing of Nuclear Fuel Services (a subsidiary of W. R. Grace) for the reprocessing of irradiated fuels from nuclear power reactors. The reprocessing plant, located southwest of Buffalo, New York, and scheduled to begin operation in 1966, marked another major entry of private enterprise into the uranium route. In the meantime, pending operation of the plant, the AEC had made arrangements in 1963 to provide for spent fuel storage and to make payments for the plutonium and uranium contained in the spent fuel. Some appreciation of the order of magnitude and the economics involved in the spent fuel operation may be gained from the knowledge that the value of the spent fuel from one reactor charge might range from two to ten million dollars. Such charge would probably be removed once every three years.

Further indication of the diminished need for atomic production for military purposes came early in 1964 when it was announced that three of the eight reactors at Hanford would be shut down and that one of the five reactors at Savannah River would be shut down. At the same time a new production reactor (NPR) was nearing operation at Hanford which was designed for the production of plutonium, but also had design features which permitted the generation of steam from by-product heat, which in turn could be used to produce electricity. The AEC signed a contract with the Washington Public Power Supply System whereby the latter was to build an 800,000 kilowatt power plant using the by-product steam from NPR. Seventy-six public utilities, of which five were privately owned, participated in the power project. By congressional action 50 percent of the power was offered to a publicly-owned group of companies and 50 percent to private utilities.

The budget of the AEC was also indicative of a trend. While as late as 1962 70 to 75 percent of the AEC budget was devoted to military uses, by 1965 about 50 percent was devoted to military uses and about 50 percent to peaceful uses. And Glenn T. Seaborg, the Chairman of the AEC, projected a continuing increase in the budget for peaceful uses.

In conclusion, the *uranium route* had its great impetus from military applications under government sponsorship; but the United States through the AEC has progressively shifted to peaceful uses and increased private ownership of the various stages of operation along the route.

APPLICATION OF NUCLEAR DEVELOPMENTS

Nuclear research and development before World War II probably can be attributed more to the investigating urge of scientists than to an end-use application. The great urgency to beat Germany in the development of an A-bomb caused the United States to undertake the tremendous research and development program, greatly accelerated research, made possible the development through government expenditure, focused attention on the military aspects of the program, and caused the general public to lose sight of the fact that the applications of nuclear developments are twofold: for military purposes and for purposes of peace.

By mid-1965, according to the AEC, the total U.S. investment in atomic energy from the beginning of the program had been about 34 billion dollars. Of that amount 28 billion dollars had been for military programs, and 6 billion dollars for nonmilitary, or peaceful uses.

We will turn our attention to a detailed examination of the military applications and peaceful uses of atomic energy.

Military Applications

Major military applications include explosives, motive power, and radiological use. Obviously many peacetime applications are jointly shared with military use.

Explosives. To achieve an explosion was the purpose of the World War II atomic energy program. A chain reaction will not occur until there is present a minimum amount (a critical mass) of some atomic explosive. When the critical mass is brought together an explosion is spontaneous. Stated simply, an atomic bomb is a device containing at least two pieces of U-235 or plutonium, each slightly smaller than a critical mass, which slaps these pieces together at the moment an explosion is desired. The H-bomb differs in that very light atoms are combined or fused, releasing perhaps a thousand times more energy than splitting U-235 or plutonium in an A-bomb. The problem is that to bring about the fusion a temperature reaching millions of degrees is required. To produce this extremely high temperature, an A-bomb is required as a "kicker."

An appraisal of the problems and progress of developments of explosives is of course not a matter of public knowledge. Evidence indicates, however, that the 1945 A-bomb was a "rather clumsy and inefficient piece of mechanism." One of the major tasks of the AEC was to improve the bomb. This was the task of the AEC's Los Alamos Scientific Laboratory in New Mexico and the Western Electric Laboratory at Sandia.

The first job was to increase the efficiency of the A-bomb, and it appeared that substantial success had been achieved with the bomb tested at Eniwetok in the summer of 1948, which reportedly developed about 50 percent efficiency and released energy equivalent to about 100,000 tons of TNT. The establishment of the Nevada proving ground and the frequent additional tests have indicated further improvements in efficiency.

An additional improvement was made in the weight of the firing mechanism. A B-29 superfortress was required to carry the Hiroshima bomb. There were hints as early as 1951 that fast fighter bombers could carry the bomb, which made enemy interception harder. Other developments which perhaps resulted from improvements in the firing mechanism include the application of the bomb so that it would be fired from oversized mortars at targets twenty or thirty miles away.

Of tremendous significance was the use of an atomic warhead in a V-2 type of rocket, which in 1951 had ranges of around 200 miles. These rockets could be launched by land or sea. This of course was followed in a few years by the development of intercontinental guided missiles with atomic warheads.

New nuclear weapons which have been produced by the AEC under Presidential authorization are more effective, more reliable, and safer than older weapons that are gradually retired from the stockpile. Weapons research is performed by Sandia Corporation at Albuquerque, N. Mexico, at the Los Alamos Scientific Laboratory, Los Alamos, N. Mexico, and at the Lawrence Radiation Laboratory, Livermore, Cailfornia.

The H-superbomb and nuclear explosives were so well perfected by 1954 that a Congressional committee concluded that nuclear energy could "ravage this planet beyond recognition."

Finally, one interesting application of explosives which lends itself to peacetime use is cratering or excavation experiments which are being conducted by the AEC under the Plowshare program with the objective of achieving a refined nuclear excavation technology. This technique is deemed feasible as a fast and cheap means to "dig" a second canal to replace and/or supplement the Panama Canal.

Motive Power. The main obstacles to the use of nuclear fuel in transportation for military or peaceful uses have been (a) the extremely high cost of a nuclear reactor, (b) the difficulty of safeguarding its operation—for example, in an aircraft—so that if the reactor and its shielding were accidentally damaged it would not be a source of dangerous radiation, and (c) the immense weight of shielding required to contain the radiation from even a small reactor.

The most intriguing thing about nuclear fuel is the packing of ten million kwh into a pound—practically a weightless fuel. This makes it possible for the first time for moving vehicles to cruise almost indefinitely without needing to stop at refueling bases.

For the above reasons, naval craft were the first to use nuclear fuel. The nuclear-powered submarines, the *Nautilus* of 1954 and the *Sea Wolf,* were the first of the navy ships. A reactor is an ideal power source for a submarine not only because it will operate for months without refueling but also because it requires no oxygen and will propel the submarine with unmatched speed. Nuclear-fueled vessels are here—economics is the limiting factor.

In 1962 the United States Navy had 28 nuclear-powered submarines and three nuclear-propelled surface ships in operation. These surface ships were the aircraft carrier Enterprise, powered by eight reactors, the guided-missile destroyer leader Bainbridge, and the cruiser Long Beach, each powered by two reactors. A total of 51 reactors were to be used to power 47 submarines and two guided missile destroyer leaders under construction.

Nuclear-powered aircraft have been a government project since the end of World War II. Not much progress was made while it was an Air Force—Fairchild—project, but by 1951 it was on the development schedule after being approved by the AEC, the Navy, and the Joint Chiefs of Staff. The AEC in 1955 was spending more than 5 million dollars on the aircraft program at the National Reactor Testing Station in Idaho. General Electric and United Aircraft were working on the power cycle for the aircraft and, at the same time, other companies were concerned with airframe design. Eventually the problems appeared so difficult to resolve that the nuclear-powered aircraft project was abandoned. But in the area of airflight the world's first nuclear rocket engine system test was conducted late in 1965 at the Space Nuclear Propulsion Office's nuclear test site in Nevada.

Radiological Warfare. The deliberate use of radioactive materials as weapons is possible. They could be used effectively to keep troops from entering a contaminated area or workmen from entering a contaminated plant. The length of period of contamination could be controlled by selecting isotopes with the right rates of decay. Waste materials are available from the Hanford and Savannah plants and other radioactive materials could be manufactured to required specifications.

Peacetime Applications

The same Congressional committee that reported that nuclear energy could "ravage this planet beyond recognition" went on to say "or make it fair beyond the wildest dreams of our fathers." Two of these amazing develoments which reached early application were (1) nuclear power and (2) isotopes.

Nuclear Power. The reactor is the "key" machine of peacetime nuclear power. One approach toward the understanding of the role of the reactor is to state that at Hanford the end-product is plutonium, and, as a by-product, heat is produced unavoidably. Water is flushed through the piles (or core) of the reactor in order to keep them cool and in sufficient quantity to carry away all the heat without raising the water to the boiling point. This hot water is then dumped into the Columbia River. As a result, the Columbia is warmed and heat is lost. Obviously this intense heat could be used in the form of boiling water to make steam which would spin turbine-generators to produce electric power—that is of course, if they were high temperature reactors rather than low temperature reactors. Since the older Hanford reactors are of the low-temperature type, they must be kept cool and the water comes out below the boiling point.

When the Savannah River reactors were designed the AEC gave serious thought to installing reactors with a temperature high enough to make the energy output usable. Successful experience with the low-temperature reactors and the time element were the decisive factors. The AEC thus had two huge reactor installations which were throwing away several million kilowatts of energy at the same time they were draining several million kilowatts of electricity from the country's power facilities for the purpose of operating the plants.

Although there were certain complicating technical matters, it was clear in the early 1950's, that it was possible for future AEC reactor installations to produce utilizable heat converted into electric power at the same time they were producing plutonium or tritium. It was thought that this would put the government farther into the power business and would lessen the cost per kwh as most of the capital investment would be made to turn out end-products for military applications. Thus, it was clear that nuclear power for peacetime uses was technically possible and would be economically advantageous three ways: electric power would not be used from existing facilities, energy in the form of heat would not be thrown away, and the cost per kwh would be reduced.

Private industry looks at the reactor as a machine to produce an end-product of heat to drive a turbine to make electricity. The major difference between a conventional steam plant and a nuclear power plant is that the former uses heat produced by combustion of fossil fuels in a furnace, but nuclear plants use heat produced by fission of nuclear fuels in a reactor. Basically a nuclear reactor is substituted for a fossil fuel boiler. The reactor becomes a machine to receive a nuclear fuel. Suppose the fuel being used is natural uranium or enriched uranium. It contains some U-235 and the rest is U-238. The reactor burns the U-235 and produces heat for the conversion into electric power. At the same time the burning of the U-235 expels neutrons which strike and transmute the U-238 into fissionable plutonium. Some of the plutonium formed during the operation of the reactor will fission and release energy. The rest of the plutonium produced in the reactor (and unused U-238) is removed during the discharge of the fuel, and is separated at a chemical plant either to be reinserted as fresh fuel into the same reactor, or inserted in other reactors to produce additional energy.

A reactor that produces somewhat less than the amount of fuel that it burns is called a *converter*. But what nuclear scientists have as an objective is to develop a *breeder* reactor—a reactor in which more than one atom of plutonium, or U-233 is produced for every atom of fuel burned in the process. The achievement of this objective would make it possible for a reactor to produce more fuel than it burns, and at the same time produce power.

In order to explore a broad range of reactor types the U.S. nuclear power program has included a wide range of research, design, construction, and operation of a number of experimental and small prototype nuclear power plants. Many concepts of thermal reactor power plants have been studied and tried. These have included the use of fissionable U-235 fuel, and in some instances plutonium or U-233, in various concentrations and in metallic and ceramic materials with various protective coatings, such as stainless steel, and zirconium alloys, and in physical configurations, such as rods, plates, and tubes, and even in liquid form as liquid metals, molten salts, or slurries.

The principal components of a reactor are shown in Figure 6.2. Heat may be removed from the fuel by circulation of ordinary or heavy water, steam, gas, organic liquid, and liquid metals. The moderator which slows down the movement of the neutrons may be ordinary water, heavy water,

Figure 6.2: Principal Components of a Nuclear Reactor.

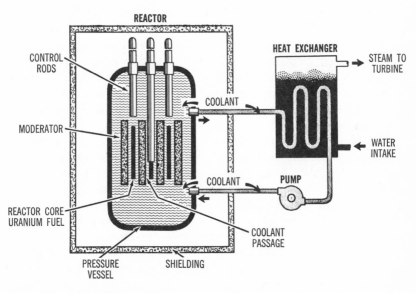

SOURCE: Atomic Energy Commission.

graphite, beryllium, or organic fluids. The heat removing fluid may also serve as a moderator. In general the goals are a simple economical fuel and reactor system from which heat can be extracted at high rates and temperatures and a fuel form which can be operated for a long time without replacement. In addition neutrons should be conserved for production of as much new fuel as practicable.

The feasibility of producing electric power by using a reactor to replace the boiler in a conventional power plant (or to replace a hydro plant) was proved by the AEC in 1951 with its Experimental Breeder Reactor, which developed 100 kilowatts of electricity.

In 1955, *Business Week*, in its June 18 issue, reported that the AEC had underway a 5-year Reactor Development Program, given below:

Reactor Type	Builder	Total Estimated Cost	Scheduled Completion
Pressurized Water	Westinghouse Electric Duquesne Light (Operator)	$85,000,000	1957
Sodium-graphite	North American Aviation	10,000,000	1955
Boiling water	Argonne National Lab.	17,000,000	1956
Fast breeder	Argonne National Lab.	40,000,000	1958
Homogeneous	Oak Ridge National Lab.	47,000,000	1959

With the exception of the pressurized-water reactor, which was a prototype plant, these projects were all reactor experiments. The Pressurized Water Reactor at Shippingport, Pennsylvania was scheduled to be the nation's first large-scale (at least 60,000 kilowatts) civilian nuclear power plant. First of the reactors to begin operation was the Experimental Boiling Water, which began producing power early in 1957. All of the other experimental reactors ran into testing difficulties and were not completed on schedule.

The Shippingport Atomic Power Station also went into operation in 1957, and thus became the first nuclear plant to produce commercial electric power. The plant is operated by the Duquesne Light Company, and by 1964 had supplied more than 1.7 billion kwh of electricity to users in the Pittsburgh area. The plant became the leading representative of one of the two most intensively developed reactor concepts—the pressurized water reactor. The other was the boiling water reactor.

As of July 1, 1964 there were thirteen operable civilian nuclear power plants in the United States, varying in sizes from 11,400 kilowatts to 200,-000 kilowatts, with a combined net capability of about 970,000 kilowatts. Three of these were pressurized water plants, six were boiling water, and one had a sodium cooled-graphite-moderator, one used heavy water for coolant and moderator, and one was a sodium cooled fast breeder. These plants are listed in Table 6.6, with their individual capacities, start-up dates, and other relevant information.

TABLE 6.6

Operable Nuclear Power Plants[1] as of July 1, 1964

Name, owner or operator	Location	Type	Capacity net kw	Startup
Shippingport Atomic Power Station (AEC and Duquesne Light Co.)	Shippingport, Pa.	Pressurized water	60,000	1957
Dresden Nuclear Power Station (Commonwealth Edison Co.)	Morris, Ill.	Boiling water	200,000	1959
Yankee Nuclear Power Station (Yankee Atomic Electric Co.)	Rowe, Mass.	Pressurized water	175,000	1960
Big Rock Nuclear Power Plant (Consumers Power Co.)	Big Rock Point, Mich.	Boiling water	72,000	1962
Elk River Reactor (AEC and Rural Cooperative Power Association)	Elk River, Minn.	Boiling water	23,000	1962
Hallam Nuclear Power Facility, Sheldon Station (AEC and Consumers Public Power District)	Hallam, Nebr.	Sodium graphite	75,000	1962
Indian Point Unit No. 1 (Consolidated Edison Co. of New York, Inc.)	Indian Point, N.Y.	Pressurized water	255,000[2]	1962
Carolinas-Virginia Tube Reactor (Carolinas-Virginia Nuclear Power Associates, Inc.)	Parr, S.C.	Pressure tube, heavy water.	17,000	1963
Enrico Fermi Atomic Power Plant (Power Reactor Development Co.)	Lagoona Beach, Mich.	Fast breeder	60,900	1963
Humboldt Bay Power Plant, Unit No. 3 (Pacific Gas & Electric Co.)	Humboldt Bay, Calif.	Boiling water	50,500	1963
Piqua Nuclear Power Facility (AEC and City of Piqua)	Piqua, Ohio	Organic cooled and moderated	11,400	1963
Boiling Reactor Nuclear Superheat Project (AEC and Puerto Rico Water Resources Authority)	Punta Higuera, P.R.	Boiling water, integral nuclear superheat.	16,300	1964
Pathfinder Atomic Power Plant (Northern States Power Co.)	Sioux Falls, S. Dak.	Boiling water, nuclear superheat.	58,500	1964

1 Based on tables included in AEC report TID–8200 (10th revision).
2 Approximately two-thirds contributed by the nuclear reactor and one-third by the oil-fired superheater.
SOURCE: *National Power Survey, A Report by the Federal Power Commission,* Washington, D. C., 1964.

Table 6.7 gives similar data for the five major plants then under construction and expected to be placed in service in 1965 to 1967. The total capacity of these plants is about 1,730,000 kilowatts. The largest plant in this list, rated at 800,000 kilowatts, is also unique in that it is a dual-purpose plant. With it comes the breakthrough that was always deemed possible at Hanford. The reactor, a plutonium production reactor, is owned by the U.S. government and operated as one of the AEC's defense facilities. Production of plutonium began in 1964. The by-product heat which it generates is used to drive turbines at a power plant constructed for the Washington Public Power Supply System, which began to produce electric power late in 1965. Each of these plants, except in the special case of the dual-purpose plant, will have costs of power production higher than from alternative conventional sources.

Business Week reported as a result of so little to show for so much effort: "there's a growing wave of skepticism over the prospects of civilian nuclear power. A bitter argument continues over how much the Atomic Energy Commission and individual companies ought to be spending on further research and development in a field that has produced so many disappointments." However, there was growing evidence that 1964 might be the turning point, and that the nuclear power effort might be on the brink of paying off.

The chances of the nuclear power breakthrough were dependent on technology and economics.

Technology of nuclear power is directly related to the research and development effort that is concentrated upon reactor development. The AEC in its 1962 Report to the President on the Civilian Nuclear Power Program included three segments: (1) converter type light water-saturated steam reactors; (2) advanced converter type reactors; and (3) breeder reactors.

Converter type reactors in operation by 1964 were ten in number. The Atomic Energy Act of 1954 made available to industry for private use previously classified reactor technology and established the Power Reactor Development Program. These ten plants and others under construction were the result of the joint efforts of government and private industry in converter-type nuclear reactors. These converter reactors are cooled with light water (ordinary water), produce less fissionable material than they consume in operation, generate saturated (wet) steam, and are of two types—pressurized water and boiling water. As a result of these efforts, the light water saturated steam reactors were the most highly developed and the AEC had decided by 1964 that future government support would be largely limited in this area to conducting economic and technical analyses of operating reactors.

Advanced converter type reactors are considered by the AEC to hold promise of early marked improvement over saturated steam reactors in

TABLE 6.7

Nuclear Power Plants Under Construction[1] as of July 1, 1964

Name, owner or operator	Location	Type	Capacity net kw	Startup
Peach Bottom Atomic Power Station-HTGR (Philadelphia Electric Co.)	Peach Bottom, Pa.	Gas cooled, graphite moderated	40,000	1965
La Crosse Boiling Water Reactor (AEC and Dairyland Power Cooperative)	Genoa, Wis.	Boiling water	50,000	1965
Hanford New Production Reactor (AEC and Washington Public Power Supply System)	Richland, Wash.	Pressure tube	800,000	1965-6
San Onofre Nuclear Generating Station (Southern California Edison and San Diego Electric Co.)	San Clemente, Calif.	Pressurized water	375,000	1966
Connecticut Yankee Atomic Power Station (Connecticut Yankee Atomic Power Co.)	Haddam Neck, Conn.	Pressurized water	462,000	1967

1 Based on tables included in AEC report TID–8200 (10th revision).
SOURCE: *National Power Survey*, A Report by the Federal Power Commission, Washington, D. C., 1964.

power costs, have markedly higher conversion ratios (the ratio of the amount of fissionable material produced to that consumed), and to have direct and important technical bearing on breeder systems. Reactors of these advanced converter types are considered advantageous to accelerate the nuclear industry, increase operating experience, and to help provide the plutonium needed for added installations. The following concepts are employed in the advanced converter type: organic-cooled, nuclear super-heat, sodium-graphite, and gas-cooled.

Breeder reactors constitute the third implementing phase of the AEC's civilian nuclear reactor power program. The objective is to conduct an intensive, long-range effort to develop breeder reactors which would make possible the use of the full potential energy available in nuclear fuels. The AEC reported in 1964 that good technical progress had been made in the breeder concept. "Its technology, however, is extremely complex and much research and development remains to be done before breeder reactors approach an economically attractive stage of development."

Economics of nuclear power is caught up in a series of factors that make nuclear power more costly than conventional steam power. Equipment costs are higher, for they include not only all the items used in steam plants (except firebox and conventional boiler) but the nuclear reactor and auxiliary equipment as well. Construction costs are higher because of the requisite safety rules. The site is much larger, covering 100 to 1,000 acres or more, and all other activity is excluded from it. Since the plants are located in areas of low population density, the cost per acre is low, but transmission lines must be longer. Shielding around those parts of the plant containing radioactive materials adds to the cost of construction, as does provision for protective measures against accident. Because construction costs are higher for nuclear plants, and construction periods are longer, interest charges on construction are higher than for a steam plant of the same capacity. Depreciation charges are still arbitrary because of the short time the nuclear power plants have been in operation. The AEC uses an estimated 30 years service life as against 35 years used by the FPC for modern thermal plants. Fuel cost is compounded mainly of the cost of fuel itself, cost of fabricating the fuel units (the core), and cost of processing the partly consumed cores in order to recover unexpended uranium and plutonium. The fuel is the property of the U.S. government and is leased to the reactor operator. The user pays for the fuel consumed or lost, at prices set by the AEC. Ultimate fabricating and reprocessing costs will be those determined by the private operators responsible. However, perhaps the most important factor affecting costs will be improved efficiency in the ratio of the amount of fissionable material to that consumed and increases in the length of time the fuel cores can be used. Since the cost of fuel, fabricating, and reprocessing is high there is a strong incentive to produce a fuel that has high enough integrity to last a long time. For example the approximate value of the fuel charge of the Yankee Nuclear Power Station when new was $7,500,000, which was made up of a cost of $6,000,000 for U-235 plus $1,500,000 fabrication costs. The value of the uranium and plutonium at discharge was $5,112,000 less $986,700 for reprocessing to leave a net value of recovered material of $4,125,300.

The Report of the National Fuels and Energy Study concluded that the cost of producing nuclear power remains speculative and illusive, but gave the following figures as the most commonly quoted for a plant of 400,000 to 500,000 kilowatt capacity:[2]

Capital costs per kilowatt $160-190
Capital costs, mills per kilowatt-hour 3.2-3.65
Fuel costs, mills per kilowatt-hour 1.7-2.1
Operating and insurance, mills per kilowatt-hour 0.5-0.6
TOTAL generating costs, mills per kilowatt-hour 5.4-6.4

By way of comparison, in 1960 the capital cost per kilowatt of a 500,000 kilowatt conventional plant averaged $124 per kilowatt. Average costs of producing a kilowatt of electricity have been declining over the years due to the continuing reduction in the amount of heat necessary to produce a unit of electricity. In 1964 the average costs of producing a kwh of electricity stood roughly in the range of 4.5 to 7 mills per kwh. These conventional steam costs of course were firm, while nuclear plant costs were still "speculative."

But the economics of nuclear power costs in 1964, as previously indicated, gave some evidence of having reached a turning point. Table 6.8 shows three additional plants announced as of July 1, 1964. Their aggregate capacity is some 1.5 million kilowatts. All are water reactor plants and each was considerably larger than any of the existing U.S. nuclear plants except the Hanford dual-purpose plant. The last plant, the Oyster Creek Station, was the object of all the 1964 optimism. The Jersey Central Power and Light Company was predicting (and enthusiasm within the AEC seemed to confirm the prediction) that its Oyster Creek 515,000-kilowatt boiling water reactor would produce power at less than 4.5¢ per kwh. It appeared that this would be fully competitive with any fossil fuel —coal, oil, or gas—plant in Ocean County, New Jersey. Other utilities were considering plants ranging in the 400,000 kilowatt capacity, and they too believed that they would be able to compete with comparable fossil fuel plants. In each case the plants were in areas where power is relatively expensive. By the end of 1965 six other utilities had announced plans for nuclear plants with a total rated capacity of over 4 million kilowatts. All

[2] *Report of the National Fuels and Energy Study Group*, Washington, D.C., 1962, p. 273.

TABLE 6.8

Planned Nuclear Power Plants Announced as of July 1, 1964

Name, owner or operator	Location	Type	Capacity net kw	Startup
Malibu Nuclear Plant (Los Angeles Department of Water and Power)	Corral Canyon, Calif.	Pressurized water	463,000	1967
Nine Mile Point Plant (Niagara Mohawk Power Co.)	Oswego, N.Y.	Boiling water	500,000	1968
Oyster Creek Station (Jersey Central Power & Light Co.)	Oyster Creek, N.J.	Boiling water	515,000	1968

SOURCE: *National Power Survey,* A Report by the Federal Power Commission, Washington, D.C., 1964.

seven of the plants were designed to generate power at a cost of 4 to 5 mills per kwh. Optimistic sources were declaring 1965 to be the long-awaited "breakthrough" year for nuclear power.

Additional enthusiasm was generated in 1965 when the Commonwealth Edison Company gave nuclear power a vote of confidence by announcing plans for its second atomic plant—Dresden II—to be located at Chicago, Illinois. This plant was to be even larger than the Oyster Creek Station plant—715,000 kilowatts capacity at first with expectations of a total of 792,000 kilowatts. This tends to confirm the finding of many economic studies of power plant costs that with increase in size atomic plants decline more rapidly in fixed costs and costs of generation per kwh than conventional fuel plants, and thus become more competitive in larger installations.

Thus, there was a surge of confidence in 1964 and 1965 that the AEC's short range goal of 5 million kilowatts of nuclear electric power by 1970 at least seemed possible.

On the other hand, the economics and the technology were considered by some to have possibly suffered from the AEC's decision to stop its reactor development program. The AEC's fiscal 1965 budget had no requests for reactor construction. *Business Week* concluded that "AEC's decision to back out of nuclear reactor construction won't hurt the 1970 forecasts, but it will really cut back into the 1980 hope of having 40 million kilowatts of nuclear electrical power available in the United States." The Federal Power Commission did not see it this way in the *National Power Survey* published late in 1964. The Commission felt that there had been a number of developments since the AEC's projections for 1980 which made them appear too conservative. Foremost of these were the results of the bids for the Oyster Creek nuclear plant. As a result the FPC raised the earlier estimates by about 70 percent, and projected approximately 70 million kilowatts of nuclear capacity for 1980.[3]

Isotopes. One of the most significant applications of nuclear developments has been with radioactive isotopes. Artificial radioisotopes were made and used before the atomic age. They were manufactured with atom smashers, such as a cyclotron; but only a few kinds of isotopes could be made and they were expensive. The nuclear reactor changed this. Reactors are now used regularly to change atoms from one kind to another (transmutation).

Transmutation occurs because of the way that fission works in the nuclear reactor. As we have seen, when a fuel atom splits it releases heat and it releases neutrons. The neutrons cause the transmutation. As they are electrically uncharged, they are not repelled by the other constituents of atoms. Often they get inside the cores of atoms and stay there. When

[3] *National Power Survey*, A Report by the Federal Power Commission, Washington, D.C., October, 1964, p. 204.

that occurs, one kind of atom is converted into a different kind. In other words, transmutation occurs.

When the core of an atom gains a neutron or two, it sometimes does not change into an atom of an entirely different element, but into a different isotope of the element it was before. The very useful cobalt 60, for example, is made by adding a neutron to the core of ordinary cobalt 59. Both are the same element, alike physically and chemically, but cobalt 60 contains an extra neutron and is radioactive. We know that the reason that both cobalt 59 and cobalt 60 are the same element is that elements are determined not by the number of neutrons but by the number of protons.

In order to transmute one element into a different one, the number of protons must be changed. The neutron can do this indirectly. When an atom absorbs a neutron to become a different isotope, it also becomes radioactive. Sometimes its rate of decay is so rapid that it almost immediately loses or gains a proton, forming a new element. This is what occurs in the case of U-238, the abundant but nonfissionable isotope of uranium. When placed inside a reactor, it takes up a neutron, becoming U-239, another uranium isotope. U-239 is a very short-lived isotope, half of it decaying in 23 minutes. It emits an electron which converts a neutron into a proton in its core, and becomes neptunium 239. (Neptunium 239 is an artificial element unknown in nature.) Neptunium 239 is also short-lived, half of it decaying in 2.3 days. It also throws off an electron, changing a neutron into a proton in its core, and becomes plutonium 239 (another artificial element). Plutonium decays quite slowly. Thus, a neutron indirectly changes uranium into plutonium.

In the manner described, elements are transmuted inside a reactor. In the case of plutonium, an entirely new and valuable element is manufactured, for, as we have noted, plutonium is a fissionable atomic fuel. Hundreds of other useful materials can be made by the same process, and thus the ability of the reactor to make artificially radioactive atoms may in the long run prove to be one of its most valuable attributes.

Radioactive isotopes are extremely useful because of their radioactivity and they are the best *tracers* known. Their radioactivity causes them to continuously throw off atomic parts that are easily detected. They may make a mark on a photographic film, and they also register on electrical instruments such as Geiger counters and electroscopes. Presently, we will note some of the specific applications of radioisotopes.

Artificial isotopes can be made in any kind of nuclear reactor. All that is needed is access holes to admit the material to the reactor core, and machinery for putting the material in and getting it out. Most of the big reactors designed to produce electric power are not so equipped as the holes and the insertion of foreign material into the reactor core would interfere with the operation. Isotopes are made in reactors designed for production, test, or research work.

The material to be irradiated is usually packed in a can and pushed into the reactor, where it stays until the desired amount of transmutation is completed. Then it is pulled out, frequently into a heavy metal coffin which protects the workers from radiation. All this must be done with extreme care and with long-handled tools, or even more complex remote control apparatus.

Some of the radioisotopes are so short-lived that they must be used in a laboratory at the reactor. Long-lived isotopes are the ones that are now in wide use. They are shipped all over the world in small quantities by mail or express and marked with distinctive orange radiation warning. In 1946 the AEC initiated a policy of distributing isotopes at cost. The isotopes program is principally carried out at the Oak Ridge National Laboratory, Oak Ridge, Tennessee; Hanford Works, Richland, Washington; Brookhaven National Laboratory, Long Island, New York; Mound Laboratory, Miamisburg, Ohio; and the Savannah River Plant, Aiken, South Carolina, as well as at private research and development laboratories and universities. The isotopes used in the program are produced under the production programs at Oak Ridge and at Hanford and Savannah River. Each year since the policy of distributing isotopes was initiated, new record levels have been reached in production and sales. By 1965 there were about 100 different radioactive isotopes being used.

The vast growth and interest in isotopes may be attributed in part to the fact that they could be used and studied without access to classified information, their cost has rendered their use economically possible, and they have numerous applications. These uses may be thought of as falling into three general types: industrial, agricultural, and medical. In reality, their uses may be thought of as innumerable and unpredictable.

Industrial users of isotopes were estimated to be in excess of 1,000 as early as 1955. One important early use of isotopes was their application as thickness gauges. Sheet metals, as well as plastics and other products are made by passing the material between two heavy rolls, a fixed distance apart. To maintain proper thickness, it is necessary to check the product, and readjust the rolls if there is any variation. When this is done with hand-operated calipers, it is necessary to stop the process and take a measurement. Now, continuous process control is possible with beta rays. (A beta ray is an electron which has been ejected from an unstable nucleus.) All that is needed is to place on one side of the sheet material a source of beta rays (such as strontium 90) of known intensity, and on the other a radiation detector that measures the amount that passes through. The thinner the sheet, the stronger the transmitted beam: thus the gauge may be calibrated to indicate directly the thickness of the metal, plastic, or other material as it moves along at high speed. Moreover, a degree of automation may be introduced, by having a type of automatic control over the space between the roll, which, in turn, is regulated by the reading of the thickness gauge.

While beta rays can go through things such as aluminum, plastics, and paper, their low penetrating power does not enable them to penetrate thicker substances. Gamma rays, on the other hand, like X-rays, may penetrate even considerable thicknesses of iron and steel. (A gamma ray is energy in the form of electro-magnetic radiation released from an unstable nucleus. Its properties are comparable to the properties of X-rays.) Radium had been used in the past as a source of gamma rays to take radiographs to test the structural soundness of steel castings, but now such reactor-produced radioisotopes as cobalt 60, yttrium 88, or tantalum 182 can be used in the same way.

Radioisotopes are also finding many industrial uses as tracers, where their radioactivity permits some particular substance to be followed, even through an intricate process. One such use is sending oil through pipelines used to carry various kinds of petroleum products. After one kind of product has gone through, another will be sent along immediately following, and there is very little mixing at the interface. However, at the receiving end it is necessary to know accurately when this interface arrives. Then a quick shift is made in the valves so as to send the next product into a different tank. Now in the atomic age, at the refinery, just as the new product starts, a radioisotope is injected and carried along with the flowing oil. At the other end a pipeliner waits with a Geiger counter against the pipe; when the interface arrives there is an outburst of clicks that indicates that a new product has arrived and must be shifted to another tank. Antimony 124 is the isotope generally used since it emits gamma rays as well as beta and can be easily detected in the pipe.

The use of gamma rays is coming into use in the chemical industry as these rays can initiate chemical reactions. In making plastics, for example, the raw materials must combine to form new, very long molecules (polymerize). Ordinarily, polymerization is started with the help of catalysts. Now gamma rays from radioactive isotopes can be used to take the place of the catalysts. They have also been used to "crack" petroleum into gasoline. In addition, there are many other ways in which radiation is used to change the characteristics of materials. One product that has been improved by radiation is polyethylene, a plastic that is widely used to make bottles, containers, and piping. Until recently this plastic could not stand heat as it softened. Radiation has corrected this so that plastic containers can be put in dishwashers and plastic pipe can carry hot water.

The above and many other industrial uses of isotopes prompted the AEC to estimate that by the middle 1960's the savings as a result of this use were a billion dollars annually, and, in addition, at this time, the future held great promise for further savings.

The Southern Interstate Nuclear Board was under contract to the AEC to search for industrial applications of atomic energy, and in July, 1965, based on a report made by the Board to the AEC the conclusion was drawn that: "Furniture processed with atomic energy may become a reality within five years, depending on the availability of atomic processing plants." The report, an object of some enthusiasm within the AEC, suggested that a completely new material for furniture making, combining the desirable properties of both wood and plastic, might become available.

The new material is made by removing air from the pores of natural wood, either solids or veneers. The pores are then filled with liquid materials, of which one is methyl methacrylate. Wood parts treated with these liquids are placed in a nuclear reactor or subjected to the gamma rays of cobalt 60. This causes the liquid material to solidify and become a plastic. The material is then wood-plastic retaining properties of both.

Without changing the grain structure of natural wood, through irradiation and impregnation the wood takes on characteristics which are entirely new. The wood becomes resistant to scuffing, cigarette burns, nail polish or other harmful materials. The process improves on nature by making wood resistant to warping and twisting, and causes it to become a more stable material for furniture making. In addition, because the process allows the finish to be impregnated directly into the wood, furniture makers look forward to the economies that will be possible.

Thus, while economies of industrial isotopes were already estimated at a billion dollars a year in 1965, the prospects for the future were for a cornucopia of new uses and savings.

Agricultural application of isotopes is of growing importance. Radioactive materials have been used to induce genetic changes. A rust-free variety of oats and a strain of peanuts with a 30 percent greater yield have been developed.

Radioisotopes have also given data as tracers to show the proportion of nutrients that a plant obtains from the soil, and how much is taken from the fertilizer applied. An AEC official has estimated that tobacco farmers in North Carolina alone could save more than 100,000 pounds of phosphate fertilizer each year by applying the knowledge yielded by research from isotopes. With other crops in other states, this figure would doubtless be increased many times.

In animal husbandry, the value of nutrient sources can now be studied more effectively. For example, by feeding radiophosphorus alfalfa to lambs it was possible, by tracing nutritional values, to establish the benefits of feeding alfalfa, which had previously been thought to be of little value.

After fruits and vegetables are harvested, animals slaughtered, and other products made ready for distribution, they must be preserved long enough to reach the consumer in good condition. In spite of all efforts, sizable amounts of foods spoil before they reach the table because of the presence of bacteria, molds, insects, or other organisms. But in many foods, including meat and grains, vegetables, and fruits these can be killed with gamma rays or electrons. These, in turn, may be produced from a reactor, fission by-products, or with special generators. Yet such processes do not leave any residual radiation in foods as they do not acquire radioactivity. Experiments have shown that irradiated foods can be preserved for long periods without refrigeration.

Finally, another way in which isotopes may help agriculture is by providing insight into photosynthesis which has been often described as the most important chemical process in the world. This is the process whereby the living plant takes carbon dioxide and water and then with energy supplied by sunlight falling on its green leaves, manufactures sugars, starches, and fats. Animals eat these, add nitrogen to them, and turn them into proteins. All mankind's food supply comes from this process; if it did not occur, no life of the kind we know could exist. Using radioisotopes, particularly carbon 14, plant scientists are learning its details, which heretofore have been a profound mystery. With such knowledge in prospect, forecasts of the effect of nuclear applications on agriculture appear to have unlimited potentials.

Medical applications of radioactive isotopes and materials may revolutionize medical science. The increased availability and lower price of radioactive materials have been factors that have placed medical use of isotopes in the forefront of the peacetime applications of nuclear developments. Radioactive cobalt 60, which maintains its emission of gamma rays for a relatively long time, is a case in point. The value of radium in the treatment of cancer has been known for some time; now the attention is focused on the external use of radioactive cobalt 60 for therapy in cancer. Significantly, a small piece of cobalt 60, manufactured in a nuclear reactor at a cost of about $100 can take the place of $20,000 worth of radium.

In the area of research concerning biological processes, radioisotopes are a delicate tool for following normal life processes. They have been fed to or injected into healthy people to reveal much new knowledge about the complex workings of the human body. They have proved particularly helpful in explaining the circulation of the blood, the routes followed by food and oxygen, and the uses to which the body puts various chemicals, especially those that are required in tiny amounts.

In the diagnosis and treatment of disease one isotope alone, namely radioactive iodine 131, has proved so useful in the diagnosis and treatment of certain thyroid disorders that in 1965 it was estimated that about 500,000 "atomic cocktails" were served each year in hospitals in the United States in this connection. The iodine is taken in the form of a colorless solution. It then is possible, for example, to make a diagnosis of a hyperthyroid condition by measuring the rate of uptake of the iodine into the thyroid. Then if the patient has this hyperthyroid condition as diagnosed by the radioactive iodine, a subsequent series of larger doses of the same isotope is administered as treatment through the same process of drinking the solution of the radioactive iodine. The radioactive iodine eliminates that portion of the thyroid, more or less selectively, that led to the particular condition.

Radioactive iodine, in conjunction with another radioisotope, phosphorus 32, also helps to locate elusive brain tumors. These growths are quite difficult to detect from outside the skull, and when found they are almost indistinguishable in appearance from healthy brain tissue. The tumors, however, absorb certain dyes much more readily than healthy tissue. If an iodine dye containing iodine 131 is injected into the body, it quickly concentrates in the tumor. The iodine 131 throws off gamma rays which signal their source to a detector held outside the patient's head so that the tumorous area can be located. The iodine 131 throws off such strong rays that once the operation takes place the delicate diseased tissues cannot be located. This is the point at which the previously injected phosphorus 32 goes to work. It concentrates in the tumor, but it emits mild electron rays with a short range. During the operation for removal of the tumor, a detecting instrument shows where the electron rays begin to decrease, indicating the limit of the diseased tissue.

One of the first diseases to be treated successfully with artificially radioactive material was polycythemia vera, a condition in which the bone marrow is overactive and produces red blood cells too rapidly. It was found possible to control it very satisfactorily by giving the patient an occasional "atomic cocktail," a solution of sodium phosphate in which some of the phosphorus is the radioactive P-32. This concentrates in the bones, where its radiation slows down the formation of red cells in the marrow.

Radioactive phosphorus has also been used in the treatment of leukemia, another blood disease, believed to be closely related to cancer, in which abnormal numbers of white blood cells appear. While this treatment has not had the striking success that was achieved in polycythemia, it has been some benefit to leukemia sufferers, whose lives have been made more comfortable and probably prolonged.

The above and many other examples can be given. Every day new discoveries are being made and applied. In summary, one can note that medical research, using these new radioactive isotopes and materials made from them, is being carried out along three main lines: (1) for obtaining a better knowledge of biological processes, (2) for diagnosis of diseases, and (3) for treatment of diseases. One leading authority in the field stated that as early as 1955 the use of radioactive isotopes had already advanced the state of medical knowledge to what it would otherwise have been in 1980. And this was just the beginning.

Summary and Future of Peacetime Applications. We have seen the growing importance of the peacetime uses of atomic energy in the generation of electric power and in the use of isotopes. Peacetime applications of nuclear developments will multiply as a result of private and government research. Christopher P. Keim, director of stable isotope research and production at Oak Ridge, correctly predicted in July, 1955 that "the constructive peacetime uses of atomic energy will increase in emphasis" and indicated that vast new developments in the fields of industry, agriculture, and medicine would soon be ready for public usage. Most significantly Dr. Keim concluded: "Controlled climate is also a distinct possibility of the future."

Much more imminent is the possibility of using nuclear applications in the desalinization of water. Plans were underway in 1965 for the building of the free world's first nuclear-powered desalinization plant. If the plans were approved, building was to begin in 1966 at Riverhead, N.Y., on the northeast shore of Long Island, and in 1968 the plant should start turning out fresh water. The process to be used at Riverhead is called "multistage flash distillation." Water from Long Island Sound will be pumped into the plant, where it will be heated by an open-pool reactor. It will then pass through a series of large chambers, each with different pressure levels; the heat and the changes in pressure will cause the water to form steam and separate from the brine; the steam will then be condensed and piped out as pure, distilled drinking water.

While in 1965 more than 200 desalting plants were already operating around the world, including nine in the United States, they have yet to solve one vexing problem—cost. The desalting plants have been unable to produce fresh water for much less than $1.00 per 1,000 gallons, which may be economical in a parched country such as Kuwait, but can scarcely compete against the average 35¢ per 1,000 gallons that U.S. communities pay for water. What is significant about the proposed new nuclear plant is that, in theory, the plant will be able to sell its water for 35¢ because it will produce two valuable by-products—electricity and radioactive isotopes. It will turn out 1,000,000 gallons of water per day—enough for the average needs of 10,000 rural-area people—as well as 2,500 kilowatts of electricity per hour and up to 500,000 curies of cobalt 60 isotopes per year, which together could be sold for $500,000 annually.

This amount of water would be only a beginning, but the project was an expression of confidence in the economic viability of small nuclear plants capable of many applications. Federal experts forecast that water shortages will become acute in large areas of the western part of the United States within the next twenty years. Though desalinization is only a partial answer to the problem of a nation whose water demand is expected to almost double by 1980, it is a challenge that has aroused scientists, the government, and businessmen. And there is growing optimism in regard to nuclear contributions to the solution of the problem, for Dr. Glenn T. Seaborg, Chairman of the AEC, predicted that by the 1980's there would be huge dual reactors with a capacity of a million kilowatts of electricity, or more, and perhaps desalting water to the extent of 500 million gallons a day. This amount of electricity and water would take care of the requirements of a city of one million people. Further, the U.S. Interior Department's Office of Saline Water optimistically predicts that by the year 2000, between 7 and 10 percent of the nation's fresh water will come from the sea.

The conclusion is that technology is the indispensable finder, developer, and multiplier of natural resources, and nuclear developments have indeed made the "horizon unlimited."

STRUCTURE OF THE ATOMIC ENERGY INDUSTRY

By the early 1960's atomic energy had attained the status of a major industry. While the relative immaturity of the field, as well as the great variety of applications of nuclear developments makes it impossible to estimate the size of the industry, a useful measurement of activity is provided by the fact that as of 1963, the AEC and its contractors employed more than 123,000 workers. Most important, as previously noted, by mid-1965 the U.S. government had spent about 34 billion dollars on the country's atomic energy program. Significantly, 6 billion dollars of this total had gone to develop peaceful uses of atomic energy.

In an established industry the observer can study the organization and structure of the industry. In the case of the new atomic energy industry, however, the AEC set up and defined for Congress in its 1962 Report eight major segments of the atomic industry: (1) raw fuel materials; (2) materials processing and fabrication; (3) components and equipment; (4) reactor applications; (5) radioisotopes; (6) material reprocessing; (7) waste disposal; and (8) services. Figure 6.3 gives in depth the various functions performed by each of these categories of the atomic industry.

The significance of this organizational grouping is that it shows the extent to which this infant industry has become a major industry, and it provides the student with guidelines to follow in the further development of the industry in its many ramifications.

The following brief comments on each of the categories will provide the status of each part of the industry in the mid-60's and furnish the basis of study of future developments.

Raw Materials

Uranium mining and uranium concentration were fully discussed in a previous section of this chapter. All activities in this category of the atomic energy industry are in the hands of private industry. Government contracts for the purchases of U-308 concentrates will all expire by 1970

Figure 6.3: Organization of the Atomic Energy Industry.

I—RAW FUEL MATERIALS

A. Uranium
1. Exploration
2. Mining (Uranium ore)
3. Milling (U3O8)

B. Thorium

II—MATERIALS PROCESSING AND FABRICATION

A. Fuel Materials
1. Feed preparation & enriching
  a. Uranium Hexaflouride
    (1) Conversion
    (2) Enriching
      (a) Depleted
      (b) Enriched
2. Processing (includes oxides, compounds, metals)
  a. Depleted Uranium
  b. Normal Uranium
  c. Enriched Uranium—
3. Fabricating
  a. Metal shapes
  b. Non-fueled control rods (excluding those shipped as part of complete cores)

C. Coolants
1. Production
  a. Heavy water
  b. Lithium-7
2. Processing
  a. Gases
  b. Heavy water
  c. Light water
  d. Liquid metals
  e. Organics

D. Moderators and Reflectors
1. Processing
  a. Beryllium
  b. Graphite
  c. Heavy water
  d. Light water
  e. Organics
2. Fabricating
  a. Beryllium
  b. Graphite

E. Cladding & Matrix Materials
1. Processing
  a. Beryllium
  b. Graphite
2. Fuel handling equipment
3. Instrumentation for reactor control
  a. Reactor power control instruments
  b. Reactor coolant instruments
  c. Reactor switchboards and consoles
4. Safety and containment
  a. Vapor suppression systems
  b. Containment spheres and shells
5. Other reactor equipment
  a. Primary vessels and tanks
  b. Heat exchangers and condensers
  c. Pressurizers, components, and auxiliary equipment
  d. Pumps
  e. Valves

B. General Nuclear Equipment
1. Shipping containers
  a. Radioisotopes
  b. Irradiated fuel
  c. Waste products
2. Health and safety
  a. Nuclear monitoring instruments: area
  d. Laboratory hoods
  e. Glove boxes
4. Scientific instruments (excluding systems for reactor control)
  a. Scalers
  b. Analyzers
  c. Count rate meters
  d. Amplifiers
  e. Miscellaneous nuclear instruments and accessories (excluding radiation sources and film badges)
5. Particle accelerators

IV—REACTOR APPLICATIONS

A. Power
1. Central station (electric power)
2. Space auxiliary power
3. Packaged power plants

B. Propulsion
1. Space
2. Other

C. Production
1. SNM
2. Isotopes

D. Process & Space Heat
1. Low temperature
3. Labeled compounds
4. Power sources
  a. For space applications
  b. For other applications

VI—MATERIAL REPROCESSING

A. Irradiated
1. Uranium
  a. High-enriched
  b. Low-enriched
2. Plutonium
3. Thorium
4. Uranium-thorium mixtures

B. Non-irradiated
1. Uranium (all chemical forms)
  a. Enriched
  b. Normal
  c. Depleted
  d. U-233
2. Thorium (all chemical forms)
3. Plutonium (all chemical forms)
4. Uranium-thorium mixtures
5. Precious metals

VII—WASTE DISPOSAL

5% or less U-235
d. Enriched Uranium—more than 5% U-235
e. Thorium
f. Plutonium
g. U-233
3. Fabricating (includes fission foils and sub-critical and critical fuels)

B. Control Materials
1. Enriching
a. Boron-10
b. Lithium-6
2. Processing
a. Boron
b. Cadmium
c. Hafnium
d. Silver-Cadmium-Indium
e. Rare earths

c. Aluminum
d. Stainless steel
e. Zirconium & Zircaloy
f. Niobium
g. Molybdenum
2. Fabricating
a. Metal shapes

F. Shielding Materials
1. Fabricating
a. Boron
b. Concrete
c. Lead
d. Carbon steel
e. Uranium
f. Light water
G. Other In-Core Materials
1. Fabricating
a. Metal shapes and supports not included elsewhere
b. Piping and tubing

III—COMPONENTS & EQUIPMENT
A. Reactor Components
1. Control rod drive mechanisms and components

and personnel
(1) Portable
(2) Fixed
(3) Hand and foot counters
b. Nuclear monitoring instruments: environmental

(Gas, liquid and particulate)
c. Dosimeters and accessories
d. Whole body counting equipment
e. Protective clothing
f. Emergency monitoring equipment
g. Decontamination equipment
h. High efficiency filters
i. Film badges
j. Packaged disposal systems
3. Hot laboratory type equipment
a. Shielding windows
b. Remote control manipulators
c. Periscopes and borescopes

2. Intermediate temperature (an "intermediate temperature" reactor system may be considered one which produces useable saturated steam at 200 psi or above but not higher than 600 psi)
3. High temperature
E. Testing
F. Research & Training (including criticals and sub-criticals)
G. Medical Therapy
H. Multipurpose

V—RADIOISOTOPES
A. Production (including separation)
1. Fission products
2. Reactor produced
3. Accelerator produced
B. Products & Equipment
1. Radiation sources
a. Alpha
b. Beta
c. Gamma
d. Neutron
2. Nuclear industrial instruments

A. Sea Disposal
B. Land Burial

VIII—SERVICES
A. Irradiations
1. Neutron
2. Gamma
B. Health & Safety
1. Environmental monitoring
2. Film badge service
3. Calibration and maintenance
4. Bio-assay
5. Laundering and cleaning
C. Analytical (other than for health purposes)
D. Testing
1. Radiographic
2. Non-destructive
E. Architect-Engineering
F. Construction
G. Transportation
H. Insurance
I. Consulting Services
J. Research & Development
K. Education & Training

SOURCE: Atomic Energy Commission.

as shown in Table 6.5, and after that date this segment of the industry will have to survive in the commercial market.

Materials Processing and Fabrication

Uranium feed preparation, which we have seen to have been initially a function of two government-owned plants, was also a function of the privately owned Allied Chemical Corporation plant at Metropolis, Illinois which has the capability to produce uranium hexafluoride (UF_6) from either concentrates ($U-308$) or refined UO_3.

Uranium enriching was provided by the government facilities still in operation. This was the only major area in the fuel cycle which was still performed by the government. There were three possibilities for greater private participation in the enriching process: sale or lease of AEC facilities, private use of gas centrifuges, or toll processing. Of the three approaches, toll processing of privately-owned fuel in government-owned facilities offers the most promising possibility if the necessary legislation is enacted.

Uranium processing involves the conversion of slightly enriched UF_6 to forms in which uranium fuel elements could be fabricated. As previously noted, ten private companies were engaged in this activity in 1964; and the AEC reported that "adequate industrial capability and competition exists to produce uranium metals and various compounds of all assays from UF_6."

Uranium fabrication of the various types of reactor fuels and shapes from metal and compounds was engaged in by twenty firms in 1964, and the number of firms in this already highly competitive field was increasing yearly in the middle sixties.

Components and Equipment

All the nuclear components listed in Figure 6.3 are available commercially. These components are produced, in large part, by companies not dependent on atomic energy for their growth and profitability. This is not true, however, of the nuclear instrument industry, which is characterized by small firms building intricate and specialized equipment.

Reactor Applications

An analysis has already been made in depth of the reactor research and development program. In the reactor industry a relatively large number of firms (fourteen) are competing for a limited volume of business, with two companies (General Electric and Westinghouse) dominant in the field.

Radioisotopes

The AEC is the principal producer and distributor of radioisotopes although the packaging and encapsulation are mostly performed by private industry. Private industry has shown an increased interest and participation in the production and distribution. In April 1963, the Atomic Industrial Forum held a meeting to discuss the industry and government roles in radioisotopes and identified the four major policy issues as: (a) criteria for AEC withdrawal from the production and distribution of particular radioisotopes in favor of industry; (b) AEC radioisotope pricing criteria; (c) submission of formal petitions to the AEC by private firms requesting AEC withdrawal from production of particular radioisotopes, and public comment thereon; and (d) whether the AEC should contract with private firms for research and development on radioisotope production technology. The hope was that determinations could be made in these policy areas to bring about greater participation by private industry.

Materials Processing

From Figure 6.3 can be seen that materials reprocessing involves irradiated fuels and unirradiated fuels. As previously noted, the limited amount of irradiated fuels that was reprocessed from power reactors was a responsibility of the AEC, but with the licensing of Nuclear Fuels Services for the reprocessing of irradiated fuels from nuclear reactors, private enterprise entered another category of the atomic energy industry. Unirradiated fuels of enriched uranium are recovered from all types and forms of scrap. Adequate private capability exists to recover uranium but only a limited capability to process plutonium scrap is available at two firms. Additional capability in the plutonium field will be required as plutonium becomes more commonly used as a reactor fuel.

Waste Disposal

Radioactive waste disposal, which was shown in such a simple fashion in Figure 6.1, has been one of the major problems of the atomic energy program. This includes the disposal of low-level and high-level waste by land burial and sea disposal. A number of private companies are licensed to collect, store and dispose of low-level waste, either by burial at sea, or by shipment to authorized sites. Arrangements for the construction of the Nuclear Fuel Services commercial fuel reprocessing plant included provision for high-level waste disposal facilities.

Services

Figure 6.3 shows the broad range of activities included in the services category of the atomic energy industry. For the most part the companies providing these services were not dependent on atomic energy as a primary source of income. Nevertheless, each of these areas is of great importance to the atomic energy industry.

Conclusion

In conclusion, the atomic energy industry is growing into a major industry, and the AEC is endeavoring through the cooperation of private enterprise to pursue a policy of government exit and private entry into the field. The AEC has sketched the organization of the industry and its functions, and in so doing has presented a much clearer understanding of the scope of the atomic energy industry.

PROBLEMS AND POLICY

The atomic energy industry in its short life-span of two decades has been beset with many problems. Probably one of the most debatable issues has been what the roles of government and private enterprise should be. However, we have seen that the AEC has fostered a policy of encouraging the entry of private enterprise into the atomic energy industry. This the AEC has done in executing its fourfold mission of: (1) making the maximum contribution to the common defense and security; (2) supporting the research and development necessary for the advancement of nuclear technology for both military and peaceful uses; (3) fostering the participation of science and industry in the atomic energy program; and (4) regulating the possession and use of nuclear materials in the interest of the public welfare.

Of the many problems of the atomic energy industry, two will be singled out for study: uranium ore and the impact of atomic energy on other energy sources.

Uranium Ore

Once the United States was committed to a policy of using nuclear energy, the basic problem was to develop an adequate source of uranium ore for the expanding United States atomic energy needs.

Facts Bearing on the Problem. Before the AEC was charged with atomic energy activities in 1947 the uranium industry did not amount to much. For centuries the Navaho and Ute Indians used carnotite, a bright yellow uranium-vanadium ore, as a ceremonial paint. After 1900, carnotite was mined for its radium content, and the Colorado Plateau (a 65,000 square mile area of Colorado and Utah) was the leading source of radium during and after World War I, supplying more than 200 grams at $120,-000 a gram. But the U.S. uranium boom ended in 1923 when the Union Miniere du Haut-Katanga used the fabulously rich radium-bearing uranium ores of the Shinkolobwe mine in the Belgian Congo to command the market. For several years the chief market for the Colorado Plateau's uranium ores was as a coloring agent for ceramics. Then in the late 1920's it was found that the vanadium content, which up to then had been re-garded only as a nuisance adding to the difficulty to separating the radium from the ores, was a valuable hardening agent in steel. Mills, to recover the vanadium, were constructed in Colorado and produced some 62 million pounds of vanadium by 1949. For many years the uranium passed through the mills into tailings, unrecovered and valueless.

During World War II the Manhattan Engineering District, charged with the development of the atomic bomb, engaged in a secret worldwide search for uranium. Twelve hundred and fifty tons of high-grade ore owned by Union Miniere turned up in a Staten Island warehouse. It was used in the atomic experiments and, thereafter, tailings of Congo radium mines were reprocessed to recover the discarded uranium, and so were those at the Colorado vanadium plants. Because of the wartime security, every effort was made to conceal the source of uranium shipments, and the official records on ore procurement were juggled by the Manhattan District. As they were later sorted out by the AEC, the records indicated that out of the 11,590 tons of uranium oxide purchased during the 1943-1947 period, only 1,440 tons came from U.S. mines.

The charge is made that when the AEC took over in 1947 it ignored the existence of a secret wartime report—only declassified in the 1960's—which placed domestic uranium reserves at 11,611 tons of recoverable U-308. It used instead outdated estimates that put the total at 1,000 tons for January, 1948, as previously shown in Table 6.1.

As a result, the AEC set its early procurement policies in the belief that most of the uranium would have to come from abroad, even though as one spokesman said, "this was not the happiest situation to be in." The Shinkolobwe's rich pitchblende deposit was regarded as probably the greatest single source of uranium that would ever be discovered, and everything possible was done to encourage production there. The AEC paid the costs of pumping out the Shinkolobwe, which had become flooded; and also paid the Union Miniere to explore for new deposits. In addition, the AEC through the Combined Development Agency, a joint United States-British-Canadian purchasing agency, encouraged explora-tion and, eventually, signed long-term contracts for production in Canada, South Africa, Portugal, and Australia; and the last deliveries to the United States under these contracts are not due until 1967. (See Figure 6.4.)

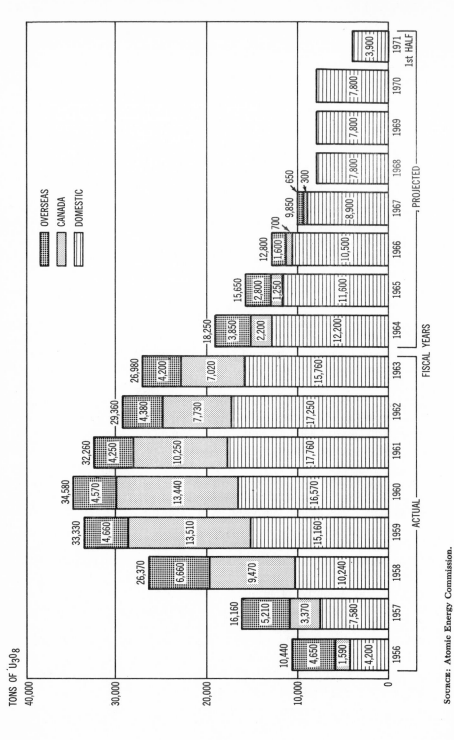

Figure 6.4: Uranium Deliveries.

Source: Atomic Energy Commission.

218

During this early period, just after the AEC succeeded the Manhattan District, the Commission saw its problem as one of keeping the overseas producers happy. The thought was that if higher prices were paid to uranium producers in this country, Union Miniere might increase the price of its ore, and the AEC had not yet seriously considered the possibility that major uranium deposits could be found in the United States, if adequate incentives were offered. In addition, its early price schedules were unduly soft toward the domestic vanadium producers. For them uranium was a by-product and they wanted to limit production to avoid upsetting the vanadium market.

The rationale for going along with this restrictive policy was explained in December, 1948, by John K. Gustafson, then manager of the AEC's raw materials operation: "Since the estimated annual production of the Colorado Plateau, even under an accelerated program, would be small in relation to the total United States requirements and to supplies available from foreign sources, it appeared more economical to obtain the uranium as a by-product from the vanadium operations which were geared to the vanadium market."

The emphasis on foreign ores and lack of interest in domestic sources brought a growing rise of public protest and the AEC changed its policy in 1948 to one of encouraging exploration and production wherever uranium might be found, and by 1950 a new policy of providing incentives for domestic producers was well established. The AEC offered a guaranteed price for uranium oxide in ore which reached $3.50 a pound in 1951. As a result the domestic uranium rush was on, and the AEC joined in with an 80 million dollar prospecting program of its own. As we have seen the guaranteed minimum prices for ores of various types and grades held until April, 1962.

As a result of this new policy the AEC had hoped to secure an orderly development of the domestic uranium industry. Instead, all of the excitement due to the bite of the uranium bug created a surge effect. This can clearly be observed from the more than three-fold increase in domestic uranium reserves between 1955 and 1956 (Table 6.1).

By early 1956 some AEC experts foresaw that the procurement program was in danger of reaching absurd proportions unless it was quickly modified. But military needs still seemed too urgent and too unpredictable. In 1957, however, Jesse Johnson, who succeeded Gustafson as head of the AEC's raw-materials division, declared: "We have arrived at a point where it is no longer in the interest of the government to expand the production of uranium concentrate." It was still another year, however, before the AEC announced that its guarantees would not apply to any ore deposits discovered after November 24, 1958. The lack of the guaranteed market for new deposits meant that the uranium prospecting boom was ended. This was reflected, as shown in Table 6.1 in an almost immediate slow down in the additions to domestic reserves.

But while withdrawing its guarantees for new discoveries the AEC continued to stimulate domestic production. As we have seen, after April, 1962, the AEC shifted from a policy of purchasing ore from mines, and instead for the period 1962–1966 set a flat rate of $8.00 a pound of U-308 concentrates from the mills. This $8.00 a pound was considered to be an overly generous figure because before 1962 mills producing more than half the domestic U-308 were selling it to the AEC for less than $8.00 a pound. The General Accounting Office calculated that the $8.00 price gave these mills extra profits of 34 million dollars.

Thus we can see that the AEC dramatically shifted its policy to domestic sources, and once having done so, felt under obligation to continue to support the domestic industry.

Further, with the end of a guaranteed concentrate market in sight in 1966, the AEC announced a stretch-out program late in 1962 whereby the concentrate mills with contracts through 1966 would be allowed to defer to the period 1967–1968 a portion of the material scheduled for delivery to the AEC prior to 1967. In return, during 1967–1970, the Commission would purchase at fixed formulated prices U-308 concentrates equal to the quantity deferred and delivered in 1967 and 1968. Thus, as we have seen, as it now stands there will be a commercial market for U-308 concentrates after 1970 since the AEC will be out of the market.

Thus, the AEC shifted its policy from almost exclusive dependence on foreign sources of uranium ore, to one of greatly stimulating domestic discoveries and production, and finally to one of letting the commercial market determine future discoveries and production. Uranium deliveries in the United States by domestic, Canadian, and overseas sources are clearly shown in Figure 6.4.

The impact of the AEC's policies on domestic uranium reserves is clearly presented in Table 6.1—first a few discoveries, then a sudden upsurge, and finally a decline in new discoveries. What the future holds is uncertain. But as we have seen, the AEC has estimated that with no further discoveries of uranium, the January 1, 1964 domestic reserves of 160,-000 tons of U-308 will be reduced by usage to 95,000 to 100,000 tons by the end of 1966 and to about 86,000 tons by the end of 1970. Since requirements are rather firm through 1966 based on known and planned reactor requirements, and estimable to 1970, actual reserves in 1970 will depend on company mining practices, the quantities of ore discovered in the intervening years, and the prevailing U-308 prices at the time. The amount of exploration work will depend on the industry's assessment of the future market for uranium.

In 1962 the AEC estimated that civilian uranium requirements would remain small rising to the order of 3,000 tons in 1970; growing to 10,000 to 20,000 per year by 1980. It was thought that foreign requirements for uranium enriched in AEC facilities might be of the same order of magnitude. During the period prior to 1970 there will be a continuing requirement for military propulsion, but these total requirements are estimated by the AEC to be much less than domestic requirements for industrial power reactors, and it is not felt that weapons requirements will be an important market factor. Comparing these requirements to 1970 with the annual domestic production of 17,250 tons U-308 in 1962, one can see that the commercial market prior to 1970 is not a bright one. After the early 1970's with requirements increasing, the AEC estimates that new sources of uranium production will be needed to meet the demand. As will be noted later, a more favorable outlook for nuclear electric power led in 1964 to an increase in the AEC's estimate of uranium requirements in 1980 to a range of between 20,000 to 30,000 tons for nuclear generation.

Jesse C. Johnson, in a study of the outlook for uranium, concluded that the industry should prepare for the possibility of a smaller market and lower prices in the period after 1966.[4] He pointed out two downward pressures on prices: (1) Foreign competition would be strong and foreign producers, especially Canadian and South African producers, had become reconciled to lower prices, and (2) Manufacturers of power reactors and the utility companies are concentrating on reducing the cost of power; so much so that one tenth of a mill per kwh is important. Johnson saw prices in the bracket of $4.00 to $5.00 a ton of U-308 as a possibility, and he suggested that uranium will be available at prices below the level necessary to support an expanding uranium industry— an industry developing new mines and constructing new facilities. He concluded that the domestic uranium industry should be working to improve its post-1966 competitive position. It should plan its operations to survive in a limited market with prices well below the $8.00 level. Such a market possibly may extend to the mid-1970's. In his report, Mr. Johnson drew this conclusion: "Based upon past experience in developing uranium production, when the market expands to a point where new sources of uranium must be found and brought into production, prices should return to an $8.00 level."

Conclusion and Recommendations. The challenge to the domestic uranium industry is to survive until 1975, and then to prepare to meet expanded requirements. Just how great these requirements will be depends on many variables; but the AEC predicted by the year 2000, 90,000 tons of U-308 would be needed if converter reactors would be required and if breeder reactors are used 40,000 to 50,000 tons a year would be needed. The schedule of these requirements is such that they are slow at first but build up rapidly in the last years.

These predicted requirements point up the eventuality of a much larger uranium industry and the need for careful, well-planned explora-

[4] Jesse C. Johnson, *The Outlook for Uranium*, Washington, D.C., U.S. Atomic Energy Commission, March 17, 1962, p. 3.

tion and production expansion after the period of low requirement the United States will face in the early 1970's. Undoubtedly when the demand occurs more companies and more activity will characterize the uranium business, but the recommendation is that it is important to have a domestic industry in operation, even on a curtailed basis, from the end of government market until the requirements begin to grow in the late 1970's.

The United States uranium ore policy should be to begin long range exploration programs for future uranium reserves. Admittedly this is an expensive proposition, and an unattractive one in view of the short-range market, but it is a necessary one if the United States is to solve the uranium ore problem which will run full cycle through what *Fortune* magazine called a "glut" to a long-range one to develop an adequate source of uranium ore for the expanding U.S. atomic energy needs.

As for the availability of future reserves, the AEC has concluded:

> In addition to the discovery of large amounts of uranium during the 50's, discoveries were made over a wide geographic area, and in a multitude of geologic environments. As modification of the AEC's procurement program reduced incentives for further exploration, many of these areas are essentially undeveloped and their true potential is unknown. When future requirements develop a need for additional reserves, we can expect that the exploration will be done and the ore will be found.[5]

But one should add, only if the uranium industry holds its geologists in research and development intact, for uranium reserves and production cannot be expanded in time for the increased requirements to come, if the United States has to rely on a dead industry.

Nuclear Energy and Other Energy Sources

The development of nuclear energy has brought the dawn of a new energy age. One of the basic problems raised by this new energy source was: Does this have serious implications for other energy sources? The answer is "Yes," but in almost all instances the long-run effects appear to be favorable. This conclusion is drawn because energy needs are expanding so rapidly that the ultimate problem is not what fuel is going to be replaced, but what new sources can be developed to meet the increasing needs of an expanding economy.

Facts Bearing on the Problem. The major uses where nuclear fuel appears as a possible substitute or supplement for coal, petroleum, and natural gas are: power generation, transportation, and space heating.

In 1960, just as atomic electric power was beginning to enter the

---

[5] John A. Patterson, *Domestic Uranium Reserves,* Speech delivered for the AEC before the National Western Mining Conference and Exhibition, Denver, Colorado, February 8, 1963.

picture, the total installed electric generating capacity in the United States was 168.0 million kilowatts, of which 31.1 million was hydro, 123.1 million steam, and 2.8 million internal combustion generated. The generation of electric power by fuels was 571,883 million kwh, and the coal equivalent of all the coal, oil, and natural gas was 266 million tons required to generate this electricity. Actual coal consumption in steam generation was 173.9 million tons. By 1963 the generation of electric power by fuels had risen to 748,500 million kwh, and the coal equivalent to generate this electricity was 320 million tons. Coal's actual consumption in steam generation was 209 million tons. Thus, in a short span of three years the use of coal in electric power generation was up over 20 percent, and it was holding its position with oil and gas. The question was could coal continue to gain in the light of encouraging developments in nuclear fueled steam generated power?

The FPC made an intensive study of the electric power requirements in the United States up through 1980. This study, published as the *National Power Survey*,[6] made a thorough analysis of the type of generating facilities and fuel that would be required by the electric power industry. Table 6.9 presents the results of this study in terms of energy sources required for generation of electric power in 1980 as compared with 1963.

TABLE 6.9
Energy Sources for Generation

	1963		1980	
	Billion kwh	Percent of total	Billion kwh	Percent of total
Coal	494	54	1,264	47
Natural gas	201	21	458	17
Oil	50	6	107	4
Total fossil fuel	745	81	1,829	68
Nuclear	3	0.1	514	19
	748	81	2,343	87
Water power	166	19	340	13
Total	914	100	2,683	100

SOURCE: *National Power Survey*, A Report by the Federal Power Commission, Washington, D.C., 1964.

[6] *National Power Survey, op. cit.*, p. 53.

It is clear from this study that nuclear fuel will skyrocket from negligible use to about 19 percent of 1980 requirements. All thermal generated power will increase from 81 percent to 87 percent as hydro sites become more difficult to develop. Coal which was generating more than half the electricity will continue to be the workhorse for electric generation throughout the survey period although its percentage share will decline from 54 to 47 percent. Natural gas is expected to remain dominant in areas near sources of gas supply with an increase of 40 percent in requirements, although it can expect increasingly stiff competition elsewhere, and on a nationwide basis its share will also decline from 21 percent of generating capacity in 1963 to 17 percent in 1980. Oil will, it is anticipated, remain the source of fuel confined to coastal areas having access to cheap water transportation, where its share will depend to a large extent on the availability of imports of residual fuel at competitive prices. Overall, it is expected that oil will more than double its volume while it will decline on a proportionate basis by a third from 6 percent to 4 percent of the market.

Although the share of thermal sources (including nuclear) is expected to increase to 87 percent of total kilowatt-hours generated in 1980 as the share of hydroelectric power declines, the FPC concluded that continued progress in reducing fuel requirements per kwh should offset the impact of the increased reliance on thermal sources. Thus the rate of increase of use of fuels projected for the electric power industry closely parallels the rate of growth in electric power requirements projected in the *National Power Survey;* for 1980 both the electrical load and the fuel requirements are approximately $3\frac{1}{3}$ times the 1960 level.

The Survey projected the total use of fossil and nuclear fuel for electric power generation to increase from 6,500 trillion Btu in 1960 to approximately 22,000 trillion Btu in 1980. The latter figure is equivalent to 900 million tons of coal with a heat content of 12,500 Btu per pound. This 900 million tons should be compared with the previously indicated total coal equivalent of 266 million tons in 1960 and 320 million tons in 1963.

The National Power Survey summarized its findings on fuel requirements for electric power generation as follows: "In order to meet the tremendous growth in the demand for electricity expected for the coming decades, our projections indicate that by 1980 demand for fossil and nuclear fuels will be using annually some 500 million tons of coal, 4 trillion cubic feet of natural gas, 100 million barrels of residual fuel oil, and 20 to 30 thousand tons of uranium for nuclear generation."[7]

The most significant figure in the above estimate is the 500 millions tons of coal expected to be required in 1980, for it had been feared that coal would be the most seriously affected of the fossil fuels since the first

[7] *Ibid.,* p. 51.

applications of nuclear energy were likely to occur in the generation of electric power. Further, as fuel requirements for transportation and space heating increase and the best hydro sites are utilized, coal had been expected to become the chief source of energy for the United States rapidly expanding power demands. Thus, even though coal falls to less than 50 percent in furnishing kwh in 1980, the estimated 500 million tons of coal required will be almost three times as great as coal used to generate electricity in 1960. Most important, we need to review the fact that total coal consumption for all uses in the United States was only 380.4 million tons in 1960.

The conclusion seems justified that the coal industry will have expanding demands for coal in electric power generation long before coal will feel the impact of nuclear fuel. When the impact does come it is likely to occur as costs reach a competitive level in regions like New England, where present power costs are relatively high because of the high transportation costs of coal.

Similarly the potentialities for the increased use of nuclear fuels for power purposes are great and may come earlier in underdeveloped areas where the need is great and the demand for electric power is growing and coal is unavailable or its cost is high. Thus the conclusion can be drawn that nuclear fuel will supplement coal in producing electric power in the United States and elsewhere, but the expanding demand for electric power will create a larger market for coal.

Transportation and space heating offer fewer opportunities for nuclear fuels than does the electric power industry. The Standard Oil Company (New Jersey) sees three main obstacles to the widespread use of nuclear energy in transportation and space heating. "The first is the extremely high cost of the reactor. The second is the difficulty of safeguarding its operation—for example, in an aircraft—so that if the reactor and its shielding were accidentally damaged it would not be a source of dangerous radiation. The third obstacle is the immense weight of the shielding required to contain the radiation from even a small reactor."[8]

In transportation, petroleum is the fuel. Ships, locomotives, automobiles, and aircraft are the users.

Nuclear-fueled ships, as we have noted, are already a technical reality and in operation for military purposes. Critics insist that the experience with the N.S. Savannah, the first atom-powered commercial ship, was not very satisfactory. But Dr. Glenn T. Seaborg, Chairman of the AEC looks upon the Savannah as a successful venture that opened ports in many countries to nuclear ships; and even though it was not intended to be an economical ship he believes that the follow-on reactors that will be coming along will lead to economical nuclear power for merchant

[8] *Oil and the Atom,* New York, Standard Oil Company (New Jersey), 1955, p. 12.

ships. In response to the question in July, 1965—"Do you foresee the day when nuclear power will be the principal, even exclusive, means of ship propulsion?"—Dr. Seaborg replied: "Oh, yes. Again, it's only a matter of when, you see. At some stage we are going to run out of oil at the price that would, by then, be competitive with nuclear power." About 20 percent of residual fuel oil is used for ships, but the oil industry does not believe that nuclear-fueled commercial vessels will be an important factor by 1975. Moreover, the petroleum industry does not appear to be worried about the impact of nuclear fuels for bunkers, for as one industry official stated: "If we should lose the fuel-oil business of some of the larger ships after 20 years or so—what of it?"

In locomotive use, Robert E. Wilson, Chairman of the Board of the Standard Oil Company (Indiana), reported to the Atomic Energy Conference of the National Industrial Conference Board, New York, October 14, 1954: "But even if this should be both safe and economical in normal service (which I seriously doubt), can you imagine either the railroads or the regulatory authorities being willing to risk a possible wreck of an atomic engine in one of our large cities? I realize that a theoretically safe 'package' might be designed, but I think psychological factors would bar it for many, many years."

Nuclear-powered highway vehicles appear to the petroleum industry to be precluded by the shielding problem. There is of course the possibility of using electricity from nuclear power plants to charge some new kind of highly efficient storage batteries for electric automobiles (direct solar radiation also might be used). Here again the petroleum industry is not worried because it does not believe an electric car will give what the public demands—fast acceleration, agility in traffic, and other qualities that come under the general heading of "performance."

An atomic-power military aircraft was once believed to be possible, but for commercial planes the shielding problems have always seemed to constitute an almost insuperable bar. Again, reporting in July, 1965, Dr. Seaborg of the AEC stated: "My opinion is that aviation is not a field where there will be an advantage in using nuclear power. There is the shielding problem, the heavy weight of taking off, and the possibility of crash with a nuclear reactor that has highly radioactive fission products aboard."

In the field of space heating both oil and natural gas are affected. Coal is also affected, but coal's competition has and will come from the conventional fuels. The use of nuclear fuels appears to be ruled out by all of the general obstacles. The consensus of industry was that the displacement of large numbers of oil- and gas-burning units appeared to be a remote possibility. There is of course the chance that in low-cost power areas electric radiant heating and electric-driven heat pumps will become a substantial competitor for space heating. But as has already been noted, this electric power is likely to be coal generated for many years to come.

Conclusions. The conclusion that the long-run implications of the impact of nuclear energy on other energy sources will be favorable seems justifiable. The two following statements of Robert E. Wilson, while coming from the oil industry, may well be used to summarize the position of the competitive fuels.

"I believe that the impact on our industry will be negligible over the next 20 or 25 years. Beyond that, I believe we will welcome its aid in helping to take care of the country's rapidly growing needs for power."

"As a former chairman of the Atomic Energy Commission has pointed out, when we attempt to predict the future of atomic energy, we are in the same position as those who tried to predict the future of electricity ten years after Benjamin Franklin's experiment with the kite in the thunderstorm. In the period immediately ahead, however, it is clear that anything atomic energy does to promote industrialization and raise standards of living will create new needs for liquid energy."[9]

The Panel on Peaceful Uses of Atomic Energy concluded: "The realization of nuclear power as a practical source of energy should be welcomed by the American people including those related specifically to conventional fuel industries. While in particular instances nuclear power may displace power generated from conventional fuels, in most cases it will provide a necessary supplement to those fuels in meeting the Nation's rapidly expanding power requirements. But even where it does displace conventional fuels, those fuels may find uses that are more profitable to those who produce them and of greater value to the Nation's economy."

SUMMARY

In a little over 20 short years the atomic energy industry has given birth to the atomic bomb which has been developed to such an extent that mankind must now live under the perpetual threat of self-destruction. Yet at the same time, the possibilities of peaceful uses of the atom hold out unlimited horizons. In line with the shifting use of the atom to peacetime service as a source of energy, and in uses of isotopes in industrial, agricultural, and medical applications the structure of the industry has been shifting gradually from one of tight military-security and governmental control to private industry operation.

Once the United States policy shifted toward domestic procurement of uranium, resources were developed at a fantastic rate. The future of these resources is now in the hands of private enterprise as the U.S. government withdraws its subsidized procurement program.

The future impact of atomic energy on other energy sources is favorable and in the national interest as this new energy source supplements

---

[9] *Ibid.*, p. 13.

conventional sources of energy to meet the expanding energy requirements of the U.S. economy. The electric power industry stands ready to
benefit first, as will be observed in detail in the following chapter.

But how can one draw conclusions and predict the future at the
dawn of a new energy age? The horizon, indeed, is unlimited. However,
we can share the best thoughts of President Dwight D. Eisenhower as
he introduced his atomic energy program a little over ten years ago in,
appropriately, a commencement address at Pennsylvania State University
on June 11, 1955.

Nuclear energy is too new for any man to chart its limits or predict its
course with accuracy. But in ten short years the curtain has been pushed aside
sufficiently to afford glimpses that have aroused atomic hopes commensurate
with the awful dimension of atomic fears.

The extent of the economic and industrial changes that we can anticipate
is indicated by estimates that world sources of uranium potentially available
contain as much as twenty times the energy of the world's known reserves of
coal, petroleum, and natural gas combined. And power is only one of the results of nuclear fission. Many engineers and scientists believe that radiation and
radioactive isotopes may provide even greater peacetime benefit. They are
already opening new horizons in medicine, agriculture, and industrial processes.

Our nation has no desire for a monopoly on the knowledge and practice of
these possibilities. We want the world to share—as we always have.

Moreover, we know that the human talents essential to the advancement
of science are not restricted to this country. Throughout the free countries there
are men and women of great ability who, given the opportunity, can help further to advance the frontiers of knowledge and contribute to the peace and
progress of the peoples of all nations.

Progress to date in nuclear science is not, of course, exclusively an American achievement. An international cooperative effort broke the barriers and
made possible man's use of atomic energy. For maximum progress in the future,
we must work for a continued partnership between the world's best minds—in
science, engineering, education, business, and in the professions.

SELECTED REFERENCES

"Atoms and Automation," *Saturday Review,* Special Issue, January 22, 1955.
Civilian Nuclear Power a Report to the President—1962, Oak Ridge, U.S.
    Atomic Energy Commission, 1962.
Crawford, John E., "Uranium," in *Mineral Facts and Problems,* Bureau of Mines
    Bulletin 556, Washington, D.C., 1956, pp. 945–951.
Davis, Kenneth, Shield Warren, and Walker L. Cisler, *Some Peaceful Uses of
    Atomic Energy,* Proceedings of the National Academy of Economics and
    Political Science, Atlanta Session, December 29, 1955.
"Exploration Widens the U.S. Uranium Belt," *Business Week,* March 3, 1951,
    pp. 102 ff.

Johnson, Jesse C., *The Outlook for Uranium*, Washington, D.C., U.S. Atomic Energy Commission, March 17, 1962, p. 3.

McCune, Francis K., *The Race for Atomic Power*, New York, General Electric Company, March 23, 1955.

"Nuclear Power," in *National Power Survey*, A Report by the Federal Power Commission, Washington, D.C., October, 1964, pp. 77–92.

"Nuclear Power," *Report of the National Fuels and Energy Study Group*, Washington, D.C., 1962, pp. 272–273.

Oil and the Atom, New York, Standard Oil Company (New Jersey), 1955.

Patterson, John A., *Domestic Uranium Reserves*, Speech delivered for the AEC before the National Western Mining Conference and Exhibition, Denver, Colorado, February 8, 1963.

Peaceful Uses of Atomic Energy, Report of the Panel on the Impact of the Peaceful Uses of Atomic Energy to the Joint Committee on Atomic Energy, 84th Congress, 2nd. Session, Washington, D.C., 1956.

Poane, James, "Uranium," in *Mineral Facts and Problems*, Bureau of Mines Bulletin 585, Washington, D.C., 1960, pp. 919–940.

United States Atomic Energy Commission, *Annual Report to Congress of the Atomic Energy Commission for 1963*, Washington, D.C., January, 1964, and later reports.

"Uranium," *Commodity Year Book*, New York, Commodity Research Bureau, 1955, pp. 350–352.

7

ELECTRIC POWER

ELECTRIC power is not a natural resource. It carries the energy developed from coal, petroleum, natural gas, and nuclear fuels, and from falling water. By transmitting energy from these sources, electric power with its industrial, commercial, and residential uses has truly revolutionized man's capacity to do work. In the United States over 90 percent of the power in industry is provided through electric motors. Expressed in another way, over 90 percent of industrial production depends on electricity, as do almost all commercial establishments. Residential consumers are so dependent on electricity that modern man can hardly function during a power failure. About 98 percent of all U.S. homes, both urban and rural, are served by electric power.

By 1962, eighty years after Thomas Edison started the first central station at Pearl Street, New York City for the generation and distribution of electricity, U.S. production of electricity was 946,949,000,000 kwh. The United States, with only 6 percent of the world's population, led all other countries in the production of electricity, generating 37 percent of the world total in 1962. United States production was almost as much as the combined output of the next six countries—Russia, United Kingdom, Japan, Western Germany, Canada, and France—and was 2¾ times that of second-ranking Russia.

Over the 50-year period 1912–1962 the long-term growth rate in the use of electricity was at an average rate of 7.16 percent per year compounded, as compared with the average growth rate of the GNP of 3.06 percent per year. Over this period the use of electricity doubled about every ten years. After World War II the growth in the use of electricity was at an annual average rate of 8.2 percent. This was about 2½ times the rate of growth of the whole economy as measured by the GNP. Indeed a case can be made for the existence of a close correlation between the rate of growth of electric power generated in the United States and the rate of growth of the economy. Thus electric power production is an excellent measure of productive strength. Expanding electric power capacity is requisite to continued increases in productive capacity.

ELECTRIC POWER PRODUCTION

An electric current is created when a certain kind of wire is passed through the lines of force emanating from the poles of a magnet, called the magnetic field. This principle is used in the commercial generation of electricity. A generator is a device for passing many wires through a strong magnetic field at a rapid rate. In this manner large amounts of electricity can be generated. The generator is a means of converting mechanical energy into electric power.

There are two main sources for the mechanical power needed to turn the generator—water power and steam power. In the early 1960's almost 20 percent of the electric power generated in the United States was from water (hydro) power, while almost 80 percent was generated by steam plants. Internal combustion accounted for the remaining fraction of 1 percent.

Water Power

Hydro power is of course an ideal major source of electricity because the use of water power (a flow resource) does not cause a drain on the mineral fuel resources. The amount of power at a given site depends on the amount of fall or head (height of site), and on the amount of water the stream is carrying. A typical water power development would include: plenty of rainfall throughout the year; relative freedom from floods, droughts, and severe freezes; forests along the streams and lakes; and such geological conditions that a dam could be constructed to create, or aid in creating, a large pond or lake. To this natural environment must be added: penstocks for conducting water to hydraulic turbines in the powerhouse; an electric generator; and a trailrace to return the water to the stream after it has passed through the turbine.

For centuries, man has used water, falling on the paddles of the water wheel, for producing power to grind grains or operate pumps. This principle, combined with the principle of the generator, is used in modern hydro plants. Water from a higher level, flowing through penstocks, exerts force against an arrangement of blades called a *turbine*, which is mounted on a shaft. The shaft is connected to a generator, causing it to rotate and generate electricity. One advantage of hydroelectricity is that while electricity cannot be stored, it is possible to store the water used to make electricity, so that it may be released in time of peak demands.

On the other hand, the above advantage is offset by the wide seasonal variation in stream flow. Streams are usually low in the summer, so that water is not always available when needed. As a result there are only a few instances where water power alone can be relied upon, and it becomes necessary to have supplementary stand-by steam plants. Thus to the initial capital cost of the dam and power site, must be added the cost of steam facilities. This duplication of equipment may offset the so-called advantage of free water power.

One important fact about the water power plant is that its location is determined by natural conditions. Favorable sites are likely to occur long distances from the market for electricity (load centers). Some few industries are foot-loose and may move to the energy source, but most industries and commercial users have other locational factors. And, of course, residential demand is where the homes are. As a result, hydroelectricity has the disadvantage of having to be transmitted over long distances from its point of production to load centers. Indeed, some sites are so inaccessible and remote from the market for power that they must remain undeveloped because of this factor alone.

The FPC is authorized under section 4(a) of the Federal Power Act "to make investigations and to collect and record data concerning the utilization of water resources . . ." For studying the hydroelectric power resources of the United States the Commission groups the river basins into 16 major drainages. These major drainages, and their description are shown in Figure 7.1. Also shown in this figure is a summary of the Commission's study of developed and undeveloped hydropower potential in the United States. These data, although subject to constant revision, do show that the North Pacific drainage basin has the greatest developed and undeveloped resources. This area has 33 per cent of the United States installed hydro capacity and 39 percent of the potential. Next in potential is the South Pacific area with 11 percent. However, most favorable indications are the North Atlantic with 8 percent of the U.S. total, the Ohio River with 7 percent, and the Missouri River with 10 percent of the undeveloped potential. Nevertheless, the map does indicate that favorable hydroelectric sites do tend to occur in areas removed from population centers.

In a more recent report in the *National Power Survey*,[1] the FPC estimated that as of January 1, 1964 hydroelectric power potential of the 48 contiguous states was 134 million kilowatts of capacity, capable of producing an average of about 500 billion kwh of electric energy annually. Of the total installed capacity, about 40 million kilowatts, or 30 percent, generating 175 billion kwh a year, was installed as of that date.

[1] *National Power Survey*, Report by the Federal Power Commission, Washington, D.C., October, 1964, p. 94.

Figure 7.1: Developed and Undeveloped Hydroelectric Power by Major Drainages.

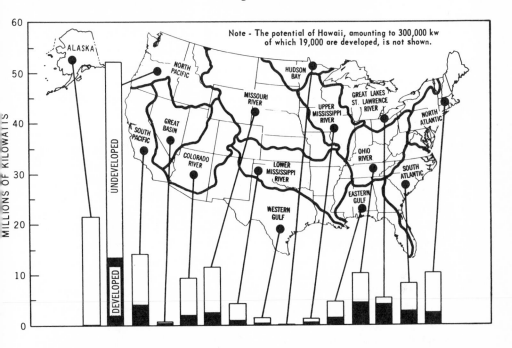

NOTE: The river basins of the United States are grouped into 16 major drainages. Each covers an area with boundaries coinciding with natural drainage features. The boundaries of these major drainages conform generally to the boundaries of the areas adopted by the U.S. Geological Survey as a basis for its publication of streamflow measurements, with some adjustments in the grouping of river basins. The states of Alaska and Hawaii are included as separate major drainages.

These major drainages and the river systems which they comprise are: *Hudson Bay:* the U.S. portions of river systems draining into Hudson Bay; *Great Lakes–St. Lawrence:* all river systems in the United States draining into the Great Lakes or the St. Lawrence River; *North Atlantic:* the U.S. portions of river systems draining into the Atlantic Ocean starting with the St. John River, Maine, and extending to and including the York River, Va.; *South Atlantic:* the remaining river systems draining into the Atlantic Ocean starting with the James River, Va.; *Eastern Gulf:* river systems draining into the Gulf of Mexico east of the Mississippi River; *Western Gulf:* river systems draining into the Gulf of Mexico west of the Mississippi River; *Lower Mississippi River:* Mississippi River and tributaries from its mouth to the Missouri River, excluding the Ohio River Basin; *Upper Mississippi River:* Mississippi River and all tributaries above the mouth of the Missouri River; *Ohio River:* the Ohio River and its tributaries; *Missouri River:* the Missouri River and its tributaries; *Great Basin:* all river systems within the Great Basin; *North Pacific:* river systems draining into the Pacific Ocean along the Washington-Oregon coastline; *South Pacific:* river systems draining into the Pacific Ocean along the California coastline; *Colorado River:* the Colorado River and its tributaries; *Alaska:* the U.S. portions of river systems in the state of Alaska; and *Hawaii:* all river systems in the state of Hawaii.

SOURCE: *Hydroelectric Power Resources of the United States*, Washington, D.C., Federal Power Commission, January 1, 1964.

Water resources have multiple uses, and the problem of their development is a complex one, leading to government supervision and regulation. Dams for hydropower impound and conserve water that is in increasingly short supply; they affect navigation and flood control; they flood areas of heretofore useful land which may thereafter provide recreational areas; and finally, they generate electric power. In short, private property rights and public rights become commingled. This has led, through the Federal Power Act, to the licensing by the FPC hydroelectric power developments located on streams over which Congress has jurisdiction. It has also led to a high degree of public ownership and participation in hydroelectric power development.

In the United States, the federal government owns almost 50 percent, and lower levels of government over 5 percent, of all hydroelectric capacity. Much of the growth of the U.S. power capacity during the 1930's was due to public or federal power projects. These were large multiple-purpose water installations which could not have been undertaken by private enterprise. Federal government ownership or control is effected through three administrative channels: (1) In the Tennessee River Valley, the Tennessee Valley Authority, a public corporation, has jurisdiction over aspects of the valley involving electric power production, flood control, navigation, irrigation, and recreation; (2) Along rivers and streams where navigation is the principal purpose, the Corps of Engineers of the Department of Defense is responsible for building and maintaining federal dams; (3) In areas where irrigation and land reclamation are the major objectives, the Bureau of Reclamation of the Department of Interior is responsible.

Largest of the federal government's hydroelectric plants is the Grand Coulee in the North Pacific drainage area, followed by the Hoover Dam in the Colorado River area. This in spite of the fact that the Tennessee Valley complex is probably the best known of the federal hydroelectric projects.

Privately owned hydroelectric plants, while not as spectacular in size as the federal projects, do account for a major portion of the nation's developed hydro capability. They tend to be located more predominantly east of the Mississippi and thus are closer to the market. In addition, many of the privately owned facilities have most favorable site locations.

Steam Power

Thermoelectric power is produced from coal, petroleum, natural gas, or nuclear fuels. The term *steam power* once referred to power produced by a reciprocating steam engine driving a generator. Today, in a conventional steam plant, the heat of the fuel is used to transform water into steam, which is directed against the blades of a turbine, which in turn rotates a generator. In the previous chapter we saw how in a nuclear powered plant the reactor was used to replace the boiler used in a conventional steam power plant. By use of the turbine, the full expansive effect of the steam is utilized. It is adaptable to high rotative speeds, commonly operating at 3,600 revolutions per minute (rpm) as contrasted with the old Corliss piston engine speed of 90 rpm. This factor enables the turbine to be built in very large units requiring the minimum floor space.

The National Fuels and Energy Study Group emphasized that there had been two notable developments in electric generation technology: the trend to larger plants and the trend to large generating units, i.e., larger capacity per boiler. At the time of the report there were a number of steam plants with a capacity of greater than a million kilowatts. But more outstanding was the trend toward large units. At the time of the report one unit in excess of a million kilowatts was being planned for the Tennessee Valley Authority's Bull Run plant. The FPC estimates that the maximum size of turbine-generator units will reach the 1½ to 2 million kilowatt range by 1980. Most significant about these large units is that they require less space and weight per kilowatt than earlier units of lower rating. This accomplishment has been made possible mainly by the development of alloys that permit operation at higher temperatures and pressures. High-temperature and high-pressure steam engenders high efficiency in heat use. The effect in boiler design is to extract every possible Btu of heat from the fuel. The past and projected record of coal requirements per kwh shows a decrease from 3 pounds of coal per kwh in 1920 to a projected rate of not much above $\frac{7}{10}$ of a pound of coal or coal equivalent per kwh in 1980.

Table 7.1 gives the amount of coal, fuel oil, and gas consumed by the electric power industry in 1962 compared with 1937. In addition, this table gives further data on the improved efficiency of thermoelectric plants. The amount of electricity generated by fuel in 1962 was 9.1 times that produced in 1937, although total consumption of fuel or its equivalent in coal was only 5.5 times as much.

Steam plant location is much more flexible than that of hydro plants, and at first thought, it may appear that location would simply be a matter of building a plant near the center of the market. But location is much more complicated. As with a hydro plant, water is the controlling factor. Not only are considerable quantities of pure water required for conversion to steam in the boiler, but tremendous volumes are required to condense the steam leaving the turbines as water is pumped through the condensers to absorb the heat given up by the steam. Return of the water to the stream may cause thermal pollution. In general, given available

TABLE 7.1

Fuel Consumed by the Electric Utility Industry*

(1937 compared with 1962)

Fuel	1937	1962p
Coal (thousand short tons)	42,930	193,134
Fuel oil (thousand 42-gallon barrels)	13,829	85,643
Gas (million cubic feet)	169,127	1,965,590
Total fuel in coal equivalent (thousand short tons)	53,560	292,345
Net generation by fuels (kwhr in millions)**	74,502	681,286
Heat rate, Btu per kwhr***	17,850	10,493
Pounds of coal per kwhr	1.44	0.86

° Except Alaska and Hawaii.
°° Excludes generation by wood. waste and nuclear fuels.
°°° EEI estimate.
p Preliminary.
SOURCE: *National Power Survey*, A Report by the Federal Power Commission, Washington, D.C., 1964.

water, plant location then becomes a matter of economics, and a weighing of the relative costs of transporting fuel or electricity to the center of demand. In some areas it is cheaper to transport electricity by way of the transmission line than it is to move fuel, and in such cases the power stations are located near the source of fuel. When the conditions are reversed, the power stations tend to be near the market. Two developments that are modifying locational factors with opposite effects are the development of integral trains which lower the cost of coal transportation, and high voltage transmission which lowers the cost of delivery of electricity. It goes without saying that available land supply for plant location becomes important in many locations.

Thermoelectric units have two major advantages over hydroelectric plants: (1) mobility and (2) low initial costs. The first point has been covered above with the conclusion that steam plant location, given adequate water, tends to be a problem of determining the most economic location. Low initial costs tends to be an understatement and should be considered relative to hydroelectric initial costs. Initial costs of the thermoelectric unit are those of the generator, the turbine, the structure in which to house them, the arrangement for the storage and application of fuel, and the plant site. In contrast, the initial costs of the hydroelectric plant involve the construction of a major dam, the purchase of thousands of acres of ground which must be flooded, plus the turbines and generators, and usually longer transmission lines must be built. Thus the lack of operating costs for fuel in hydro plants tends to be offset by higher fixed costs for plant.

The ownership of thermoelectric plants is 90 percent in the hands of private enterprise, as compared with the majority ownership of hydroelectric plants by governmental interests.

Coordinated Use of Hydroelectric and Thermoelectric Plants

While the difference between hydro plants and steam plants is clear, there are different types and functions within this dichotomy that require the combined use of all types of plants within a system.

A specific illustration of the above point is the case of base and peak load hydro and steam plants. There are two extreme types of hydro sites: one with a high head in a narrow gorge, and one with a low head spread across a wide river bed. A high head lends itself to giant turbines and generators, whereas a low spread-out head favors the installation of a number of small generating units. For most satisfactory services, large turbo-generators should operate constantly, supplying what is called the base load, the core of sustained demand. On the other hand, smaller turbo-generators suitable for the low heads permit more flexible use, and they are well suited to handle peak loads over shorter periods of time. Similarly, generally speaking, large steam units are best suited to carry base loads and smaller units to handle peak loads. Thus we have the classification of plants: hydro base load, hydro peak load, fuel base load, and fuel peak load. Clearly the best results are achieved by the interconnection of the peak and base load plants in the appropriate combinations for the coordinated use of the installed capacity.

Two other types of plants are important: stand-by plants and pumped storage plants. Stand-by plants are used primarily in connection with hydro plants. It is often desirable to build hydropower plant capacity in excess of the water power available through the year. Power available only part of the year is called "secondary" power as contrasted with "firm" power which is available all during the year. Unless secondary power can be "firmed-up," i.e., made available throughout the year, it is known as "dump power"; this can be sold only on a "when and if available" basis and at a very low rate. Secondary water power can be firmed-up by connecting the hydro system with a steam plant which "stands by" for the emergency when the flow of water is inadequate. It follows that stand-by plants operate at a low capacity factor and therefore at a relatively high cost.

Pumped storage is of growing importance and is now set aside as a special type of generating facility by the FPC. A pumped storage plant generates electric energy during system peak loads, using hydroelectric units driven from a headwater pool. During offpeak periods energy from other sources, usually from steam plants, is used to pump water from a lower pool back to a headwater pool. The water in the upper pool may thus be regarded as the equivalent of stored steam-generated energy. Pumped storage installations can be divided into two general categories, those in which pumped storage facilities are added to a conventional hydro installation, and those which are exclusively pumped storage and generate power by recirculating the water between a lower and higher reservoir. Pumped storage generating plants have most favorable advantages for peaking and reserve use, and, in addition, utilize the offpeak power of steam plants.

The New England states appear to be set for a new application of pumped storage. Most authorities agree that before 1975 nuclear reactors will generally be chosen over conventional coal and oil fired boilers for base load power plants in high cost fuel areas such as New England. Residential, commercial, and industrial demands for power normally are at their lowest between midnight and 6 AM (Figure 7.2). With the growth of nuclear plants, utilities will face the prospect of having to shut down or curtail output from nuclear plants during this offpeak period. However,

Figure 7.2: Electric Power Demand Pattern in New England.

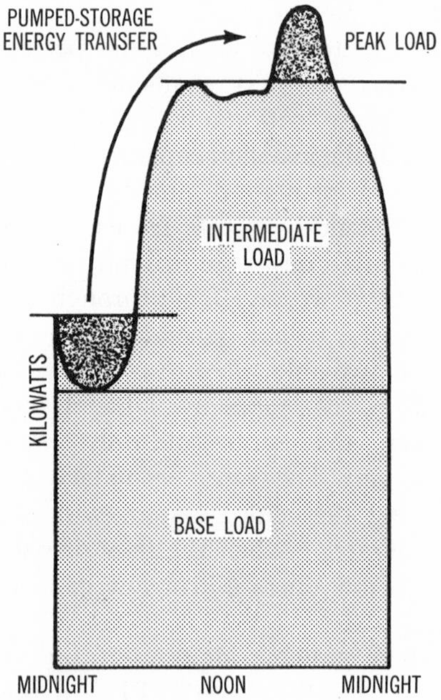

SOURCE: Federal Reserve Bank of Boston.

since the cost of continuing to operate a nuclear reactor in an offpeak period will be relatively low, an estimated $.0015 per kwh, these plants will probably be kept running at or near capacity around the clock, utilizing the offpeak period to provide low-cost power for pumped storage operations.

Thus, in this new application of pumped storage, water is pumped to a high elevation reservoir during the offpeak period of the day when the lowest cost power is available to run the pumps. The stored water is held in the upper reservoir until the next peak use period when it is dropped through a turbine located at a lower level reservoir. The economic efficiency of such an installation depends in part on the cost of electric energy used to run the pumps and the resultant loss of energy. The newness of this operation of course is found in its application of the low base load cost of nuclear plants as they fit into a coordinated use of electrical facilities.

Capacity, Production, Loads, and Reserve Margins

In our discussion of production of electricity we have been using terms which we need now to state clearly as we look at the relationship between capacity, production, loads, and reserve margins. The capacity to produce electric energy is measured in kilowatts. The kilowatt is also a measure of demand for electric power at an instant of time. Production and demand (or "load") over a period of time are measured in kwh. One kilowatt of electric generating capacity operating for 1 hour will produce 1 kwh of electric energy; for one entire day, 24 kwh of energy; and constantly for one year, 8,760 kwh of energy.

The demands for electric power fluctuate over each twenty-four-hour period and through the months and seasons of the year. The normal sustained demand or requirement on a particular generating capacity is referred to as the *base load*. The total of this base load and additional fluctuating demands (for example, evening home lighting and cooking requirements) is referred to as the *peak load*. Since electric power cannot be stored, there must be an installed capacity to produce the peak load. Since all generating plants must be taken out of service for repairs, electric generating systems must maintain as a part of their capacity a stand-by idle maintenance reserve. Stand-by reserve fuel capacity, as we have noted in detail, is often required to supplement fluctuating hydro capacity due to irregular stream flow. In addition, the electric power industry usually has a so-called *spinning reserve*, which is the excess capacity, over the load being furnished, of the operating units actually in use.

Peak load, peak capability, and reserve (gross margin as a percentage of peak load), is given for the United States for the years 1948 through

1967 in Figure 7.3. *Peak capability* represents the maximum kilowatt output with all power sources available. It must, therefore, provide the necessary allowances for maintenance, emergency outages, and system operating requirements. *Gross margin* includes the provision for maintenance, emergency outages, and system operating requirements. Any remainder, after these needs are met, is available for unforeseen loads.

Figure 7.3: Peak Capabilities, Peak Loads, and Gross Margins.

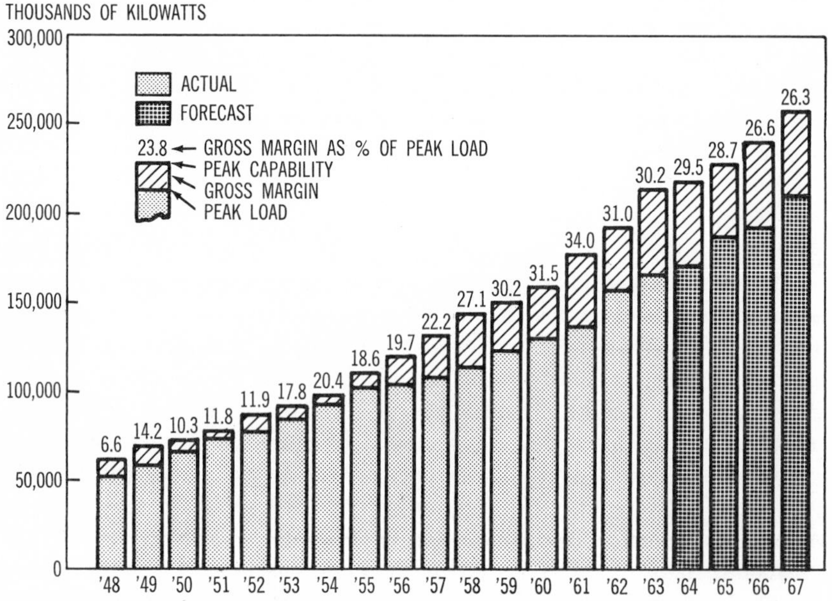

THOUSANDS OF KILOWATTS

SOURCE: Edison Electric Institute.

Before 1938 the electric power industry had about 50 percent reserve requirements. The high pre-World War II reserve margins were the result of two factors: "(1) As a rule, each ownership unit operated on the principle of self-sufficiency, providing its full reserve requirements of generating capacity to carry peak loads and provide for shutdowns; (2) although there were some limited capacity interconnections between systems, no regions were tied together for large-scale transfers of power."[2]

Out of World War II came a development that had a dramatic effect on capacity and reserve margins—interconnection—which was facilitated both by government and by private industry. The Power Act of 1935 au-

[2] George A. Lincoln, *Economics of National Security*, Englewood Cliffs, N.J., Prentice-Hall, 1954, p. 224.

thorized the Federal Power Commission (FPC) to consider the availability of power for national defense production. In 1938 the FPC was authorized to order interconnection and interchange of power that might be required for war. During the summer of 1941 a serious power shortage developed in the southeastern United States. Following recommendations by the FPC, electric power systems operating in adjacent areas voluntarily coöperated to furnish power to the deficient areas. Experience gained from this project solved many operational problems which had previously been considered as limitations and led to the realization of the advantages of generating systems serving combined rather than separate system loads. Interconnection action taken from 1941 on was equivalent to a major expansion in power-generating capacity which was available for World War II. This was possible because of the more efficient utilization of generating capacity. Greater efficiency in the utilization of capacity through interconnection has had the permanent effect of reducing the reserve margin requirement to the point that 15 percent is now considered a safe minimum.

Figure 7.3 reveals that during the span of years of the Korean War the reserve margin fell sharply below this 15 percent minimum. During this time some regions had serious power shortages, and aluminum production which requires 10 kwh per pound was curtailed. Since then the reserve margin has been more than adequate, and interconnection has served to further reduce the amount of installed capacity required.

There are additional benefits of interconnection: Lower reserve requirements and capacity have made possible a higher capacity factor and lower fixed costs; greater diversity of demand has leveled out peak loads among systems; the effects of fluctuating water supply have been smoothed out in the case of hydro power; and continuity of power supply has been more effectively assured during peace and wartime emergencies. Indeed, so important is interconnection, that we will consider it as a special problem and policy question. Also, as we shall see, interconnection is a part of the next function of the electric power industry set apart for study—transmission.

ELECTRIC POWER TRANSMISSION

Transmission is the middle part of the three distinct functions of an electric power supply system—generation, transmission, and distribution. The purpose of electric power transmission is to deliver electric power from a generating source to a market area, or to connect one electric power system with another. After discussing the technical aspects of electric power transmission, we will look briefly at its effects on the location of industry and its significance in interconnection.

Voltage and Distance

An electric transmission system may be likened to a hydraulic system, in that the flow is the result of pressure, hydraulic head in one case, voltage head (differential) in the other. If a switch is closed in a factory, electric energy flows in from the local generating plant to start the factory's motors. The voltage of a circuit is the electric potential difference between conductors or between conductors to ground, usually expressed in volts or kilovolts.

The voltage selected for a given line or system is determined by several factors, of which the power to be transmitted economically and the distance are particularly important. Voltages in use range from 22,000 to 345,000. More than 60 percent of all lines in the early 1960's were at 90 kilovolts or less, reflecting the usual short distance between terminals, which at that time averaged about 50 miles. High voltage circuits averaged between 100 and 150 miles in length, with the longest line being the 265-mile 287-kilovolt line from Hoover Dam to Los Angeles.

Higher voltages permit larger amounts of power to be moved longer distances. For example, a 500-kilovolt line can move a given quantity of power more than twice as far as a 230-kilovolt line. A 150-mile 230-kilovolt line and a 500-mile 345-kilovolt line have about the same transmission capacity. Thus for a given capacity, increasing the voltage increases the distance more than proportionally. For a given distance, increasing the voltage increases the capacity more than proportionally. As line voltage goes up, construction costs increase almost in proportion to voltage, but the power capacity goes up basically as the square of the voltage, so that cost per unit of power transmission decreases sharply.

But higher voltage transmission brings with it a number of technical disadvantages which were only nuisances at about 300 kilovolts. The principal probblem is leakage (corona loss); others include interference with radio and television and danger from lightning. In addition, transformers and towers need better insulation. Nevertheless, the *National Power Survey* of the FPC concluded that the most important fact about extra high voltage technology, is that higher voltages bring lower transmission costs.

There is some professional opinion that use of direct current (DC) will enable more power to be delivered longer distances. Alternating current (AC) has been almost exclusively used in the United States because it is readily transformed from one voltage level to another. The fact is that high voltage direct current is feasible and that the cost of DC lines is lower than the cost of AC lines, but the terminal facilities for conversion between AC and DC are relatively expensive. Thus it appears that transmission by AC will remain the rule in the United States.

Transmission and Plant Location

Electric power transmission distances have important effects in the location of industry. These involve problems whether plants should move to the source of power or the power should be transmitted to the plant. In many instances in which a plant has important locational factors there is no alternative except to move the power. Where the location is too far from hydro sites for efficient transmission of electric power, fuel plants are required. The same reasoning applies to the movement of fuel to thermal plants. In the discussion of coal two observations were made: (1) A short-run continuation of a long-term trend was seen in the move of industry to coal as a source of fuel and for multipurpose use, and (2) the possibility of moving coal by pipeline to more remote thermal stations was already being replaced by the reality of moving coal at lower costs by unit trains. To these it should be added that the ease of shipment of nuclear fuel to the required source of power may help solve some of the electric transmission problems.

The strategic military implications of electric power transmission were summarized as follows by the U.S. Military Academy Department of Social Sciences:

Transmission distance seems certain to increase. The meaning of 300-mile versus 500-mile transmission distances in the economics of power and in the development of emergency measures is indicated by a simple exercise in plane geometry. A circle with a 300-mile radius covers approximately ½ of the United States; a circle with a 500-mile radius covers more than ⅓ of the United States. As transmission distances increase, generators can be located near sources of cheap fuel rather than near load centers. Some hydro power sites may become more economically feasible. If power costs less and can be transmitted farther, the location of defense industries can be determined by strategic reasons rather than the proximity of sources of power. Finally, in case of atomic attack or similar disaster, emergency power can be transmitted to afflicted areas from more distant sources.[3]

Interconnection

Interconnection (an intertie) is a transmission line between generating centers, or power systems or pools. A system interconnection is a connection between two electric systems permitting the transfer of electric energy in either direction. A power pool is two or more electric systems interconnected and coordinated to supply power in the most economical manner for their combined load requirements and maintenance

[3] *Ibid.*, p. 226.

program. The intent is to so integrate the operations that the various generating plants will operate as a single economic unit.

To illustrate we may return to our example of a factory closing a switch. If the local generating plant is already running at capacity, the switch closed at the factory will automatically lead in electricity generated in a neighboring plant some distance away; the second station may draw in a third, if need be, the third station draws on a fourth and so on. In effect the electricity used to run the factory came from the fourth station, possibly 500 miles away. The result is if the load is shed by one plant, it is pushed up by another. If one plant can be operated more economically than another, the more efficient plant is loaded first to satisfy a base demand, additional plants being brought in later, as needed, in order of their economy of operation.

This example, given above, could apply to generating centers in one system under one ownership, or to system interconnections and power pools under multiple ownership. The net effect of an intertie is to pool the generating resources of adjacent regions and beyond, resulting in the economies mentioned above.

In addition, we have already seen that interconnection permits a two-way movement of electricity from one system that has a surplus to one that has a deficit. This in turn reduces the need for each system to maintain reserve capacity for peak or emergency demand or to protect against failure or catastrophe.

By 1965 the FPC reported that 97 percent of the U.S. generating capacity was to a greater or lesser extent interconnected in five large networks. The largest existing group of interconnected systems involved 167 million kilowatts of electrical generation operating in parallel.[4] This system covered roughly the entire portion of the United States east of Texas and the Rockies, as well as much of eastern Canada—39 states and two Canadian provinces in all. It consisted of the so-called Interconnected Systems Group, the Pennsylvania-New Jersey-Maryland Interconnection, and the Canada-U.S. Eastern Interconnection. Two other major networks, the Northwest Interconnected Systems Group, and the Pacific Southwest Interconnected Systems Group, each represented about 11 percent of the total industry load. In addition were the Texas Power Pool and the Rio Grande-New Mexico Pool.

Most of these existing networks were not designed for and were incapable of achieving full coordination. Nevertheless, the FPC felt they were a solid beginning for stronger interties. One major question is how to facilitate these interconnections, and this we shall discuss in more detail in the problems and policy section of this chapter.

---

[4] The phrase "operating in parallel" means that the electric power systems in the group are normally operated on a continuously interconnected basis in which some electric energy can flow from one system to the other.

ELECTRIC POWER CONSUMPTION

We have already noted that the growth in the total use of electricity in the United States has been remarkably steady throughout the industry's 80-year history, with usage doubling approximately every ten years. This phenomenal growth has been due in large part to the many advantages of electricity.

One leading advantage of electricity over other forms of energy is its almost unlimited degree of divisibility. By simple mechanical devices such as transformers, the amount of energy tapped can be adjusted from a fraction of a watt to thousands of watts per hour. This is of tremendous importance to control the speed of machines and the heat in furnaces. Another advantage that we have just studied is transmission. The energy is conveyed to the point of need, and by means of wires and plugs in strategic places, machines and appliances can be moved from one place to another. Contrast this with the use of other energy sources such as the use of steam power or even internal combustion engines. A third major advantage of electricity is its cleanliness. There is no dust, dirt, or grease to be encountered where electricity is used, because the power plant for the generation of electricity is not located at the point of demand. Finally, capable of being used for mechanical energy, heat, light, refrigeration or any one of a dozen different purposes, electricity proves itself adaptable to use where any form of energy is needed.

In general the use of electricity falls into three major classifications: residential, industrial, and commercial. But there are many other categories: all of which are shown in Table 7.2 which gives the U.S. annual electric power requirements in 1960 and projected use in 1970 and 1980. These projections of electric power requirements were based on a comprehensive study by the FPC. Thus, starting from the vantage point provided by a knowledge of the industry's past achievements and future plans, the Commission projected a possible tripling of the country's use of electricity by 1980.

Residential Use

How the growth of electric consumption is expected to develop can be seen by looking first at the residential segment which is expected to continue to be the fastest growing market. The projected increase of 555 billion kwh in residential use—corresponding to an average increase of more than 150 percent per customer—highlights the potential for residential space heating and air conditioning and for greater use of electricity for appliances and improved lighting.

TABLE 7.2

Annual Electric Power Requirements by Categories of Use, 1960–1980

Category of use	1960 actual		1970 projected		1980 projected	
	Billion kwh	Percent total U.S.	Billion kwh	Percent total U.S.	Billion kwh	Percent total U.S.
Electric utilities:						
Residential (nonfarm)	174	22.7	373	25.2	729	27.1
Irrigation and drainage pumping	10	1.3	17	1.1	25	0.9
Other farm[1]	22	2.9	35	2.4	52	1.9
Commercial	121	15.9	241	16.2	430	16.0
Industrial[2]	330	43.4	615	41.5	1,098	40.8
Street and highway lighting	7	0.9	13	0.9	22	0.8
Electrified[3] transport	5	0.7	6	0.4	6	0.2
Other uses	22	2.9	42	2.7	71	2.6
Losses and unaccounted for	70	9.3	142	9.6	260	9.7
Total utility requirements	761	100.0	1,484	100.0	2,693	100.0
Industrial establishments:						
In-plant generation[4]	85		105		127	
Total	846		1,589		2,820	

1 Includes farms actually used for farming; other residential uses in farming areas included under "Residential."
2 Includes AEC loads which are expected to decline.
3 This projection reflects recent U.S. experience trends but could be far too low if the progress of electrified transport in other countries should prove a guide to future use in this country.
4 Excludes industry sales to electric utilities.
SOURCE: *National Power Survey*, A Report by the Federal Power Commission, Washington, D.C., 1964.

The industry has an announced target of 19 million electrically heated homes by 1980. The potential market for electric heating of homes is very large since only slightly more than one million homes were fully electrically heated in 1960. In addition, the average annual use of about 20,000 kwh of electricity in homes with electric heating and cooling contrasts with an average of 4,100 kwh in nonelectrically heated homes. If we assume that one home in four will be electrically heated in 1980—which is consistent with the projection of 19 million electrically heated homes—this heating load would account for 225 billion kwh of electricity annually, over 30 percent of the total projected for nonfarm residential use. To achieve the industry's goal in this market of unrelenting competition will require considerable technological and promotional effort which will have to accompany reduced costs and rates.

Air conditioning offers another potentially undeveloped market as only 10 million of the 55 million homes in the United States in 1960 had a means of air cooling and most of those were only partially cooled. Greater future use of electrical appliances will result from more homes, and perhaps additional units of appliances already owned.

In order to accomplish this electric consumption, the industry is not only going to have to promote all-electric homes, as it is doing, but it is also going to have to stress the necessity of adequate wiring and service entrance facilities having a minimum of 200 amperes capacity to accomodate increased household appliance loads.

These projections for 1980 contemplate a rise in the average annual consumption per nonfarm residential customer from about 4,200 kwh in 1963 to 10,000 kwh. The FPC thought that this goal might not be considered to be too difficult to reach since 10,000 kwh had already been reached in the TVA and Pacific Northwest regions; however it was felt that the task would be made much harder because of the large and growing number of apartment-dwellers who use less electricity than those living in single-family homes.

Industrial Use

Industrial consumption, the largest of all the use categories shown, is projected to increase by 768 billion kwh to over a trillion kwh annually by 1980; or a rate of growth of 6.4 percent per year. Much of this increase will come from existing intensive users of electricity, particularly the aluminum, steel, glass, plastics, and chemical industries. However, new industries stemming from the rapid development of new materials and new processes following World War II will be making increased demands for electricity. One example is the potential market for the manufacture of titanium, a promising newcomer to the group of structural metals and noted for high strength to weight ratio and temperature resistance, in which twice as many kwh are required to produce a ton of titanium as are required per ton of aluminum or magnesium.

Another new and expanding market for industrial uses of electricity is in consumption beyond the primary manufacturing needs. This market is to be found in the rapid growth in the lighting and air conditioning of industrial plants to improve working conditions and the requirements for critical temperature and humidity control in many industries. In these instances, however, the cost of the equipment may have a greater impact on electrification than the cost of energy itself.

Commercial Use

Commercial consumption of electricity is expected to grow at a rate of 6.5 percent a year to a total of 430 billion kwh in 1980—an increase of 309 billion kwh from the existing load in 1960. This projection is based on an accelerated expansion of lighting, air conditioning and electric space heating, much more electric office equipment, and the growth of electric cooking in restaurants and institutions. Certain is the air conditioning of commercial buildings which is rapidly becoming a necessity in almost all areas of the country and thus affords a large and growing market.

Another important and growing use of electricity is in outdoor and indoor display lighting. Also, increased lighting will be required for organized recreation as the rapid trend toward night sports spreads. A dramatic example is the electric lighted and air conditioned indoor stadium at Houston, Texas, which may be a prototype of mammoth-scale air-conditioning installations. These particular types of markets may be most advantageous to the electric power industry as in most instances they would occur in off-peak hours from regular commercial uses.

Total Requirements

In addition to residential, industrial, and commercial uses, Table 7.2 shows the amounts of electricity required in other use categories. In summary, the *National Power Survey* of the FPC visualizes increased dependence on electricity in all areas of the U.S. economy. We note from Table 7.2 that the United States will probably require approximately 2.8 trillion kwh of electricity by 1980, or slightly more than three times the amount generated in 1960. The FPC concludes that to produce this energy will require a well interconnected and coordinated utility industry with an installed capacity of about 523 million kilowatts, compared with about 200 million kilowatts of capacity in existence at the end of 1963.

The basic problem of how to expand the generating capacity to meet the growing demands for electric power will be the major topic considered in the problems and policy section of this chapter.

STRUCTURE OF THE ELECTRIC POWER INDUSTRY

The United States' electric power industry is made up of four distinct ownership segments: investor-owned, state and local public agencies, cooperatives, and federal agencies. The industry includes 3,600 systems which vary greatly in size, type of ownership, and range of the power supply functions performed.

As shown in Table 7.3 the investor-owned segment is the largest with 480 private systems, which own 76 percent of the industry's generating capacity and serve 79 percent of the retail customers.

Second in number of retail customers served is the public (non-federal) owned segment which consists of 2,124 state and local public agencies—including municipalities, public utility districts, and state and county entities. This group of public agencies accounts for 10 percent of the generating capacity and serves 13.5 percent of the retail consumers.

Cooperatives, the next largest segment, are a major factor in rural areas. Their principal role is distribution to 7.5 percent of the retail customers, but they own less than one percent of the industry's generating capacity.

The federal segment has 13 percent of the generating capacity. It consists primarily of five large agencies which market the federally generated power, most of which is produced as part of multipurpose river basin programs. Publicly owned systems and cooperatives are preference customers for federal power and purchase much of the output of the federal power plants. However, federal power is also sold to investor-owned utilities, to industries such as aluminum plants, and to government users. For example, The Atomic Energy Commission in 1963 purchased approximately 40 percent of the entire output of the TVA system.

Since 1930 there have been dramatic shifts in the relative share of power production by the private investor-owned segment and the public agencies. The change in the public share in this period has been substantial, increasing from 5.5 percent in 1930 to 23.6 percent in 1962. The greater part of this increase has resulted from huge federal projects notably the hydroelectric and steam generation of the TVA and the large-scale hydroelectric programs in the Columbia, Missouri, and Colorado River Basins.

Development and Institutional Organization

Investor-Owned Systems. The 480 investor-owned systems which serve approximately 79 percent of the nation's customers are themselves largely the result of the consolidation and combination of perhaps as many as 4,000 separate investor-owned systems and some 1,000 additional municipal systems which were once in existence. About 320 of the 480 existing companies are vertically integrated systems, generating most of the power they distribute. These systems account for 70 percent of the total electricity generated by the entire industry, public and private. Most of the remaining 160 investor-owned systems are primarily engaged in distribution.

One principal factor contributing to the development of the investor-

TABLE 7.3

Number of Systems, Generating Capacity, and Customers Served by U.S. Electric Power Industry[1] by Ownership Segment, 1962

Ownership	Number of systems			Generating capacity, percent of total	Retail customers served	
	Total	Engaged in generating and transmission	Engaged in distribution only		Number	Percent
Investor-owned[2]	480	318	162	76	47,500,000	79.0
Public (non-Federal)	2,124	864	1,260	10	8,118,000	13.5
Cooperatives	969	76	893[3]	1	5,095,000	7.5
Federal	44	42	2	13		
Total	3,617	1,300	2,317	100	60,713,000	100.0

1 Excludes Alaska and Hawaii.
2 Includes 34 industrial concerns that supply energy to other customers.
3 Many of the distribution cooperatives are also members of generating and transmission cooperatives (the so-called "G&T's") and hence participate indirectly in the generation and transmission function.
SOURCE: *National Power Survey*, A Report by the Federal Power Commission, Washington, D.C., 1964.

owned segment was the growth of the holding companies after 1900 and especially in the decade after World War I. The holding company was a means of combining in a single economic unit, a number of separate operating corporate entities, many of which were operating in noncontiguous areas. Moreover, the holding companies provided a means of achieving such combinations while meeting the requirements in certain states that a utility operating in such states be a domestic corporation. Unfortunately, however, holding companies were also used by some for financial empire-building, accounting and financial misrepresentation, and circumventing the intent of regulation.

By 1929, approximately 60 percent of the industry's electrical energy was provided by systems controlled, directly or indirectly, by seven holding companies. As an outgrowth of many of the abuses of concentration, the Public Utility Holding Company Act of 1935 provided comprehensive controls administered by the Securities and Exchange Commission (SEC) to end the abuses of the holding company instrument, including limitation of each holding company to a single interconnected system serving contiguous territory. The SEC has under the Holding Act eliminated unnecessary corporate complexity, and has provided continued regulatory control of the remaining holding company systems. There remained in 1965 eleven electric holding company systems, subject to all of the provisions of the Holding Company Act, which represented 21 percent of the sales of electric energy by the investor-owned electric power industry.

State and Local Public Agencies. Local public agency ownership began early in the industry's development, when numerous municipal systems were organized to provide electricity to previously unserved areas. There were more than 700 public systems in 1900, and over 3,000 by the early 1920's as compared with approximately 2,100 in 1965.

There are many types of public agencies that maintain their own electric generations, transmission, or distribution facilities, or combinations thereof. These include towns and cities of greatly varying sizes from the smallest to the city of Los Angeles, whose Department of Water and Power serves over a million customers in the city with power generated at Hoover Dam some 250 miles away, as well as by the Department's own hydro and steam plants and a new atomic energy plant. However, the most common forms of public entities, other than municipalities, providing electric service are special utility districts (as illustrated by the numerous public utility districts of Nebraska, Oregon, and Washington), municipal utility districts (such as the Sacramento Municipal Utility District in California), irrigation districts (such as the Imperial Irrigation District in California), and the various kinds of State "authorities" (such as the Grand River Dam Authority in Oklahoma, the Colorado River Commission of Nevada, the Arizona Power Authority, and the Power Authority of the State of New York).

The statutory and constitutional framework within which these public entities were created has tended to maintain their separate identities, and there is great diversity in the nature of their operations. Many municipalities and other local public agencies generate their own power requirements in varying degrees, while others purchase their power from federal, investor-owned, cooperative, or other local public systems, and sometimes from a combination of such suppliers. A few are largely confined to the generation and transmission functions. An example is the Power Authority of the State of New York, which sells at wholesale the power it generates at its two big hydroelectric projects at Niagara Falls and the St. Lawrence Seaway.

Rural Electric Cooperative Systems. The electric cooperative became a significant part of the electric industry after the enactment of the Rural Electrification Act of 1936. Prior to that time, the investor-owned segment of the industry had extended electric service to only about 10 percent of the farms in the United States, because it was generally believed that rural service would not yield an adequate return on the required investment.

The Rural Electrification Act of 1936 was designed to stimulate farm electrification through low cost loans by the Rural Electrification Administration (REA), of the U.S. Department of Agriculture, originally established in 1935 by executive order of President Franklin D. Roosevelt. The REA makes self-liquidating, interest bearing loans (currently fixed by statute at 2 percent) to finance the construction and operation of generating plants and of electric transmission and distribution lines to serve persons in rural areas who are not receiving central station service. Since the enactment of the Rural Electrification Act, electric cooperative cooperation laws have been adopted in many states for the purpose of providing an effective corporate means for furnishing electric service in rural areas on a cooperative basis, with the aid of REA financing. Although REA may make loans to investor-owned and public systems, the cooperatives have come to be the preferred vehicle for the extension of rural electrification with federal funds.

The vast majority of cooperatives are merely distributors and purchase all of their power at wholesale from the federal power marketing agencies or investor-owned utilities. However, some groups of distributing cooperatives have formed generating and transmission cooperatives to generate part or all of their electric power requirements.

As a result of the REA program, and the expansion of investor-owned companies' programs, 98 percent of the farms in the United States are electrified. There are about 1,000 cooperatives participating in the REA program, serving about 50 percent of the rural customers.

Federal Systems. The federal government is an important contributor to the electric power supply. Federal power is produced at approximately 125 projects which are part of federal multipurpose water resource developments, and at steam plants of the Tennessee Valley Authority (TVA). The agencies primarily responsible for the operation and maintenance of federal projects are the Bureau of Reclamation, the Army Corps of Engineers, and the TVA.

Almost all federal power is marketed by the TVA and four Department of Interior agencies—Bureau of Reclamation, Bonneville Power Administration, Southwestern Power Administration, and Southeastern Power Administration.

The TVA was created in 1933 as a means of controlling floods and of promoting navigation on the Tennessee River and its tributaries. Accomplishing these goals required the construction of dams and other facilities that had hydroelectric potential. Some of this electric energy was needed for operational purposes, but the act specified that surplus power could be marketed and also authorized the necessary transmission and related facilities. The TVA has grown to where it serves 80,000 square miles in the Tennessee River Basin area, and is the only federal agency with full responsibility for meeting all electric power supply requirements in any sizeable area of operation. In 1965, with over 13,000 megawatts of generating capacity, 9,300 of which was in steam plants, the TVA was the largest electric system in the United States with approximately twice the capacity of the next largest.

The Department of Interior agencies market power under the following procedures. The Bonneville Power Administration markets power generated at hydroelectric projects, located in the Pacific Northwest, of both the Corps of Engineers and the Bureau of Reclamation. The Bonneville Power Administration has constructed an extensive regional transmission system which facilitates the coordination of the total power supply in the area. The Bureau of Reclamation markets all the power generated by that agency, except that in the Pacific Northwest. The Bureau also markets power generated at Corps of Engineers' projects in the Missouri Basin. The Bureau has constructed transmission facilities to interconnect plants in the Missouri Basin, the Pacific Southwest, the Central Valley of California, and in the Upper Colorado River Basin. The Southwestern and Southeastern Power Administration (SWPA and SEPA) have the responsibility for marketing power from the Corps of Engineers' projects within their respective regions. SWPA has constructed some transmission facilities, but the SEPA does not operate transmission facilities.

Sales of electric power from federal projects are wholesale, except that the TVA both retails and wholesales electricity. The government sells power to approximately 1,050 electric utility systems in all sections except in the northeastern and portions of the north central United States. Public agencies and cooperatives systems are given statutory preference to buy the output of all federal projects. As a result, the federal system will occasionally displace an investor-owned system as a supplier to a preference customer. In addition, the availability of federal power at wholesale may encourage a preference agency to acquire its own distribution system in an area previously served by an investor-owned system. A further result of this preference system will be noted in the following section.

Areas Served

Investor-Owned Systems. The investor-owned systems generally serve prescribed areas pursuant to certificates or territorial franchises granted by one or more state or local governmental agencies. Sometimes such franchises are prescribed in the certificate of incorporation of the investor-owned utility; sometimes they are granted by state-wide public service commissions; and sometimes they are granted by counties or municipalities.

In the early days of the industry there was a significant amount of competition between investor-owned systems for particular territorial franchises and some duplication of facilities resulted. As a result, in some rare instances, two investor-owned systems provide electric services in a few communities.

State and Local Public Agencies. The local public agencies generally serve areas prescribed by municipal charter or state statute. In some instances (e.g., Cleveland, Ohio), a municipal system and an investor-owned system both serve the same community, but territorial competition between municipal systems and investor-owned systems is not frequent.

Rural Electric Cooperative Systems. In most states cooperatives do not have a franchise or other prescribed service areas and are free to serve in the state except as they may be limited by the basis upon which they may obtain their capital funds. The principal limitations are those set by the Rural Electrification Act, since most of the cooperative systems borrow funds under the Act.

The Rural Electrification Act requires that cooperatives financed under the Act be initially established to serve communities of not more than 1,500 persons which are without central station service. However it has been held that once this test has been met, REA funds may be used to serve all persons within the area and to expand the area of service to additional rural customers who are without service.

With growth in population and the annexation of municipalities of nearby areas there has grown up a considerable amount of competition between investor-owned companies and cooperatives for existing and new customers. In some areas this has led to the construction of duplicate facilities, and in all areas it has led to increased demands on the part of investor-owned companies that cooperatives have undue advantages which are gained at the taxpayers' expenses. This contention is made on the basis of their ability to borrow from the federal government at 2 percent, and their cooperative status which exempts them from paying federal and state income taxes.

Federal Systems. With the exception of the TVA, none of the federal systems possesses the equivalent of territorial franchise rights. Instead, they primarily sell power at wholesale to other systems, with statutory preference being given to public agency and cooperative systems on the output of the federal system. This gives rise, as noted above, to competition between the federal systems and investor-owned systems since the federal system may replace one of them as a supplier to the preference distribution system. In addition, the investor-owned systems claim that they should be given the right to distribute the low-cost federal power. As a consequence, the investor-owned segment of the industry is of the opinion that the preference system should be done away with and investor-owned systems should be given equal rights to purchase federal power.

Regulation

There are significant differences in the regulation of various segments of the power industry.

Investor-Owned Systems. The statutes of 46 states provide for public service commissions with varying degrees of statewide jurisdiction over investor-owned electric utilities. The commisisons typically regulate rates for retail sales, standards of service, issuance of securities, and accounting. Local regulation, directly and by franchise, is practiced in three of the four states where statewide regulation does not exist, namely Minnesota, South Dakota, and Texas. In Nebraska all electric utilities are publicly owned.

The interstate wholesale rates and services of investor-owned utilities are subject to the jurisdiction of the FPC. In addition, utilities making such sales or owning or operating facilities for the interstate transmission of electric energy are subject to the Commission's jurisdiction with respect to their interconnections, mergers, interlocking directorates, accounting, and, in certain instances, issuance of securities.

State and Local Public Agencies. In ten states public agency systems are subject to varying degrees of regulation at the state level by a public utility commission or its equivalent. In the other 40 states they are not subject to such regulation, but are subject to state statutes and are governed by boards of elected public officials. Normally, rates and rules for service are established only following public hearings.

State and local public agencies are also regulated in varying degrees by the federal government, e.g., agencies operating hydro projects under the Federal Power Act must comply with requirements established by the Federal Power Commission, and purchasers of federal power from the Department of Interior and the TVA must comply with so-called "resale rate" requirements set forth in purchase contracts.

Rural Electric Cooperative Systems. Rural electric cooperative systems are not subject to regulatory agencies in 30 of the 50 states. In the remaining states, varying degrees of regulation exist. One significant complaint of the investor-owned segment of the industry is that electric cooperatives are not subject to the same degree of state regulation as investor-owned companies.

However, the loan contacts of cooperatives which obtain their funds from the REA contain provisions reserving extensive control to the REA administrator over the operations of the cooperatives. Cooperatives are also controlled by their member-consumers who elect their Boards of Directors.

Federal Systems. No regulatory agency has comprehensive regulatory authority with respect to federal systems. Congress has reserved the regulatory power to itself, through enactments and committee control. The FPC allocates costs between functions in the case of certain federal projects and participation in the allocation of costs of others, and in this fashion has a voice in the determination of the allocated investment which affects the determination of rates.

Power rates established by the Bonneville Power Administration, the Southwestern Power Administration and the Southeastern Power Administration are subject to confirmation and approval by the Federal Power Administration. Rates for power sold by the TVA are not subject to such approval and, except for a few specified projects of the Bureau of Reclamation, power marketed by that agency also is not subject to FPC approval. It is not so much this lack of rate regulation that riles the private-power sector of the industry as it is the fact that federal rates do not reflect the total costs of power generation. More on this point will follow under the section, The Yardstick Method of Rate Regulation.

Public Utilities and Rate Regulation

The dictionary defines a public utility as "a business organization (as a public service corporation) performing some public service and subject to special governmental regulation." Another source says: "A public utility is an industry essential to the public interest with some element of necessary monopoly. To protect consumers utilities are either owned or regulated by the government."

Most economists would insist that a public utility should be the required form of business organization where two conditions exist: (1) The industry is a "natural monopoly," that is, the efficient scale of enterprise is very large relative to the market, so that splitting the market would obviously involve higher-cost production. (2) The industry is vital to the public welfare as electricity, public transportation, gas, and water.

Even the beginning economist can see that the initial capital costs for generation, transmission, and distribution are such that most communities should have only one efficient electric power system. To insist on several competitive firms in each area would probably lead to higher prices and certainly to a big waste in duplicate facilities. Further, under a competitive system perhaps none of the companies would be willing to serve an isolated house except at a very high price.

Thus, as a means of accomodating a natural monopoly in the public interest, a public utility is established. A public utility usually is given an exclusive franchise, or at least the entrance of other firms is controlled by the government in accordance with public interests. The public utility is required to provide service satisfactory to the regulating government agency, and its prices are controlled by the agency. But the question is: what price or what rate should be charged by the public utility? It follows that there ought to be a two-way responsibility. If the public utility must provide adequate services for the public, then the public has a responsibility to see that the public utility receives an adequate rate of return on its investment.

The investor-owned segment of the electric power industry operates as a public utility with rates regulated by the appropriate government agency. In general what has evolved is that rates should be regulated in such a fashion so as to give "a fair rate of return on a fair value," but it has also been suggested from time to time that a government agency should produce the electric power and let its rates be used as a "yardstick" to measure the adequacy of the rates charged by the investor-owned segment of the industry.

A Fair Rate of Return on a Fair Value

The landmark legal decision in utility pricing stems from a ruling by the Supreme Court in the case of Smyth vs. Ames in 1898. This ruling establishes a formula under which utility rates are calculated by ascertaining a fair value for the utility property in accordance with measures set forth by the Court (known as the rate base), ascertaining a fair return (known as rate of return) and then multiplying rate base by rate of return and adding allowable expenses. Thus a *fair value* for the base and a *fair rate* of return must be determined.

Should fair value of the investment be based on: (1) Original cost (minus depreciation), or the sum of all past prudent investments; or (2) Current reproduction or replacement costs (minus depreciation), or the cost of replacing the company's equipment at present prices corrected for age and condition of the property.

The second alternative is the choice of the companies because costs have been increasing and this method will give them a bigger investment base rather than a lower one based on outmoded costs. But customers, of course, favor original cost less depreciation. Which method is better depends on whose interests one puts first. If the price level were constant the two would amount to about the same thing. The courts have vacillated between the approaches. Some states use plant reproduction cost to determine the rate base, others original costs, still others some measure of fair value. Most economists do not like either approach, but reproduction costs appear more realistic since it gears public utility costs, prices, and earnings more directly to current conditions.

A fair rate of return is ascertained in line with guideposts set forth by the Supreme Court in the Bluefield Water Works case in 1932. The Court's decision states:

A public utility is entitled to such rates as will permit it to earn a return on the value of the property which it employs for the convenience of public equal to that generally being made at the same time and in the same general part of the country on investments in other business undertakings which are attended by corresponding risks and uncertainties; but it has no constitutional right to profits as are realized or anticipated in highly profitable enterprises or speculative ventures. The return should be reasonably sufficient to assure confidence in the financial soundness of the utility and should be adequate, under efficient and economical management, to maintain and support its credit and enable it to raise the money necessary for the proper discharge of its public duties.[5]

Using the above case as a guidepost, the courts have often selected 5, 6, or 7 percent as the fair rate of return.

Utility rate regulation then becomes a matter of pricing to give a fair rate of return on a fair value. The principal factor affecting differences in rates charged different classes of customers is the extent to which plant facilities are utilized (the capacity factor). The intent is to adjust rates to encourage increased use during offpeak periods. Thus the rates for industrial customers generally consist of a combination of: (1) a charge related to the customer's maximum demand (because this maximum demand determines the facilities necessary to provide the service), and (2) a charge related to the number of kwh consumed.

Residential and commercial rates are sometimes similarly divided in two parts, but this is not typical. Most residential customers are served under block meter rates, and commercial customers under both block meter and two-part rates. Residential pricing is heavily oriented toward balancing the load to achieve a high capacity factor. In regions of the country where peaks in electric consumption occur in the summer months, special winter heating rates are offered; in areas where winter peaks predominate, summer air conditioning rates are offered. The unit cost to the

[5] *Report of the National Fuels and Energy Study Group*, Washington, D.C., 1962, p. 233.

consumer in both of these cases is considerably less than the average paid for regular service.

In conclusion, it can be seen that the method of rate regulation of investor-owned electric utilities is designed to adjust individual prices to achieve the highest capacity factor, and in so doing to yield a fair rate of return on the fair value of the utility's investment.

The Yardstick Method of Rate Regulation

One suggested method of rate regulation was the idea advanced at one time that the TVA power costs should be used as a "yardstick" to measure the adequacy of the rates charged by the investor-owned segment of the electric power industry. Although for the moment it appears that this suggestion has been completely abandoned, it generated so much ill feeling between public and private interests that the idea needs to be examined briefly.

One of the fundamental contentions was that the TVA could not determine what part of its total costs should be attributed to power, and that in addition, the agency was not paying all the costs that private enterprise was.

In the first instance the contention was that in a multipurpose project, such as the TVA, there was no cost accountant alive who could determine what part of the total cost should be allocated to flood control, navigation, irrigation, and finally to electric power generation. In the second place the point was made that since appropriations for capital were being made out of general funds the TVA had no capital costs, and, further, it paid no taxes.

The fact is that all capital funds for federal power systems have been supplied entirely by capital appropriations and that no interest has been paid for the use of this money. On the other hand, private companies must pay investors for the use of capital. However, since 1959, perhaps as a direct result of this controversy, the TVA has been on a self-financing basis. The TVA was empowered to obtain funds in the private capital markets by the issuance of revenue bonds. The federal government's appropriation investment in TVA, as well as retained earnings, are treated as equity junior to the revenue bonds sold to the public. Since the 1959 self-financing Act, TVA is required to pay the U.S. Treasury a "return" or "dividend" on the appropriation investment equivalent to the average rate of interest paid by the United States on its outstanding marketable debt. TVA was also required to repay one billion dollars of the appropriated investment of 1.2 billion dollars within the next 59 years.

The fact on taxes is that federal power systems are not subject to federal and state income taxes or to local property taxes; whereas, the private companies must pay all these taxes. However, the TVA makes substantial payments in lieu of taxes to state and county governmental units. But private companies have long contested the adequacy of "in lieu of tax payments."

Under the circumstances it is understandable that investor-owned companies have objected violently to the idea of the yardstick method. In their objections they have accomplished the result of putting one federal operation, TVA, on a more self-financing basis.

The prevailing viewpoint of the investor-owned segment appears to be that the yardstick method is totally meaningless for the reasons mentioned above, and the general opinion is that the yardstick method of rate regulation wouldn't be fair because of the many different costs of power generation under different systems. Rather, it appears that the present governmental regulation of investor-owned electric public utility systems is working effectively to bring about the desired results: (1) to see that an area is provided with adequate electric service at reasonable rates, and (2) to see that the company receives a fair return on the fair value of the property used in furnishing the service.

Conclusion

The conclusion can be drawn that the structure of the electric power system is made up of four distinct ownership segments: investor-owned, state and local public agencies, cooperatives, and federal agencies. The industry includes 3,600 systems supplying power to over 60,000,000 customers. The private sector has been given public utility status and is regulated in the public interests. The cooperatives and the public sector are less subject to regulation but, nevertheless, especially in the case of the cooperatives and many of the federal projects, they have brought lower cost electric power to many consumers who might not otherwise have received it. It is quite possible that some of the costs of this latter service have been paid by taxpayers. In any event, the structure of the industry is such as to assure adequate electric power to residential, commercial, industrial, and other markets at reasonable rates.

PROBLEMS AND POLICY

The basic problem is to expand the generating capacity to provide for the growing demands for electric power and for an adequate reserve requirement. The FPC has established a definite target of 2.8 trillion kwh of electricity by 1980, or slightly more than three times the amount generated in 1960. The Commission has estimated that to produce this energy will require a well interconnected and coordinated electric power industry with an installed capacity of 523 million kilowatts, compared with about 200 million kilowatts of capacity in existence at the end of 1963.

Three of the subsidiary parts of the central electric power problem that will be considered are: (1) the type of generating capacity, (2) the class of ownership, and (3) the role of interconnection.

Types of Generating Capacity

Before World War II, 36 percent of electric power was produced by water power. By 1945 this figure was only slightly lower at 35 percent, but by 1962 less than 20 percent of the United States power production was hydro. This is most significant as it is indicative of the increasing dependence on thermal-produced electric power. The FPC estimates that by 1980 conventional hydro will contribute less than 15 percent of the generating capacity in the United States. This is part of the answer to the problem of what type of electric generating capacity the future holds which has been answered for us by the Federal Power Commission.

The general plans projected by the FPC for 1980 result in the following overall distribution of capacity by types: (1) Conventional hydro —14.5 percent; (2) Steam-power (fossil fueled)—67.3 percent; (3) Steam-power (nuclear fueled)—13.3 percent; (4) Pumped storage—3.6 percent; and (5) Diesel and gas turbines—1.3 percent. Table 7.4 shows the projected make-up of the generating capacity required in 1980 by sectors.

Hydroelectricity. The basis of determining hydroelectric feasibility was a study of potential hydroelectric capacities at existing or new projects which were economically feasible and might reasonably be expected to be completed by 1980. Such additions from 1967 to 1980 total 33 million kilowatts, which amounts to about 11 percent of the total required additions for this period.

The Pacific Northwest and the Southeast are the areas where most of the new hydroelectric facilities will be located, and it is estimated that about two-thirds of the new capacity will be constructed in these areas. About 50 percent of the new capacity is projected for the Pacific Northwest, where the FPC believes that hydroelectric capacity will be serving both base and peak loads well into the 1970's, but in later years of the decade base load thermal power will be required to meet total demands. Outside the Northwest the new hydroelectric capacity will be used primarily to serve peak loads.

The FPC believes that about one-half of the new hydro power will probably be built as a part of federal multipurpose development programs, but, nevertheless, is of the opinion that there are many locations that should be economically attractive for development by private enterprise.

A strong case can be made for adopting a policy of first priority for developing hydro power sites. Hydroelectric power is unique in that it is an energy source that requires no fuel for generation. The recurring cy-

TABLE 7.4

Estimated U.S.[1] Generating Capacity 1980
(Gigawatts[3])

Generating capacity	Northeast sector	South sector	North central sector	West sector	Total	Percent
Hydroelectric:						
In 1966	6.7	10.2	3.9	21.8	42.6	8.2
Added 1967–1980[2]	3.5	6.8	0.2	22.7	33.2	6.3
	10.2	17.0	4.1	44.5	75.8	14.5
Fossil fueled steam:						
At load center:						
In 1966	53.0	57.4	21.9	18.9	151.2	28.9
Added 1967–1980[2]	40.8	51.2	14.8	7.0	113.8	21.8
	93.8	108.6	36.7	25.9	265.0	50.7
At mine mouth:						
In 1966	13.9	4.5	2.0	0.5	20.9	4.0
Added 1967–1980[2]	22.8	18.9	19.0	5.0	65.7	12.6
	36.7	23.4	21.0	5.5	86.6	16.6

262

Nuclear fueled steam:						
In 1966	0.8	0.0	0.3	1.5	2.6	0.5
Added 1967–1980[2]	25.3	13.4	10.0	18.4	67.1	12.8
	26.1	13.4	10.3	19.9	69.7	13.3
Pumped storage:						
In 1966	0.6	0.1	0.4	0	1.1	0.2
Added 1967–1980[2]	10.9	4.0	2.0	1.0	17.9	3.4
	11.5	4.1	2.4	1.0	19.0	3.6
Diesel and Gas Turbines						
In 1966	1.2	1.5	1.4	0.2	4.3	0.8
Added 1967–1980[2]	1.4	0.7	0.5	0	2.6	0.5
	2.6	2.2	1.9	0.2	6.9	1.3
Total:						
In 1966	76.2	73.7	29.9	42.9	222.7	42.6
Added 1967–1980[2]	104.7	95.0	46.5	54.1	300.3	57.4
	180.9[4]	168.7[2]	76.4[4]	97.0[4]	523.0[4]	100.0

1 Excludes Alaska and Hawaii; also excludes imports from Canada.
2 Additions less retirements.
3 Millions of kilowatts.
4 The capacity provided for each sector takes into account diversity savings, potential imports from Canada, and the relative difference in reserve requirements for hydroelectric and thermal capacity.
SOURCE: *National Power Survey*, A Report by the Federal Power Commission, Washington, D.C., 1964.

cles of rainfall, runoff, evaporation, and transpiration make hydroelectric power a renewable flow energy source. Hydroelectric plants have several important advantages which have not been stressed in an earlier study. They neither consume water, nor do they heat the water of rivers as thermal plants do. The maintenance costs of hydroelectric plants are relatively low, and in many instances the plants can be designed for automatic or remote control. They have long life, low depreciation expenses, and relatively predictable costs because fixed charges are a much larger part and current operating expenses a much smaller share of total costs than in the cases of fuel-burning plants.

Perhaps the strongest policy argument for the development of hydropower stems from the fact in many cases it provides such associated benefits as flood control, recreation, water supply, fish and wildlife enhancement, and cooling water for thermal electric and industrial plants. Many multipurpose projects would not be economically feasible without the inclusion of power as one of the project purposes.

The favorable characteristic of hydroelectric power and the frequent multiple use benefits associated with its development provide strong incentives for utilizing the remaining potential of the nation's water power resources that can be developed economically.

Fossil Fueled Steam Power. The projections of the FPC show that conventional steam plants will provide in excess of 350 million kilowatts of the total installed capacity by 1980. This represents about 67 percent of the needed capacity, of which about 17 percent is shown to be at mine-mouth. Fossil fuel plants will add about 60 percent of the capacity from 1967 to 1980. The indications are that the central areas of the United States will continue their major dependence on fossil fuel steam generated electricity.

The trend of the future appears to be the location of a large number of plants in the coal fields of Appalachia and the Ohio and Tennessee Valley which are situated in mining areas or within short hauling distances, and the location of generating plants near the natural gas fields of Texas, Oklahoma, Kansas, Arkansas, and Louisiana.

The choice between locating a conventional steam plant at the fuel source or at the load center has been determined, as our past study has indicated, largely by economic comparisons between the cost of delivering energy to the load by fuel transport and the cost of transporting energy by wire. These will still remain the principal considerations but the comparisons will be sharpened by improved efficiencies and reduced costs among the competing forms of transportation, and alternative choices in types of generation.

But there is a group of additional factors that may lead to policy decisions favoring locations away from the load centers. Finding suitable sites near load centers is becoming more and more difficult, and when found they are expensive. In addition, stream and air polution are significant problems in steam generation and federal, state, and local governments are likely to become much more strict in controlling contamination. The result is that good sites available for large generation stations are decreasing in number with the increase in population, expansion of the economy, and the more active interest of the general public in matters of stream and air pollution. Therefore it follows that it is in the best interest of the electric utilities to use each site selected for the largest generating plant that can be economically justified. Fortunately, as has been noted, the industry has been making great strides in increasing the size of generating units. Not only will the increased size of these generating units make possible the maximum use of site location, but also they are likely to have significant effects on reducing the cost of power generation.

Another factor favoring mine-mouth generation, is the opportunity for multiple use of transmission lines from mine-mouth stations to load centers. Many of the lines serving mine-mouth stations as well as remote hydroelectric plants can become components in transmission interconnection networks. Certainly, the incorporation of such lines into interconnected grids should be the rule for electric power systems having generating plants in the extensive coal fields of Appalachia.

The construction of the required additional fossil fuel plants of such large scale and the investment in transmission facilities require that these plants have adequate fuel supplies. It is expected that for new generating capacity coal, oil, and natural gas will share in the proportion of 75 percent, 5 percent, and 20 percent respectively. The geographic distribution of the plants using these fuels is expected to remain about the same with coal predominating in the heavy load areas surrounding the extensive coal fields in a broad east to west belt from Pennsylvania to Arkansas and certain areas in the West; natural gas will be the leading fuel in the load areas bordering on the large gas fields in the Southwest; and oil will be limited generally to the coastal areas where other fuel costs are higher. The Federal Power Commission's projections indicate that by 1980 the electric power industry will more than triple its 1960 demands for fossil fuels and will be using annually some 500 million tons of coal, 4 trillion cubic feet of natural gas, and 100 million barrels of fuel oil. Based on our past study of these three fuels, the conclusion can be drawn that adequacy of supply will not be a problem. To the contrary, increased demands for coal by the electric power industry are expected to help coal out of its sick-bed. Further, an additional factor protecting the availability of the fossil fuel supply is that steam-electric units can be designed to burn alternative types of fuel and can change from one fuel to another in accordance with availability and price.

Since the U.S. economy must continue to depend on conventional steam-electric plants as the principal source of power, it is fortunate that this source of power has earned its present position. The impressive continuity in increasing unit size at ever-continuing economic gain has brought about lower capital costs, improved heat rates, and reduced costs of operation. In the six-year period alone 1957 through 1962, unit costs of generation of steam electric power were reduced from 3.90 mills to 3.54 mills per kwh for fuel, operation, and maintenance. In 1962 the average total cost, including fixed charges, for producing steam-electric power in investor-owned plants was slightly over 7.5 mills per kwh, and in 1964 the more economical of the privately-owned conventional steam electric plants were producing high load factor power at less than 5 mills per kwh.

There is reason to expect further improvements in all the elements that have produced all the best plants with their outstanding records of reducing the cost of conventional steam-electric power. These are: (1) reduction in the delivered cost of fuel, (2) reduced annual operating and maintenance expense, (3) lowered investment cost per kilowatt of capacity, and (4) improved heat rate.

Nuclear Fueled Steam Power. Nuclear (atomic) power has been discussed in detail in the previous chapter. Nuclear power is expected by the FPC to account for approximately 70 million kilowatts of generating capacity by 1980, or a little over 13 percent of the total installed capacity. This is a tremendous increase from the thirteen civilian nuclear power plants operable in the United States in 1964 with a combined net capacity of about 970,000 kilowatts, supplying only a fraction of the nation's power needs. Nuclear plants operating at the base of the load at an average factor of 85 percent are expected to supply about 19 percent of the electric power requirements in 1980.

Nuclear power is expected to make its strongest showing in New England, Florida, and the West Coast. These are areas where generating costs are sufficiently high to permit some of the projected plants to be competitive. Moderate projections are made for nuclear power in the Great Lakes and mid-continent region.

Tables 6.6, 6.7, and 6.8 presented the data as of July 1, 1964 for the nuclear power plants operable, under construction, and planned in the United States. As early as the first part of 1964, the AEC had what was thought by some an optimistic target of 40 million kilowatts of installed capacity by 1980. The projection of 70 million kilowatts made late in 1964 is a most optimistic revision made on the basis of the cost estimates for Oyster Creek Station, New Jersey, the last plant on the list in Table 6.8.

We learned in Chapter 6 that the Jersey Central Power and Light Company was predicting that its Oyster Creek 515,000 kilowatt boiling water reactor would produce power at less than 4.5¢ per kwh. This plant was constructed at a cost per kilowatt considerably less than any earlier plant; and the FPC was of the opinion that this and other then current proposals appeared to mark the beginning of marketing practices by major nuclear reactor manufacturers which took into account the opportunities for repetitive use of established reactor designs.

Another factor working in favor of lower costs was the construction of nuclear reactors with larger generating capacity. We have already noted that a nuclear plant has higher construction costs than a conventional plant. However, comparative design studies have indicated that the capital costs per unit of capacity for a nuclear plant should decline even more rapidly with increasing capacity than do conventional plant costs. Accordingly, the capital cost disadvantage of nuclear plants in comparison with conventional plants will be less significant for larger plants.

The FPC in the *National Power Survey*, after a thorough study of costs involved, projects the following range of generating costs for nuclear power assuming an 80 percent capacity factor.

Table 7.5
Projected Range of Nuclear Generation Costs

	1967	1970	1975	1980
1. Year plant placed in service	1967	1970	1975	1980
2. Nominal plant output—kilowatts	300,000	500,000	1,000,000	1,200,000
3. Range in generating cost (at busbar) for nuclear plants—mills/kwh	5.4–6.0	4.3–5.0	3.5–4.1	3.2–3.8

Source: *National Power Survey*, A Report by the Federal Power Commission, Washington, D.C., 1964.

The rate of installation of new nuclear generating plant capacity will be dependent not only upon the realization of projected declines in nuclear plant and fuel costs, but also on the attitudes of utility management. It seems likely that management will be alert to use proven types of nuclear plants, but will be hesitant to undertake the construction of unproven types. But it does appear that the range of projected costs for proven reactors will make nuclear fuel installations economically feasible in many areas. Areas of high fossil fuel costs will be the first to increase their nuclear power capacity, but when nuclear costs are sufficiently reduced, other areas are likely to install nuclear capacity. In some cases there may be other than economic reasons for installing nuclear plants. For example, the FPC judged it advisable in its projection to include in a few instances nuclear installations for densely populated metropolitan areas on the grounds that such plants, located on the fringe of metropolitan areas, could assist in meeting total loads without contributing further to the problem of air pollution.

In conclusion, it must be noted that the projections which stress nuclear power in New England, Florida, and the West Coast are based on the assumption that nuclear plants and production costs have a greater opportunity for future cost reduction than conventional thermal generation under the fuel supply which exists. We have seen that the suppliers and transporters of fossil fuels (especially coal) are actively competing for the electric power market. Thus part of the answer as to how fast nuclear generating capacity will be expanded will depend on the vigor with which suppliers of these competing forms of energy pursue their respective advantages to achieve lower-cost power.

Class of Ownership

How the required addition to generating capacity is to be achieved is the fundamental issue of the basic electric power problem. Central to the solution of the issue is the much debated public and private ownership of generating facilities.

Facts Bearing on the Problem. Just prior to the completion of the *National Power Survey,* a 20-year summary of the relative position of public and private power would show that in 1962 the investor-owned companies accounted for 75.5 percent of total electric industry capacity, and governmental agencies plus cooperatives provided 24.3 percent, while in 1942 the investor-owned companies had 83.1 percent of total capacity and governmental agencies plus cooperatives comprised only 16.9 percent. During the twenty years from 1942 to 1962 the private companies installed a total of 107 million kilowatts, of which about three-fourths of the total was installed in the last 10-year period. At the same time governmental agencies and cooperatives added almost 39 million kilowatts, including 29 million kilowatts during the last ten years.

Of the governmental additions to capacity during the 1942–1962 period, federal agencies, including the TVA, Bonneville, Grand Coulee, and Hoover Dam were responsible for 21 million kilowatts, and municipal plants, aided by federal loans and grants, installed over 9 million kilowatts. Power districts, state projects, and cooperatives added over 8 million kilowatts. Table 7.6, which follows, gives the complete comparison of investor-owned, cooperatives, and governmental agencies.

The electric power industry, partly because of the great depression of the 1930's, was conservative in estimating future demand. The result was too slow expansion of capacity, which had a drastic effect of retarding industrial growth. As already noted, the growth in power capacity in the 1930's was due to public or federal power projects. These were large multipurpose installations which could not have been undertaken by private enterprise. Yet this was the big surge forward in public power that ultimately led, for example, to the TVA buying out practically every investor-owned electric utility in Tennessee—there now remain only three investor-owned facilities. And although begun with hydroelectricity as the prime source of power, the TVA now generates about two-thirds of its electricity through the use of steam generators.

TABLE 7.6

Comparison of Investor-owned, Cooperatives and Governmental
Generating Capacity, 1942–1962

	1942		1962	
	Installed capacity, kilowatts in thousands; (Name-plate)	Per-cent	Installed capacity, kilowatts in thousands (Name-plate)	Per-cent
Investor-Owned Companies	37,442	83.1	144,577	75.7
Cooperatives			1,537	0.8
Governmental Agencies				
Federal (TVA, Bonneville, etc)	3,216	7.2	24,315	12.7
Municipal governments	3,527	7.8	12,929	6.8
Power districts and state projects	868	1.9	7,709	4.0
Total Governmental	7,611	16.9	44,953	23.5
Total Electric Industry	45,053	100.0	191,067	100.0

Source: *National Power Survey*, A Report by the Federal Power Commission, Washington, D.C., 1964.

The investor-owned companies themselves helped the growth of public power by their reluctance to serve customers in remote, high-cost-of-service rural areas. This gave rise to the Rural Electrification Administration which greatly increased farm and rural use of electricity through sponsorship of "farm cooperatives" and other types of cooperatives. The REA did a commendable job in making low-cost loans to the cooperatives so that distributive systems could be set up. But in recent years it has actively sponsored the construction of steam-generating facilities by the cooperatives. And as we have noted, much to the dissatisfaction of the investor-owned companies, these cooperatives borrow their funds from the REA at a cost of 2 percent for interest, and in most instances these cooperatives are tax free, nonregulated undertakings. This is indeed an interesting public policy which permits a government agency to lend money at 2 percent, when the federal government itself has had to pay in excess of 4 percent for long-term bond financing.

There is no question about the contribution of the REA to the rural economy, or that, for example, of the TVA to the economy of the Southeast. Further, there was great good fortune in having the electric power of the federal multipurpose facilities available at the beginning of World War II. However, the growth of federal power facilities brought with them the controversial issue of the yardstick method of gauging rates charged by private utilities, one aspect of which we have previously discussed.

There have been at least two fundamental points at issue in the yardstick method that have been vigorously debated. First was the pricing policy advocated by the TVA—that low electric power rates would result in increased demand for electric power and increased total revenue with lower costs. Prior to the TVA, private power companies were reluctant to experiment with the effect of lower rates, knowing that once rates had been lowered it would be difficult to raise them if the experiment proved unsuccessful. Erich Zimmermann, who had a real sense of feeling for the TVA rate approach, argued the point: "Low rates for electricity attract industries, electrical machinery raises the productivity of labor, this in turn raises incomes and the standard of living, and this again calls for the use of more electricity. Similarly on the farm, the liberal use of electricity renders labor more productive and sets in motion a spiral of forces which raises the whole level of the economy." Private power companies will agree with this conclusion, but they want to know what the effect is on their cost-income-profit position. This led to the second and most heated part of the yardstick debate. What was the cost of multipurpose, by-product-produced power and did the rates cover the costs? The argument has been over whether low-rate policies made it possible for the public power facilities to pay their way or whether they were operating at a loss. Public power supporters advance the Zimmermann point of view and in addition claim that most of the projects show a return on the public's investment. The private power companies disagree with this view and contend that the cost allocations in the public power accounting and in the yardstick have not included interest charges and taxes, which private companies must use.

The effect of this whole argument was that private power utilities were uncertain as to the role of public power, and an additional element of conservatism was added to the private electric power industry. Power shortages and low reserve margins after World War II were results of this conservatism, results which only served to add fuel to the fire of the postwar debate over public and private power.

There seems to be some general agreement that federal power projects are justified when private capital is unable to undertake an investment. The points of disagreement arise in determining the circumstances under which this is true; in addition, where the federal facilities are established in an area, such as the TVA, should private power facilities be allowed to establish new fuel plants within the area to serve expanding demands? There are unlimited subsidiary issues which are a part of the debate.

Policy. Two reports on this controversial issue of public versus private power will point up and summarize many issues and policy problems involved. The first of these reports was from the President's (Truman) Water Resources Policy Commission in 1950. This Commission recommended as a part of *A Water Policy for the American People:*

Full development of the Nation's undeveloped water power resources, as an integral part of comprehensive basin programs, should be considered a major federal responsibility, to be exercised in such a way as to assure ample supplies of hydroelectric energy well in advance of expanding regional and national needs.

Federal hydroelectric plants should be designed to produce ultimate capacity and energy which will best fit into the requirements of potential markets on the assumption of complete regional integration of power supply.

Future licenses for new non-federal water power developments should be issued only with the joint consent of the federal agencies responsible for power in basin programs. In exercising this responsibility, the federal agencies should continue to recognize the preferential position accorded state and municipal applicants under the Federal Power Act.

The federal power marketing policy heretofore adopted by Congress, authorizing federal agencies to build transmission facilities, giving preferences in power sales to public and cooperative bodies, and fostering low rates for residential and rural consumption, should be continued.

Federal power marketing policy should be carried out flexibly to assure sound adaptation of federal power supply responsibility to regional power resources and the most effective cooperation of all power systems, public and private, in the task of assuring ample supplies of power at the lowest possible rates.

Since private power systems will probably continue to provide a large share of the new capacity required to meet future needs, federal arrangements for marketing power should where possible take full advantage of private power facilities, provided the contracts preserve the preferential right of public bodies and cooperatives to a share of the power, or its equivalent, at the lowest possible rates.

Where the Federal Government assumes a major responsibility for the power supply to distribution systems, this should be recognized as a utility responsibility, requiring the construction of new generating capacity, whether hydroelectric or steam-electric, well in advance of expanding needs.

The second report was made in 1955 by the Commission on Organization of the Executive Branch of Government. This Water Resources and Power Report to Congress called for a revolution in federal power policy and in summary recommended an end to the expansion of federal power. Four of the twelve Commission members, including two top Republicans—Attorney General Herbert Brownell, Jr., and Defense Mobilization Director Arthur S. Flemming—dissented vigorously in the findings and recommendations, which included the following:

. . . A large number of the great multipurpose dams . . . were . . . beyond the financial and technical strength of private enterprise or the nongovernmental agencies. . . . But this situation does not prevail today.

The growth of savings in the hands of private citizens and institutions now enables both private companies and nonfederal public bodies to obtain enormous sums for the building of power plants. . . . Financially there is no present or prospective need for financing of power activities.

Federal power development might also be deemed necessary if privately owned electric utilities could not be regulated effectively in the public interest. The regulation of electric utilities . . . by both State and federal governments has become effective.

Federal power development might be deemed necessary if nonfederal sources could not supply whatever power was required for the current and prospective defense activities of the Federal Government. There is nothing to indicate any necessity of this sort.

It is clear that in the field of power the government is conducting functions and activities which are competitive with private enterprise. This competition "has taken on many aspects which are the negation of our fundamental economic system" of free competitive enterprise.

Rates charged for federal power are too low because "exemptions from tax charges and other economical rate making practices caused revenues from federal power sales in 1953 to fall about 40 percent below the value of the power."

Rate making authority over federal power should be given to the Federal Power Commission and the FPC be directed to fix rates high enough to cover all costs—including amortization and interest on the federal investment, and amounts equal to federal, state and local taxes paid by private utilities.

All the federal multiple-purpose projects should be self-supporting and made subject to the Government Corporation Control Act. These federal projects should be "required to secure their capital for future improvements when authorized by Congress, by issuing their own securities to the public. . . ."

In addition, the Commission on Organization insisted:

That private enterprise be offered the opportunity to provide the capital for the electric component of multiple purpose dams and dispose of the power through their own systems.

That Government cease the building of steam plants and connect federal power facilities with grids of neighboring systems.

That Government undertake no further building of transmission lines where such transmission services can be provided by nonfederal agencies.

That . . . private utilities be permitted to purchase a fair share of federal power.

The net effect of this second report was to recommend that all existing federal projects be made self-supporting and that no additional federal projects should be undertaken. Republican (!) Commissioners Brownell and Flemming believed that "the recommendations taken together would impede the federal government in exercising its proper role in the development of the nation's water resources."

Much of the public versus private power controversy has had expression in specific regions where public power is dominant—principally in the East South Central states (TVA) where over 75 percent of the electric power generated is publicly owned, and in the Pacific area (Columbia River Basin) where over 50 percent of the kwh is public.

The real clamor for public power began in the 1920's, with Senator George Norris of Nebraska the most vociferous advocate. He sponsored and created the TVA with the stated purpose of flood control and navigation, using the maximum generation of electric power consistent with these aims. The first major dam of the TVA is named for the Senator. If one looks at the purpose of the TVA, power generation was incidental and presumably only in sufficient quantity to supply the power needs of the TVA. Actually, as we have already seen, electric power generation became anything but incidental, and a whole regional complex known all over the world has grown up in the Valley as depicted and described in Figure 7.4. As a result, the Tennessee Valley has produced many ardent spokesmen for public power who have continued the battle championed by Senator Norris.

With many swift rivers and waterfalls, it was only natural that the states of the Pacific Northwest, particularly Idaho, Oregon, and Washington, became the focal point for advocates of public power. Today the Department of Interior operates the world's largest generating facilities at Bonneville-Grand Coulee on the Columbia River. In addition, as a result of public advocates in many areas of these states, organizations known as Public (or People's) Utility Districts (PUD) were formed. These PUDs were given broad powers by the states, and they were able to condemn various investor-owned electric properties, including generating stations. But the federal government, through Bonneville and other developments, supplies the bulk of the power used by the PUDs. The privately-owned utilities in the area also can buy federal power, but first choice is given the PUDs and similar groups such as REA cooperatives and municipalities. Out of the Northwest has come much political support for public power, although there has been some evidence that public opinion is shifting. Under the so-called partnership principles of the Eisenhower administration, private companies renewed their construction of large power projects. But at the Snake River in Idaho, one of the last remaining sites on which a large power dam could be built, the debate was whether the plant should be built by private companies (which received approval by the FPC), a combination of local PUDs, or the federal government itself.

The debate over the activities of the REA cooperatives is less regional

Figure 7.4: The Tennessee Valley Authority.

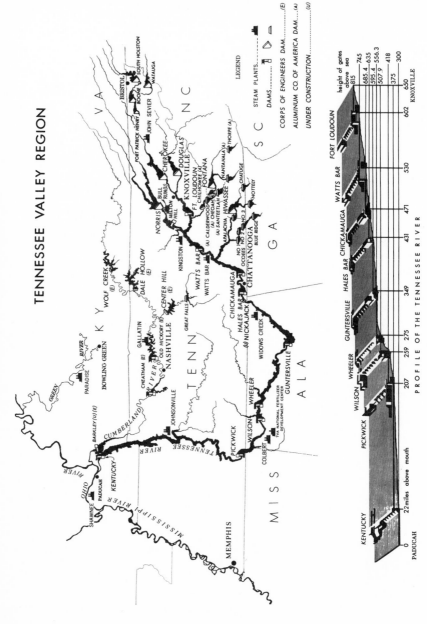

NOTE: The Tennessee River has its principal headwaters in the Appalachian Mountains of Virginia and North Carolina. Ranked by volume of streamflow, it is the fifth largest river system in the United States. The Mississippi, Columbia, Ohio, and Missouri outrank it. The main stem of the river forms at Knoxville, Tennessee, where two of its major tributaries join—the Holston River from southwestern Virginia and the French Broad from western North Carolina. Its course goes southwest through eastern Tennessee, gathering the flow of important tributaries: the Clinch carrying water from southwestern Virginia, the Little Tennessee from North Carolina, and the Hiwassee and Ocoee rivers, whose headwaters are in North Carolina and Georgia.

Thus grown, the Tennessee flows into the northern part of Alabama, where it turns generally west, crosses that state, and swings north through western Tennessee and Kentucky. About 650 miles from Knoxville it joins the Ohio River to flow into the Mississippi River at Cairo, Illinois; the streamflow of the Tennessee accounts for about 25 percent of the Ohio's discharge into the Mississippi. The watershed of the Tennessee River is about 40,000 square miles.

This is the river system that in the early 1930's wasted its great power in destruction of land, property, and human life. Now, the Tennessee River is the most completely controlled river system in the United States.

The Tennessee Valley Authority (TVA), by Act of Congress, signed on May 18, 1933, was created as a new agency to supplement the efforts of a region to develop its total resources for the benefit of the area and the nation. A summary of the many purposes of the project is found in Section 23 of the Act: "for the especial purpose of bringing about in said Tennessee drainage basin and adjoining territory . . . (1) the maximum amount of flood control; (2) the maximum development . . . for navigation purposes; (3) the maximum generation of electric power consistent with flood control and navigation; (4) the proper use of marginal lands; (5) the proper method of reforestation . . . and (6), the economic and social well-being of the people living in said river basin.

In 1965, 32 major dams and 10 large steam plants were generating electric power which was sold to cities and rural cooperatives for distribution, and which was used by the Federal Government in atomic energy projects and for other defense purposes. The TVA power system generated more than 73 billion kwh of electricity in fiscal year 1964. About 38 percent of the power was used by atomic defense plants. More than 1,800,000 consumers used TVA power in 1965, nine times as many as had electricity in the same area in 1933. Nearly all the region's farms were electrified com-

pared with 3.5 percent in 1933. Residential consumers paid less than half as much per kwh as did those in the nation as a whole and they used over twice as much, on the average.

The TVA helps in the industrial development of the region. Its multipurpose dams, its forestry and agricultural aids, and its service to industry had helped make it possible by 1963 for the people to increase their per capita income 897 percent since TVA began; in the nation the increase had been 553 percent. By 1962, the number of jobs in manufacturing had increased by 350,000.

The dams have created a series of slack water lakes with a nine-foot navigable depth for 650 miles, from Paducah, Kentucky, to Knoxville, Tennessee. In 1958, river traffic ton-mileage was nearly 70 times as great as it was before TVA. An all-year navigation channel connects the great trans-Appalachian region with the inland waterway system directly connecting twenty states.

The TVA operates chemical laboratories and plants for research in improved fertilizers and processes for their manufacture, the object being to lower the cost of fertilizers to farmers. Since 1950, the cost of plant nutrients in the United States has declined 15 percent. Fertilizers are made in times of peace and munitions in times of war. The TVA made it possible during World War II to mobilize quickly the resources of a strategic region in the nation's scheme of defense to produce aluminum, chemicals, and the materials for atomic weapons.

TVA reservoirs have up to 12 million acre-feet of storage space reserved at the beginning of the flood season for flood control alone. This makes possible the reduction of floods in the Valley and aids in control of lower Ohio and Mississippi River floods. At times as much as four feet have been cut from the crest of a Mississippi River flood south of Cairo, Illinois.

Recreation, the bonus of river development, had become a major industry in which states, counties, cities, and private individuals had invested by 1965 some 170 million dollars.

Many TVA achievements have been noted, but the full development of the Tennessee Valley is something more than the mobilization of economic assets for the achievement of greater material rewards. The Tennessee Valley's greatest asset is its people who prefer to live there because they like its hills and valleys, and its mountains and forests, its prevailing sense of community, and the depth of the region's cultural roots and traditions. These folk have now found productive and satisfying work and exercise their initiative freely. As a result, the freedom, security, and strength of these people and the nation have made significant gains which only one who has lived with this regional revolution can fully appreciate.

SOURCE: Tennessee Valley Authority.

in character because of their widespread activities throughout the United States. As a result, at many local levels the battle between public and private power goes on with intensity because of the growing conflict of interest between investor-owned companies and REA cooperatives.

At the national level, as we have seen, the public versus private power issue has had its more recent reflections in the role of the government in sponsoring nuclear power developments. Our intensive study of nuclear power has revealed that nuclear development is being turned progressively over to private enterprise.

But what should the policy be between public and private power? We have seen the difference in the recommendations of two government commissions and how the support for the various policies is conditioned by differences in interest. But whatever differences exist, the investor-owned electric power and light companies, through the Edison Electric Institute, have prepared a booklet, *We Believe,* which sets forth clearly their recommended policies for federal operation, rural electrification, and atomic development that are summarized in the following paragraphs.

Federal government generation of electrical power should be undertaken only under the following rules:

1. In multipurpose federal projects all capital investment required for the construction and installation of the power facilities should be charged to the power function of each project.
2. Investment in power facilities should be self-liquidating over a reasonable period, as to both principal and cost of money.
3. The power should be sold without discrimination or preference.
4. Such sums as electric companies carrying on the same business would pay in federal, state, and local taxes should be included as part of the cost of making power.
5. All proceeds from the sale of power should be paid into the federal treasury. Rates should yield to the government not less than the cost of power, including interest, charges for taxes, depreciation, operation, and maintenance. The power should be distributed by nonfederal distributors under adequate regulation.
6. The government should not build transmission lines from federal dams to market where existing distributors have built or are willing to build them.

Rural electrification cooperatives are serving a good purpose in retailing electricity to farms. The power companies will continue to sell power to them at the lowest rate consistent with sound economic principles. But the investor-owned companies believe that the following practices should prevail in passing loans to rural electric cooperatives for generating plants and transmission lines.

1. The cost analyses upon which the loans are justified should be open to inspection and not held in secret as at present.

2. In determining economic feasibility, a proper cost of money should be used, rather than the artificial 2 percent rate.
3. The analyses should allow for the taxes which will be foregone when the power supply is government-financed.

Atomic power development should be effected according to the following principles.

1. In the building and operation of prototype and commercial-type nuclear power reactors maximum utilization should be made of the American free enterprise system and free market financing.
2. The statutory requirement of mandatory ownership of special nuclear material should be abolished and legislation should be enacted calling for industry ownership of such nuclear material, provided there is an adequate transition period to allow the nuclear industry to make the necessary adjustments to the change.
3. The role of the federal government should be one of engaging in fundamental and experimental research rather than in building power plants. Beyond fundamental research, the role of the government should be in research and advanced reactor concepts. In general this work should be followed as part of the research program by small experimental units.

Thus we have a clear-cut policy recommendation by the investor-owned companies on public power in three areas—federally-owned, cooperatively distributed, and in atomic development. How near one comes to accepting these recommendations depends upon one's position as a consumer, voter, and owner and upon one's geographical location; or it may depend on one's fundamental philosophy about the role of government. However, it does appear, as we have noted previously, that policy now favors development of nuclear power by private interest in effecting the full recommendations of the investor-owned companies.

Further, even under the Kennedy administration, the investor-owned companies seemed to be making some headway. This was indicated by two developments. First, President Kennedy in one of his statements before the Committee for Economic Development indicated that when a private company could develop a hydro site or provide service more satisfactorily than the federal government, then the private company should go ahead, and the burden of the proof should be on the federal government to show that the job would not be done otherwise. The second development was a bill (HR6852) introduced in Congress calling for certain amendments to the Rural Electrification Act of 1936. It provided, among other things, for certain restrictions on the granting of loans for generation and transmission facilities, and to eliminate the secrecy that surrounds loan deliberations.

There was also a third development underway during the Kennedy administration and culminated during the administration of President

Johnson which set a pattern for public power and private enterprise co-operation. That was the development of the dual-purpose reactor at Hanford. In this instance, it will be recalled, the AEC signed a contract with the Washington Public Power Supply System whereby the latter was to build a 800,000 kilowatt power plant using by-product steam from a new production reactor. By Congressional action 50 percent of the power was offered to a publicly-owned group of companies and 50 percent to private utilities.

Conclusion. We can conclude that the battle between public and private power is nowhere near resolved, and there is nothing in the voting records of either President Lyndon B. Johnson or Vice President Hubert Humphrey to give the investor-owned companies anything to cheer about. On the contrary, most executives of privately owned utilities expect to see a continuing fight with their greatest enemy—public power.

The Role of Interconnection

The FPC was authorized under the authority of the Federal Power Act to project the nation's power needs for the 1970's and 1980 and to suggest the broad outline of a fully interconnected system of power supply for the entire country. The results of the FPC study have been reported in the *National Power Survey* in terms of anticipated demand and recommended generating facilities. However, Joseph C. Swidler, chairman of the FPC, said that the basic finding of the *National Power Survey* was that each of the 3,600 power systems, large and small, could achieve savings in the costs of generation and transmission of electricity by moving away from "isolated or segmented operations and from existing power pools of limited scope, to participate in fully coordinated power networks covering broad areas of the country."

The *National Power Survey* divided the United States into sixteen "coordination study areas" shown in Figure 7.5, and lettered A to P. The report showed as we have previously indicated, that great progress had been made in interconnection; but drew the conclusion, however, that in many situations the depth of coordinated system planning had not progressed to the point of taking full advantage of joint planning of generating capacity. The report felt that many systems were still installing relatively small and inefficient generating units.

The FPC found that the survey analysis justified the conclusion that it would be economical and practical for all utilities to effect interconnection and coordination within each of the sixteen study areas by 1970, with full coordination within each of the four sectors (Figure 7.5) to be well on its way by that time, and completed by the mid-1970's. By 1980 virtually full coordination should be completed both east of the Rockies and west, and substantial interconnection between the east and west zones should be established.

Figure 7.5: Coordination Study Area and Sector Boundaries.

SOURCE: *National Power Survey*, A Report by the Federal Power Commission, Washington, D.C., 1964.

Prior to the release of the *National Power Survey*, one of the fears of the investor-owned segment of the electric power industry was that the recommendations on interconnection would lead to further government participation and regulation of the industry. This gave rise to a basic problem that was considered by the National Fuels and Energy Study Group: What should be the role of the government in the encouragement of electrical interconnection?

What follows are the facts and recommendations which were made prior to the release of the *National Power Survey* based on information obtained from the FPC, and it bears the stamp of approval of the Committee on Interior and Insular Affairs of the United States Senate.

Facts Bearing on the Problem. There are several pertinent definitions that bear on the problem. A system interconnection is a connection between two electric systems permitting the transfer of electric energy in either direction. A power pool is two or more electric systems interconnected and coordinated to supply power in the most economical manner for their combined load requirements and maintenance program.

By 1965, as previously reported, about 97 percent of the United States generating capacity was to a greater or lesser extent interconnected in the five large networks. Large amounts of power in the aggregate flow back and forth from system to system and, by displacement, from region to region, but the net exchange is small, because receipts from and inputs into the pool tend to balance out.

By 1965 about 80 percent of the nation's electric energy was supplied by investor-owned public utilities which paid conventional corporate income taxes. As early as 1961 the investor-owned utilities announced plans for adding 100,000 miles of high-voltage lines by 1970 at a cost of 8 billion dollars, with the expectation that at that time all major investor-owned systems would be interconnected. In 1963 the Edison Electric Institute in its second *Report on the Status of Interconnections and Pooling of Electric Utility Systems in the United States* showed that plans indicated it was possible that all the major systems would be capable of operating in parallel as early as 1966.

The National Fuels and Energy Study Group pointed out that one pertinent fact bearing on interconnection was the relative costs of moving energy, and that moving electricity ranges up to 30 times the next least costly means. Therefore the decision to transport electrical energy for long distances, as opposed to transporting fuel, is taken only when this high cost balances out in the economic equation of fuel costs, freight rates, load centers, and generating efficiency. Further, the mere fact that inexpensive fuel is available in one part of the nation does not mean that an interconnection will make it available to another part. This kind of availability depends more on transmission costs than on a simple connection allowing power to be exchanged. The more removed the generating plant, the more displacement steps are required and the more high-voltage transmission is involved, and this must somehow be financed. This is one of the reasons for the intense research in ultra high-voltage and direct-current transmission.

The Study Group found that the major benefit from pooling is that larger and more efficient units, operating at high capacity factors, can be built to supply a pool than can be built to supply an individual system. The result is cheaper power for the pool as a whole and a more flexible and dependable supply.

A fully coordinated national transmission system would mean somewhat cheaper power because the generating capacity above peak loads, needed for emergencies and operating reserves, could be reduced. The FPC judges that the normal reserve requirement, which it estimates at 15 percent, could be reduced to 10 percent. Some estimates place the savings derived from smaller investment in the billions of dollars.

Savings would also derive from lesser consumption of fuel resulting from the use of large efficient units, and from lesser cost per kilowatt because of operating at high load factors. Some estimates place the fuel savings in hundreds of millions of dollars a year; one estimate from the

FPC places it at 300 million dollars in 1980 at 1964 fuel prices. Whatever the figure, professional opinion is in agreement that the benefits from operating larger plants at high capacity factor are great. But while the quantities of fuel per unit may be smaller, the lower cost per kilowatt may induce a greater use of electricity so that the total quantity of fuel used might be greater than before.

The National Fuels and Energy Study Group saw the subject of the government's involvement in interconnection as part of the broad and basic problem of public power versus private power, which was beyond the scope of its report. Nevertheless, the Study Group had this to say:

1. A system of interties sponsored, constructed, and operated by the Government would cost the Treasury a great deal in direct outlay, because transmission facilities are expensive. Moreover, fully interconnected operations under private sponsorship, presumably will appear in due course (by 1970, they say), so that the more the Government participation the less the private participation and the less the Treasury revenue.[6]

2. The devoting of public funds and resources to promote something that is going to happen in any event can be considered a social cost and the justification would have to be that the saving in time is an overriding gain. An argument advanced by persons who oppose more Government participation is that billions of dollars would be spent toward promoting a consumer expenditure that represents only about 1½ percent of personal income and manufacturing revenues, and the public funds and resources so devoted are thus withdrawn from serving more significant social needs.[7]

Conclusion. The FPC performed a proper governmental function in its *National Power Survey* which laid out a guideline pattern for the development of the nation's electric power industry designed to encourage full regional and countrywide coordination of all systems by 1980. It appears that the projected transmission network for 1980 would serve the following purposes:

1. Permit construction of larger and more economical generating units, both nuclear and conventional, and transmission of bulk power from generating sources to major load centers.
2. Permit savings in fuel transportation costs possible in mass shipments to large plants.
3. Permit location of large steam plants in less heavily populated areas to alleviate air pollution problems in large metropolitan centers.
4. Permit reduced reserve requirements by sharing capacity between areas and sectors.
5. Provide savings by seasonal exchange of capacity between areas with opposing summer and winter peaks.
6. Permit more efficient use of hydroelectric plants for peaking purposes.

[6] *Ibid.*, p. 358.
[7] *Ibid.*, p. 359.

7. Permit capacity savings from time zone and random diversity.
8. Facilitate transmission of offpeak energy.
9. Provide flexibility to meet unforseen demands.

The vital links in the efficient power supply networks which the *National Power Survey* suggests, are extra-high voltage transmission lines which enable large amounts of power to be transmitted economically over long distances. Facilitated by this link, the program for coordinated planning proposed by the FPC suggests that it could bring about an 11.7 billion dollar saving in plant investment and annual net savings to consumers of 11 billion dollars by 1980. These savings would amount to a reduction of about 27 percent in the average unit price of electricity for residential, commercial, and industrial users.

Representatives of REA cooperatives, and municipal and other local, publicly owned electric power companies were more dubious about accomplishing the goals of the *National Power Survey* than were the investor-owned companies. The doubts were based on: (1) the ability of many of the smaller systems to take advantage of the economies of scale suggested by the Survey, and (2) skepticism about the investor-owned segments' willingness to undertake the program and, if the goals were achieved, to pass the benefits on to consumers. The investor-owned interests had already had their say before the National Fuels and Energy Study Group and they were willing to stick by their ability to supply the nation's electric power needs in a coordinated manner.

The investor-owned companies had expressed their opinion through the Edison Electric Institute. The Institute estimated that to provide for the growth in electric energy requirements of the nation in the next twenty years would require capital expenditures of some 175 billion dollars.

The electric utility companies are confident these expenditures can be financed by them in the free market without Government subsidy. Were the Government-operated and/or financed segment of the industry to maintain the 20 percent position it now holds, it would cost the American taxpayer some $35 billion in capital outlay and some $15 billion in taxes to the Federal Government. The total drain on taxpayers' funds in simply maintaining the present proportion of Government power would be in the order of $50 billion. The position of the investor-owned electric utilities is that such a drain on the Federal Treasury is wholly unnecessary when the electric power requirements of the Nation can be supplied by the so-called private sector of the economy without the use of Government funds. In addition, the investor-owned electric utility companies will be contributing about $100 billion in taxes to Federal, State, and local governments.[8]

Thus, the investor-owned segment of the electric power industry saw

[8] *Ibid.*, p. 403.

the role of interconnection as a part of the coordinated plan to supply electric power, and they challenged the question of federal participation in interconnection as part of the broader and basic problem of public versus private power. But the vested interests in public power are too strong and memories of the inactivity of the investor-owned companies in remote and rural areas are too old and powerful to leave the total job of a coordinated electric power industry to private enterprise.

The final conclusion is that the burden of completing the recommended interconnection program will rest upon the investor-owned segment of the industry, but the *National Power Survey's* fully coordinated national transmission system is going to require the effort and cooperation of all segments of the industry. However the rate of progress toward accomplishing the goal of a nation-wide power pool received a sharp setback in November, 1965 when an electric power failure plunged the entire Northeastern United States and part of Canada and over 30,000,000 inhabitants into total darkness and brought all electrical equipment to a halt. Here was an area served by a power pool designed to prevent such a disaster, which apparently found itself a victim of a failure in the pool.

The breakdown occurred just as New York City was at its peak demand for electric power and was drawing on large amounts of power from upstate New York. When a failure occurred and one system was knocked out this immediately put a strain on the rest of the power pool as other members attempted to make up the lost power. The strain apparently proved too much. In order to prevent permanent damage to their equipment, each utility's system has a built-in safeguard in the form of circuit breakers. When an overload on the system occurs, these circuit breakers switch off the power of each utility system the same way a household fuse blows out when too many appliances are put on a circuit. When the circuit breakers switch off the power flow, the generating plants have to shut down as there is no place to send their power. What happened in the dramatic blackout of November, 1965 was that a failure in one part of the giant power pool triggered a chain reaction as circuit breaker after circuit breaker switched off, and utility after utility closed down, withdrawing from the power pool.

Once the circuit breakers started switching off each utility's power, the utility had to withdraw or segregate itself from the power pool and start relying on its own generating capacity. The circuits were restored as engineers cracked the triggered circuit breakers and gradually built up the power flow to the area it served. Only when the utility had restored its own system's power could it reconnect with the power pool.

If what occurred is indeed a weakness in the power-pooling idea, it could have long, lasting repercussions on the entire utilities industry in its attempts at power pooling. The possibility was raised that all the lights in the entire United States could go out in less than a second if all the utilities tie their systems into a single network operated by automatic controls that act almost instantaneously. Such a power pool was, of course, the recommendation of the FPC just one year prior to the failure in November, 1965. One thing was certain. The utilities and the federal government were going to have to restudy power-pooling systems. In addition, one thing had been proven: the very strength of the power pool can turn, with frightening speed, into its greatest weakness. Finally, this incident of a major power pool failure was certain to lead to support of public power advocates to supervision of power pools by the FPC.

SUMMARY

The U.S. electric power industry is truly a growth industry which has grown at an annual rate of 8.2 percent, or about 2½ times the rate of the whole economy since World War II. Residential, commercial, and industrial uses of electricity are expected to continue to grow and by 1980 will require 2,820 billion kwh as compared with 846 billion kwh in 1960. To accomplish this goal will require a fully interconnected and coordinated electric power system with an installed generating capacity of 523 million kilowatts in 1980 of which 14.5 percent will be hydroelectric, 67.3 percent fossil fueled steam, 13.3 percent nuclear fueled steam, 3.6 percent pumped storage, and 1.3 percent diesel and gas turbine.

The investor-owned segment of the industry is sure to take a more aggressive role, seeking to confine state and local public utilities and REA cooperatives to their existing territories and federal government operations to multipurpose hydroelectric projects. The issue of public versus private power will prevail and investor-owned companies will be given a high priority to develop nuclear facilities and coordinated electric power systems through interconnection and power pools, but always under the watchful eyes of public power advocates.

SELECTED REFERENCES

Bauer, J., and N. Gold, *The Electric Power Industry*, New York, Harper & Row, 1939.

Bauer, J., and P. Costello, *Public Organization of Electric Power*, Harper & Row, 1949.

"Electric Transmission Interties," in *Report of the National Fuels and Energy Study Group*, Washington, D.C., 1962.

The Electric Utilities, The 60 Largest U.S. Companies, New York, Merrill Lynch, Pierce, Fenner & Smith, 1963.

Federal Power Commission, *Hydroelectric Power Resources of the United States, Developed and Undeveloped*, Washington, D.C., 1960.

Lincoln, George, A., "I: Electric Power," in *Economics of National Security*, Englewood Cliffs, N.J., Prentice-Hall, 1954, pp. 219–233.

National Power Survey, Report by the Federal Power Commission, Washington, D.C., October, 1964.

National Power Survey, Part II, Advisory Reports, Report by the Federal Power Commission, Washington, D.C., October, 1964.

Report on the Status of Interconnections and Pooling on Electric Utility Systems in the United States, New York, Edison Electric Institute, May, 1963.

"Statement of the American Public Power Association," *Report of the National Fuels and Energy Study Group,* Washington, D.C., 1962, pp. 388–396.

"Statement of the Edison Electric Institute," *Report of the National Fuels and Energy Study Group,* Washington, D.C., 1962, pp. 402–403.

A Water Policy for the American People, Summary and Recommendations, from the report of the President's Water Resources Policy Commission, Washington, D.C., 1950.

Water Resources and Power Report to Congress, Commission on Organization of the Executive Branch of Government, Washington, D.C., 1955.

We Believe, New York, Edison Electric Institute, 1964.

Zimmermann, Erich W., "Electricity—A Modern Refinement of Energy Use," *World Resources and Industries,* New York, Harper & Row, 1951, pp. 595–612.

8

MINERAL RESOURCES

MINERALS are classified by the Bureau of Mines as mineral fuels, metals, and nonmetals. The mineral fuels have been the basic source of our inanimate energy supply, and the metallic minerals have been the basic materials of modern industrialization which have been used to harness and apply this energy. Prior to this chapter we have studied energy sources and energy in the form of coal, petroleum, natural gas, atomic energy, and electric power. This chapter will discuss mineral characteristics, the nonfuels minerals position, and minerals policy of the United States. And this will be followed by three separate chapters dealing with the metallic minerals—steel, copper, and aluminum.

MINERAL CHARACTERISTICS

Localized Occurrence

As compared with agricultural resources, most mineral resources are highly localized in occurrence. This leads to possible dominance of production control by individual firms and to uniform price patterns which are said to be the result of prices administered to the public or "administered prices." In addition, since minerals are not evenly distributed among countries, the control of minerals is localized in those nations where they occur. The localized occurrence of the combination of iron and coal, the basis of heavy industry, is found very infrequently. The control of these localized fund mineral resources has been the basis of power of the modern fuel-power-metal civilization. In addition, the worldwide dispersion of many localized minerals has led to the necessity of international trade in minerals. Technological developments have increased the need for special-purpose minerals and therefore have increased this international independence. Thus localized occurrence of mineral resources has resulted in the dominance of a few nations as world powers; and technological developments have not lessened this dominance, but they have tremendously increased the interdependence of nations.

Exhaustibility

Most minerals differ from other natural resources in that they are funds, which when used long enough become exhausted. This is in sharp contrast to the flow resources of agriculture, which when used properly tend to be renewable. The exhaustible nature of minerals creates several problems.

From the standpoint of the individual firm, adequate reserves against depletion must be set up. From the standpoint of nations, the exhaustion of mineral reserves becomes of critical importance because of the effect upon the total strength to produce and resultant position among the world powers. Great Britain's declining position as a world power during and after World War II was in part a direct result of the decline in her coal production.

The exhaustible nature of minerals creates a problem of increasing costs. High fixed costs are combined with rising variable costs. Since mines have no alternative use they may often be operated at a loss as long as variable costs can be covered and only a small portion of fixed costs paid. This is of course not an abnormal condition in competitive enterprise. But because mines have no abandonment value, and because they are very often the principal source of income to a community, both economic and social pressures are at work to keep them open over a long period of time, even when it is not economically profitable to do so. Political pressures often become dominant in these decisions, and the combination of forces may result in government aid of some type.

A final and critical problem created by the exhaustibility of mineral resources is the development of the most efficient uses of the minerals, the use of scrap as secondary sources, the development of substitute commodities where feasible, and the use of more efficient methods of recovery, and development of known reserves. In addition, continuous programs must be carried on for exploration and development of new sources of supply.

Discovery Problems

Most mineral deposits are hidden from view. Many major metal discoveries have been made by following surface exposures in mountain regions; but the conclusion has been drawn that few of these exposures remain undiscovered in the United States. Usually the most obvious reserves are found first, and subsequent discoveries are more difficult and costly. Adequate incentives for discovery are thus necessary. In the United States the legal right of ownership of mineral reserves on one's property has been fundamental as an incentive to discovery. However, as discovery has become more costly in the United States, additional incentives have been provided through indirect means of restrictive tariffs and quotas and direct subsidies of government exploration assistance and purchase, and high depletion allowances.

The cost of discovery and development of foreign reserves is much higher than that of domestic reserves. The risks are greater and consequently U.S. companies have undertaken this discovery and development only when they thought the returns would justify the investment. In most instances, costs have been so high that only very large corporations have been able to undertake the commitments. Further, many underdeveloped countries have been forced to seek outside capital because of the investment required for discovery and development. Although this reciprocal dependence would appear to be mutually beneficial, serious problems are involved. For example, initially United States and other companies are often more powerful than the governments of those areas in which investment is made; later, as the governments become more powerful and more autonomous, they begin to demand and to secure greater rights and revenues from their mineral enterprises. These greater risks of foreign investment in minerals have led to demands by U.S. concerns for investment guarantees.

Demand

An elementary fact about the demand for minerals is that requirements arise from the mechanization of modern society and are more a function of technology and industrialization than population. Between 1900 and 1950, U.S. population doubled. National output during this same time increased five times. Total consumption of agricultural products of all kinds increased only two and one-half times and thus was closely related to population growth. However, U.S. consumption of minerals in 1950 was six times 1900 totals.

In 1950 we were taking from the earth
> two and one-half times more bituminous coal;
> three times more copper;
> three and one-half times more iron ore;
> four times more zinc;
> twenty-six times more natural gas;
> thirty times more crude oil;

than in the year 1900. The quantity of most metals and mineral fuels used in the United States since the first World War exceeds the total used throughout the entire world in all of history preceding 1914.[1]

[1] *Resources for Freedom, Summary of Vol. I,* report by the President's Materials Policy Commission, Washington, D.C., June, 1952, p. 7.

A study by the United Nations[2] of the demand for minerals has shown the close correlation that exists between world mineral and industrial output. This clearly indicated the fundamental importance of minerals for industrial production. The United Nations then projected the world demand for major mineral products for 1975, based on a trend incorporating the relationship between the absorption of the minerals and some independent variables such as time, population, gross domestic product, value added in manufacture, changing technology, and innovations. These projections indicate a sustained increase in demand for metals ranging up to as high as 6.7 percent a year for aluminum.

In the United States the interrelationship between mineral trends and industrial activity can be seen from Figure 8.1. Separate trends are

Figure 8.1: Indexes of Physical Volume of Mineral Production in the United States.

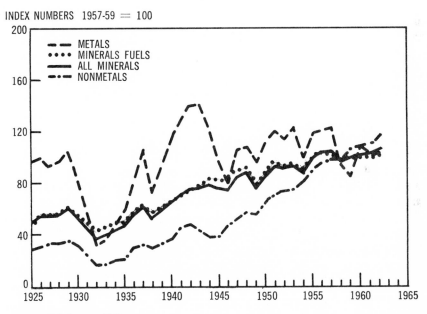

INDEX NUMBERS 1957-59 = 100

SOURCE: U.S. Bureau of Mines.

shown for mineral fuels, metals, and nonmetals as well as for all metals. Clearly discernible is the steady upward trend of all mineral production. Mineral fuel has been the leader in the increase and closely follows the total trend. Petroleum and natural gas, which we have studied, have been the principal leaders in this increase. The nonmetals also have come into

[2] *Study of Prospective Production of and Demand for Primary Commodities,* New York, United Nations Secretariat Report, 1962.

their own since the end of World War II. Metals, however, fluctuate sharply and do not show the steady upward trend. Production declined incisively during the depression of the 1930's and then increased during World War II, only to decline sharply and fluctuate thereafter with the recessionary periods. One contributing factor to the differential rate of growth of production between fuels and metals is that the nature of demand is such that fuels are consumed in their initial use, while metals can be reclaimed as scrap and thus a secondary reserve can be built up. An important effect of this is that during a depression or recession metallic mineral production is reduced sharply as more scrap is used from nonexpendable metals. However, during war years mineral production is accelerated because so much of metal is used up. Thus the end use to which metals are put is of critical importance in evaluating the role of scrap as a secondary reserve.

The rapid rise in production of minerals as a result of increasing demand poses the fundamental question as to the adequacy of mineral supplies for the future. The UN studies are now attempting to throw some light on the future world demand for minerals. A more accurate picture of future demand would be most helpful as one part of the answer to the question of adequacy of mineral reserves. One thing is certain, however: with goals of economic progress throughout the world, the demand for minerals will increase at an accelerated rate.

Reserves

The other major element of uncertainty in the adequacy of mineral supplies is the extent of reserves. Study of this problem requires an appraisal of known reserves, the outlook for future expansion, and technological developments which will affect production. Discovery problems have already been discussed. Not only are estimates of mineral reserves difficult to make, but mineral terminology used is so varied that what is difficult is compounded by confusion. Known mineral reserves must be thought of as those that are known to exist and that can be recovered with the application of present technology. In addition, economic feasibility must be taken into consideration. When technology and economic considerations are taken together, reserves become commercially feasible and are then thought of as available resources and ore. These may also be referred to as actual, proved, and indicated reserves, resources, and ore. In addition, references are made to potential and ultimate reserves, sub ore, sub resources, neutral stuff, and assorted other nomenclature.

When considering the extent of knowledge about world mineral reserves, the fact should be kept continuously in mind that even in the United States geological investigations have not been carried out intensively. The Minerals Subcommittee of the Senate Committee on Interior and Insular Affairs reported that less than one percent of the area of this nation has been included in geological investigations, only 12.7 percent has been geologically mapped, and 31.1 percent has been topographically mapped by the U.S. Geological Survey.

However, within the limit of all the above considerations, an attempt was made by Elmer W. Pehrson of the Bureau of Mines of the U.S. Department of the Interior to bring together the present judgments of experts concerning world reserves and to consider these data in the light of current rates of use and other factors that will condition the mineral economy of the future.

The results of this effort in a summary of world reserves of thirteen important industrial minerals and a comparison of these reserves with the then current rate of production are given in Figure 8.2. The reserve fig-

Figure 8.2: World Position in Reserves of Major Industrial Minerals.

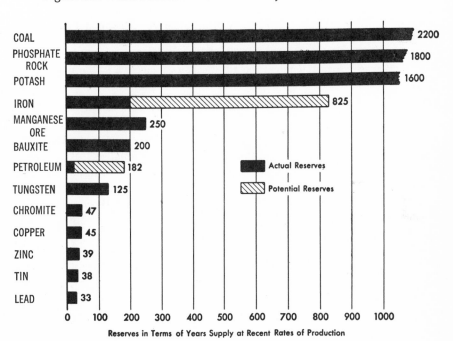

Reserves in Terms of Years Supply at Recent Rates of Production

Source: Olin T. Mouzon, *International Resources and National Policy* (Harper & Row, 1954), p. 230.

ures represent the judgment of various experts on the quantity of known reserves amenable to commercial recovery under technological and economic conditions present and those likely to exist in the foreseeable future. Estimates of potential reserves of iron ore and petroleum are also given; similar data for other commodities shown were not available.

After taking into consideration estimates of known reserves and the outlook for discovery, the above study summarizes the world outlook for mineral reserves as follows:

Conclusions about the adequacy of mineral resources differ whether the appraisal is made for the world as a whole or for an individual country. No curtailment of current rates of use due to resource limitation is imminent for the world as a whole. Known reserves of some minerals, however, particularly the ores of certain of the nonferrous metals, are small. Although this situation doubtless will be modified to some extent by discovery, total resources appear to be inadequate to support large and widespread expansion of consumption in the underdeveloped areas. Such expansion, however, is not likely to occur suddenly. Moreover, as mineral shortages arise, science and invention, motivated by economic considerations, will provide acceptable substitutes or adapt presently unused resources to industrial requirements. Thus it appears that drastic consequences resulting from exhaustion of mineral resources need not be feared. Temporary shortages can result from failure to anticipate expanding requirements in time to permit construction of necessary production facilities, or from destruction of the incentives necessary to maintain vigorous mining enterprise. On the whole, however, it may be concluded that if relatively free and unhampered access to world mineral resources can be maintained, and resort to military action to preserve national security becomes unnecessary, the mineral resources of the world are adequate.[3]

However, the assumptions behind the above conclusions are totally unrealistic. Nations will probably continue to use their mineral reserves to their own advantage and to consider mineral deficiency as the most fundamental detriment to economic progress and national security.

The United States is and will continue to be in competition with other nations for a limited nonrenewable supply of mineral reserves. The resulting summary problems and policy issues will be discussed in the final section of this chapter after study of the United States' nonfuels minerals position.

UNITED STATES NONFUEL MINERALS POSITION

There are many nonfuel minerals problems but they are all a part of one central issue: How can the United States increase its supply of nonfuel minerals in order to meet the anticipated growth in demand and to provide for an adequate emergency reserve?

Consumption

One of the most spectacular features of our economy has been the rapid growth in the use of minerals. Figure 8.1 which was discussed in the section on mineral demand, shows this growth quite clearly for all

[3] William Van Royen, and Oliver Bowles, *The Mineral Resources of the World,* Englewood Cliffs, N.J., Prentice-Hall, 1952, pp. 5–6.

minerals, and for mineral fuels, metals, and nonmetals. The consumption of minerals has increased in two ways. First, the demand for each mineral has increased. For example, in 1950 as compared with 1900 the United States used three and one-half times more iron ore, three times more copper, and four times more zinc. These are the metals long known to man. Second, the number of minerals required continues to expand as technological developments call for special-purpose minerals. In 1900 few metals were used—iron, copper, lead, tin, zinc, gold, and silver. Aluminum has grown from a laboratory experiment just before 1900 to a position where it is competing with copper for leadership in the nonferrous field. Technological developments have now made some 45 metallic elements and 8,000 alloys of these metals essential to modern industry. Thus technology has made us more dependent on sources outside the United States rather than more self-sufficient.

This past growth in consumption seems Lilliputian when compared with estimated future requirements. Figure 8.3 presents estimated future U.S. consumption of selected major materials in 1975 as compared with 1950. This chart has the advantage of making possible a comparison of estimated rates of growth by classes and individual materials. Minerals are classified into mineral fuels, construction materials, and other nonmetallic minerals; and the metals are subdivided into: (1) iron and ferroalloys; (2) nonferrous metals (except ferro-alloys). This latter sub-classification of the metallic minerals is particularly helpful. The anticipated expansion of iron will call for much greater expansion of the alloy metals for steel. The other nonferrous metals show a continued growing requirement for the older metals; gigantic increases in the consumption of the "light" metals, aluminum (bauxite), and magnesium; and anticipated spectacular gains for the new metal, titanium.

Military requirements for certain metallic and nonmetallic minerals are such that the wartime demands far exceed peacetime consumption. This necessitates special preparation in the nature of a reserve to fill these requirements immediately. In addition, the military requirement for minerals is similar to the long-range peacetime trend. For example, the jet plane of the early 1950's used more than twice as much copper, steel, and aluminum as the plane of World War II; and artillery in Korea used ammunition more than five times as fast as in World War II.

The U.S. Bureau of Mines maintains a continuously revised estimate of 1975 consumption of non-fuel minerals. These quantitative statements classified as ferrous, nonferrous, and nonmetals are shown in Table 8.1.

Supply

The increased consumption and changing pattern of mineral use immediately raise the question of the availability of an adequate supply.

Figure 8.3: How United States Consumption of Minerals Might Rise by 1975 (Assuming no relative change in prices).

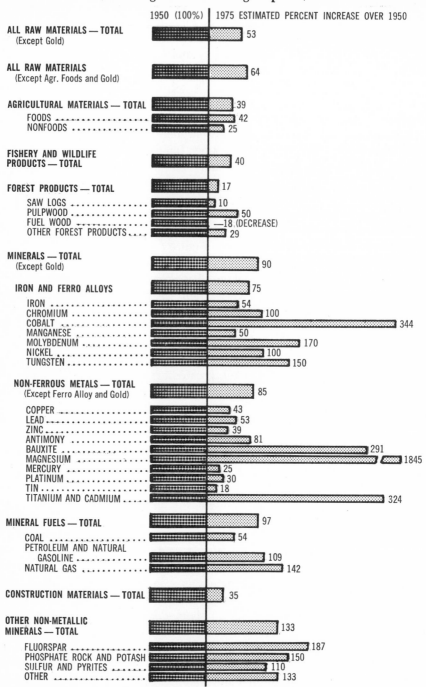

	1950 (100%)	1975 ESTIMATED PERCENT INCREASE OVER 1950
ALL RAW MATERIALS — TOTAL (Except Gold)		53
ALL RAW MATERIALS (Except Agr. Foods and Gold)		64
AGRICULTURAL MATERIALS — TOTAL		39
FOODS		42
NONFOODS		25
FISHERY AND WILDLIFE PRODUCTS — TOTAL		40
FOREST PRODUCTS — TOTAL		17
SAW LOGS		10
PULPWOOD		50
FUEL WOOD		—18 (DECREASE)
OTHER FOREST PRODUCTS		29
MINERALS — TOTAL (Except Gold)		90
IRON AND FERRO ALLOYS		75
IRON		54
CHROMIUM		100
COBALT		344
MANGANESE		50
MOLYBDENUM		170
NICKEL		100
TUNGSTEN		150
NON-FERROUS METALS — TOTAL (Except Ferro Alloy and Gold)		85
COPPER		43
LEAD		53
ZINC		39
ANTIMONY		81
BAUXITE		291
MAGNESIUM		1845
MERCURY		25
PLATINUM		30
TIN		18
TITANIUM AND CADMIUM		324
MINERAL FUELS — TOTAL		97
COAL		54
PETROLEUM AND NATURAL GASOLINE		109
NATURAL GAS		142
CONSTRUCTION MATERIALS — TOTAL		35
OTHER NON-METALLIC MINERALS — TOTAL		133
FLUORSPAR		187
PHOSPHATE ROCK AND POTASH		150
SULFUR AND PYRITES		110
OTHER		133

SOURCE: Data from *Resources for Freedom, Summary of Vol. I,* a report to the President by the President's Materials Policy Commission, Washington, D.C., June, 1952.

TABLE 8.1

Estimated United States Consumption of Major Mineral Products for 1975

Mineral products		Quantity
Ferrous:		
Steel ingot	million short tons	130
Pig iron	do	85
Ferrous scrap	do	55
Iron ore	million long tons	150
Manganese ore	thousand short tons	3,000
Chromite ores:		
Metallurgical grade	do	1,850
Refractory grade	do	650
Chemical grade	do	200
Molybdenum	million pounds	63
Tungsten	short tons	1,250
Nonferrous:		
Bismuth	thousand pounds	2,400
Copper, primary, refined	thousand short tons	2,000
Lead	do	1,350
Zinc, slab	do	1,400
Aluminum	do	7,200
Alumina	do	12,000
Bauxite	do	25,000
Antimony, primary	short tons	11,000
Antimony, secondary	do	20,000
Silver	million troy ounces	414
Platinum	thousand troy ounces	1,100
Titanium, ilmenite including titanium slag	thousand short tons	1,600
Titanium, rutile	do	150
Nonmetals:		
Asbestos	thousand short tons	1,000
Cement	million barrels	600
Clays	thousand short tons	59,700
Lime	do	22,000
Phosphate rock (P_2O_5 content)	do	9,000
Potash (K_2O content)	do	6,000
Sulfur	do	8,000
Salt	million short tons	50
Crushed stone	do	1,200
Sand and gravel	do	1,300

SOURCE: U.S. Bureau of Mines, *Minerals Yearbook*, Washington, D.C., 1964.

In 1947 the staffs of the Bureau of Mines and the Geological Survey prepared the most comprehensive appraisal of the mineral position of the United States which had been attempted up to that time. The report summarized:

Describing the mineral position of a nation in terms of its self-sufficiency or its ability to produce to meet its own needs is a well-established practice. Self-sufficiency is readily and effectively determined by comparing production and consumption during a chosen period, for such a comparison considers all the factors—resources, technologic, and economic—that influence the production that develops in response to a specific demand. For most commodities the basic factor is the quantity of the raw-material resource—the reserves—exploitable under prevailing conditions, particularly the spread between cost and price. Under special circumstances other factors, such as availability of labor and equipment and the limitations imposed by installed capacity, are equally important. Also, with the byproduct materials, output frequently is restricted more by the rate at which the associated metals or minerals are produced than by the size of the reserve or by other factors. However, the influence of factors other than reserves usually is relatively temporary, so that, for long periods, the degree of self-sufficiency provides a rough measure of the economic availability of resources.

Figure [8.4] compares the self-sufficiency of the United States in 39 important industrial minerals during the 5-year periods 1935 to 1939 and 1940 to 1944. Before the war, production equaled or exceeded consumption in 11 commodities. For 12 minerals, production ranged from 50 to less than 100 percent of consumption, for 6 commodities from 10 to less than 50 percent, and for 10 minerals less than 10 percent of requirements. During this period, there were few if any labor or equipment shortages or restraints imposed by production facilities. Thus, except for the byproduct minerals, the production record affords a fairly reliable index of the availability of domestic resources under the economic and technologic conditions prevailing at that time.

It will be noted that, from 1935 to 1939, the United States was fully or highly self-sufficient in coal and iron ore, the raw materials required to support an industrial economy based on steel. It was equally well situated with respect to supplies of other important minerals, such as petroleum, copper, sulfur, and phosphate rock. However, the record also reveals that this country depended on foreign sources for substantial proportions of its needs of other minerals that are indispensable in this machine age.

During the war there were notable increases in the ratio of production to consumption in some minerals and decreases in others. Significant improvement in self-sufficiency was obtained in iron ore, fluorspar, nitrates, mercury, potash, bauxite, vanadium, arsenic, tungsten, ilmenite, and flake graphite, whereas dependence on foreign sources of copper, zinc, lead, rutile, platinum metals, and tantalum increased substantially. It should be noted, however, that flake graphite produced during the war was substandard and unsuitable for some important uses.

On the whole, there was only a moderate improvement in American self-

Figure 8.4: United States Self-Sufficiency in Principal Industrial Minerals, 1935–1939 and 1940–1944 (Production is expressed in percentage of domestic consumption).

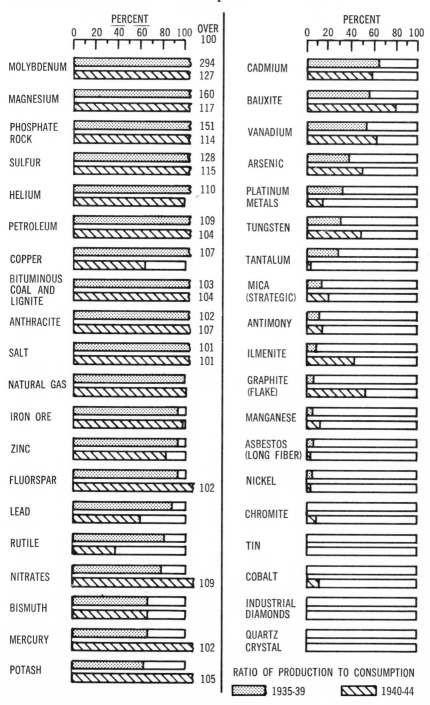

SOURCE: Data from U.S. Bureau of Mines and Geographical Survey.

297

sufficiency during the war. In view of the tremendous need for minerals for the war program and the pressure for larger output, a more striking result might have been expected. Failure to achieve a larger measure of self-sufficiency under these conditions may be ascribed to many factors. Lack of reserves precluded significant production of many minerals, including chromite, nickel, tin, industrial diamonds, and quartz crystals. For some of the other metals and minerals, depletion of the reserves undoubtedly was an important but by no means solitary factor. During the war, shortages of manpower and equipment and the limitations of installed production capacity were real bottlenecks that prevented full realization of the reserve potential. Opinions differ as to the relative importance of these causes, but the fact remains that the war experience demonstrated weaknesses in the Nation's mineral position and emphasized the need for doing something about it.[4]

This 1947 report has been presented because of its comprehensive and comparative scope, and because it was an outgrowth of the post World War II realization of the need for an appraisal of the United States' mineral position.

The sustained and accelerated demand for minerals after World War II gave rise to the comprehensive report of the President's Materials Policy Commission in 1950. In an attempt to answer the fundamental question of the availability of an adequate mineral supply the Commission prepared Table 8.2, which gives the domestic supply position of selected mineral materials, dividing them into three major measures of adequacy: known economic reserves adequate for well over twenty-five years; known economic reserves inadequate; and little or no known economic reserves, significant discoveries not expected. Although the work of the Commission has been subject to subsequent revision, it stands out as a landmark work which has promoted further investigation.

Another partial measure of adequacy is the degree to which U.S. production is dependent on foreign sources. Again on this matter, the U.S. Bureau of Mines prepares each year a table for ferrous, other metallic ores, and nonmetals which indicates the extent to which the United States depends on primary shipments, secondary production, and imports. Table 8.3 on page 300 is an abstract of this information for ferrous and other metallic ores. Nonmetals are omitted because of the emphasis placed herein in the nonfuel metallic minerals.

In the ferrous categories the following percentages were imported in 1963: iron, 22 percent; manganese, 94 percent; chromite, 100 percent; cobalt, 98 percent, nickle, 86 percent, and tungsten, 57 percent. Only in molybdenum of the principal ferrous metals is the United States self-sufficient.

---

[4] *Investigation of National Resources*, Hearing before a Subcommittee of the Committee on Public Lands, United States Senate, 80th Congress, 1st Session, on Investigation of the Factors Affecting Minerals, Fuels, Forestry, and Reclamation Projects, May 15, 16, and 20, 1947, Washington, D.C., 1947, pp. 177–178.

TABLE 8.2
Domestic Supply Position of Selected Mineral Materials

Known Economic Reserves Adequate for Well Over 25 Years

magnesium	lime	gypsum
molybdenum	salt	borax
coal	sand	barite
phosphate	clay	feldspar
potash		

Known Economic Reserves Inadequate

Discoveries geologically likely—though not necessarily adequate:

copper	vanadium	petroleum
lead	tungsten	natural gas
zinc	antimony	sulfur
uranium		

Beneficiation progress expected:

iron	beryllium	fluorine
aluminum	thorium	graphite
titanium	oil from shale	

Synthesis progress expected:

oil from coal	gas from coal

Little or No Known Economic Reserves, Significant Discoveries Not Expected

Beneficiation progress expected:
    manganese

Synthesis progress expected:

industrial diamonds	quartz crystals
sheet mica	asbestos

Significant beneficiation or synthesis not expected:

chromium	tin	platinum
nickel	cobalt	mercury

SOURCE: *Resources For Freedom,* Vol. 1, Washington, D.C., 1954.

In the nonferrous metallic categories the following percentages were imported: copper, 14 percent; aluminum equivalent, 85 percent; lead, 35 percent; zinc, 44 percent; tin, 85 percent; magnesium, 2 percent; and titanium concentrates, 22 and 86 percent. Thus of the major nonferrous metals, only in magnesium is the United States self-sufficient.

TABLE 8.3

Net Supply of Principal Ferrous and Other Metallic Ores in the United States
and Components of Gross Supply[1]

(Thousand short tons unless otherwise stated)

Commodity	Net supply			Components as a percent of gross supply (gross supply = 100)						Exports as a percent of gross supply	
	1962	1963	Change from 1962 (percent)	Primary shipments[2]		Secondary production[3]		Imports[4]			
				1962	1963	1962	1963	1962	1963	1962	1963
Ferrous ores, scrap, and metals:											
Iron (equivalent)	93,147	100,864	+8	48	48	28	30	24	22	4	5
Manganese (content)	965	1,038	+8	5	6			95	94	1	1
Chromite (Cr₂O₃ content)	612	631	+3					100	100		1
Cobalt (content)	12,640	10,717	-15			2	2	98	98		
Molybdenum (content) thousand pounds	34,762	39,012	+12	100	100					31	41
Nickel (content) do	142	133	-6	9	11	4	3	87	86	1	
Tungsten ore and concentrate (W content) short tons	6,447	4,679	-27	61	57			39	43	1	1

Other metallic ores, scrap, and metals:

Commodity	Unit										
Copper (content)		1,779	1,859	+4	58	56	20	19	22	25	16	14
Lead (content)		1,077	1,119	+3	22	23	41	42	37	35	4	3
Zinc (recoverable content)		1,064	1,018	−4	46	50	5	6	49	44	8	9
Aluminum (equivalent)		2,732	2,638	−4	9	11	4	4	87	85	1	3
Tin (content)	long tons	58,097	56,356	−3	5		20	22	80	78		
Antimony (recoverable content)	short tons	37,092	39,337	+6		4	52	52	43	44		
Beryl ore (BeO content)	do	990	710	−28	2		3	3	95	97		
Cadmium (content)	do	5,769	4,834	−16	33	36			67	64	6	11
Magnesium (content)		74,498	89,112	+20	85	82	12	16	3	2	8	4
Mercury	76-pound flasks	63,405	72,309	+14	41	26	9	15	50	59		
Platinum-group metals	thousand troy ounces	821	1,423	+73	3	3	15	8	82	89	7	4
Titanium concentrate:												
Ilmenite and slag (TiO₂ content)		531	604	+14	79	78			21	22		
Rutile (TiO₂ content)		40	77	+93	18	14			82	86	3	1
Uranium concentrate (U₃O₈ content)	short tons	28,728	23,020	−20	59	62			41	38		

1 Net supply is sum of primary shipments, secondary production, and imports minus exports. Gross supply is total before subtraction of exports.

2 Primary shipments are mine shipments or mine sales (including consumption by producers) plus by-products production. Shipments more nearly represent quantities marketed by domestic industry and as such are more comparable to imports. Use of shipment data rather than production data also permits uniform treatment among more commodities.

3 From old scrap only.

4 Imports for consumption except where otherwise indicated; scrap is excluded wherever possible in both imports and exports, but all other sources of minerals through refined or roughly comparable stage are included except when commodity description indicates earlier stage. Exports of foreign merchandise (reexports), if any, are included when imports are general.

SOURCE: U.S. Bureau of Mines, *Minerals Yearbook*, Washington, D.C., 1964.

In the nonmetals, which are not shown in Table 8.3, asbestos, fluorspar and mica are our principal deficiencies.

The Importance of the Ferrous and Nonferrous Minerals

The ferrous minerals consist of iron and its alloys, and thus derive their importance from the role they play in the iron and steel industry. The nonferrous metals are significant for their diversified special uses.

Ferrous Minerals. The ferrous minerals that are of significance to the iron and steel industry are iron and its alloys: manganese, chromium, nickel, tungsten, molybdenum, cobalt, and vanadium. The iron and steel industry will be studied in great detail in the next chapter, and special consideration will be given to the iron ore problem. It is appropriate at this point to comment briefly on the importance of each of these ferro-alloys.

Manganese is a necessary ingredient in making steel and is therefore vital to industry. Its main function is to remove impurities, and in the performance of this job it leaves the furnace as slag. Between 13 and 14 pounds of manganese are required in the production of each ton of steel. The portion of manganese that remains in steel improves its strengths and workability. It is a relatively common metal occurring throughout the world; however, a minimum manganese content of 35 percent is necessary to allow commercial ore to be shipped directly without concentration. The United States has no high grade deposits. The only present commercial reserves are in Montana, and are estimated to contain not quite one million tons of manganese of about 15 percent content. Thus 100 percent of this essential alloy must be imported. Estimates indicate about 450 million tons of major deposits around the world, but only about 185 million tons are located in non-Communist countries, principally in Africa, Brazil, and India.

Chromium along with nickel is quantitatively the most important alloying agent used in the production of steel. Chromite processed into a ferroalloy lends strength and hardness to steel and along with nickel is used in the manufacture of stainless steel. Reserves of chromic oxide in the United States are estimated at 4 million tons. Most of these reserves are located in Montana, but only a few thousand tons are suitable for use by the steel industry. No chromite has been produced in the United States since 1961, and metallurgical grade, refractory grade, and chemical grade chromite are on the United States strategic and critical list for stockpiling. The most important foreign sources are South Africa, Southern Rhodesia, Turkey, and the Philippines. There are low-grade deposits in Cuba which are of little value until technological and political considerations undergo remarkable changes. Since there are no good known chromite deposits in the Western Hemisphere, chromium supply will continue to be of serious concern to the United States since many of the present sources are not only far removed for security purposes, but they are also subject to political instability.

Nickel is used as an alloying element in steel to make it hard and heat resistant. Just as in the case of chromium the United States is almost completely dependent on foreign sources for nickel. However, large reserves are located within fairly secure reach in Canada. The Canadian deposits are rich in sulfite ore in which nickel, copper, platinum, and other metals occur in a manner that permits ease of separation. The second commercial source is New Caledonia, where nickel is extracted from silicate ores that are low in iron and chromite. Other sources of nickel are in nickel-bearing iron ores which are found in Cuba, the Philippines, and Indonesia. Total reserves of nickel in Canada and New Caledonia, plus those that are minable in Cuba, are estimated at no more than 16 million tons of nickel content. There is evidence that many of the technological problems had been resolved in using the low-grade Cuban deposits before the Castro take-over, but for the present the future supply of nickel will have to come from further extensions in Canada, and from new discoveries elsewhere in potential ore.

Tungsten is a metal with a wide range of uses. As an additive to steel it imparts great hardness and resistance to heat, is used in electric and electronic components, and, like tungsten carbide, provides shaping and cutting ability in tools. Domestic deposits of tungsten consist mostly of low-grade, high-cost material. Estimates of the quantity of tungsten reserves are unreliable in the United States unless they are quoted at some specified price. In the first half of the 1950's the U.S. government paid over $60 per short ton unit of tungsten (equivalent to just below 16 pounds of tungsten metal), and as much as 7,000 short tons were produced in a year from 700 mines. In 1958 after the incentive price program ended the price dropped to below $20, and the amount mined was less than 2,000 tons from two mines. From Table 8.3 it can be seen that U.S. consumption is of the order of magnitude of 5,000 tons a year. Of the world's estimated tungsten reserves, only about 20 percent of the 1.4 million ton total is located in non-Communist countries. Over one million tons are in mainland China and additional amounts are in North Korea and the Soviet Union. The world reserves are unknown, but commercial reserves are known to exist in other countries including Bolivia, Malaysia, and Burma. The need is for some major discoveries of tungsten, and if these are not forthcoming, molybdenum may have to be accepted as a substitute.

Molybdenum imparts qualities to steel of strength, toughness, and resistance to shock and vibration such as would be required in automobile gears. Unlike most other metals, molybdenum is not only sufficient for domestic uses but is exported. United States reserves have been estimated at 3 billion pounds out of a world total of 4 billion pounds. About one-third of the U.S. total is contained in copper-bearing ores of the western states. Production of molybdenum in the United States comes principally from the Climax mine in Colorado. Recently a new discovery has been made in New Mexico. At current rates of U.S. production and consumption, and with new discoveries on the horizon, molybdenum is one ferrous metal about which the United States can be optimistic.

Cobalt is used both as a ferrous and as a nonferrous alloy. It has a high resistance to corrosion at high temperatures which makes it a desirable element in missiles, jet engines, generators, and similar technical applications. Cobalt is also used in magnets, and has another wide variety of uses ranging from blue pigment to cancer treatment. U.S. resources are small with about 43,000 tons, and an estimated additional potential of 107,000 tons. Table 8.3 shows that annual consumption is 5,000 to 6,000 tons a year, thus the United States must look to outside sources. Foreign reserves are known to be large, but for some time the Congo has supplied the major portion of the cobalt production in the non-Communist world. Cuba has sizable deposits of low-grade ore. Other areas known to have cobalt-bearing deposits are the Philippines, New Caledonia, Northern Rhodesia, and Canada. Thus, here again, in the light of limited domestic reserves the United States is going to have to rely on imports to supply domestic requirements.

Vanadium imparts many of the same properties when used as an alloy as does molybdenum. It finds its principal usefulness where high speed, heat resistant steel alloys are required. We have already seen from our discussion of uranium, that the best known source of vanadium is the Colorado Plateau where the requirements for uranium have increased its availability. Vanadium, now produced as a by-product of uranium, provides enough ore for domestic use and export. Estimated reserves in the United States total about 600,000 tons of contained vanadium metal. Recoverable vanadium annual production and consumption has been running around 5,000 tons, and thus vanadium along with molybdenum offers no problem in the United States in the production of specialty alloy steels requiring its properties.

Nonferrous Metals. The five traditional nonferrous metals are copper, aluminum, lead, zinc, and tin. There are also relatively new ones such as magnesium and titanium and a large number of minor metals that have recently come into use. Copper and aluminum will be the subject of two separate chapters following the one on iron and steel. What follows will be a brief statement with respect to the United States' position in lead, zinc, tin, magnesium, and titanium.

Lead is a soft heavy metal that is easily worked. The addition of a small amount of antimony imparts great strength and hardness. Lead is remarkably resistant to the action of many chemicals. Paints made from compounds of lead, especially white lead and red lead, possess excellent coloring power and resist weathering. Lead's resistance to acids adapts it to use in storage batteries. Its capacity to harden when alloyed with antimony and other elements renders it suitable as a bearing and a type metal. United States reserves of lead are less than 5 million tons, and measured and indicated ore in the rest of the non-Communist world is estimated at around 33 million tons. Intelligent guesses have been made that, if potential ore were added to measured and indicated ore, the total in the non-Communist world might be between 70 to 75 million tons. Estimates have been made that the total consumption of lead in the United States alone over the next 35 years will be about 38 million tons. Thus, the United States must continue to depend on outside sources for supply, and the rest of the world with increasing demands must look for new sources of supply. United States imports of lead have been coming from Australia, Mexico, Peru, Canada, and to a lesser extent from Yugoslavia, the Republic of South Africa, and Belgium-Luxembourg. Thus there may be some security in diversity. In some instances substitutes have been found for lead; for example, polyethelene, aluminum, and other sheathings continue to replace lead in anticorrosion cable sheathings, and to some extent titanium has replaced lead in paints. It appears then if lead is to continue to serve where no acceptable substitutes are readily available, new discoveries must be made. It is encouraging that new occurrences of lead have been located in southern Missouri, in eastern Tennessee and in New Brunswick, Canada. This Canadian deposit, unknown in the 1950's, is estimated to have reserves about equal to that of the entire United States.

Zinc has a most remarkable property which imparts virtual immunity to the harmful effects of moisture and air at ordinary temperatures. Even a very thin layer of it protects iron and steel sheets and adds greatly to their life. Hence the galvanizing industry is the largest consumer of zinc. Zinc is alloyed with copper to make brass, which in time of war is a larger use for zinc than galvanized products. Other uses include plates for battery cans, photoengraving, zinc oxide in paint, and pharmaceutical applications. United States reserves of measured and indicated zinc are about 13.5 million tons, which is equal to about 16 percent of the world's reserves. Inferred reserves are thought to be about the same order of magnitude. United States reserves, as well as world reserves, are fairly widely scattered. Zinc is produced in fifteen states but the total production ranges around only 500 thousand tons a year of recoverable zinc as compared with consumption of about twice that amount. Zinc appears to be more abundant in domestic reserves than lead, but there are disturbing features of both supply positions that indicate the inferred or potential ore position may not be favorable. For example, during both World War II and the Korean War the government offers to subsidize the exploitation of what normally would be potential ore received a disappointing response. The subsidy was large in relation to market price, but the resulting increase in production was only modest and insufficient for the then current need (including stockpiling). The General Service Administration continues to operate a stabilization program for small domestic producers of lead and zinc; and since October 1, 1958, import quotas on zinc (and lead) have been in effect. Since 1952 domestic producers had sought additional protection through the "escape clause" of the Trade Agreements Extension Act of 1951, and in 1958 the President, acting on the recommendation of the Tariff Commission established import quotas at 80 percent of the average dutiable imports into the United States during the base period 1953–1958, and the tariff duties remained at the existing rates of 0.7¢ and 0.6¢ a pound respectively on zinc slab and ore. The chief sources of U.S. imports of zinc have been Canada and Mexico. But despite the proximity of these sources the United States has adopted a policy that for defense and safety considerations this country should be assured an active zinc-producing industry. Part of the policy stems from the fact that up until about 1940, the United States was self-sufficient in zinc supplies. Thus, domestic interests have hoped to maintain their position under changed conditions which include additional consumption, the creation of a national stockpile, a decrease in domestic mine and secondary production, and an increased dependence on imports. Nevertheless, the facts point toward a continued dependence of imports of zinc to satisfy the United States requirements with the hope that continued development of zinc ores outside the United States will expand at a greater rate than world consumption.

Tin for many years was used chiefly in the making of bronze, an alloy of copper. More recent uses of tin stem from the fact that tin is highly malleable and nontoxic. Even a thin coating provides reliable protection against acids, atmospheric effects, corrosion, the influence of water, etc. This property coupled with its malleability has given rise to the modern tin-plate industry which manufactures the ubiquitous tin can, which is made of steel with a thin tin coating. Tin also possesses the useful properties of low melting point and easy fusibility, softness, lightness, and attractive appearance. These properties have led to many metallurgical uses and chemical applications. Tin is almost unique in the extent to which the areas in which it is produced are geographically separated from the areas in which it is consumed. The United States is virtually devoid of domestic tin ores, and uses about one-half of the world's output, the consumption of which is concentrated in about half a dozen industrialized countries. Tin reserves occur in several tin provinces, but by far the largest is a belt which lies in an area extending for 1,000 miles from Yunnan province in China through Thailand, the Malay Peninsula, and into Indonesia. This region has produced about 70 percent of the tin to date. There are other provinces in Africa, especially in Nigeria, the Congo, and South Africa; in South America, in Bolivia; and small deposits in Europe and Australia. North America is distinguished for her virtual lack of tin. Production of tin in six countries representing 67 percent of total production is under the International Tin Agreement, which through the International Tin Council operates a Buffer Stock Pool to control supply and prices. The International Tin Agreement was signed by twenty producing and consuming countries to become effective in 1956, but the United States did not sign or ratify the Agreement and is not a member of the Council. About 80 percent of the world output of primary tin is smelted by eight companies operating eleven major smelters—three in Malaya, two in Great Britain, one each in the Netherlands, Belgium, West Germany, Australia, the Congo, and the United States.[5] The United States had no smelter until World War II, when under government sponsorship one was built at Texas City, Texas. All the United States' supply of tin consists of imported tin and metal recovered at the Texas City tin smelter from imported casiterite concentrates. Thus the United States as a tin consumer is confronted with the problems of: (1) coping with tin supply and prices as a result of dependence on outside sources operating through the International Tin Agreement, (2) developing a primary source of tin from virtually nonexistent, known reserves, and (3) improving secondary sources of scrap recovery which accounts for about 30 percent of domestic tin consumption each year. From the standpoint of domestic dependence on tin the only favorable aspects are: (1) the establishment of a strategic stockpile, (2) the use of the electrolytic process of tinplating replacing the hot-dip method of tinplating which required more tin, and (3) the use of substitutes for tin such as aluminum to replace tin in foil and collapsible tubes, and the development of alternative containers to replace the tin can. All the tin problems are of increasing significance because of the sustained political instability in the producing areas.

Magnesium, a relative newcomer to the nonferrous metals, is the light metal *par excellence.* It weighs only 109 pounds per cubic foot compared with 165 for aluminum and 490 for steel. However, magnesium is used both for distributive and structural purposes. Its distributive uses are in applications in aluminum alloys, and as a reducing agent principally to produce titanium, with smaller quantities being used for the production of zirconium, hafnium, uranium, and beryllium. A little less than half of the U.S. consumption of magnesium is used for structural purposes, principally in the manufacture of aircraft, missiles, consumer products, machinery, and tools. Magnesium has been substituted for other more

[5] Thailand, the third largest producer of tin ores and concentrates in the world, completed its first tin smelter late in 1965 to be operated by a joint venture organized and financed by Union Carbide Corporation and the Eastern Mining and Development Company, Ltd., of Thailand.

scarce or heavier materials; a practice which was begun in World War II when supplies of raw materials to produce other strategic materials were cut off. Magnesium is produced by two methods in the United States: the electrolysis of magnesium chloride obtained from sea water, sometimes referred to as the Dow process, and the thermic reduction of dolomite with ferrosilicon. Large domestic deposits and wide distribution of magnesium-rich dolomite ores, plus the virtually limitless supply of magnesium in seawater, assures self-sufficiency in the United States. The producing industry is composed of three firms and four plants. Annual production capacity of the two seawater magnesium plants in Texas is 89,000 tons. The two other plants with a capacity of 11,000 tons produce magnesium from dolomite in Alabama and Connecticut. United States consumption in the mid-1960's was around 55,000 tons. During World War II the U.S. government built six magnesium plants. One of these in Texas was sold to the Dow Chemical Co., and the other five plants with an annual capacity of 58,000 tons, have not operated to produce magnesium since 1953. The government also holds a strategic stockpile of magnesium which was acquired during the Korean emergency when the government-owned magnesium plants were reactivated. In studying this newcomer to nonferrous metals, it is good to be able to conclude that the wide distribution of virtually limitless quantities of magnesium assures a plentiful supply of this lightest of structural metals for new and increased uses. The U.S. Bureau of Mines in *Mineral Facts and Problems* certainly gave an unusual statement of the magnesium problem: "The basic problem of the magnesium and magnesium compounds industries is utilization of abundant raw materials."

Titanium is used as a pigment and in metallic form. Titanium pigment has had a phenomenal growth which may be attributed principally to its high hiding power per unit of volume. Titanium in its metallic form was first produced commercially in 1948, and it has been highly touted as the metal of the future because of a combination of strength, lightness, and resistance to corrosion. Ilmenite ore is required for the manufacture of titanium pigments (manufactured titanium dioxide). Rutile ore is required for the manufacture of titanium metal. Deposits of titanium ore minerals, ilmenite, and rutile, are widely scattered with major economic deposits found in Australia, Canada, Finland, India, Norway, Senegal, South Africa, and the United States. The United States is dependent on Australia for about 80 percent of its supply of rutile but it is largely self-sufficient in ilmenite—Table 8.3 shows 23 percent imported in 1963. Titanium metal seemed tailor-made for the space age, and it received large-scale financial encouragement from the government. Thought of as a miracle metal by 1952, titanium seemed to be headed rapidly into the group of major tonnage metals. Annual consumption of 100,000 tons was freely predicted, and the U.S. government had a target for productive capacity of 35,000 tons a year, which was later reduced to 22,500 tons. Production rose from 500 tons in 1951 to over 17,000 tons in 1957 only to drop to under 4,000 tons in 1954, and recovered slightly to 5,000 tons in 1960. Capacity has settled down at some 21,000 tons of metal sponge (the stage preceding ingots). Titanium metal has been suggested for many applications, but its major use at the beginning of the 1960's was for military purposes, especially for airplanes in both airframe and power plant. Civilian aircraft also used titanium for similar applications. The outstanding characteristics suggest many uses such as surgical instruments, orthopedic appliances, and textile machinery; but large-scale civilian use had still not materialized midway through the 1960's. Over 90 percent of titanium was still used for defense purposes in aircraft and missiles. The development of the A-11, a military jet capable of flying at three times the speed of sound, is believed to have been made possible largely because of the use of titanium. Once this type of plane is produced in volume the consumption of titanium is expected to derive quite a boost. Even as early as 1960, commercial jet transports used from 700 to 2,500 pounds of titanium in each airplane. Total consumption of titanium has been on the rise since the low of 1959 and reached almost 8,000 tons in 1963. Titanium metal can replace many other metals in applications where a high strength to weight ratio or a certain type of corrosion resistance is desired. The price of titanium sponge metal declined steadily from $5.00 a pound in 1958 to $1.27 in 1963. Expansion of titanium metal production and widespread use of this metal for civilian, as well as military purposes, depends mainly on continued reduction in the cost of production and fabrication, and growth in knowledge of the properties of titanium and its alloys. Should titanium ever become a large tonnage metal the sources of rutile, which is largely imported, might have to be supplemented by domestic ilmenite, provided technology can be developed satisfactorily to produce titanium metal from this source. For example, when production reaches its 1965 capacity of 21,000 tons, the titanium metal industry will require about 45,000 tons of rutile or some other material of equivalent TiO_2 content. Fluctuations in prices of rutile from overseas sources has been a continuing problem to domestic producers, and is a deterrent to the development of sources which would be accessible to the United States in time of war.

UNITED STATES MINERALS POLICY

Enough evidence has been presented to prove that there is a nonfuels mineral supply problem with almost all the ferrous and nonferrous metals discussed above. It is not a problem about which the United States should be alarmed, but it calls for awareness and actions to solve it. Although each specific mineral may require special study, certain measures are applicable to all nonfuel minerals. In addition, because of the time needed to develop, transport, and process minerals, policies required for peacetime are for the most part the same as those required for war.

There are several areas where appropriate policy and action will help solve the supply problem. Among these are exploration and development, stockpiling, imports, and the development of outside sources.

Exploration and Development

The Materials Policy Commission concluded that the critical problems of domestic mineral supply center in those minerals still produced in the United States but having reserves which no longer seem adequate. For these, e.g., copper, lead, zinc, tungsten, etc., the job ahead is to find and develop new reserves. More difficulties stand in the way of discovery than of development. Two fields of action seem appropriate—factual knowledge and financial incentives.

Factual Knowledge. Factual knowledge and analyses concerning reserves of the various minerals, costs and rates of exploration and development, and other pertinent factors were found to be seriously lacking by the Materials Policy Commission. The Commission recommended:

. . . that the Department of the Interior strengthen its programs for gathering and analyzing basic facts about minerals, that industry groups undertake an integrated complementary program, and that a complete census of mineral industries be taken in 1954 and every 5 years thereafter (see P.M.P.C. vol. I, p. 26).

. . . that the U.S. Geological Survey accelerate the geologic mapping of the United States and Alaska, by 50 percent within five years and 100 percent as soon thereafter as possible, with priorities given to localities of most probable mineralization; that the Geological Survey and the Bureau of Mines, in cooperation with State mining agencies and the mining industry, develop a program for a coordinated national system of libraries of core samples and other geologic evidence; that an intensive program of basic scientific research and technical development be undertaken, led by a special committee under the National Science Foundation, on methods and instruments of exploration for minerals, enlisting experts in Government, private industries, and universities; and that direct exploration by Government—limited to situations in which private industry cannot be expected to undertake it—be part of the continuing activities of the Geological Survey and the Bureau of Mines (see P.M.P.C. vol. I, p. 29).

Financial Incentives. Financial incentives to exploration and development of several types have been used by the federal government. These include tax policies, special provisions of the Defense Production Act of 1950, and use of a two-price plan.

Tax provisions of the federal income tax which offer special incentives to the mineral industries are: percentage depletion allowance, the privilege of expensing certain costs of exploration and development, and accelerated amortization. These are powerful incentives to investment in discovery and development.

The annual depletion allowance, which was studied as a petroleum problem, is a deduction from taxable income permitted because of the gradual exhaustion of depletable property. The percentage depletion deduction allowed by the Internal Revenue Code is a stated percentage of gross annual income, ranging from 5 percent for certain common minerals like sand and gravel, through a 10 percent and 15 percent bracket, to 23 percent for sulfur and 27½ percent for gas and oil; but it may not exceed 50 percent of the net income from the property. Over the life of a property it is possible for tax-free recovery to reach a total far greater than the taxpayer's investment. This is justifiable because percentage depletion is used not only to permit recovery of investment in a wasting asset but also as an incentive for discovery and development in a risky business. There is a need, however, to adjust the percentage depletion among the minerals so that the rate will be higher where the risk is greater and/or the national need for the particular mineral is greater.

Expensing is the privilege of deducting as current expense certain outlays for exploration and development which would otherwise have to be treated as a capital outlay recoverable over a period of years. In oil and gas, all "intangible drilling and development costs" are expensible. These include most of the outlays for exploration and development. In the mining industries exploration costs may be treated as current expense only up to $75,000 a year, with a cumulative limit of $300,000. There is no limit on expensing the cost of developing a mine once a discovery has been made. Since expensing provides such a powerful direct incentive for discovery, it would appear logical that the present limitation on minerals other than oil and gas should be removed.

Another provision of the federal income tax which has been used to encourage development of minerals is the rapid tax-write-off program for new defense plants which was started in 1950 after the Communist invasion of South Korea. Under this program of accelerated tax amortization, applications are made to the Office of Defense Mobilization for a "certificate of necessity" for the construction or expansion of a facility "in the interest of national defense." The certificate holder is allowed to amortize over a period of five years that percentage of the cost of the new facility covered by the certificate, instead of the normal rate of twenty years as fixed by the International Revenue Code. This has presented a tremendous tax advantage to the applicant and resulted in an accelerated investment program. Certificates of necessity are granted mainly on the basis of the essentiality of the project to national defense.

The rapid tax-write-off program requires continuous review, and may result in inequities between firms. This review was under way in 1955, and in August, Mobilization Director Arthur S. Flemming issued an order ending the rapid write-off for nineteen industries including asbestos, lead, manganese ore, cement, tungsten, zinc, and various alloying minerals. In addition, thirty-eight others were indefinitely suspended—these included iron ore and oil among the minerals.

Under the fast tax-write-off plan many serious abuses occurred in the name of "defense." During 1956 the plan was thoroughly studied and the government was moving toward a policy in what *Fortune* described as a "commendable intention to overhaul and in so far as possible do away with the whole system." The last week in December, 1956, Director Arthur S. Flemming of the Office of Defense Mobilization rejected all pending applications for rapid amortizations. Of the original 228 items eligible, expansion goals and fast tax write-offs were still available for only 22. These included chromite; research and development laboratories; manganese ore; medical supplies and equipment; mercury; nickel; oil and gas pipelines and petroleum storage facilities for specific defense programs; electric power facilities for military, Atomic Energy Commission, and defense-related needs; aircraft and other production facilities for military and AEC procurement; roll-on, roll-off ships; scientific instruments; selenium; steam boilers; steam turbines; steel castings; substitutes for strategic natural mica; ocean-going tankers; and titanium-processing facilities.

The announced fast tax amortization policy on January 1, 1957, after advice from the full Defense Mobilization Board, was that "The only consideration for new tax write-offs would be if a case could be clearly made that in a full mobilization—and only then—there would be a scarcity of materials for military, atomic energy, defense-supporting, or 'rock bottom' civilian requirements."

The Defense Production Act of 1950 had two important provisions to encourage exploration and development of minerals: one making possible loans for exploration, and the other providing for purchase of minerals.

Under the Defense Production Act of 1950 as amended, the Defense Minerals Exploration Administration (DMEA) was authorized to grant loans in some instances up to 50 percent, and for other minerals up to 75 percent, of approved costs for exploration of specified minerals. Authorization of the DMEA expired December 31, 1958. Public Law 85-701, enacted August 21, 1958, provided the authority for the new Office of Minerals Exploration (OME) in the Department of Interior which took over the DMEA activities. This loan incentive program met with varying success, but it was particularly effective in southern Missouri where important new ore bodies were found which may contain several million tons of recoverable lead.

Another financial incentive authorized by the 1950 Defense Production Act as amended is the purchase of raw materials for government use to encourage the exploration, development, and mining of strategic materials. Long-term contracts and standing purchase offers between the U.S. government and domestic producers are desirable for use with certain minerals which either are chronically scarce or are expected to be so during the period of the contract or offer. These measures are very effective when substantial amounts of marginal production of minerals will be taken only if otherwise prohibitive market risks are eliminated by the assurance of sale at a price high enough to cover all costs. These contracts and offers are well adapted to preserving an active domestic production nucleus for certain minerals of which a quickly expansible domestic source is needed as a security measure. The Materials Policy Commission concluded: "The standing offer to purchase is administratively more practical than the long-term contract if the mineral is one produced by a large number of producers each operating on a small scale. Either device should be used with great caution and only where it promises a substantial amount of needed domestic production or productive capacity not otherwise obtainable at lower cost." Both types of these purchase agreements may prove politically difficult to terminate even when they may be deemed no longer justified.

The two-price plan, also referred to as the premium price, is the last financial incentive to discovery and development that will be considered. This is a program that is especially designed for emergency periods when price ceilings are in effect. During World War II the premium price plan was used to obtain additional quantities of copper, lead, and zinc, and oil from stripper wells. Premiums above ceiling prices were paid for output in excess of quotas based on "normal" production. The program was considered successful. During the program premiums were paid on 20 percent of the copper produced domestically, 40 percent of the lead, 70 percent of the zinc, and about 10 percent of the petroleum. Administrative expenses were under one percent of total payments. Costs in higher prices sufficient to induce this additional production would have been greater. The Materials Policy Commission concluded that in an emergency period when price controls are in effect the premium price plan can be a valuable device for stimulating production without undercutting a stabilization program or creating windfalls for low-cost producers. "Applied over long periods, however, it entails increasing administrative expenses, particularly in revising cost analyses and adjusting quotas. Moreover, since premium price plans primarily stimulate production from known reserves, their use might tend in the long run to divert energies from discovering and developing new sources of supply. In addition, they may set up a heavy drain on small reserves of scarce materials." Both of these latter conclusions would appear to be highly debatable, and equally applicable to other programs.

Stockpiling

Because of the critical importance of many minerals and other raw materials for military purposes and because of the time needed to develop, transport, and process these materials, reserve supplies must be accumulated and held in stockpiles during peacetime. In addition, the sharp rise in the demand for minerals during war periods require stockpiles as a cushion against the sudden increase in requirements.

Stockpiling should be against specific requirements. This necessitates a determination of (1) the total requirements of a major emergency, (2) the anticipated production during the emergency, and (3) the difference between (1) and (2) for each item in the stockpile. This difference is the quantity to be purchased and held in stockpile. The President's Cabinet Committee on Minerals Policy reported in November, 1954:

> To the degree that minerals are stockpiled within the United States prior to the start of a war, there will be less need, or no need at all for forced draft wartime expansion of raw materials production involving unreasonable increases in prices or substantial Government investment. Likewise, there will be less need for stringent wartime allocations, ceiling prices, and limitation orders on raw materials. In addition, stockpiling can greatly reduce the need for diversion of naval, air, and military efforts to the secondary task of protecting overseas sources of materials and supply lanes when they should be employed in the primary task of fighting the war.

The first Congressional stockpiling legislation was authorized by the Act of June 7, 1939. Inadequate funds were appropriated. Action was "too little too late." On July 26, 1946, the 79th Congress approved the Strategic and Critical Stockpiling Act (Public Law 520). At the end of World War II the government had a large unbalanced stock of materials on hand. These were not legally handled as a reserve for stockpile; instead, a large part was sold as war surplus. The act of 1946 made possible the transfer of the desirable remaining unbalanced and depleted war stocks to the stockpile. Once again Congress did not provide adequate stockpiling appropriations and they were not made available until after the beginning of the Korean War. Once again action was "too late."

The President's Cabinet Committee on Minerals Policy concluded in 1954:

> Twice within the last 15 years, the United States has been drawn into international conflicts with almost no stockpile of strategic and critical materials. The absence of an adequate stockpile required the Nation in 1942–44 and again in 1950–52, to undertake costly and disruptive expansion programs to obtain materials which a stockpile, accumulated in advance, could have supplied. It was necessary at a most difficult time to divert scarce machinery and equipment, manpower, and military forces to obtain these materials.

Two of the costly and disruptive effects of 1950–1952 were as follows: First, the demand for raw materials for mobilization plus the stockpile purchasing resulted in tremendous increases in prices and costs. Second, since our allies had to buy materials at these high prices, the effect was quite serious and disruptive for them as they were already critically short of foreign exchange. A third disruptive effect which came later was that while foreign sellers of raw materials benefited initially from higher prices, they suffered greatly from the drastic drop in prices when the United States stopped buying some commodities for stockpile purposes. These suppliers prefer a sustained purchase program. Where individual materials constitute a large part of the national income of producing countries, intermittent purchases on the part of the United States drastically upset the economies of the suppliers.

These errors of the past suggest the conclusion that building of a stockpile is a long-term and continuous matter and that major additions to the stockpile should be made so as to bring about the least possible disturbance to the mineral market.

There are other stockpile problems which require continuous attention. One such is the concern of producers that the stockpile is a surplus hanging over the market. A most serious problem is the constant need for revision of the stockpile in terms of new military plans, new total requirements, new metals, and new supply sources.

The President's Cabinet Committee concluded that the objectives of the stockpile program were "minimum" in that they assumed substantial wartime imports, as well as stringent conservation measures. Therefore, the Committee recommended a complete review of all stockpile objectives for strategic and critical metals and minerals and the establishment in lieu of the "minimum" objective of new long-term goals that would assure, over a period of time, the acquisition of adequate stocks of these materials and thereby reduce and where possible eliminate foreseeable wartime shortages. This recommendation was to be implemented as follows: (1) It is assumed that supplies from abroad will not be available to the United States in time of war except from a limited group of countries. (2) A supply sufficient to offset possible destruction of major metal- and mineral-producing facilities within the United States must be assured. (3) Materials will be upgraded and refined to the point at which they will be readily usable in an emergency. (4) Stockpile objectives were to be fulfilled from all sources as quickly as possible, but purchases of materials will be made to stabilize and to alleviate distressed conditions in domestic minerals industries that are an important element in the mobilization base of the nation. (5) Preference will be given to newly mined metals and minerals of domestic origin. (6) Acquisition will continue to be made by obtaining strategic and critical metals and minerals in exchange for surplus agricultural commodities which have already been paid for by the government. (7) In acquiring metals and minerals for the "long-term" stockpile objective, care should be exercised to avoid interfering with the normal relationships of regular trade in the United States and in friendly foreign countries.

These recommendations and their implementation were ordered into effect by President Eisenhower. In aggregate they would appear to put the stockpile on a much sounder basis. However, two interrelated points should be singled out for further comment because of their debatable character: (4) stabilization and (5) domestic priority.

The question has been raised: Is the strategic stockpile for security or stabilization? The answer is "Both" under the new program, because price and industry stabilization are clearly defined objectives: "Acquisitions should take place ordinarily at such times as the Government decides that purchases will help to reactivate productive capacity and in other ways to alleviate distressed conditions in connection with domestic mineral industries that are an important element of the Nation's mobilization base. . . ." "Upgrading of stockpile materials should normally be done only when it can be accomplished at favorable prices and in periods of lowered economic activity."

The military have expressed the opinion that "The stockpile should not be used as a stabilization device except in very extraordinary circumstances. This is not to say that we should flout incidental benefits of stockpiles to the stabilization of a peacetime economy. These can be reaped, since assured steady purchasing over a long period is a strong force for stabilization and for a high rate of production."[6] Putting it in proper context and perspective, the military have opposed the inclusion of stabilization as a stockpile objective because they have seen the stockpile depleted for this purpose, because they know that it confuses the primary issue of security, and because it increases the problems of political manipulation. The military would prefer to see other devices used to obtain stabilization.

One example of the use of the stockpile as stabilizer under the new program occurred early in 1955 when U.S. producers of lead and zinc were in such serious trouble that they were, as in the past, asking for higher tariffs to protect themselves from cheaper foreign metals. President Eisenhower rejected the tariff increase, but instead almost doubled the rate of stockpile buying.

This example shows the interrelation of stabilization to the second point singled out for further comment—domestic priority. The first stockpiling legislation in 1939 contained a "Buy American" clause. "Buy American" legislation requires government agencies to buy only domestic goods, unless they are not available in sufficient commercial quantities or

---

[6] George A. Lincoln, *Economics of National Security*, Englewood Cliffs, N.J., Prentice-Hall, 1954, p. 19.

their cost is unreasonable or "otherwise inconsistent with the public interest." This clause was continued as part of the 1946 legislation. Commenting on the 1946 act, the military concluded: "The Act provided a sound basis, with the exception of one aspect, for proceeding with stockpiling. The major weakness was the 'Buy American' clause. This is incongruous since one of the chief purposes is to get within the United States a larger supply of materials needed than would otherwise be available. If we merely move materials from United States ground to United States stockpile we gain time and save labor and other resources in case of emergency, but we do not expand our total supply. Development of the available U.S. reserves should go forward, but other methods such as subsidies should be used to encourage domestic producers."[7]

This "Buy American" clause is clearly contained in the Committee on Minerals Policy recommendation: "Accordingly, in making purchases, preference should be given to newly-mined metals and minerals of domestic origin." The justification for such an approach is the subsidization and stabilization of the domestic industry plus what *Time* called a goal "that would make the U.S. virtually self-sufficient in strategic materials." *Time* made the following comment on this approach:

> The program assumed that in wartime all sources of supply except Canada and Mexico would be cut off from the U.S., and that even some metal-processing plants in the U.S. might be blasted out of commission. But if the stockpile assumption is that the U.S. will be cut off from all supply, it is the only aspect of U.S. defense based on that idea. All the armed forces have planned their strategy with the idea that the U.S. will have allies, and that it will be able to maintain supply lines back and forth across the oceans. Furthermore, if self-sufficiency is the goal, the U.S. should be spending its money only for those highly critical metals that cannot be found at home, instead of buying aluminum, nickel, molybdenum, etc., which are available in the U.S., Canada and Mexico.

Obviously, *Time* oversimplified the problem in stating only one goal out of a number of stockpile objectives. However, the President of the United States instructed his Committee by letter on October 26, 1953, to use as one of its guide lines: "To preserve the added economic strength represented by recent expansion of facilities by the domestic mining industry, through policies that would be consistent with our other national and international policies." It was also suggested: "That the prudent use and development of domestic mineral resources and assured access to necessary sources abroad are indispensable to the operation of an active economy and sound defense." The U.S. international policies have called for international trade. There is considerable evidence that the Cabinet Committee on Minerals Policy has in its stockpile policy overemphasized

[7] *Ibid.*, pp. 193–194.

the domestic interests and deëmphasized the continued necessity of importing minerals from outside sources.

A final summary conclusion is that, while clearly stating that "overriding in importance in any consideration of policies relating to mineral production and utilization is the security of the Nation," the Committee may have partially reduced the role of security of the stockpile program by stressing the use of stabilization in its implementations. The military have expressed the opinion that there is some danger that the possession of a large stockpile may develop a complacency which would be a brake on the necessary peacetime efforts of exploration, expansion, and technological improvement which need to be pressed because of our worsening raw materials situation. If the recommendations of the Cabinet Committee are carried out properly, this danger certainly should not materialize because the Committee's recommendations were in two parts: "I. The Problem of Security," and "II. The Development of Domestic Mineral Resources." The stockpile is one part of the first and an integrated part of the whole.

Responsibility for the stockpile program rests with the Office of Emergency Planning (OEP). In 1965 rather than there being one big reserve of materials there were three stockpiles: (1) the National Stockpile, of strategic and critical materials built up after World War II; (2) the Defense Production Act of 1950 inventory; and (3) the Commodity Credit Corporation and Supplemental stockpile built up under the Agricultural Trade and Assistance Act of 1954 which provided for trading surplus agricultural products for strategic and critical materials.

One of the basic problems faced with such a complexity of inventories was the development of an integrated stockpile policy for accumulation and disposal. The President of the United States appointed an Executive Stockpile Committee under the Chairmanship of the OEP which reported to the President on *Disposing of Excess Stockpile Materials* on January 16, 1963. One of the recommendations was that disposal plans should be based on maximum objectives and that those objectives be predicated on supply-requirements studies that reflect current strategic concepts and up-to-date information about emergency requirements to meet military, war-supporting, and essential civilian needs. The Committee found that the then present stockpile objectives were based on conventional war assumptions, military, defense-supporting, and essential, that might not reflect current needs for such a conflict. In large part the requirements were found to be based on requirements that were several years old, and that stockpile requirments for nuclear war had not been developed.

Thus again investigation showed that the stockpile was not functioning to serve its proper purpose, and this was discovered as a result of concern about disposal problems. The net effect of these findings was that the OEP began an attempt to develop up-to-date, single objectives for each stockpile material which reflect the calculated deficits in military, industrial, and other essential needs in the event of a conventional war emergency. The OEP is also attempting to determine stockpile needs to meet the requirements of a general nuclear war including reconstruction. The OEP has completed a postattack economic model, referred to as a "rough-cut" study for agency guidance in developing postattack supply-requirements studies. When commodity objectives for nuclear war differ from those established for conventional war, the higher of the two objectives will prevail.

Once proper stockpile objectives and levels are achieved, disposal of surplus must then fellow definite, recommended lines which would cause the minimum harmful effects on the U.S. domestic economy and international relations. One recommended simplification of the stockpile problem was to reduce the three existing stockpiles in 1965 to two: (1) the National Stockpile of strategic and critical materials, which then contained 3.3 billion dollars worth of inventory; and (2) a Material Reserve Inventory, which then contained 5.2 billion dollars of material. Sales could then be made from the latter stockpile, but not from the National Stockpile. But such a plan would have to be administered with great caution. Some of the intricate and interrelated problems involved are the impact on the domestic minerals industries and on the world market, and the economic reliance of certain countries on one or more of the minerals. However, there was real evidence in 1965 that the government stockpile policy would continue to stress both security and stabilization, and that the policy would be directed toward a specific impact on a domestic industry. The case in point was that in response to the industry's increase in the price of aluminum the government announced a sale of 300,000 tons of aluminum from the stockpile. The industry rescinded the price increase as the government initiated a policy of selling from the stockpile to hold prices down just as previously, purchases had been made to support prices as was the case cited for lead which occurred ten years earlier.

Import Policy

One of the most widely debated issues is the use of tariffs and quotas in the minerals supply problem. On the one hand the contention is that tariffs and quotas are essential as protective and development devices for the domestic industry. On the other hand, the argument is waged with equal force that these devices retard the importation of essential minerals and misdirect productive efforts which should be put to more effective use. These and other arguments have been developed extensively in the discussion of petroleum.

The increased dependence of the United States on imports of minerals already has been shown. In no commodity group has a greater change taken place in the trade of the United States than in metals and minerals. As has been seen, the United States produces a number of minerals either in very small quantities or not at all, and thus must depend on outside sources. Some are available from nearby sources, and others must be imported from less assured sources. In the next three chapters we will study the leading ferrous metals—iron and steel—and the two leading nonferrous metals—copper and aluminum. A few brief remarks about the United States import position with respect to them are in order at this point.

Iron ore, the basic nonfuel mineral of industrialization, is expected to be imported in much greater quantities. Domestic grades of high-grade ores are being depleted. Very large low-grade reserves and the technology to develop them are available in the United States. To supplment these reserves high-grade ore is being imported principally from Venezuela, Canada, and to a lesser extent from Chile and Brazil. Sweden is also a source of United States imports.

In copper, the first of the two most important nonferrous metals, the United States has shifted from an exporter to an importer. Imports of copper come primarily from Chile and Peru, where production is for the most part owned by the United States. Table 8.3 showed that in 1963 imports of copper were 25 percent of the net supply, with 56 percent coming from primary domestic production and 19 percent from scrap.

Aluminum, the second most important nonferrous metal, is produced from bauxite. Imports of bauxite have grown in the United States until they constitute between 85 and 90 percent of total domestic uses. Originally most of the U.S. imports came from Surinam, but new sources of supply have been developed in Jamaica. United States companies control most of the production in South America and the Caribbean area. The outlook is that with increased aluminum production in the United States, the nation's dependence on bauxite imports will increase.

In view of the United States increased dependence on imports of ferrous and nonferrous metals there is a need for some clear direction in the determination of this country's minerals import policy. The objective of obtaining an adequate flow of minerals at least cost has general appeal, but it has to be reconciled with such other considerations as national defense, the position of domestic industries and regions that might be affected by larger imports, and the interests of friendly nations. It is hard to reconcile these general objectives and even harder to translate objectives into policy.

One specific attempt to formulate a U.S. minerals policy was made by the Public Advisory Board for Mutual Security. The writer was privileged to serve on the staff of the Board which formulated its recommendations in a report to the President on *A Trade and Tariff Policy in the National Interest*, in February, 1953. Since this states a recommended minerals import policy in a concise fashion, the resultant discussion, conclusions, and recommendations are repeated.

United States Needs and Foreign Sources—The United States would be following a dangerous policy if it were to close its eyes to its dependence on foreign sources for a substantial part of its supply of many of the most vital mineral commodities, or to disregard the importance of keeping down the materials costs of goods entering into the United States economy. When domestic production of some mineral is substantial, it is necessarily in competition with imports; but if this country depends on such imports, it must give the foreign producer access to the American market on a reasonable and fair basis and United States industry access to foreign supplies on as favorable terms as possible.

There can be only one valid policy on minerals: to assume adequate supplies for this country and the free world in the present and the future. Such a policy should encourage domestic and foreign production, and provide for the exploration and development of domestic and foreign deposits. The United States must give every encouragement to the expansion of production abroad and the participation of American companies in such development on equitable terms. Foreign countries will not offer such opportunities to American investors if the ores and metals cannot be exported to the United States on fair terms.

Nor can the United States expect to have assured sources of imports in the future, when its needs are greater, if it is unwilling to allow imports in the present, when its needs may be less acute. After foreign producers of minerals develop markets in other countries, they cannot cut off supplies to their usual customers to meet emergency needs of the United States. Finally, since a producing country abroad may be a source of various minerals, a policy of encouraging imports of some and restricting imports of others may be regarded as discriminatory by the supplier country. To participate in the development and use of the mineral production of other countries, the United States must permit imports to come in without serious restrictions and without penalizing the reduction and refining of ores abroad.

Tariffs on Metals and Minerals—With few exceptions, the duties on metals and minerals, including import excise taxes, are low, and many ores and unprocessed minerals are on the Free List. The duties are generally specific, and their ad valorem equivalent is seldom more than 15 percent and often below 10 percent on the basis of 1951 market prices. There has been a marked reduction in the impact of the specific duties because of the rise in prices. For many of these minerals and metals, moreover, duties have been reduced under the Trade Agreements, often by half and occasionally by more than half of the 1930 rate. Much of the reduction in duties has occurred since the war.

For most ores and unprocessed minerals, the relatively small duty has little restrictive effect on imports under ordinary conditions; it is a low hurdle over which imports pass easily, and does no more than give domestic producers a slight price advantage. For many imports, including the major nonferrous metals, such relatively low tariffs cannot possibly provide a significant inducement for expanding or maintaining the high cost segment of domestic output.

The specific duty on some metals provides a fixed differential between the price of domestic and imported metals. It thus becomes more protective when prices are high. As metals prices are subject to greater fluctuation than the prices of manufactured goods, the tariff does operate to keep prices in the domestic market from falling as low as they otherwise might when there is a sharp decline in demand. In fact, however, for most minerals and metals present duties are too low to have any significant effect on price stability.

A suggestion has been made to replace present duties with a sliding scale tariff. For example, in place of the present duty of 1 1/16 cents a pound on lead in metal, the duty would be placed at 4¾ cents a pound when the price of lead is 5 cents a pound and would be reduced by one-fourth cent a pound for each 1 cent a pound rise in the price of lead. Whenever lead is over 20 cents a pound, imports would be duty free. The proposal has several objectionable features, apart from the high rates which are recommended. Its stabilizing effect on the domestic price of lead would be great. But this stability would be achieved at the expense of very much greater instability in the price of lead abroad. Whatever contribution it would make to encourage domestic production would be more than offset by the serious blow it would give to production abroad. The United States cannot isolate itself from the world market and from the world supply of a commodity for which 50 percent of domestic requirements, and probably a larger proportion in the future, must be met by imports.

Tariffs and Domestic Needs—The effect of small duties in encouraging domestic exploration and development is very uncertain. Search for minerals is undertaken in response to the prospect for profit. Incentive is not provided by a tariff as such, but by an expanding market at profitable prices. Tax provisions covering exploration costs and depletion allowances offer far greater incentives for the metals and minerals industry than could be provided by tariffs. It would be dangerous to exclude imports which meet the needs of the American economy in order to encourage exploration and development of possible domestic sources of these minerals. If additional incentives are necessary to stimulate exploration and development in the United States, they can be better and more economically provided in other ways. The use of tariffs to encourage exploitation of low-grade ores now is particularly objectionable.

Tariffs on the minerals for which the United States produces all of its current needs and is a net exporter are unnecessary. Their effect in excluding imports is negligible, and their elimination would contribute to the simplification and rationalization of the tariff. Such minerals include molybdenum ore and concentrates, and magnesium metal. They should be transferred to the Free List.

The basic principle that a tariff is unjustified when imports are necessary to supply a large part of American conseumption is as applicable to metals and minerals as to other commodities. At present, the excise tax of 2 cents a pound on imported copper is suspended. There is no reason to restore it at all. For lead and zinc, the present tariff is equivalent to about 6 percent ad valorem. The world market for these metals has not been as strong as that for copper; and high cost domestic producers have been more dependent on the tariff to maintain output. For this reason the tariff should perhaps be retained for the time being, but provision should be made to remove it when prices of these metals rise and conditions become favorable for eliminating the tariff.

A change in tariff policy is also desirable for the minerals of which domestic production supplies less than one-third of domestic needs. The principal reason for encouraging domestic production is to meet emergencies. In part this can be accomplished by stockpiling. If it is also necessary in the case of some minerals to foster a going domestic industry of moderate proportions in peace time, the Government purchase programs now in use for mica, chrome and manganese could be extended to other commodities and accomplish the same purpose as a tariff. Imports of such minerals, however, should be on the Free List.

The tariffs on metals and processed minerals should be no more than the equivalent of the tariffs on the ores and crude minerals from which they are derived. The existing differentials are undesirable. The reason for admitting an ore free of duty and placing a duty on the metal is to induce the establishment of smelting facilities in the United States instead of the country of origin. Continuation of such duties is prejudicial to the countries on which this country must depend for import supplies and places an unnecessary burden on domestic metals manufacturing industries. The assessment of an additional duty on the minor presence of a mineral in an imported ore, such as vanadium in iron ore, should also be eliminated.[8]

The above recommended trade and tariff policy follows the principle that national interest includes both the United States domestic and international considerations. It is obvious that this policy recognizes the United States dependence on foreign sources for imports of minerals and tends to favor a lessening of restrictions to trade. It is equally obvious that recent examples of U.S. minerals policy in the case of quota restrictions on crude petroleum and lead and zinc have tended to emphasize domestic and security interests over international interests. Thus, the United States continues to attempt to reconcile such considerations as national defense, the position of domestic minerals industries, and the interest of friendly nations in obtaining an adequate flow of minerals at least cost. There still is not, and there may never be, a clear-cut direction in the determination of this country's minerals import policy.

Development of Outside Sources

Ample proof has been given for the need of imports and of the dependence of the United States on foreign sources for nonfuel minerals. The question then is what policies, in addition to changes in import policies, might effectively help develop outside sources for nonfuel minerals and thus help alleviate the supply problem. The development of these sources is important because of the increasing requirements of both the United States and the rest of the free world. There is a need for policies

[8] *A Trade and Tariff Policy in the National Interest*, Public Advisory Board for Mutual Security, Washington, D.C., 1953, pp. 33–35.

and action which are advantageous to both the United States and the source countries.

The President's Materials Policy Commission concluded that the areas to which the United States must principally look for expansion of its minerals imports are Canada, Latin America, Africa, the Near East, and south and southeast Asia. The Commission found that in the high-tonnage materials, such as oil, iron ore, zinc, manganese, bauxite, and possibly copper, there is little doubt that the less-developed areas have high-grade reserves, which after satisfying their own expanding requirements can supply the rest of the free world beyond the 1975 terminal date of the study. The same was considered to be true for a wide range of other essential materials. "The real question, therefore, is whether capital, equipment, technology, and management skills will flow into the expansion of lowest cost sources of supply in the less developed countries at a rate sufficient to yield the necessary production."

To this real question should be added the question of the assured availability of this production to the United States as a part of a long-term peacetime program and during wartime.

The Commission saw need of action along four lines: "(1) to provide better inducements both abroad and at home for private investors in foreign materials production; (2) to assist resource countries in the progressive improvement of their productive capacity; (3) to relieve restrictions on trade in raw materials; and (4) to curb the violent fluctuations of materials markets."

All of these lines of action have much broader applications than to nonfuel minerals alone. Point one and two would require an intensive study as to the effective role of capital resources. Point three was considered in detail in the previous discussions of imports and of the "Buy American" clause. Also point four has been referred to several times. However, a brief consideration of one, two, and four as they affect minerals will point up the required policy action to improve the nonfuels minerals supply position.

Private Investment. It would appear that private investment on the part of U.S. nationals is the best source for the development of minerals in raw material countries. But many of the primary resource countries have been extending government control over their minerals and other raw materials.

The President's Materials Policy Commission made a survey of fifty companies, together with underwriters, brokers, bankers, management engineers, and law firms active in materials enterprises abroad. It concluded that, in general, private investors recognize the legitimate interests of resource countries and are ready to work on equitable terms including, in cases, the sharing of investment, ownership, and management with local interests. However, the private investors want relief from threat of expropriation, foreign administrative restrictions on conversion of earnings into dollars, discriminatory taxations, and interference with operations. They also want relief from penalizing provisions of U.S. tax laws.

The results of this survey suggest that the U.S. government should extend its diplomatic efforts to create a more favorable basis for bargaining and the conclusion of agreements between investors and the governments of resource countries. The President's Materials Policy Commission believed that in achieving such ends there was considerable value in the investment treaties which the United States was negotiating with other nations. These treaties give the investor greater assurance of the right of appeal to the International Court of Justice in case of unresolved disputes over the interpretation of treaty terms, and against arbitrary and unfair treatment. In addition to investment treaties, the Commission recommended the negotiation of government-to-government special resource agreements when new investment in minerals would occur in a given place in a given country if legal and administrative deterrents were lifted. The suggestion is that these agreements would run from five to ten years, during which the private investor would have the pledge of the foreign government in specific terms concerning tax laws, ownership and management, exchange, restrictions, compensation in event of expropriation, and other familiar points of issue.

The Commission also concluded that the amount of private capital invested in the development of mineral resources abroad could be considerably spurred and new investors attracted by certain changes in the tax laws. The Commission recommended a series of actions:

Allowing taxpayers to elect annually between "per country" and "over-all limitations" in claiming credits on their U.S. tax bills for taxes paid abroad; permitting deferral of reporting income until actually received; extending the privilege of filing consolidated returns with foreign subsidiaries; allowing stockholders in foreign corporations which have invested in exploration and development to treat part of their dividends as tax-free return of capital rather than a taxable income.

Up until the early 1960's the United States did follow a policy of encouraging investment in other countries; not only private investment, but the government itself actively participated in loans. However, beginning in 1965 the U.S. government began to be concerned about the nation's unfavorable balance of payments which was causing a drain on the gold supply. Although there were many causes of this drain, chief among which were the government's own expenditures for military and civilian foreign aid, the decision was made to attempt to check private investment abroad. President Lyndon B. Johnson asked the Commerce and Treasury Departments to "enlist the leaders of American business in a national campaign to limit their direct investments abroad, their deposits in foreign banks, and their holdings of foreign financial assets until their efforts—and those of all Americans—have restored balance in the country's international accounts."

This whole change in policy toward foreign investment is regressive and runs counter to U.S. policy which has favored the growth of the international economy. The charge is that these capital outflows for investment constitute a big part of the drain. The argument is that this change in U.S. policy is remarkably myopic, for the outflows of the moment tend to be compensated, and more than compensated, by later return. It was estimated in 1965 that past direct investments abroad were yielding a 4 billion dollar annual inflow of dividends and other payments to the United States, or twice the then current new investment. In other words, continued heavy foreign investment is a long-term strength, rather than a weakness for balance of payments. There is no question about the fact that investment on the part of U.S. companies in minerals abroad has opened up new sources of minerals to this country, and it does appear that U.S. policy should continue to favor such investment.

Assisting Resource Countries. One would hope that assisting resource countries in the progressive improvement of their productive capacity is a task that private enterprise could perform and would be encouraged by U.S. policy. However, in some countries the task may be too great for private capital, and public loans and technical assistance may be called for to aid in educational programs and the diversification of economic development.

To accomplish this task the United States should encourage a wider use of the United Nations technical assistance in geological surveying and minerals exploration in the underdeveloped countries. The United States might also expand its own technical assistance program in return for the assurance that the recipient countries will develop the new mineral resources discovered.

In addition, the expansion of minerals output is often impossible in some countries without public improvement in transportation and electric power. In such instances, public capital supplied by the United States Export-Import Bank and by the International Bank is called for. The President's Materials Policy Commission recommended that the International Bank should be the principal source of such public loans and that the Bank should consider the effect of the loans on materials output in reviewing requests from member countries.

Reducing Market Instability. Reducing market instability would aid tremendously in the development of outside sources for minerals. This problem was considered as a part of the minerals stockpile program. In that connection the recommendation was made that the United States as a buyer enter into long-term purchase contracts and buy in an orderly fashion rather than in the spasmodic economy-upsetting fashion that had been practiced in the past. The same thing holds true for the disposal of commodities from the stockpile which currently is the order of the day. There is real need on the part of the U.S. administrative officials to consider the impact of purchases and sales on raw material suppliers. More orderly markets with more stable prices would greatly encourage mineral production.

Intergovernmental commodity agreements have been used with varying degrees of success. In the past they have been dominated by producer interests and therefore have not been acceptable to the United States. In general, it has not been the policy to approve such agreements, although this country has entered into a wheat agreement and a coffee agreement. There is some opinion that multilateral agreements might work for selected commodities. But as time passes the United States is getting more and more disenchanted with the wheat agreement, and delayed a long time in the renewal of a coffee agreement to stabilize prices.

International buffer stocks have been suggested and discussed over the years as a means of stabilizing prices. Mention was made of the fact that there is now in operation a buffer stock for tin. The idea behind the buffer stock is that when world prices for a mineral fall, the buffer stock would act as a residual buyer; when prices rise, the stock would act as a seller. "The object is to confine price fluctuations to a moderate range, but not to interfere with the market price mechanism." This stated objective makes absolutely no sense in so far as the "but not" clause is concerned. United States policy makers have never approved a buffer stock. The complications of its administration would be many, and it would inevitably result in international interference with the market mechanism.

The President's Materials Policy Commission concluded that it was aware of the extreme difficulties inherent in such international undertakings. But it believed "that the alternative to giving them a trial would be an open door to the evils of restrictions and the monopolistic practices of cartels, limiting production, consumption and trade."

Conclusion

The basic problem of the nonfuel minerals position is this: How can the United States increase its supply of nonfuel minerals in order to meet the anticipated growth in demand and to provide for an adequate emergency reserve? The solution to this problem has been seen to be possible in the development of policies and their implementation which will further domestic exploration and development; provide for an adequate stockpile integrated with a growing economy and a mobilization base; establish an import policy in the national interest; and aid in the development of outside sources of supply through encouraging private investment, assisting resource countries, and reducing market instability.

Policy Recommendations

One of the basic objectives of our economic system is to raise our plane of living through economic growth. This objective of economic progress places an ever-increasing burden upon our mineral resources. Requirements for security add to this burden.

World War II proved emphatically the productive strength of the United States economy, and showed the possibility of channeling this strength to achieve economic progress; but at the same time the drains of the war on the resource base gave rise to the question this nation had never before taken seriously: Have we the resources for freedom?

To answer this question the President appointed the Materials Policy Commission on January 22, 1951. The Commission saw "as its central task an examination of the adequacy of materials to meet the needs of the free world in the years ahead." The report was made in June, 1952. The problem was found to be larger and more pervasive than a "shortage" problem, local and transient, which in the past has found its solution in price changes that have brought supply and demand back in balance.

Powerful historical streams have converged to make the problem uniquely intense today. First, there has been a profound shift in the basic materials position of the United States—a worsening relationship between our requirements and our means of satisfying them. Second, other high-consuming nations, primarily in Western Europe, are in difficulties which stem from the serious depletion of their own domestic resources coupled with the weakening or severing of their former colonial ties. Third, many resource-rich but less-developed nations, especially of former colonial status, now focus on industrialization rather than materials export. Fourth, there lingers from the Great Depression a worldwide fear of the possible collapse of markets, which dampens the willingness of private investors and resource-rich countries to develop new free world resources. Finally, a great schism divides the world between the totalitarian and democratic nations, disrupting normal trade patterns and making necessary costly measures of armed preparedness.

The fundamental concepts upon which the report was based were clearly stated:

First, we share the belief of the American people in the principle of Growth. Granting that we cannot find any absolute reason for this belief we admit that to our Western minds it seems preferable to any opposite, which to us implies stagnation and decay. Whether there may be any unbreakable upper limits to the continuing growth of our economy we do not pretend to know, but it must be part of our task to examine such apparent limits as present themselves.

Second, we believe in private enterprise as the most efficacious way of performing industrial tasks in the United States. With this belief, a belief in the spur of the profit motive and what is called "the price system" obviously go hand in hand. This method, motive, and system have served uniquely well in America. We believe in a minimum of interference with these patterns of private enterprise. But to believe this is not to believe that this minimum must be set at zero. Private enterprise itself has from time to time asked for helps, or restraints, or counterpoises from Government to keep the system working at its best; for this reason, among others, we have experienced for a long time a mixture of private and public influences on our economy. The Commission sees no reason either to blink this fact or to decry it; as we see the future, the coexistence of great private and public strength is not only desirable but essential to our preservation.

Third, we believe that the destinies of the United States and the rest of the free non-Communist world are inextricably bound together. This belief implies, for example, that if the United States is to increase its imports of raw materials —as we believe it must—it must return in other forms strength for strength to match what it receives. It is this Commission's belief that if we fail to work for a rise in the standard of living of the rest of the free world, we thereby hamper and impede the further rise of our own, and equally lessen the chances of democracy to prosper and peace to reign the world over.

Security and economic growth for the United States and the rest of the free world must be the essential aim of any policy worth the name. Materials strength is a prime ingredient of general economic strength and growth. This Commission is convinced that if the United States and other free nations are to have such strength they must coordinate their resources to the ends of common growth, common safety, and common welfare. In turn, this means that the United States must reject self-sufficiency as a policy and instead adopt the policy of the lowest cost acquisition of materials wherever secure supplies may be found: self-sufficiency, when closely viewed, amounts to a self-imposed blockade and nothing more.[9]

The major premise upon which all the report was based was as follows: "The over-all objective of a national Materials Policy for the United States should be to insure an adequate and dependable flow of materials at the lowest cost consistent with national security and with the welfare of friendly nations."

The Commission found in brief that "In area after area we encounter soaring demands, shrinking resources, the consequent pressure toward rising real costs, the risk of wartime shortages, the strong possibility of an arrest or decline in the standard of living we cherish and hope to share." "The Materials Problem now demands that we give new and deep consideration to the fundamentals upon which all employment, all daily activity, eventually rests: the contents of the earth and its physical environment."

The dynamic nature of changing demands, technology, resource availability, political, economic, and military factors continuously create new problems and call for sustained study and policy recommendations and action. There is plenty of evidence that the U.S. government and pri-

[9] *Resources for Freedom, Summary of Vol. I, op. cit.,* pp. 5–6.

vate industry have been alerted to the dynamic nature of the energy and material problems and have taken action.

The United States government followed the President's Materials Policy Commission Report with: *A Trade and Tariff Policy in the National Interest,* a report to the President, February, 1953; *Commission on Foreign Economic Policy,* a report to the President and the Congress, January, 1954; *The Report of the President's Cabinet Committee on Minerals Policy,* November, 1954; and *The Report on Energy Supplies and Resources Policy* by the President's Advisory Committee, February, 1955. In 1956 the Bureau of Mines published *Mineral Facts and Problems* and revised this comprehensive study in 1960. In 1962 the *Report of the National Fuels and Energy Study Group* was issued, and in 1964 the FPC published the definitive *National Power Survey.* These major reports were augmented by hundreds of significant separate studies which led to the establishment of policy and its implementation.

Private industry, on the other hand, became acutely aware of the post-World War II energy and materials problems and has progressively solved many of them, and thus contributed to the sustained growth and strength of the U.S. economy.

SUMMARY

This chapter has considered carefully mineral characteristics and the United States nonfuel minerals position and problems and policy pertaining thereto. But what of the future? In summary, sustained action is required in the domestic and in the international area, and in the integration of the two to provide for an adequate mobilization base and its expansion for security purposes. The coordination and implementation of these three inseparable parts must be accomplished by government-industry cooperation.

In the domestic area more energy and materials can be obtained by working on the supply and use problems. On the supply side more resources can be made available by exploration and discovery, more efficient extraction, using lower-grade reserves, employing flow resources, using presently unemployable reserves, synthesizing new material, and developing technologies to accomplish unknown tasks. On the use side "phantom resources" can be created by shifting from the scarce to the abundant, using energy and materials more efficiently, and using more scrap.

In the international area these same recommendations will increase the available supplies of resources. The United States role is to make available its technology and its capital, and to adopt a trade policy which will lead to the most efficient use of the world's energy and material resources.

Mobilization and security plans must be continually revised, while we remain ever mindful of the fact that energy and materials are one of the basic requisites of productivity; and "only the productive can be strong and only the strong can be free."

Government-industry cooperation is required to study the ever-changing problem, to formulate policy, and to initiate and execute the required action in the above three inseparable areas. To this end, the President's Cabinet Committee on Minerals Policy recommended "that the Secretary of Interior develop ways and means of establishing and maintaining through some workable body the contacts between the mining industry and Government necessary to give force and effect to policies recommended herein." This is not enough. Workable bodies must be developed to aid in the development and implementation of energy and material policies present and future. This is a required, sustaining and reciprocal task.

SELECTED REFERENCES

Commission on Foreign Economic Policy, Report to the President and the Congress, Washington, D.C., January 23, 1954.

Domestic Problems of Non-Fuel Minerals, Section IV, Mid-Century Conference on Resources for the Future, Washington, D.C., Resources for the Future, Inc., December 2–4, 1953.

Landsberg, Hans H., *Natural Resources for U.S. Growth,* Baltimore, Johns Hopkins, 1964.

Lincoln, George A., *Economics of National Security,* Englewood Cliffs, N.J., Prentice-Hall, 1954.

Mineral Facts and Problems, Bureau of Mines Bulletin 585, Washington, D.C., 1960.

Netschert, Bruce C., and Hans H. Landsberg, *The Future Supply of Major Metals,* Washington, D.C., Resources for the Future, Inc., 1961.

Report of the President's Cabinet Committee on Minerals Policy, Washington, D.C., Executive Office of the President, November 30, 1954.

Report on Energy Supplies and Resource Policy, Washington, D.C., Executive Office of the President, February 26, 1955.

Resources for Freedom, Summary of Vol. I, a report to the President by the President's Materials Policy Commission, Washington, D.C., June, 1952.

Stockpile Report to Congress, Washington, D.C., Office of Emergency Planning, 1963.

"Strategic Stockpile—Is it for Security or Subsidy?", *Time,* October 4, 1954, p. 90.

A Trade and Tariff Policy in the National Interest, Public Advisory Board for Mutual Security, Washington, D.C., 1953.

Van Royen, William, and Oliver Bowles, *The Mineral Resources of the World,* Englewood Cliffs, N.J., Prentice-Hall, 1952.

"Will Lack of Minerals Strangle U.S. in War?", extracts from the official text of the report "Accessibility of Strategic and Critical Materials," issued by the Minerals Subcommittee on Interior and Insular Affairs, *U.S. News & World Report,* July 9, 1954, pp. 106–109.

9

STEEL

STEEL is the basis of industrialization. Since steel in one form or another enters into every part of the economy, the steel industry has always been considered an important barometer of general business conditions. More fundamentally, however, the capacity to produce steel, sustained production, and the availability of raw materials are excellent measures of the productive capacity and strength of a country.

Steel's dominant position rests on certain fundamental properties of this alloy of carbon and iron. To mention only a few: (1) It has a relatively high ductility and toughness compared with other metals, (2) It has a high modulus of elasticity which allows it to withstand great stress without appreciable distortion, (3) It has a definite proportional strength limit, and if not stressed beyond this limit, it will return to its original form and size, and (4) It can be alloyed with other metals which imparts to it properties that have widened its field of application.

TYPES OF STEEL AND MARKETS

There are three different broad categories of steel: carbon steels; alloy steels; and stainless steel, which is technically an alloy steel, but is usually classified separately.

A precise definition of carbon steels is not possible, except to state that these contain very little alloying elements, while the carbon (C) content ranges from 0.08 percent up to 1.7 percent. Low-carbon steels (0.08 percent to 0.35 C) are largely used for flat-rolled products because these grades are readily formed and are easily welded; increasing the carbon content results in greater hardness, tensile strength, and yield strength. About 93 percent of finished steel shipments are carbon steels, or so-called "tonnage grade" steels.

Alloy steels, which account for about 6 percent of the volume, are grades with substantially improved physical properties resulting from the addition of varying quantities of alloying elements. The wide range of products in this category consists of steels that have more than 1.65 percent manganese, 0.6 percent silicon, or 0.6 percent copper, or minimum quantities of the other major ferroalloys, including chromium, nickel, molybdenum, tungsten, titanium, vanadium, zirconium, and cobalt. Some of the special properties imparted by these alloys are corrosion resistance, strength, wear resistance, and special electrical attributes. The automobile industry usually takes about 30 percent of the alloy steel output mainly in the form of hot-rolled bars; other markets are manufacturers of machinery and industrial equipment (bar, tubing, tool steel) and electrical equipment companies, which mainly buy silicon electrical sheets.

Stainless steels account for less than 1 percent of steel shipments, but a much higher proportion of dollar sales because of their high prices. The automobile industry is a large user of stainless steel, and a growing and important market for stainless and heat resisting steels include missiles and supersonic aircraft. About 60–65 percent of stainless grades are chrome-nickel steels and the remainder are chromium steels with a minimum of 4 percent of this alloying element.

Domestic markets for steel have undergone significant changes over the years. Most remarkable has been the growth in consumer durables (automobiles and appliances). On the other hand, the demand for plant and equipment (mostly construction) has remained rather constant, while there has been a sharp drop in the freight transportation (railroad) requirements. Figure 9.1 shows these changing requirements.

The automotive market generally accounts for about 20 percent of steel use. The major automotive steel products are cold or hot-rolled sheets and bars. Production of the average car takes about two tons of steel, but the metal's weight in the finished car is less because of the scrap lost in fabrication.

The construction industry is the largest single outlet for steel and takes about 25 to 30 percent of industry shipments. About 20 percent goes to the construction market directly, but large tonnages of structurals, plates, line pipe, galvanized sheet and reinforced bars are marketed through warehouses and distributors. Steel has failed to participate in the continued construction boom of recent years because of the drop in industrial construction and sizable losses of structural steel applications to reinforced concrete.

About 15 to 16 percent of steel is shipped to warehouses and distributors. These steel service centers buy in large quantities and sell to small users.

Steel consumption by railroads—plates, structural shapes, sheets, and bars for rolling stock—has been decreasing for some time. The poor financial position of railroads, continued losses of traffic to other carriers, and technological changes point to the fact that the railroad market will not again be an important steel outlet.

Figure 9.1: Distribution of Steel Shipments by Consuming Industries, 1901–1960.

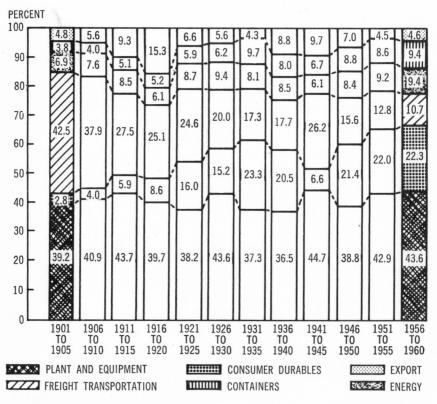

SOURCE: American Iron and Steel Institute.

The container market has shown considerable growth and takes between 9 and 10 percent of steel shipments. This growth has been helped by the packaging of beer and frozen citrus fruits in cans. Consumption of canned fruits and vegetables has been rather static due to the increased use of frozen foods. However, future growth in the container market will find steel facing stiff competition from plastics and aluminum.

Finally, one plus factor has been in the miscellaneous category of steel consumers, where the demand for refrigerators, washing machines, stoves, electrical equipment, and metal furniture has shown not only growth, but also a great amount of stability even during poor business conditions. This is certainly advantageous for a cyclical industry such as steel.

Changes in the nature of the market for steel are to be expected as well as in the rates of growth of the industry. Steel demand is essentially a derived demand largely determined by the rate of capital formation and consumer expenditure for durable goods. The fastest growth of the steel industry occurs during the earlier stages of industrialization. Thus, the growth of the industry has slowed in the United States and speeded up in Russia. However, Table 9.1 which gives a comparison of markets between the United States, the United Kingdom, Europe, and Russia shows that half of the United States' output is in thin-gauged, flat rolled steels, largely used for consumer products. The United Kingdom is closest to the United States, whereas the bulk of Russian steel is made into products for use in heavy construction and machinery.

TABLE 9.1
Breakdown of Product Mix by Major Shapes

	U.S.	U.K.	ECSC	Russia
Light flat-rolled products	56%	40%	30%	18%
Structurals and plate	17	21	17	46
Bars	15	19	25	9
Wire rods	5	8	9	8
Tubing	5	4	6	9
Rails	1	3	2	7
Semi-finished and other	1	5	11	3
Total	100%	100%	100%	100%

SOURCE: *Steel—Basic Analysis,* Standard & Poor's Industry Surveys, New York, Standard & Poor, June 20, 1963.

The tremendous consumer demand for steel in the United States accounts for a total per capita consumption of all shapes of steel of 1,100 pounds, compared with 935 pounds in the U.K., 750 pounds in the Common Market and 650 pounds per person in Russia. Further expansion of steel production in other countries will see a slowing down in the rate of growth and an increasing shift to flat-rolled consumer products just as has occurred in the United States.

RAW MATERIALS AND RESERVES

About 2¾ tons of raw materials are required to produce 1 ton of ingot steel. Into the steel furnaces go 30 pounds of alloying elements, 106 pounds of limestone, 164 pounds of iron ore, 938 pounds of scrap, and 1,251 pounds of pig iron. But to make this 1,251 pounds of pig iron, a total of 4,121 pounds of raw materials are required: iron ore 2,163 pounds, coking coal 1,371 pounds, limestone 397 pounds, and scrap 190 pounds. Thus basic requirements are coking coal, iron ore, limestone, and scrap.

The process of assembling raw materials and their conversion into steel is a basic factor in the location of an iron and steel industry.

Coal

The location of the coking coal deposits in the United States has been presented in the chapter on the coal industry. From the very first the iron and steel industry has located near coking coal deposits, possibly in large part due to the fact that the largest markets for steel were located near the coal fields as industries using steel required coal as a fuel.

Iron Ore

Factors determining the economics of iron mining are: (1) the amount of the ore, (2) the quality of the ore, (3) the location of the deposit with respect to coal and the consuming markets, and (4) the location of the ore with respect to transportation facilities, mainly water transportation.

A study of the quality of the ore must take into account more than the iron content, because even insignificant quantities of phosphorus and sulfur present obstacles to reduction. Where ore of good quality lies close to the surface, as it does in the Mesabi Range (Minnesota), it can be mined cheaply by low-cost open pit methods. On the other hand, deep deposits are minable only by more costly shaft and tunnel methods.

So much fuel is required that iron ore deposits are not usually developed unless they are strategically located with respect to a supply of coal and are available to markets by economical water transportation. The usual case is that the best, lowest-cost ores are mined first. This has been the case with the United States' deposits of the Lake Superior Region, which up to World War II supplied over 80 percent of the United States' requirements. Now more and more companies are turning to importation of high-grade foreign ores. The Great Lakes which penetrate the interior of the United States for 1,700 miles bring a vast coal and market area geographically close to the mines of the Lake Superior area. In addition, the St. Lawrence River Seaway permits Labrador-Quebec iron ore, and ore from Venezuela and other foreign sources to reach port and furnaces on the Lower Great Lakes. Thus Upper Great Lakes and foreign iron ore moves to coal.

Scrap

Scrap is equally as important as iron ore as a source of raw material. If it were not for scrap, the other raw-material sources would have their lives greatly shortened. Scrap metal originates wherever iron and steel are used. The biggest source is "home scrap" in the mills where the steel is made. "Market scrap" comes from railroads, railroad equipment builders, automobile manufacturers, machine shops, shipyards, the oil industry, used automobiles, and cannibalized defense equipment. In general the profitable collection of scrap is limited to a distance of 300 miles from the market.

Limestone

Limestone is used as a flux to draw most of the alumina, manganese, sulfur, and other ingredients (except phosphorus) out of the molten iron. Fortunately, limestone is so widely distributed and is utilized in such small quantities that it never determines the location of the industry.

Reserves of Iron Ore

Iron ore in commercial deposits is concentrated in only a few places in the United States. The iron content of commercial ore in this country now ranges from over 50 percent to about 20 percent. Lower grade ore is processed, or "concentrated," so that the product is equivalent or even superior to the direct shipping ore. There is considerable variation in the criteria that define reserves as resources. In addition to the range of iron content of ores, as we have already noted, there is also a wide variety of ores due to the impurities present. Ore of the same grade may also differ in cost of production, depending on whether it is mined underground or in open pits. But the rule is that the definition of "ore" as used commercially is the same as our definition of "resources", i.e., that part of the total deposits which can be used technically and economically.

The most recent and authoritative estimate of U.S. iron ore and potential ore is given in Table 9.2. These figures refer, as noted, not to crude ore but to direct shipping ore and concentrates. Total iron content of the reserves is nearly 3 billion tons, and potential ore, some 20 billion tons.

The Lake Superior Region is clearly the dominant source of iron ore in the United States. As has been noted, more than 80 percent of the U.S. iron ore has come from this area. Four factors account for the importance of this region to the United States industry: (1) the huge reserves of high grade hematite ore; (2) the ease and economy of mining the ore; (3) the

TABLE 9.2
Estimated United States Iron Ore Reserves

Region and type of resource	Reserves			Potential ore		
	Ore tonnage	Iron content	Iron tonnage	Ore tonnage	Iron content	Iron tonnage
	Million long tons	*Per-cent*	*Million long tons*	*Million long tons*	*Per-cent*	*Million long tons*
Lake Superior						
Direct shipping and intermediate crude ore	2,000	50	1,000			
Magnetic concentrates (from magnetic taconite)	2,000	63	1,260			
Crude ore (taconite and other)				35,000	25–45	12,250
Crude ore, presently recoverable magnetically				15,000	22	3,300
Southeastern						
Direct shipping ore	550	36	200			
Concentrates	60	50	30			
Crude ore				11,220	31–50	3,535

Northeastern						
Concentrates	300	60				
Crude ore			180	2,850	27–43	1,000
Western						
Concentrates	490	50				
Crude ore			250	500	40–50	200
Central and Gulf						
Concentrates	50	48				
Crude ore			25	116	40–50	50
Alaska, crude ore	5	45–52	2–3	large		
Total	5,455	54	2,948	64,700		20,300

Source: M. S. Carr and C. E. Dutton, *Iron Ore Resources of the United States Including Alaska and Puerto Rico*, 1955. Geological Survey Bulletin 1082–6, Washington, D.C., 1959.

location of each range well above the lake port that serves it, so that loaded trains travel downgrade to the ports; and (4) the excellent harbor and port facilities at the Western end of Lake Superior.

Of the six iron ranges in the region, the Mesabi is the most important. Although most of the close-to-the-surface, natural high-grade ore has been mined, the remaining ore is mined by open pit methods and still averages about 51 percent iron content after beneficiation. Most of the ore is carried to the surface by trucks or rail to the beneficiation plants, and finally to the docks, from which it is dropped into ore boats, and transported to the Lower Lake ports.

One major disadvantage of the Mesabi is that no ore can be mined in winter. Navigation ceases on the Great Lakes system: the St. Marys River and the Soo Canal are frozen. Hence enough ore must be shipped in the late spring, summer, and fall to keep the blast furnaces in the Lower Lakes operating throughout the year.

The other five ranges combined are less important than the Mesabi. Their mines are mostly underground, except for Wisconsin's Menominee Range. On the Gogebic Range some mines are nearly a mile below the surface. Underground mines operate throughout the year, but the ore must be stockpiled during the winter.

As the better grade ores of the Lake Superior Region become exhausted the taconite ores produced from the lean, hard, taconite rocks of Minnesota will become more important. (Similar ores from the jasper formation are known as "jaspers" in Michigan and Wisconsin.) In addition to the magnetic taconite reserves shown in Table 9.2, there are billions of tons of nonmagnetic taconite that someday may be technically and economically usable. Taconite is one of the toughest rocks known and the iron is scattered through it in minute particles. The problem has been to separate those particles of iron from the rock, and to bundle them together into pellets so they can be charged into the blast furnace.

To get 1 ton of pellets, averaging 63 percent iron, 3 tons of taconite must be drilled, blasted, mined, transported, ground fine, separated, rolled into balls and baked. The pellets which are about the size of a marble are very hard and can withstand the burden of the charge in the blast furnace. In 1960 about 20 million tons of taconite were used from the Great Lakes and the estimate was that this amount would double by 1970. Current trends indicate that before long taconite will provide a larger percentage of the blast furnace charge than regular domestic ore.

The Birmingham Ores in the Southeastern region have always been of double interest because of their close proximity to coal. However, this ore averages only 36 percent iron content. All the mining is underground, is expensive, and beneficiation costs are high. One advantage is that the ore contains about 15 percent lime and is almost self-fluxing. Fortunately, the iron ore, coal, and limestone lie in close proximity—reputedly closer than anywhere else in the world.

The Northeastern Region includes ore in New York and Eastern Pennsylvania. Adirondack deposits of iron ore have been known and used since the days of the Revolution. The ore is of high quality magnetite, and is relatively free of impurities. Mining, however, is difficult and the rock is so hard that diamond drills must be used and sometimes the shafts must be sunk a mile and a half to reach a bed of ore. Large quantities of this ore are sent to furnaces in Buffalo, Bethlehem, Cleveland, and Pittsburgh.

Although eastern Pennsylvania is an old iron-mining, and iron and steelmaking area, large-scale iron-ore production dates only from 1958. The ore which contains magnetite averaging 40 to 45 percent iron lies one mile below the surface. The ore is mined by tunneling under the deposit to force the ore to cave into large funnel-shaped openings. One of the biggest advantages of this mine is that it is only 60 miles from the mills.

The Western Region became important as a source of iron ore with World War II. The most important reserves are in Utah. Mining is carried on near Iron Mountain and Desert Mound by the open pit method and no beneficiation is required. The ore is magnetite and averages 50 to 53 percent iron. It is reduced in furnaces at Geneva, near Provo.

The other western mine is at Eagle Mountain, in San Bernardino County, California. The ore is hematite-magnetite and averages about 51 percent iron, but is upgraded to 60 percent. This ore, which is mined by open pit methods, supplies the blast furnaces at Fontana, California.

The Central and Gulf Region is new as a mining area with activity carried on near Daingerfield in northeastern Texas. Here open pit mining yields the lowest commercial-grade iron ore in the nation (excluding taconite). The ore, mostly limonite, contains 19 to 25 percent iron and must be beneficiated up to an iron content of about 50 percent. Yet it is claimed that this ore is laid down at the Daingerfield blast furnaces at lower costs than is Lake Superior ore at any Lower Lake port.

The adequacy of present reserves and the post World War II solutions to this problem will be treated at the end of this chapter. Meanwhile Figure 9.2 which follows will serve as a background for further study.

Figure 9.2 compares the projected cumulative demand through the year 2000 with the reserve-resource position of the United States with the cumulative production at the 1957 rate of 54 million tons (as the highest recent level). This is not to predict that the present resources will be exhausted before 1990. However, the important fact is that current resources of approximately 3 billion tons are little more than one half the cumulative demand through 2000 of 5 billion tons. Production cannot be maintained through the present century without the discovery of new reserves, or the creation of resources out of the present potential ore.

Figure 9.2: United States Iron-in-ore Requirements, 1960–2000 Compared with Iron in Domestic Reserves.

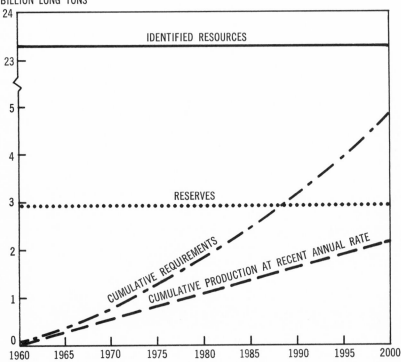

SOURCE: Bruce C. Netschert and Hans H. Landsberg, *The Future Supply of Major Metals*, Resources for the Future, Inc.

THE TECHNOLOGY OF IRON AND STEEL

How steel is made from the principal raw materials of iron ore, coal, limestone, and scrap, and the names of some of the chief products manufactured from the finished shapes are clearly illustrated and described in the flow chart Figure 9.3 which follows on page 344.

The Blast Furnace

The blast furnace makes pig iron. It may be described as the meeting place of the raw materials iron ore, coke, and limestone from which pig iron is produced. Most of the pig iron is used in its molten form, "hot metal," in the manufacture of steel. But some is also used in foundries to be cast into molds for wheels, stoves, machine parts, and other objects.

The job of the blast furnace is to liberate the iron from the ore. The furnace consists of a tall, cylindrical, brick-lined metal structure 90 to 100 feet high; powerful engines to provide the blast; and several stoves to preheat the blast before it enters the furnace. The blast furnace is filled from the top with layers of coke, iron ore, and limestone. A blast of preheated air from one of the stoves is blown in at the bottom of the furnace. The coke burns in the blast of heated air. The burning coke generates intense heat and gases. The gases formed by the combustion of the coke combine with and remove the oxygen of the iron ore. The molten limestone combines with the earthy matter of the ore, causing it to become fluid and separate as scum or slag, leaving molten iron.

Since the hot blast enters the furnace from the bottom, the furnace is hottest there, and as the raw materials melt and decrease in volume the entire mass of the charge descends. At the very base or "hearth" of the furnace, where the temperature is 3,000 degrees Fahrenheit or higher, the iron is melted, forming a pool of molten metal upon which floats the molten slag. Every four or five hours the pool of iron and slag is tapped. The slag, being lighter than pig iron, floats on top and is easily removed. Each of the large blast furnaces at a plant can produce 1,800 tons or more of pig iron in 24 hours.

If pig iron is to be used for steelmaking, it is hauled in the molten state directly to the steel department. There it is usually stored in a huge cauldron called a "mixer" which keeps it as "hot metal" until it is needed. If the iron is for use at great distance from the blast furnace, the ladle cars into which the tapped iron has been poured are taken to a department that casts the metal into "pigs."

The refining effects of the blast furnace are limited. All of the phosphorus and much of the silicon, manganese, and sulphur originally present in the ore remain in the pig iron. In addition, the iron picks up 3½ to 4 percent of carbon from the coke. Pig iron as it comes from the blast furnace is limited to use either in cast iron or steel by its high carbon content.

Historically the first great breakthrough in the manufacture of pig iron on a mass basis came with the successful application of coke as a fuel in 1730. Coke as a substitute for charcoal revolutionized the industry because: (1) It is a strong material that will sustain the heavy load of 1,500 tons or more in the furnace; (2) It is porous, permitting the hot blast to permeate it freely; and (3) It is almost pure carbon (88 percent), and hence burns little ash.

The second great technological breakthrough came with the introduction of a hot air blast in connection with the use of the stoves and the regenerative furnace principle. Sir William Siemans developed this principle in connection with the open hearth for steelmaking in 1856. The stoves, one of which is shown adjacent to the blast furnace in Figure 9.3, are the means through which the regenerative principle is applied. These stoves are heat traps which are preheated with waste gasses from the blast fur-

Figure 9.3: How Steel Is Made.

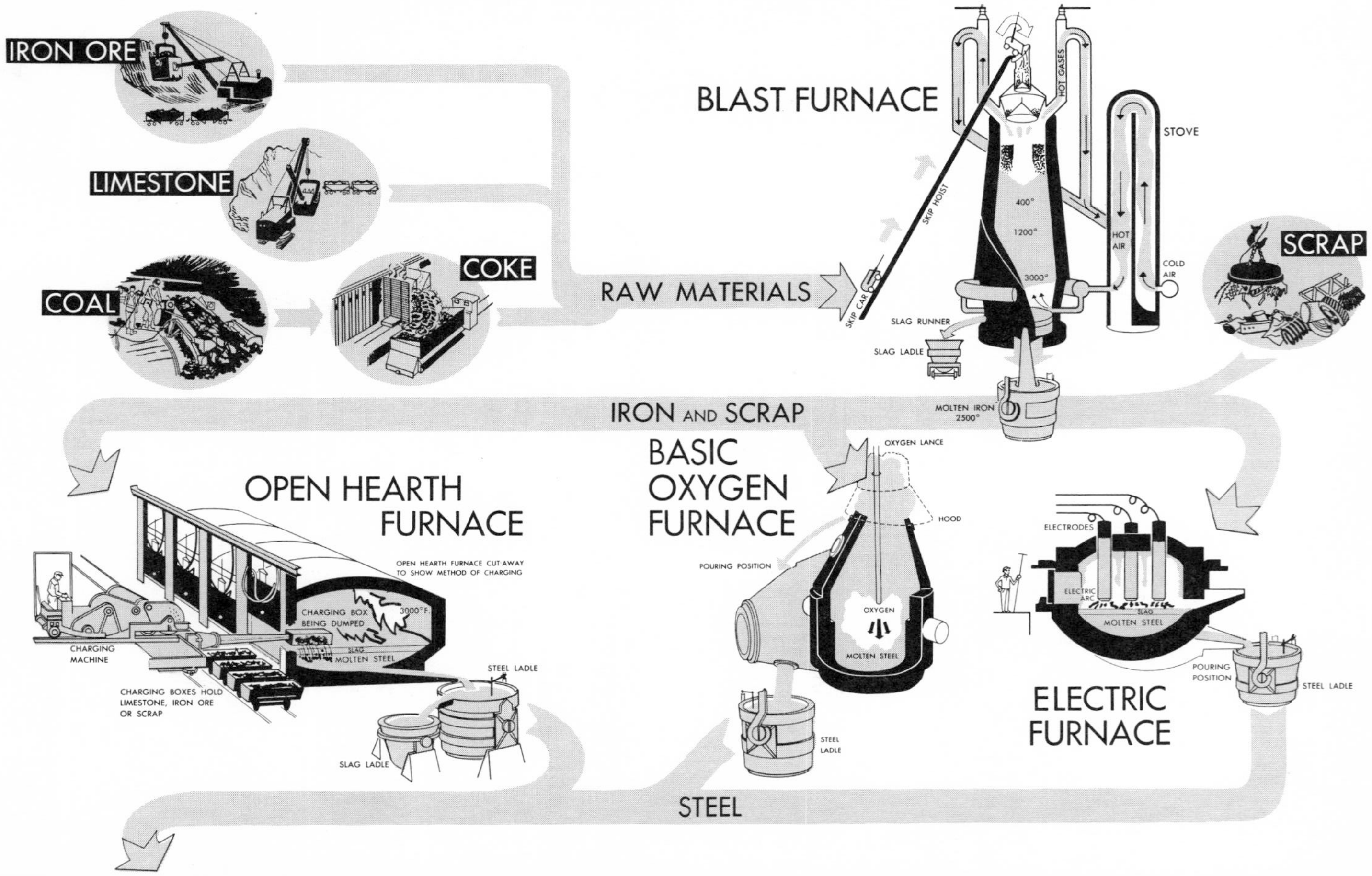

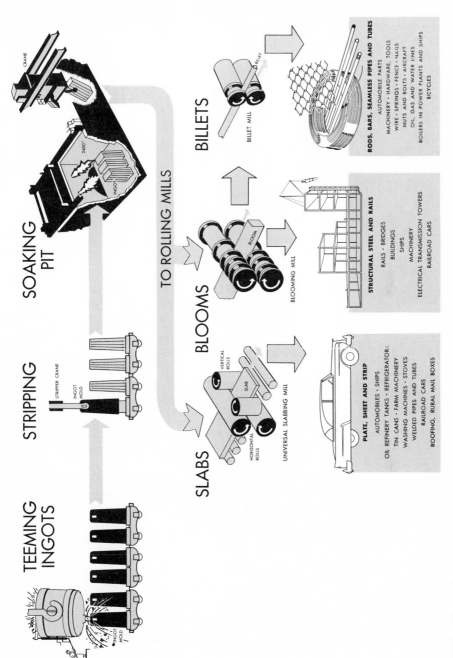

TEEMING INGOTS

STRIPPING

SOAKING PIT

CRANE

2400°

INGOT

STRIPPER CRANE

INGOT MOLD

INGOT MOLD

TO ROLLING MILLS

SLABS

BLOOMS

BILLETS

VERTICAL ROLLS

SLAB

HORIZONTAL ROLLS

UNIVERSAL SLABBING MILL

BLOOM

BLOOMING MILL

BILLET

BILLET MILL

PLATE, SHEET AND STRIP

AUTOMOBILES · SHIPS
OIL REFINERY TANKS · REFRIGERATORS
TIN CANS · FARM MACHINERY
WASHING MACHINES · STOVES
WELDED PIPES AND TUBES
RAILROAD CARS
ROOFING, RURAL MAIL BOXES

STRUCTURAL STEEL AND RAILS

RAILS · BRIDGES
BUILDINGS
SHIPS
MACHINERY
ELECTRICAL TRANSMISSION TOWERS
RAILROAD CARS

RODS, BARS, SEAMLESS PIPES AND TUBES

AUTOMOBILE PARTS
MACHINERY · HARDWARE, TOOLS
WIRE · SPRINGS · FENCE · NAILS
NUTS AND BOLTS · AIRCRAFT
OIL, GAS AND WATER LINES
BOILERS IN POWER PLANTS AND SHIPS
BICYCLES

SOURCE: U.S. Steel Corporation.

345

nace. The blast of air is generated by a blowing engine which forces the air down through one of the three or four preheated stoves located between the blowing engine and the blast furnace, into the bustle pipe that runs around the hearth of the blast furnace, and through the tuyeres into the blast furnace proper. Only one stove heats the blast of air at a time, the others are being preheated. As it takes more time to heat a stove than it takes for the blast to absorb the heat, three or four stoves are needed for the regenerative operation. The regenerative system of heating the blast with gases which formerly were wasted is a great coke saver, and renders the entire operation of the blast furnace more efficient and thus more economical.

A post-World War II development has been the feeding of oxygen or oxygenated air into the blast furnace instead of ordinary air. The idea is to reduce or eliminate the nitrogen content and thus render the blast more potent.

Recently, and most revolutionary, metallic iron has been taken from its ore by processes other than the blast furnace. These "direct reduction" processes are being developed as the iron reduction technology of the future.

The Making of Steel

Steel is composed mainly of iron, a small amount of carbon and a few other elements. Broadly speaking the steelmaking process consists in the refining of blast furnace iron to remove excess carbon and impurities from the iron. At the same time, the steelmaker controls the quantity of elements other than iron which are an essential part of the steel, and adds others. Modern steel is made by four types of processes—Bessemer, open hearth, electric, and basic oxygen.

Bessemer Converter. The Bessemer converter invented in 1856 in England by Sir Henry Bessemer (also developed by William Kelley, a Kentucky ironmaster), was the first great breakthrough that led to modern mass-produced steel. The process is remarkable in that it uses no fuel. It is a large oval-shaped vessel, lined with refractory brick (Figure 9.4). Molten iron is charged into it, and perforations in the bottom of the vessel permit air to be blown through the metal to burn out the carbon and other impurities. At the end of the blow, the purified metal is poured into a ladle, and a measured amount of ferromanganese, carbon, or spiegeleisen (a variety of pig iron containing manganese up to 15–20 percent) is added to degasify the metal, which is then poured into ingot molds. About 15 tons of molten iron may be poured into the converter, and after about 20 minutes, the steelmaking process is complete, except for adding ferroalloys.

The great advantage of the Bessemer process was and is that it can produce steel rapidly, with no fuel at a low cost. However, the process has the disadvantage of being so rapid that it does not permit adequate quality control, and scrap cannot be used unless it is previously melted.

Figure 9.4: Bessemer Converter.

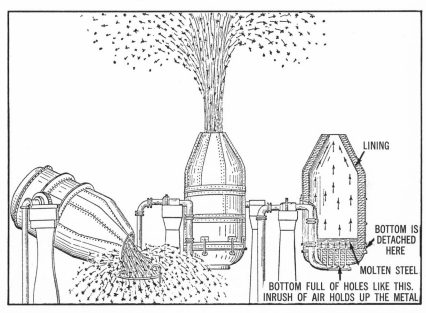

LINING

BOTTOM IS DETACHED HERE

MOLTEN STEEL

BOTTOM FULL OF HOLES LIKE THIS. INRUSH OF AIR HOLDS UP THE METAL

SOURCE: U.S. Steel Corporation.

When first developed, the Bessemer converter had an acid lining and could only be used with low-phorphorus-content ore. But two young Welshmen, Thomas and Gilchrist suggested and proved in 1878 that a basic lining in the Bessemer of limestone or dolomite would remove the phosphorus. The political and economic significance of this development had world shaking effects. Before this, Great Britain had a monopoly on the so-called "Bessemer ores" of Great Britain and Spain. Germany, victorious in the Franco-Prussian War, had occupied Alsace-Lorraine. At that time the iron reserves of Lorraine were worthless because of their phosphorus content. The invention of the basic process thus led to the industrial base in Germany. Through its later application to the open hearth process, the basic process vitally affected the steel industry in the United States and the value of the Lake Superior iron reserves, which then became "ores."

Open Hearth. This process of making steel, patented by Sir William Siemens in 1857, overcame two difficulties of the Bessemer converter—lack of quality control and the inability to use scrap. The furnace is called "open hearth" because the hearth or bottom, where the metal is held, is open to the sweep of flames which melt the steel. The hearth is shaped like a large oval dish, as Figure 9.5 shows, and is lined with heat resistant materials. The front side of the furnace contains doors through which the raw materials are charged. The refined steel is drawn off or "tapped" from the rear.

Figure 9.5: Open Hearth.

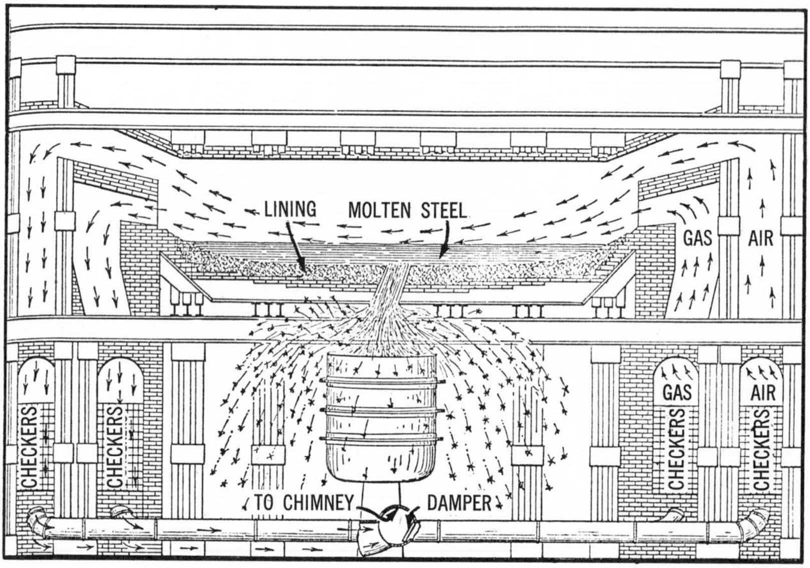

SOURCE: U.S. Steel Corporation.

Gas, oil, coal, or tar may be used as a fuel. To aid combustion the fuel is mixed with hot air in the burners located at each end of the furnace; these operate alternately (the regenerative furnace principle) and the flames sweep down and across the open hearth, directly above the metal bath, and out the opposite end. The furnace is built to operate at about 3,000 degrees Fahrenheit.

Pig iron ("hot metal" or cold) and scrap are fed into the furnace, and limestone is added. Steel can be made in the open hearth from either scrap or pig iron, but usually it is a combination of both. A frequent ratio is 48 percent scrap and 52 percent pig iron. In the process of heating, the undesirable elements are burned out by the flame playing over the liquid metal. Some impurities accumulate as scum or slag on top of the metal. Various alloying agents such as vanadium, molybdenum, nickel, tungsten, chromium, and manganese, are added to make the desired type of steel.

As much as 600 tons of steel may be made at one time in the largest open hearth. A range of 125 to 150 tons is more common, and many of the new furnaces have a capacity of 250 tons in one operation, called a "heat" by the industry. Approximately twelve hours are required to produce a heat of steel. During the first five hours the raw materials will be charged and melted, and then for about six hours more the heat is allowed to "work." During the final hour of the heat the exact composition is determined by the addition of the proper alloys to meet the desired specifications. When the heat is finally completed and up to specification, the furnace is "tapped" by knocking out a plug at the back of the furnace and the molten metal flows into a great ladle and then is poured into ingots (see Figure 9.3).

In the open hearth process, as compared with the Bessemer, a greater variety of raw materials, including scrap, may be used. The process is slower and more costly; but the process has the advantage of making more steel at a heat and at the same time permitting quality control so that the steel can be made to the exact specification required by modern industry.

The open hearth furnace is being improved and made more efficient by design and by use of oxygen through roof jets. The result is a substantial reduction in the time required to produce a heat of steel, reduced fuel consumption, and increased ingot tonnage with the same installed capacity.

Electric Furnace. The electric furnace has been used in the United States only since 1906. Steels of the most exacting composition, including stainless steels and many alloy steels, are generally produced in electric furnaces where melting and refining can be closely controlled. Electric furnaces of the type most commonly used are steel shells lined with heat resisting brick. Large sticks of carbon, called electrodes, extend down through the roof of the furnace to within a few inches of the metal in the furnace. When the current is turned on electric arcs are struck between the electrodes providing the heat (See Figure 9.3).

Electric furnaces may use as a raw material a charge consisting entirely of scrap iron and steel, although sometimes open hearth or Bessemer steel is still further refined in the electric furnace. When alloy steels are to be made, the alloying elements such as nickel, chromium, or tungsten are added either as pure metal or as ferroalloys.

When the heat is completed, the furnace is tilted to release the steel into the ladle for pouring into ingots.

The U.S. steel industry has been steadily expanding the electric furnace capacity and production due to the increased demand for high-grade steels, such as stainless and heat resisting products.

Basic Oxygen. This process is the newcomer to steelmaking methods. The refractory-lined furnaces resemble Bessemer converters in shape, but have no equipment for blowing air through furnace bottoms. Instead, jets of high-purity oxygen are directed through a lance onto the surface of the molten iron in the vessel. This serves to burn out the impurities and, in addition, the nitrogen, which makes steel too brittle for some end-uses in the Bessemer process. Figure 9.3 shows the basic oxygen furnace, which now occupies the place formerly given to the Bessemer converter in this flow chart. Here again, the basic oxygen furnace is a fuelless process in which the undesirable metalloids, such as silicon, carbon, phosphorus, and manganese serve as fuel. Unlike the Bessemer converter, scrap may be used in the process, provided it is first melted. The finished product resembles that made in the open hearth.

The capacity of oxygen vessels has grown rapidly until 1961 some of the vessels had an hourly output of 250 tons. To reach this high level of output requires vast quantities of oxygen—about 2,000 cubic feet per ton of steel. The amount of oxygen and the high price of commercial oxygen was one of the deterrents to a more rapid use of the basic oxygen process. Nevertheless, by 1961 the basic oxygen process already accounted for 4.0 million tons of steel, or 4 percent of all the steel produced in the United States. This was a 19 percent increase over 1960, and 13 times the amount of steel produced by the oxygen process in 1955. By 1963, the 1961 amount had more than doubled to 8.6 million tons, and by 1965 the 1963 amount had more than doubled again to 22.8 million tons, which represented 17.4 percent of the total U.S. production of 131.2 million tons of steel.

Trends in Steelmaking Processes. Production of steel by processes in 1965 is given in Table 9.3. Trends in steelmaking by process from 1900 to 1965 are shown in Figure 9.6.

TABLE 9.3
Production of Steel by Processes—1965

Process	Millions of net tons	Percent of total
Open Hearth	94.2	71.8
Basic Oxygen	22.9	17.4
Electric	13.8	10.3
Bessemer	.6	0.5
Total	131.5	100.0

SOURCE: *Steel Facts,* New York, American Iron and Steel Institute, February, 1966.

Figure 9.6: Changes in Steel Production by Types of Furnaces.

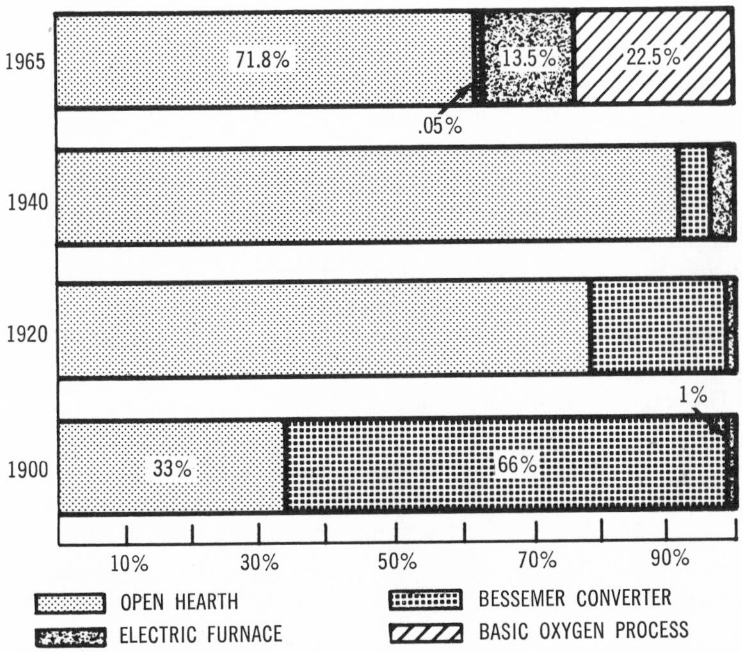

| | OPEN HEARTH | | BESSEMER CONVERTER |
| | ELECTRIC FURNACE | | BASIC OXYGEN PROCESS |

Crucible production, now insignificant, is no longer reported separately, but is included with electric furnace production. America's first direct arc electric furnace was installed in 1906. Basic oxygen process production has been reported separately only since 1955.

SOURCE: American Iron and Steel Institute.

Figure 9.6 shows clearly the growing importance of the open hearth because of its many advantages and the declining use of the Bessemer converter since 1900. The more recent shift to the electric furnace for the production of high quality specialty steels is dramatically illustrated. The dynamics of change is also shown in the basic oxygen process which only became significant enough in 1961 to be shown on a chart of this type for the first time.

Finishing Steel

Finishing crude steel begins with the ingot. From the large ladles which receive the steel at the furnace, the steel is poured into the molds. In the molds the liquid metal is allowed to solidify in whole or in part. These solidified steel castings are ingots. The molds are then stripped off, and the ingots still red hot are taken to the soaking pits. These soaking pits are really underground furnaces which have as their purpose to bring the ingots to a uniform temperature of about 2,200 degrees Fahrenheit.

The bulk of the primary steel industry's output is worked through hot rolling. A small portion is forged (hammered and pressed); an even smaller amount is sold as ingot or cast into finished products at the mill. The semi-finished shapes from the primary mill consist of blooms, slabs, and billets which are cropped and scarfed to remove ends and scales prior to further reduction.

By reference once again to Figure 9.3, entitled *How Steel Is Made*, it can be seen that the shapes of the rolls through which the steel is pressed determine the form of the mill end-product. Blooms produce structural steel and rails. Slabs produce plates, sheets, and strips. Billets produce rods, bars, seamless pipes, and tubes. Further study of this illustration will reveal the tremendous variety of products made from each of the shapes.

The average ingot yields about 72 to 75 percent finished steel. The scrap loss varies widely between different products. Increases in rolling mill yields are a major cost-reduction goal of all mills. More recently efforts have been directed toward installation of new and improved equipment, which gives better gauge and width control, and thus less off-size products and less scrap.

Probably the most significant new technological development is continuous casting. This process of finishing steel (first used in Europe and Canada) consists of direct casting of molten steel into semi-finished form, thus eliminating the need of ingot molds, soaking pit, and blooming mills. One expert predicted that by 1975, 60 percent of all steel made in the United States would be continuously cast.

STEELMAKING CENTERS IN THE UNITED STATES

Steelmaking is carried on in the following districts in the United States, and each district contributes the following approximate percentage of the nation's total capacity: Pittsburgh-Youngstown, 35 percent; Cleveland-Detroit, 10.2 percent; Chicago, 21.9 percent; Eastern, 21.1 percent; Southern, 5.7 percent; and Western, 5.7 percent. These steelmaking centers are a result of a combination of locational factors which have been at work. Although there are many factors which determine the location of the steel industry, they may be classified into two broad categories: (1) The cost of assembling the raw materials and of converting the raw materials into finished products; and (2) The cost of transporting finished products to the points of consumption. While this latter factor has not been as important as the first, in recent years the market factor has been exercising a greater location pull.

Pittsburgh-Youngstown

The Pittsburgh area consists of plants located in the valleys of the Ohio, Monongahela, and Allegheny Rivers, within 40 miles of Pittsburgh. The Youngstown area includes plants in the Shenango and Mahoning River Valleys within 30 miles of Youngstown. This center, which leads the United States in capacity, has been the nucleus of the steel industry since the integration of the iron and steel industries. Even though at the outset local ore was used, the dominate pull of Connellsville coking coal has been the principal locational factor that has led to the Pittsburgh area's continued importance. The high-quality Lake Superior ore was available via the Great Lakes, and there was less loss in weight in its processing than in the use of coal. Equally important was the fact that many coal-using industries located in the area were markets for the steel products. So coal exerted a double pull. Youngstown has been in a less favorable position than Pittsburgh, for while it is landlocked and requires rail transportation, Pittsburgh has excellent river as well as railway facilities. Pittsburgh had a major advantage in the market factor, and many of these markets were accessible by river barge. An additional and important locational factor related to markets is that they are sources of scrap. Another important factor in this area's position has been the availability of a huge supply of labor of all types. And finally, one factor which enabled Pittsburgh to compete on a nationwide basis was a result of the Pittsburgh Plus and, later, the multiple-basing point system. The Pittsburgh Plus pricing system worked so that no matter from what source in the United States steel was purchased, the price quoted was f.o.b. Pittsburgh plus transportation to the buyer.

Cleveland-Detroit

In this lower lake port district, Buffalo and Cleveland have long been the most important steelmaking centers. Lorain, about 40 miles west of Cleveland is geographically a part of the Cleveland area. Once steel began to expand from the Pittsburgh area, a logical move was toward the lower lake ports even though this was a move away from coal. One major advantage, of course, is that these mills' location on the Great Lakes puts them in a position where ore is unloaded from lake carriers directly at the blast furnace. But certainly another initial advantage was that before the move to the lower lake ports the ore was transshipped to the Pittsburgh area, and the result was railway transportation that was only used in one direction. With the location at the ports the cost of moving the coal was greatly reduced as it could be moved back in the empty cars which carried ore to Pittsburgh.

Buffalo is on the New York State Barge Canal and benefits from the St. Lawrence Seaway, and is the terminus of many coal-carrying railroads. In addition, it is in a good market position, half way between the East Coast and Lower Lake markets.

Cleveland is less important than Buffalo as a rail center, but the Cuyahoga River channel has been improved so as to enable the largest freighters on the Great Lakes to navigate the river. Cleveland is closer than Buffalo to the major coal fields, and its market factor is excellent. Lorain has all the advantages of Cleveland, plus lower locational costs and the Black River.

Detroit, which one immediately thinks of as the center of the automobile industry and thus one of the nation's largest steel-consuming markets, was a latecomer in development as a steel center. None of the original forces that accounted for the lower lake ports' expansion was at work here. Detroit did not become a producer until the twentieth century, and its big expansion did not come until the 1950's when capacity was increased by more than 125 percent in the area. Here is real evidence of steel expanding where the market is.

Chicago

The first expansion of the steel industry was from Pittsburgh to the lower lake ports, and then to Chicago and Gary. At first glance, to the Easterner, this move appeared to be one to get closer to the iron ore, but this is not the case when distances from the Superior ore to Chicago-Gary and to the lower lake ports are compared. Here was the first move of the steel industry to the market, and showed the importance of the market factor. There was a small beginning of the iron and steel industry in Chicago in 1857, but the industry only began to grow when the city became a leading rail center, and thus created an enormous demand for iron and steel products.

The Chicago-Gary district is distinctly different from the original centers of the industry in that it lies far away from the sources of raw material, iron and coal, and from the flux limestone. Yet it has been said that this district is the most scientifically located of any of the centers of the United States, because it is a center where raw material and the market meet, and shows the growing importance of the market as a locational factor.

Superior ore is unloaded directly to the blast furnace. Coal is brought principally from Kentucky and West Virginia, but also from central and southern Illinois and from Indiana. By mixing the high-quality coal of the former areas with the low quality of the latter, a suitable coke can be produced.

The establishment of the plant at Gary in 1907 is often cited as one of the first examples of scientific plant location. Here was a move by the U.S. Steel Corporation to serve the rapidly growing Midwestern market. The spot chosen was midway between coal and ore and near Chicago's manufacturers. There was plenty of cheap, level land, and water supply from Lake Michigan. In addition, labor was plentiful.

If one does not include Youngstown in the Pittsburgh total, the Chicago-Gary district outranks all others in the world, and it has grown rapidly in recent years.

Eastern

The Eastern District can be divided between the old and the new. The twin cities of Allentown and Bethlehem, astride the Lehigh River, and Easton and Phillipsburgh, east of the confluence of the Delaware and Lehigh Rivers, are among the older iron and steel centers of the United States. There locational advantages have been local iron ores, coal and limestones, excellent transportation, and the markets of the Atlantic Seaboard. The logical grouping of these plants according to locational factors, would have been with the Pittsburgh area; for Sparrows Point, Maryland and Morrisville, Pennsylvania are a product of new locational factors.

Sparrows Point was an expansion by Bethlehem Steel Corporation, which had plants in eastern Pennsylvania, but needed new sources of ore because of the dominant ownership of the Superior ores by other companies. Hence, the move to tidewater where the world's largest steel plant was built. Most of the iron ore is brought from El Pao, Venezuela directly to the blast furnaces. A special fleet of ore carriers moves about 3 million tons of ore each year from Puerto de Hierro to Sparrows Point and other eastern Pennsylvania steel centers. Coal is easily brought from the Pocahontas, New River, and Fairmont fields in West Virginia, and from the Clearfield and Westmoreland districts of Pennsylvania. Limestone is brought from West Hanover, Pennsylvania. Most importantly, the tidewater location gives excellent access to markets. Shipments can be made directly by water to the East Coast and Gulf Ports, to the Pacific Coast and to Europe and Latin America.

Morrisville, Pennsylvania represents the first fully integrated plant built at the end of World War II. Faced with diminishing Lake Superior ore reserves and a desire to capture some of Bethlehem Steel's eastern markets, U.S. Steel followed a locational plan similar to that of Bethlehem at Sparrows Point. The U.S. Steel Fairless plant was built on the Delaware River where it makes a big bend north of Philadelphia.

A search for new sources of ore had led U.S. Steel to discover a gigantic new iron mountain at Cerro Bolivar, Venezuela. The iron ore comes all the way to the plant from Puerto Ordaz at the confluence of the Rio Orinoco and Rio Caroni. The development of this mining, transportation complex in Venezuela was truly a remarkable accomplishment of modern industry. Coal for the Fairless plant comes from West Virginia and Pennsylvania, and limestone from Pennsylvania.

Thus, the two principal factors that led to the major expansion move to Sparrows Point and Morrisville were access to water-borne ore made necessary by diminishing domestic sources, and a move toward the market.

Southern

Birmingham, Alabama is one of the few places in the world where the three major raw materials of steel lie in close proximity. Since coal and self-fluxing ore (38 percent iron and 20 percent lime) are in such close proximity many observers have thought that the Birmingham area should have grown to greater importance as a center. In addition to the availability of raw materials, the plants are only 18 miles from Birmingport on the Black Warrior River where barges operate.

In spite of its many advantages Birmingham has suffered from low-grade ore which must be mined from underground. Lack of adequate markets has been a twofold handicap: (1) inadequate sales, and (2) insufficient scrap. However, since the end of World War II and the discovery of Cerro Bolivar, the high-grade Venezuelan ore is shipped in by U.S. Steel and mixed with the local ore. In addition, the abolishing of the Pittsburgh Plus plan, and later after World War II the multiple basing point system for pricing steel, has given the Birmingham mills an advantage in the growing southern market. For example, before this change in pricing policy, a buyer in Atlanta, Georgia of steel from Birmingham had to pay the same price for steel as if it were delivered, say, from Pittsburgh. In addition, the growing industrialization of the South has provided a greater amount of scrap.

Texas is a newcomer to steel production and really follows the pattern of locational factors that is responsible in the Western district. World War II saw the development of a plant at Houston which benefits from the large oil field markets and uses local raw materials, and some iron ore from Durango, Mexico. An integrated works at Daingerfield, 30 miles north of Longview, specializes in the production of steel pipe needed in the oil and gas fields. Coking coal and dolomite come from southeastern Oklahoma and ore is available close by in Texas.

These Texas plants have a favorable raw material and market situation, but other steel companies have established steel storage warehouses at market centers in order to capture this expanding market.

Western

Expansion into the Western areas, including Texas was made possible by the growing demands of World War II and the consideration of the decentralization of the industry for strategic purposes. A great many ships were built on the West Coast and rail and water transport were crowded. The result was that two new iron and steel plants were built: one at Geneva, Utah and one at Fontana, California. In addition, there was already in existence an industry at Pueblo, Colorado, and a small blast furnace south of Provo, Utah.

Pueblo was the first city in the west to have an iron and steel industry. In 1881 the first blast furnace began operation, and in 1882 a Bessemer converter made the first steel. The company uses iron ore to the west and southwest of the city, and it also uses some iron ore from Wyoming. Coal and limestone are available in southern Colorado. Although the Pueblo mill is small, it is important to the Great Plains and Rocky Mountain regions. As it is east of the Rockies the mill is not of importance to the West Coast.

Geneva, 40 miles south of Salt Lake City is the site of the first completely integrated iron and steel plant built west of the Rockies. It was built by the U.S. government as a World War II measure. Iron ore is available 255 miles to the southwest, coal 120 miles to the southeast, and limestone 35 miles to the south.

This plant is ideally located for a western plant, but its biggest disadvantage is its distance from the West Coast markets—850 to 1,100 miles.

Fontana is located about 50 miles east of Los Angeles. The ideal location would have been at tidewater, but World War II strategic considerations required that it be erected inland. Fontana gets its ore from Eagle Mountain Mine 176 miles away, and its coal from Utah 807 miles away, and limestone is available near the plant. Raw material and assembly costs are higher than at Provo, but Fontana has a great market advantage. Short hauls are made to the excellent market in Los Angeles by especially built trucks, and good rail facilities are available for longer deliveries.

Future Locational Expansion

The locational patterns of the past are the best guidelines for the future. Although the iron ore reserves of the Lake Superior Region are dwindling at a great rate, two developments indicate that existing facilities in the Pittsburgh, Lower Lake Port, and Chicago-Gary areas will continue to have adequate ore supplies: (1) the opening of the St. Lawrence Seaway Canal, and (2) the development of taconite ore.

In addition, the building of the Fairless plant by U.S. Steel at Morrisville, Pennsylvania, dramatically brought home to the steel industry the high cost of new facilities. As a result, the conclusion has been that the most economical solution to increased capacity was improved efficiency at existing locations by use of the recent developments which were discussed in the technology of iron and steel.

TABLE 9.4

†Furnace and Finishing Capacities of Leading Steel Producers As of January 1, 1960
(In net tons)

	Total ingot capacity	% Pig iron to ingot capacity*	Electric furnace capacity	Hot rolled	Cold rolled sheets	Gal-vanized	Tin mill products	Hot rolled (Strip)	Cold rolled (Strip)	Pipes and tubing	Total bars	Plates	Plain wire	Structurals
8 MAJOR INTEGRATED PRODUCERS														
U.S. Steel	41,916,000	76.4	462,000	7,677,570	2,958,190	808,970	3,082,990	526,540	236,210	4,003,560	3,740,800	4,483,640	2,248,280	2,929,540
Bethlehem	23,000,000	68.0	954,000	5,560,000	2,904,000	336,000	1,260,000	?	503,000	624,000	2,767,000	1,608,000	626,000	3,164,000
Republic	12,742,000	78.9	2,419,000	3,957,000	2,576,000	560,000	180,000	575,000	94,600	1,575,000	3,495,000	138,000	334,000	233,600
Jones & Laughlin	8,125,000	68.4	722,000	3,295,800	1,468,600	138,000	524,000	?	60,000	1,166,000	813,100	230,400	318,000	200,000
National	7,000,000	83.6		2,795,000	2,970,000	535,000	1,445,000	?	60,000		240,000			
Youngstown	6,750,000	61.3		2,250,000	1,392,000		516,000	12,000	?	1,596,000	492,000	90,000	72,000	12,000
Armco	6,800,000	56.9	1,432,000	2,904,900	1,998,600	648,500		?		828,200	671,300	876,900	355,400	133,300
Inland	6,500,000	54.8		2,562,000	1,605,000	358,000	277,000	28,000	e		678,000	726,000		718,000
9 OTHER INTEGRATED AND SEMI-INTEGRATED														
Colorado Fuel & Iron	E3,000,000	49.0		429,000	e			14,800	34,500	240,000	150,000	7,000	778,280	60,000
Kaiser Steel	2,933,000	68.1		1,734,000¹	643,680		441,000	2,700	36,000	952,000	105,800	527,300		117,000
McLouth Steel	2,580,000	84.5	654,600	250,000	700,000	324,000		?	117,020					
Wheeling	2,400,000	81.4		412,000			306,200		150,000	360,000		25,000		
Sharon Steel	1,866,000	52.1	168,000	753,000	410,000			514,000	198,000	48,000		156,000	358,980	
Pittsburgh Steel	1,620,000	58.6		906,000	312,000	225,400	227,000	?	120,000	250,000		185,000		
Granite City	1,580,000	50.1		159,100²	39,800			?	92,200					
Crucible	1,433,180	85.7	389,180						175,000	4,000	833,400		135,000	
Detroit Steel	1,400,000	54.9		600,000	420,000							26,600		

Company	Hot steel capacity *	%												
Northwest Steel & Wire	1,152,000													
Acme Steel	1,060,000		288,000	510,000		396,000		256,700		110,000	288,000	105,000	358,600	264,000
Lukens	930,000		180,000			100,000				5,900	30,000	790,000		
Allegheny Ludlum	912,000		588,000	563,000		294,800		228,440		225,000	76,080			
Phoenix Steel	866,500	23.1	[3]								300,000			259,000
Alan Wood	800,000	68.0				240,000		[8]						
Lone Star	800,000	48.1			340,000					520,000		50,000		
Keystone Steel & Wire	600,000					57,000				62,000			450,000	
Laclede	600,000									129,000	194,000		142,000	
Continental	425,000					100,000	100,000			8,000			265,000	
Atlantic	325,000		325,000			66,000				150,000	150,000		87,600	28,000

Company	Hot steel capacity *	%												
Universal Cyclops	687,410		77,410	493,100[4]		120,000		336,500			20,400	[7]		6,000
Jessop	218,990		218,990	7,700							30,700	15,000		
Carpenter	171,500		171,500					10,090		12,570	72,370	[9]		840
Eastern Stainless	72,960		72,960	36,000[5]		50,000				36,000[5]				

Company	Hot steel capacity *	%												
Ford Motor	1,940,000	77.4	220,000	1,414,000		885,000				22,000	84,000			
International Harvester	1,200,000	67.3	1,200,000	7,000		40,000				184,500	596,000	57,000		45,000
All others	5,767,670	27.7	4,193,340	179,400		40,000	184,500	2,656,110		979,000	3,866,300	2,813,180	301,900	720,340	55,500
Total	148,570,970[10]	71.9	14,395,940	39,512,570	22,007,670	8,209,190	4,153,870	3,627,260	2,656,110	16,502,960	18,349,130	10,986,740	7,256,320	8,218,940

* Open hearth, oxygen and Bessemer; excludes electric furnace. Included in hot steel capacity.
† Furnace and finishing capacities as of January 1, 1960, with revisions for later data where available.
1 Includes hot rolled strip.
2 Includes coils.
3 Includes with hot rolled strip.
4 Included hot rolled strip and plates—universal.
5 Includes plates.
6 Included with cold rolled strip.
7 Included with hot rolled sheets.
8 Included with cold rolled sheets.
9 Included with structurals.
10 Excludes latest company revisions.
E Estimated
SOURCE: Steel—Basic Analysis, Standard & Poor's Industry Surveys, New York, Standard & Poor, June 20, 1963.

STRUCTURE OF THE INDUSTRY

The steel industry may be classified into companies that are integrated, "fully" integrated, semi-integrated, and nonintegrated. Companies that have blast furnaces and coke ovens to back up their steelmaking furnaces and finishing facilities are integrated. A fully integrated company is one that furnishes most of its ore requirements. Semi-integrated companies make and finish their own steel but depend on purchased pig iron and scrap for raw materials. Nonintegrated producers only operate rolling and finishing mills, and are comparable to what are called "fabricators" in the copper and aluminum industry.

Generally the most successful producers are those whose operations are fully integrated from raw materials through finishing mill products. This includes operating iron ore, coal and limestone mines; large transportation facilities (ships and railroads); coke ovens; iron and steelmaking furnaces; rolling mills for breaking down and finishing steel ingots into a diverse list of steel products; and, in some cases, further fabrication into end products.

The steel industry is composed of a large number of companies. There are approximately 22 integrated steelmakers, 60 semi-integrated companies, and over 150 nonintegrated companies. One will note that according to the general statistical custom the so-called "fully" integrated companies are included in the one total of 22 integrated steelmakers. The important fact to know, however, is that even though the total number of companies of all types is large, the industry is dominated by eight major companies which account for approximately 75 percent of production.

Table 9.4, which is located on the two preceding pages, shows the dominant position of these eight major steel producers. U.S. Steel, with about 28 percent of the nation's ingot capacity, is also the largest producer of most finished products which make up the so-called tonnage items. The one exception is National Steel in the production of cold rolled sheets.

The largest producers of flat rolled products (plate, hot and cold rolled sheet and strip, and tin plate) in the approximate order of size are U.S. Steel, Bethlehem, National, Republic, Armco, Youngstown, Jones and Laughlin, Inland, Ford Motor, Wheeling, Granite City, Pittsburgh, and Sharon. Leading bar producers are U.S. Steel, Republic, Bethlehem, Crucible, Jones and Laughlin, Youngstown, International Harvester, Inland, Copperweld, and Armco.

Major wire producers are U.S. Steel, Colorado Fuel, Bethlehem, Keystone, Republic, Pittsburgh, Armco, Northwestern Steel and Wire, Continental, and Jones and Laughlin. Only a few companies produce structural steels; the major units are Bethlehem, U.S. Steel, Inland, Northwestern, Phoenix, and National.

The structure of the steel industry is such that the Justice Department has made it quite clear that there should be no further consolidations that will lessen competition. After the passage of the Celler Anti-Merger Act of 1950, the first major court test under the law came when Bethlehem Steel and Youngstown Sheet and Tube announced plans to merge, and were brought to court in 1958 before the merger took place. Upholding the government's argument that the proposed merger would substantially lessen competition, the Court forbade the merger in a case that appears to say that mergers are illegal whenever the companies involved are in significant competition, whether on several products or merely on one major product line.

The Justice Department had contended in the case that the defendants had a significant share of the industry's product and a merger would increase concentration and reduce competition both nationally and in important regional markets. Among the arguments which influenced Judge Weinfield in his ruling was the contention that there is no real price competition in the iron and steel industry since the industry tends to follow price patterns initiated by U.S. Steel. The principal form of competition, Judge Weinfield stated, is the assurance to buyers of continuing and alternate sources of supply; in other words, "competition is not just rivalry among sellers . . . it is rivalry among buyers for sources of supply."

PRICING POLICY

Steel is one of the cheapest of the major metals with ingots priced at 4¢ a pound in the United States at a time when the price of copper was 31¢ a pound and aluminum was 24¢ a pound.

For approximately fifty years up until July, 1948, the price of steel was administered by the basing point system in contrast to an f.o.b. mill system. Under an f.o.b. mill system a consumer at any given point in the market will be faced by a series of delivered prices equal to cost at the plant plus the actual transportation charges from each production center to that point. In contrast, under a basing point system a prospective customer is faced by identical delivered price quotations from all sellers.

The first effective control over price setting is attributed to Elbert H. (Judge) Gary, principal founder of U.S. Steel and its chief executive officer for 26 years. One of the "Gary Principles" was: "We do not advocate combinations in restraint of trade, nor action of any kind which is opposed to the laws of public welfare." Nevertheless, it is said that the Judge at his famous Gary dinners promulgated policies "to maintain to a reasonable extent the equilibrium of business, to prevent utter demoralization of business and destructive competition."

From these dinners developed the controversial Pittsburgh Plus plan. Under this pricing policy, the base price for iron and steel was in general the Pittsburgh price plus the railroad freight from Pittsburgh to the point of delivery. Under this single basing point system steel prices at any delivery point were uniform. To achieve uniform pricing three factors were required: uniform base prices, uniform delivery charges, and uniform prices for extras. (1) The base price for a ton of steel with standard specifications was given f.o.b. Pittsburgh. As a rule the base price was set by U.S. Steel and widely publicized. (2) Transportation charges for a ton of steel from Pittsburgh to every delivery point in the United States were published for many years by the American Iron and Steel Institute. (3) Extras are additions to specifications. U.S. Steel, often after consulting with other companies, set up and publicized its schedule of extras which were followed by competitors. In 1924, as a result of legal action instituted by midwestern steel fabricators, the system was modified, and instead of one city used as a basing point, a number of cities, ultimately 24, were used as basing points. However, the principle of quoting uniform delivered prices remained intact, as all mills shipping to any one city would quote the same price regardless of the sources of origin. The only difference was that cities closer to the basing points gained some transportation advantage.

Steel prices were calculated by the multiple basing point system until July, 1948, when the method was voluntarily abandoned. The reason for abandonment was the industry's concern over the continued use of the system since the Supreme Court had ruled a similar basing point system used by the cement industry to have several illegal features. The Court ruled "that concerted maintenance of the basing point system is an unfair method of competition prohibited by the Federal Trade Commission Act. . . ."

The steel industry and many distinguished economists have defended the basing point system. There have been efforts to legalize the system ever since it was declared to be in violation of the antitrust laws.

The principal argument for the basing point system is that it is necessary to prevent excesses in competition. In the steel industry, fixed overhead costs are a very large percent of total costs. It is thus necessary for steel companies to operate as close to full capacity as possible to maximize profits. Therefore, during periods of slack demand, steel companies have a very real incentive to shave prices in an attempt to increase sales. The companies will be willing to accept additional orders at any price greater than variable costs (out of pocket costs). The effect of this will be that if one company cuts the price, other companies will follow, and a disastrous price war will result. The net effect, it is argued, will be that only the firms with the strongest financial backing will survive, and there will be further concentration in the industry.

Another argument is that the basing point system may mean uniform quoted prices, but it does not mean uniform sales prices. The reason for this is that producers absorb freight to distant markets, and thus use this as a method of increasing competition that favors the consumer without engaging in disastrous price cutting.

One of the arguments most frequently advanced in defense of the basing point system is that in effect it doesn't work because of the many deviations. The point is made that base price is only one of the three components in delivered price; the others are extras and freight. Even the U.S. Department of Labor concluded that actual delivered prices paid by steel consumers deviate frequently from published delivered prices. There is no question that actual prices fall below published prices when steel mills are not operating at full capacity, and they sometimes exceed published prices during periods of full capacity.

The fact of the matter is that Judge Gary set a precedent for maintaining quoted uniform prices, and he did it because he wanted to avoid competition. Further the steel companies were very unhappy when they had to abandon the multiple basing point system in 1948.

Since that date, steel prices are quoted on an f.o.b. mill basis, which means that the customer pays the freight from the mill to his delivery site. This pricing method gives the customer an incentive to buy the steel from the nearest mill in order to get the lowest delivered price. However, a mill located in a steel export area such as Pittsburgh (which produces more steel than it uses), customarily absorbs enough of the freight charge to outlying areas (such as Chicago) to make its delivered price equal to that of a local mill.

However, it is still common practice for the f.o.b. mill price to be administered at the same price at each mill. With or without a basing point system, price leadership is a fundamental characteristic of the steel industry. The usual pattern is that U.S. Steel sets the price and the other companies follow suit in bids to private companies and to the government. Often steel producers will quote delivered prices that are identical to the thousandth of a cent. Thus, through administered price leadership the companies accomplish the same objective of the basing point system— uniform delivered prices. U.S. Steel's price leadership has remained inviolate even though other companies are more efficient as reflected in higher profit rates as a result of lower costs. Apparently, the steel companies do not see fit to compete on quoted prices; although there is evidence that there is shading of actual sales prices when the competition is great to obtain fuller utilization of plant capacity.

PROBLEMS AND POLICY

Of the many steel problems which might be singled out for study we will consider two: price trends and iron ore.

Price Trends

Since we have just completed the discussion of the steel industry's pricing policy, we shall look first at the problem which rose to the height of public controversy in the 1960's: What is the relationship between steel prices and the general price level and what should the government's policy be toward the control of steel prices?

Facts Bearing on the Problem. From the end of World War II to 1958, steel prices rose more sharply than those of almost all other major manufactured goods, including automobiles and products of other major steel-using industries. The argument was that these price increases were needed to preserve the financial strength of the industry and to permit expansion of capacity since: (1) the large advance in wages and fringe benefits had far outstripped gains in labor productivity, and (2) depreciation allowances were not adequate as an allowance was being made on plants that cost $100 a ton to build and replacement had to be made at $300 a ton.

From 1958 to 1962, despite further increases in cost, steel prices were down about 1 percent of the composite steel price index due to increased competition from both domestic and foreign sources. Price reductions on individual products ranged from 5 percent for flat-rolled, stainless steel to about 2 percent on pipe. Faced with a cost-price squeeze on profits, U.S. Steel in April, 1962 announced a general 3.5 percent price increase, and five of the other major companies followed suit. This increase was referred to as a "catch-up" adjustment needed to offset cost increases since 1958.

Immediately President John F. Kennedy in an unprecented display of power spoke out dramatically against the price increase and forced the increase to be rescinded. The reaction to the President's somewhat emotional attack on the steel industry and businessmen in general was crystalized in a statement issued by the Joint Senate-House Republican Leadership.

Beyond the administrative operations of the Federal government, it is the proper function of a President, in fact it is a duty, to help American private enterprise maintain a stable economy. In our free society he must usually find his way by persuasion and the prestige of his office.

Last week President Kennedy made a determination that a 3½ percent increase in the price of steel would throw the American economy out of line on several fronts. In the next 24 hours the President directed or supported a series of governmental actions that imperiled basic American rights, went far beyond the law, and were more characteristic of a police state than a free government.

We, the members of the Joint Senate-House Republican Leadership, believe that a fundamental issue has been raised: Should the President of the United States use the enormous powers of the Federal Government to blackjack any segment of our free society into line with his personal judgement without regard to law?

Nine actions which followed President Kennedy's press conference of Wednesday, April 11, were obviously a product of White House direction or encouragement and must be considered for their individual and cumulative effect. They were:

1. The Federal Trade Commission publicly suggested the possibility of collusion, announced an immediate investigation, and talked of $5,000 a day penalties.

2. The Justice Department spoke threateningly of antitrust violations and ordered an immediate investigation.

3. Treasury Department officials indicated they were at once reconsidering the planned increase in depreciation rates for steel.

4. The Internal Revenue Service was reported making a menacing move toward U.S. Steel's incentive-benefits plan for its executives.

5. The Senate Antitrust and Monopoly Subcommittee began subpoenaing records from 12 steel companies, returnable May 14.

6. The House Antitrust Subcommittee announced an immediate investigation, with hearings opening May 2.

7. The Justice Department announced it was ordering a grand-jury investigation.

8. The Department of Defense, seemingly ignoring laws requiring competitive bidding, publicly announced it was shifting steel purchases to companies which had not increased prices, and other Government agencies were directed to do likewise.

9. The FBI began routing newspapermen out of bed at 3 a.m. on Thursday, April 12, in line with President Kennedy's press-conference assertion that "we are investigating" a statement attributed to a steel-company official in newspapers.

Taken cumulatively, these nine actions amount to a display of naked political power never seen before in this nation.

Taken singly, these nine actions are punitive, heavyhanded, and frightening.

Although the President at his news conference made it clear that "price and wage decisions in this country . . . are and ought to be freely and privately made," there was nothing in the course of action which he pursued that supported this basic American doctrine.

Indeed, if big Government can be used extralegally to reverse the economic decisions of one industry in a free economy, then it can be used to reverse the decisions of any business, big or small, of labor, of farmers—in fact, of any citizen.

This war on the announced steel price increase by President Kennedy was because he thought this would lead to another round of inflation. A contract between labor and management, in which the federal government had played a leading role, had been signed in the early spring of 1962 which was deemed to be noninflationary as far as labor costs were concerned. A two-year contract was signed which left wage rates unchanged for a year—until mid-year 1963—but provided fringe benefits which boosted steel firms' costs by about 2½ percent in July, 1962. The contract called for renegotiation of wage increases in the spring of 1963.

This wage contract was widely heralded by the Kennedy administration as one that would stop the wage price increases. President Kennedy is reported to have thought that he had some kind of understanding that as a result of this contract, the steel companies would not advance steel prices. Thus when the steel price was announced, Kennedy saw his plan being wrecked, and he reacted violently just as if a personal agreement between him and the steel industry had been violated, when in truth this supposed agreement was more of a wish than a fact.

Basically back of all this uproar was the interrelationship between steel prices and the general price level, and labor costs and steel prices. The arguments about this interrelationship are very often distorted by applying statistics covering a very complicated subject. For example, an expert committee, set up under the administration of President Dwight D. Eisenhower to make a study of steel prices and their effect on the total economy, found that the industry was not an important factor in the sizable post-World War II inflation. On the other hand a study of the Council of Economic Advisers under President Kennedy arrived at the opposite conclusion, and thus Kennedy's concern over the effect of steel prices on the general price trend.

In looking at this problem from World War II to 1962, one notes that consumer prices went through three periods of sharp to moderately sharp inflation—during the immediate postwar period, during the Korean War, and during the 1955–1957 boom. In the 1949 recession they dipped. After the Korean War they held absolutely steady for three years, and beginning with 1958 they rose only slightly to 1962. If one looks only at the wholesale price trend from 1958 to 1962, this trend, in which steel prices are included, actually decreased. If one examines the lower chart given in Figure 9.7, the conclusion might be drawn that the fact that steel prices were slightly down from 1958 to 1962 also was partly causative in holding the price trend down that is shown for all commodities. But these interrelationships and the causes of inflation or lack of it are not quite so simple.

There are at least four factors that need to be considered in the discussion of causative forces of rising prices or inflation.

1. The classic situation of demand outstripping supply or too much money chasing too few goods, which can be brought about by government spending in excess of its receipts when the economy is operating at close to capacity.
2. An upward push of the cost of production—the cost of labor, machinery, materials, and capital.
3. The exercise of monopoly power to force up prices, that is, the use of administered prices, and this is done sometimes when the industry is operating at less than capacity.
4. Expectations—which implies that if consumers and businessmen think prices are going to rise, they will in effect cause them to rise by bidding prices up.

Figure 9.7: Steel Prices, Wages and Productivity.

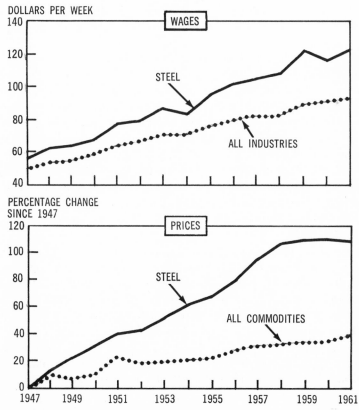

PRICES, WAGES AND PRODUCTIVITY

PERCENTAGE CHANGE SINCE 1947

EMPLOYMENT
COST PER HOUR

STEEL PRICES

HOURLY
STEEL WAGES

OUTPUT PER
MAN-HOUR

STEEL COMPARED WITH ALL INDUSTRY

DOLLARS PER WEEK

WAGES

STEEL

ALL INDUSTRIES

PERCENTAGE CHANGE
SINCE 1947

PRICES

STEEL

ALL COMMODITIES

SOURCE: *The New York Times,* April 15, 1962, © 1962 by The New York Times Company. Reprinted by permission.

The first and last of these two causes were not at issue in this great debate of 1962.

The steel industry's contention was that steel prices had to be raised because of the upward push and prices caused principally by increased wage demands. They point to the data given in Figure 9.7 which show that employment costs had gone up faster than output per man hour, and that steel prices had simply paralleled hourly steel wage increases. Thus from 1947 on, what occurred was a wage-cost-price push. Students of this question have agreed that the steel industry is correct in its position that since World War II hourly earnings in the steel industry have increased faster than man-hour productivity. However, these same students also point out that steel price increases have been made at a greater rate than warranted by wage increases.

The Kennedy administration's position was clear in that it contended that monopoly power was being exercised, or at least there was collusion in administered prices which had forced the price of steel up during the postwar period. Specifically, the contention was that the 1962 price increase was unwarranted and that improvements in plant efficiency were such that employment costs were down.

Thus the unusual display of governmental executive power was generated because the administration was convinced that administered steel prices were the cause of general price increases, that a steel price increase was unwarranted, and further, the President's personal pride was injured in view of the widely proclaimed noninflationary wage agreement that had been signed early in 1962.

On the other hand, the steel industry claims that business does not and cannot force prices up, in defiance of the consumer, but big labor can and does force up wages which generates a wage-cost-price push.

It is interesting to note that the dominant view among Washington economists was that the steel price increase in 1962 would have been inflationary, but others, including this writer and the Federal Reserve Board, drew just the opposite conclusion. The move would certainly have increased steel prices and the prices of steel products, but it might have depressed their sales and further depressed the steel business thus producing a deflationary situation.

There are others who consider that the whole outburst of activity about the price increase and resultant inflation was totally unnecessary because the contention is that the price increases could not have been maintained as proven by subsequent price concessions that were made. Thus the point was made that competition was at work, and that if left alone the price increases would have been rescinded.

It is quite clear that in 1962 the steel industry was in difficulty. The postwar boom in the demand for steel and increased capacity for steel had reached an all-time peak in the mid-1950's. But after 1958 the steel demand slacked off and in 1962 the steel mills were running at only about 60 percent of capacity. In addition, imports of steel into the United States were rising, and exports of steel were declining. Further, there was growing competition for steel markets in the United States from other materials such as aluminum. The point of all this information is that, faced with a declining market and increased competition, the basic question probably should have been: Was a price-rise good business policy?

Two events took place in 1963 and 1964 which gave further evidence of the government's attitude toward steel-pricing policy.

The year 1963 saw a substantial improvement in the demand for steel, and production rose 11 percent to 109.3 million tons. This increased demand was facilitated by increased capital plant expansion, which in turn had been helped by government action which set up revised accelerated depreciation rate schedules and initiated a 7 percent investment credit. Steel, still troubled by a declining profit margin (Figure 9.8), once

Figure 9.8: Steel's Profit Margin—Going Down Since 1955.

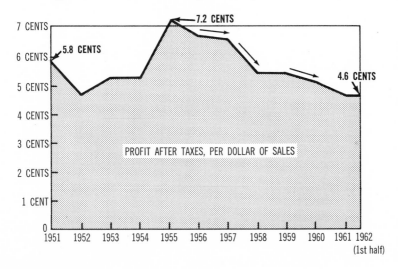

SOURCE: Reprinted from *U.S. News & World Report*, published at Washington. Copyright 1962, U.S. News & World Report, Inc.

again raised the price, but this time in a more favorable market. Price leadership this time was in the hands of Wheeling Steel which increased the price in April, 1963 on flat rolled steel ($5.00 a ton on cold rolled sheet and strip, $4.00 on hot rolled sheet and strip, and $7.00 on galvanized sheet).

The industry and the interested general public anxiously awaited the reaction of the Kennedy administration to the new attempt to raise the price. Surprisingly, President Kennedy's response was extremely mild, and indicated that the administration had no objections to "selective price increases." Why the mild response? One steel executive had said as early as August, 1962: "I really believe some White House advisers were shocked by the aftermath of the price controversy. And I do not believe we are barred in any way from seeking price relief once again when the market will take it." Part of the aftermath which has not yet been described was that steel industry investors dumped steel shares and the stocks were down as much as 50 percent from their highs in 1961. In addition, many individuals attributed the stock market crash of May, 1962 to public reaction to the Kennedy administration's antibusiness attitude.

The event of 1963 was that the Kennedy administration had obviously concluded the government had better proceed with caution in any further direct intervention in prices.

The event of 1964 that brought the industry full circle back to the realization that steel's pricing policies would not be tolerated was that on April 7, a Federal grand jury indicted eight major steel companies on charges of conspiring to fix prices and eliminate competition in carbon sheet steels. The press reported that this indictment was an outgrowth of the bitter confrontation between the late President Kennedy and the U.S. Steel Corporation over the across-the-board price increase in April, 1962. Actually the initial grand jury, that was impaneled shortly after President Kennedy's showdown with the industry, studied steel's pricing policy for nearly a year and took no action. But it was understood that leads it developed became the basis of the study by a second grand jury which led to the April 7, 1964 indictment.

Attorney General Robert F. Kennedy announced the indictment on charges of outright collusion to fix the prices of carbon sheet steel which represents about one-third of all steel products. Actually the indictment was worse than had been anticipated, as the industry had speculated that the grand jury sitting in the Southern District of New York, was primarily concerned with administered prices. That is those which we have described as being set by an industry's larger firms, rather than by market forces alone, and tacitly followed by smaller producers.

The charge was that in clandestine meetings in New York's Biltmore and Sheraton Hotels and other places, the defendants conspired to fix prices betwen 1955 and 1961. The conspiracy charges applied not to the base price of the carbon sheets but to the so-called "extras" added to the base price for particular sizes, gauges, quality, metallurgical content, and packing requirements. The jurors charged that as a result of this action carbon sheet steel prices "have been fixed at arbitrary non-competitive levels" and purchasers have "been deprived of the benefit of free and open competition."

The arguments presented by both sides in this case should be followed. One point that the steel companies are sure to make is that what they were really doing was setting up standards, which is not only a vital function of industry, but one which had actually been encouraged by the government during World War II. But while the case is being tried, the student of the history of the steel industry is bound to be reminded of Judge Gary's dinners which had as their major purpose stabilizing price and avoiding ruinous competition.

Conclusions. In concluding this study of price trends and policies it should be noted first that the price increases of April, 1963 found the steel overall index of prices about the same level as it was in 1958, since the increases offset earlier reductions. Looking ahead over the 1960's and 1970's, price trends will contrast sharply with the postwar movements, which saw prices of finished steel products rise 86 percent over the 1947–1949 base, against an advance of 18 percent in the wholesale price index and 29 percent in consumer prices. This changed price outlook reflects increasing competition from imported steel products and from other materials, particularly aluminum, concrete, and plastics.

The growth in competition from foreign steel and steel-substitute materials, has obviously lessened domestic producer's control over prices somewhat. The basic facts of economic competition indicate that steel prices over the coming years can at best only rise in line with prices of competing materials. One possible hope might be that a long-term goal of further gains in productivity stemming from capital improvements and increased capital efficiency could be passed on in terms of lower prices to consumers, instead of being channeled into higher wage costs. Wage increases at best should only be in line with increased labor productivity, and should not include the benefits of increased capital productivity.

Finally, in conclusion, it appears that in addition to sustained government policing of steel's pricing policy, steel may now have another policeman in the form of competition from substitute materials and from imports. But as early as 1964 the steel industry was beginning to ask for tariff protection from the imports.

Iron Ore

An adequate iron ore supply is basic to an iron and steel industry. In our previous study of the iron ore reserves of the United States we saw from Figure 9.2 that the U.S. current resources of approximately 3 billion tons are little more than one half of the cumulative demand through the year 2000 of 5 billion tons. Thus the problem is to develop adequate sources of iron ore to supply the continuing needs of the United States iron and steel industry.

Facts Bearing on the Problem. The iron ore problem is not new for the December, 1954 issue of *Fortune* in a feature article, "Iron Ore

Dilemma," concluded that unless the United States is to turn increasingly to foreign sources for its ore it must give new life to the wasting Mesabi. *Fortune* summarized the problem as follows:

One diagram of the U.S. economy might show it as an immense inverted pyramid, its needle base resting on a single strip of gently rolling land, 110 miles long by one to four miles wide, in northern Minnesota. Such a diagram would be oversimplified but far from fantastic. For out of this tiny strip the steel-age economy has sucked, like milk from the earth mother's breast, by far the largest portion of the principal food out of which its bones and muscles have been built: its machines and tools, its buildings and bridges, its railroads and automobiles and generating plants. Blasted and gouged from the strip's awesome open pits and scattered underground mines came a full two-thirds of the iron ore for the 400-odd million tons of steel out of which the U.S. fashioned the war plants, ships, planes, tanks, guns, bombs, and shells of World War II.

This fabulous strip, which came within an ace of being included in Canada when the boundary lines were being argued after the Revolution, is the Mesabi iron range. With the neighboring lesser ranges in Minnesota, Wisconsin, and Michigan, which combine with it to form the Lake Superior iron-ore district, it produced no less than 85 per cent of the nation's wartime iron-ore supply. Small wonder that the Sault Ste. Marie (Soo) Canal between Lakes Superior and Huron, through which its ore boats must pass on their way to the steel mills of Chicago, Gary, Cleveland, Pittsburgh, and the rest, burgeoned with barrage balloons and anti-aircraft guns to become the most heavily guarded inland spot in the U.S.

The Mesabi and its neighboring ranges have nourished the U.S. economy for half a century, through two world wars; even on their incomparably rich resources the drain, particularly of World War II, has been immense. Now some serious and farsighted men are saying that the Lake Superior District's day is almost done. In 1942 Director Edward Wilson Davis of the University of Minnesota's Mines Experiment Station reported to WPB that, at the anticipated rate of wartime consumption, the Mesabi's best ores would be gone between 1950 and 1954. Other investigators have given them up to twenty years more, at the outside. Meantime angry champions of the district insist that it can and will continue to supply the major portion of U.S. iron ore for at least a century.

One simple and reassuring observation concerning this complex controversy can be made at once: the U.S. is in no foreseeable danger of a peacetime iron-ore famine. Iron is the earth's fourth most plentiful element (the first three: oxygen, silicon, aluminum). Iron ore is now mined in twenty states, and there are abundant deposits in Russia, South America, North Africa, Australia, Newfoundland, Labrador, many another foreign land. Minnesota alone has enough known iron deposits to supply the U.S. for perhaps a thousand years.

But the fact of iron's abundance makes its economies dependent not on mere supply but on two other factors: (1) how cheaply the ore can be mined and prepared for the steel mills; (2) how cheaply the ore can be transported to the mills. Even the easily mined, high-grade ore of the Mesabi might never have been tapped if the Great Lakes did not provide cheap transportation to the coal-rich region around the lower lakes. The abundant ores of Alabama, on the other hand, are low grade and expensive to mine. They are mined—and the Birmingham steel industry therefore exists—only because Alabama happens also to be rich in the other two items of blast-furnace diet, coal and limestone.

Thus the real issues in the current controversy are two. One is how long Lake Superior ores can continue to compete with those from eastern states and foreign countries. The other is whether the U.S. can risk the prospect of another war without a large and quickly available stockpile of iron ore or pig iron. The first involves either a Bunyanesque industrial transformation of the Superior District or a conceivable major dislocation of U.S. industry through removal of midland steel mills to the Atlantic coast. The second involves the national existence.[1]

In considering this problem in 1946 the writer concluded that the steel industry would work out the solution by (1) the utilization of Class II iron ore and Class III iron reserves of Minnesota, Wisconsin, and Michigan; (2) a partial shift in new capacity location to the East Coast and increased dependence on foreign ores following the pattern of Bethlehem Steel at Sparrows Point; (3) increased imports of ore to existing facilities (in this connection, the development of the St. Lawrence Seaway project for ocean-going vessel navigation was recommended); and (4) further decentralization of the industry on a limited scale by increased facilities in the Birmingham area and in the Western region based on the local iron reserves.

The opinion of the writer was that the industry would follow past trends in solving future problems and that it was fully cognizant of these problems and to protect its own interest would work actively toward their solution. It appeared that the principal area of national policy decision was the development of the St. Lawrence Seaway project. At the state level policy decisions were required for favorable tax legislation to facilitate the utilization of Class III, principally taconite, reserves.

The post World War II experience indicates that the above predictions have been borne out.

On February 11, 1950, *Business Week* announced: "A Basic Industry Solves a Basic Problem."

One of industry's great postwar problems has been partly solved. . . . The country came out of the war with a problem: It was using steel as never before —and it had hardly more than 10 years' ready supply of ore to count on firmly.

Solution—Last week, the big final piece was fitted into a three-way program for future ore supply. It came in a surprise announcement—U.S. Steel had struck it rich in Venezuela.

Steelmen this week can relax for the first time in years. The ore they need

[1] "Iron Ore Dilemma," *Fortune*, December, 1945, p. 129.

to keep them going will come from the new Venezuelan field; from the Quebec-Labrador field, proved out in 1948; and from beneficiation of Mesabi's limitless low-grade ore, which began to look really practical last year.

The Solution. The solution to the problem has been through a two-part program; one part involves the use of new sources of foreign ores, and the other part concerns the upgrading of domestic reserves.

In *foreign ores* the U.S. Steel Cerro Bolivar deposit is believed to contain some 500 million tons of ore, with a higher iron content than in the Mesabi—better than 60 percent. Bethlehem Steel was in Venezuela in advance of U.S. Steel, but Bethlehem's leased property at El Pao is not of the order of magnitude of Cerro Bolivar.

The other big foreign ore source is in Labrador. This reserve was reported by *Business Week* on September 11, 1948. The iron deposit is 350 miles north of the St. Lawrence River. Potential tonnage estimates range from 500 million to one billion tons.

The St. Lawrence Seaway is vitally connected with the availability of these two new sources of iron ore. When the project was completed the river and the Great Lakes it drains were transformed into a man-made Mediterranean, on which seagoing ships can move 2,300 miles into North America's industrial heartland. More than 8,000 miles of new coastline were added to the United States and Canada. The lake-front cities, such as Chicago, Cleveland, Duluth, Buffalo, Toronto, and Hamilton, became genuine deep-water ports, 500 miles closer to Europe by seaway.

As early as 1895 the United States and Canadian governments began discussing the great inland seaway. The Canadian government favored the project from the beginning, but in the United States it became what *Time* magazine described in the June 6, 1955, issue as "one of the longest, most stubbornly fought issues ever introduced in Congress." *Time* briefly summarized the history of the project:

U.S. railroads, East Coast ports and industries, fearing heavy losses if traffic were diverted to the St. Lawrence, formed a powerful lobby that managed to block the project for half a century. Every U.S. President from Wilson to Eisenhower came out in favor of it. But Congress after Congress turned it down; eight seaway measures were pigeonholed or defeated outright between 1934 and 1952. . . .

After World War II, new factors tipped the scales in the seaway's favor. Mesabi's iron ore dwindled, and a rich, new field was developed in Canada's Quebec-Labrador area. The inland water route was the shortest way—and the safest in wartime—to bring the vital Quebec-Labrador ore to Midwestern U.S. steel mills.

Finally, in 1951, the Canadian government applied the maximum pressure, passing legislation to go it alone and build an all-Canadian seaway if the U.S. delayed any longer. The challenge cracked the opposition, and Congress passed the seaway bill last May [1954].

The United States dependence on foreign sources for iron ore was summarized in the mid-1950's by the U.S. Bureau of Mines as follows:

Inasmuch as it appears necessary for United States industry to go abroad for supplemental supplies of iron ore, it is fortunate that a good part of these supplies may be obtained from nearby deposits. Canada may be supplying nearly 40 million tons annually by 1975.

The Great Lakes—St. Lawrence Seaway is an important factor in the possible tonnage available from the Quebec-Labrador deposits.

Nearby, yet subject to open-sea transportation, are the rich iron-ore deposits in Venezuela. In magnitude they appear to be comparable to those of Quebec-Labrador. Security considerations favor the Canadian deposits, but year-round operation and premium grade favor Venezuela. The first shipment from Cerro Bolivar arrived at Morrisville, Pa., on January 20, 1954.

Chile, Peru, Brazil, and Cuba will provide additional supplies, but ores from Europe and Africa (with the possible exception of Liberia) will more probably find markets in Europe.[2]

The United States Steel Corporation concluded a report on *Cerro Bolivar—Saga of an Iron Ore Crisis Averted:* "For 60 years the steel industry has viewed its ore problem with all the bland indifference of the heavily endowed. But with the endowment about gone, it is apparent from all the foregoing that the challenge has unleashed a great dynamic drive from Hibbing to Venezuela, from Labrador to Liberia, from Trenton, to Pittsburgh, to Birmingham. It all involves enough imagination, ingenuity and romance to quicken the most sluggish pulse. Steelmen are long going to remember the 1950's."[3]

The increasing imports of iron ore into the United States from 1951 to 1965 and the growing importance of Canada and Venezuela as sources of supply can be observed clearly in Table 9.5 which follows on page 376.

In *domestic ores,* according to the U.S. Bureau of Mines in 1956, the principal problems of the iron and steel industry are those stemming from the approaching depletion of the readily accessible, high-grade domestic ores. By 1963 the Lake Superior district (Minnesota, Michigan, and Wisconsin) supplied only slightly over one-half of the U.S. iron ore requirements. This decline from three-quarters only ten years earlier reflected the gradual depletion of the better reserves and the discovery of higher-grade foreign ore. Other domestic mines furnished about 15 percent of the industry's ore need. And as we have just seen, the remainder largely comes from Canada and Venezuela.

Standard Lake Superior ore contains 51½ percent iron; a premium is paid for a higher-grade material and there is a penalty for ore with lower

[2] R. W. Holliday, "Iron," Preprint of chapter for *Mineral Facts and Problems,* Bureau of Mines Bulletin 556, Washington, D.C., 1955, p. 26.

[3] T. W. Lippert, *Cerro Bolivar—Saga of an Iron Ore Crisis Averted,* New York, United States Steel Corporation, 1950, p. 16.

TABLE 9.5

United States Imports of Iron Ore from Principal Countries
(In thousands of gross tons (2240 pounds))

Year	Rep. of So. Africa	Venezuela	Brazil	Canada	Chile	Mauritania	Mexico	Liberia	Sweden	Peru	Philippines	Total
1952		1,846	1,011	1,822	1,862		114	572	2,111			9,761
1953		1,950	458	1,841	2,363		242	710	2,098	844		11,074
1954		5,210	596	3,537	1,664		141	764	1,544	1,932		15,792
1955		7,160	1,011	10,077	1,035		176	928	1,221	1,559		23,472
1956		9,254	1,223	13,723	1,564		133	1,218	999	1,840		30,411
1957		12,291	1,431	12,537	2,741		236	1,013	677	2,373		33,651
1958		12,180	832	8,289	3,257		221	837	113	1,674	54	27,544
1959		13,542	1,200	13,458	3,590		106	1,105	136	2,236	71	35,617
1960		14,555	1,461	10,595	3,942		150	907	94	2,758	1	34,578
1961		10,478	889	9,683	2,604		123	715	78	1,209		25,805
1962		10,328	1,299	16,825	3,400		145	757	32	573	49	33,409
1963	21	9,231	781	18,891	2,679		1	1,310	37	290	22	33,263
1964	19	9,954	1,055	24,854	2,712	133	21	2,873	93	580		42,408

SOURCE: Data from U.S. Department of Commerce, *Commodity Year Book*, New York, Commodity Research Bureau, Inc., 1965.

iron content. As previously indicated, most ore from this area was formerly shipped as mined (direct shipping ore) or with a minimum amount of processing (mainly screening and washing). However, today, the bulk of the ore is beneficiated or upgraded before being used. In both the United States and Canada low-grade ores averaging about 25 to 30 percent iron content are now upgraded to 60–64 percent iron, and then formed into pellets which give substantial economies in blast furnaces.

The big breakthrough on the domestic ore front has been the development of technology which now permits the use of the vast reserves of taconite. As early as 1961 there were seven taconite type beneficiating plants in the United States with 19.4 million tons of annual capacity. Taconite type beneficiating plants begin with about 3 tons of hard rock with low iron ore content which is treated to obtain one ton of pellets containing upward of 60 percent iron. Pulverizers first grind up the taconite. Then the iron is separated from the unwanted silicon by methods ranging from magnetic separation to flotation. At this stage, the product is powder-rich iron. But the powder is too fine to be charged into a blast furnace, whose high winds would blow it around. To overcome this difficulty a process was developed for balling the powder into a clay-like material called Bentonite.

The resulting taconite pellets have proved advantageous to the steel industry in two ways: First, they have eased the fears that steel production would be dramatically curtailed by the exhaustion of the high-grade iron ore in the Mesabi; and second, the pellets, being richer than high-grade ore and also of constant quality and easier to handle, have increased the productivity of blast furnaces, sometimes by as much as 50 percent.

In addition, beneficiating plants have brought about dramatic changes in mining and ore shipments. Simple mining has now become a manufacturing process. As a result, even in places where transportation and housing for workers is already available, initial investment to get a mine operating runs to about $30 per ton of annual capacity, or three times the usual investment of $10 per ton. Similarly, Lake Superior ore shipments have changed radically as a result of beneficiation. As early as 1962, pellets (mainly made from Minnesota taconite and Michigan jasper) and other agglomerate products accounted for almost 30 percent of the ore shipments from the Lake Superior region. In addition to processing at the mine, about 35 percent of the industry's ore was sintered (that is, fine ore is fused into a coherent mass). Thus in 1962 over 60 percent of the blast furnace feed consisted of pellets, sinter, and other agglomerated ores, compared with 27 percent in 1957. With substantial expansion of capacity in highly beneficiated ores under way, a rising use of agglomerates is indicated, and a corresponding drop of direct shipping and lightly beneficiated ores.

In order to facilitate investment in taconite plants in Minnesota, during the general elections of 1964 a tax amendment approved by Minnesota voters guaranteed that for 25 years taxes on production of taconite would not be increased above the general corporation tax level in the state. Immediately after the election four companies announced plans to build large, commercial taconite plants in Minnesota. By August 15, 1965 a total of 30.2 million tons of taconite capacity was in operation in the United States, and total annual operating capacity was estimated to be 70.8 million tons by 1975.

The interesting part of this story of the increased use of low-grade ores is how the disadvantage was turned into an advantage of more efficient blast furnace operations, and thus capital costs were cut down in one operation of the industry to offset high costs of beneficiation. Most of this accomplishment is the direct result of the iron and steel industry solving its own problem. However, the Defense Production Act of 1950 included provision for government assistance in exploration and development of iron-ore deposits, and the Internal Revenue Act of the same year provided accelerated tax amortization for new and expanded iron ore facilities. Iron ore exploration assistance was continued until May 15, 1953, and rapid tax amortization incentives were continued through September 29, 1955. During the time the expansion goal permitting rapid tax amortization of capital invested in iron-ore facilities was in effect, planned investments under the program totaled over 1.25 billion dollars.

Conclusions. The future outlook is such that among those concerned with supplying the United States with its iron ore requirements, the U.S. Bureau of Mines reports that there is relatively good agreement that by 1975, domestic production will not exceed 90 to 100 million tons annually, and that the remaining requirements will be imported principally from Canada and South America. Figure 9.9 shows the U.S. iron ore supply by major sources projected to 1975.[4]

Projected domestic production of 90 million long tons annually, although apparently an extension of the mean for 1948–1959, is the anticipated mean of the maximum domestic output 1960–1975. Domestic output may range as low as 60 million tons annually depending on total requirements and will be less than 90 million through 1970, if the total iron ore requirements do not exceed the mean. Iron ore imports from South America and South Africa will not be much less than the forecast presented in Figure 9.9. The plus variations from the projected mean requirements will be supplied principally by Canada, and minus variations will be caused mostly by decreased Canadian imports and less domestic output.

The Lake Superior district probably reached the peak of its capacity to produce iron ore in 1953, and annual production probably will continue a gradual decline. Output of high-grade iron concentrate from the dis-

[4] This study of the requirements and sources of iron made by the U.S. Bureau of Mines is reported in detail in *Mineral Facts and Problems,* Bureau of Mines Bulletin 585, Washington, D.C., 1960, pp. 403–421.

Figure 9.9: Major Sources of United States Iron Ore Supply 1948–1958, and Predicted Sources, 1959–1975 (In million tons).

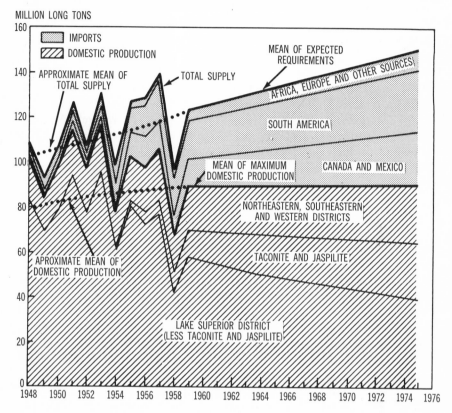

MILLION LONG TONS

SOURCE: U.S. Bureau of Mines.

trict's taconite and jasperlite deposits will probably reach 20 million tons or more annually by 1970. Iron ore production in the Northeastern district probably will continue at the rate of 4 to 5 million tons annually, and may not exceed 6 million tons annually. Iron ore production in the Southeastern district, principally in the Birmingham area, will decline slowly, but steadily due to the increased use of high grade foreign ores. Iron ore production in the western states, including Texas, Missouri and Arkansas, will increase to keep pace with the growing industrialization of the west and southwest. Some of this ore may be shipped east. The general trend appears to be that more and more ore will be beneficiated, so that the iron content of the ore fed to blast furnaces will increase.

However, the disturbing basic trend is the increased shift away from domestic ores. For if this trend continues the United States will be in a position of depending on overseas deposits for most of its iron ore. Therefore, the U.S. Bureau of Mines concludes: "Devising ways to modify the trend and assure that the Nation's future iron-ore supply will come principally from domestic sources, and also to assure that iron will be available to supply our expanding industry when and where it is needed, presents the principal problem in iron ore."

Most of the solution to this problem will have to come through technological developments which will permit the mining and processing of the medium and low-grade taconite and jasper deposits of the Lake Superior Region. The future projection of taconite plant capacity in excess of predicted ore availability in the United States is a favorable sign. In addition, complex ores (iron ore in combination with cobalt, nickel and chromium) which occur in the west may be used if beneficiation techniques can be developed which will permit their concentration.

SUMMARY

Since steel is the basis of industrialization, its continued growth is essential if the United States is to attain its objective of an expanding economy. Since the end of World War II the industry's basic financial problem has been to generate enough funds to plow back into the industry for technological improvements. With wages and other costs rising, the industry up until 1958 followed a policy of raising the price of steel in order to avoid a profit squeeze. It is argued pro and con that this policy was a contributing factor to post World War II inflation. This and previous price practices of the industry, have kept it under continued surveillance by the U.S. government.

However, the basic problem of mutual concern to the steel industry and to the United States has been the growing shortage of high-grade domestic iron ore. Over a period of twenty years since the end of World War II this problem was solved by the increased use of low-grade domestic ores, Canadian ores, and Venezuelan ores. The opening of the St. Lawrence Seaway, made possible by the U.S. government, greatly increased the availability of these foreign ores to existing plants. Technological improvements in existing plants made possible expansion of capacity without the tremendous capital requirements for new plant construction.

The outlook for the future is for increased dependence on imports of foreign ores. This increased dependence on imports of iron ore to supply the vital, basic steel industry is a matter of serious policy concern to the United States, and of critical importance in relation to our strategy of security. We are fortunate that these sources of supply are in the Western Hemisphere. Nevertheless, the industry and the United States are going to have to practice a policy of sponsoring continued technological development for the mining, beneficiation, and smelting of medium and low-grade domestic ores.

SELECTED REFERENCES

"Basing Point in the Middle," *Fortune*, September, 1948, pp. 73 ff.

Carr, M. S., and C. E. Dutton, *Iron Ore Resources of the United States, Including Alaska and Puerto Rico, 1955*, Geological Survey Bulletin 182-C, Washington, D.C., 1959.

Charting Steel's Progress, New York, American Iron and Steel Institute, Annual Issues.

Clark, J. M., "Law and Economics of Basing-Points," *American Economic Review*, March, 1949, pp. 430 ff.

The Competitive Challenge to Steel, New York, the American Iron and Steel Institute, 1963.

Fisher, Douglas A., *Steel Making in America*, New York, United States Steel Corporation, 1949.

Harris, James C. O., "Steel," in *Mineral Facts and Problems*, Bureau of Mines Bulletin 585, Washington, D.C., 1960, pp. 767–791.

Holliday, R. W., "Iron," Preprint of chapter for *Mineral Facts and Problems*, Bureau of Mines Bulletin 556, Washington, D.C., 1955.

"Iron Ore Dilemma," *Fortune*, December, 1945, pp. 129 ff.

Lippert, T. W., *Cerro Bolivar—Sage of an Iron Ore Crisis Averted*, New York, United States Steel Corporation, 1950.

Reno, Horace T., "Iron," in *Mineral Facts and Problems*, Bureau of Mines Bulletin 585, Washington, D.C., 1960, pp. 403–421.

"Republicans on Kennedy: A Display of Naked Power," *U.S. News & World Report*, April 30, 1962, pp. 109 ff.

Steel—Basic Analysis, Standard & Poor's Industry Surveys, New York, Standard & Poor, 1963, and later editions.

"U.S. Iron Ore Reserves Low," *Business Week*, April 19, 1947, pp. 20 ff.

U.S. Steel's Policies on Costs, Prices, Plants, Productivity, Testimony by Officials of United States Steel Before the Joint Committee on the Economic Report, New York, United States Steel Corporation, 1950.

World Competition in Steel, A Report to Business and Defense Administration, United States Department of Commerce, New York, American Iron and Steel Institute, 1963.

"World Steel Economy in Transition," *Monthly Economic Letter*, First National City Bank of New York, February, 1964, pp. 20 ff.

10

COPPER

COPPER has been described as "the most important nonferrous metal, both in quantity and the value of world output; among all metals it is surpassed only by iron." Copper held this position for a long time. Since the dawn of civilization copper has been an essential element in the technological development of mankind. Its value results from its high electrical and heat conductivity, its resistance to corrosion, and its ductility and malleability which will allow it to be drawn and formed without breaking.

Bronze, a combination of copper and a tenth part tin, was the first alloy in wide use by man. Bronze was used to such an extent to replace stone in making weapons, tools, and utensils that this era of importance became known as the Bronze Age. The use of copper in electrification was an important factor in the "electrical age." Today, copper faces new metals of competition. For example, aluminum has replaced copper as the leading nonferrous metal in terms of tonnage.

The copper industry consists of the functions of mining, and copper processing by concentration, smelting, refining, and fabrication.

COPPER RESERVES AND MINING

Pure copper in any significant quantity does not occur in nature. The ores of this important metal contain copper in chemical bond with iron, sulfur, and other elements. Exploration for copper-bearing ores is a continuing activity extending into the most remote sections of the world. Wherever copper deposits are found they are studied carefully to determine whether mining is justified.

Reserves and Ores

Five areas are believed to contain 93 percent of the world's measured and indicated reserves of copper. These are: Chile and Peru, Western

United States, Northern Rhodesia and the Republic of the Congo, Kazakh-stan, U.S.S.R., and Eastern Canada. Estimates of the quantities of these reserves vary widely, but the U.S. Bureau of Mines has estimated the measured and indicated reserves of the world, in terms of copper metal content, at 170 million tons.

Chile has the largest reserve with 46 million tons and is followed in order by the United States, which has 32.5 million tons, Northern Rho-desia, which has 24.5 million tons, Republic of the Congo, with 20 million tons, U.S.S.R., with 16 million tons, Peru, with 12.5 million tons, and Can-ada, which has 7 million tons. The U.S. Bureau of Mines asserts that there are substantial inferred reserves that will likely develop into measured or indicated ore upon extension of mine workings and delineation of new deposits by planned expansion and exploration projects. A typical exam-ple of the exploration project was the 1964 find at Timmons, Ontario of a 55 million ton deposit with a copper content of about 1.33 percent. With respect to the United States' official estimate of 32.5 million tons copper content ore, it has been authoritatively suggested that a more generous estimate, including a guess for inferred reserves, might allow reserves to be set as high as 50 million tons metallic content.

Copper occurs in the native state and also in a variety of ores. Three main classes of copper ores may be distinguished: (1) ore containing pure or native copper, (2) ore containing copper oxides, and (3) ore contain-ing copper sulfides. Native copper ores which contain about 98 percent pure copper are relatively insignificant, the only known deposits being in upper Michigan and Bolivia. Oxidized copper minerals are formed by weathering of primary copper sulfides exposed by erosion. Secondary sul-fides are formed when copper is leached from sulfides exposed near the earth's surface, carried down in solution, and precipitated near water level.

Copper deposits are commonly classified as porphyry, sedimentary, cupriferous pyrite, and vein deposits.

Porphyry deposits contain most of the world's estimated reserves of copper. Porphyry is an igneous rock in which larger crystals are set in a fine ground mass. In the commercial sense the term *porphyry copper de-posit* is not restricted to ore in porphyry but is applied to deposits charac-terized by huge size, uniform mineral dissemination, and low average copper content—about one percent. Many porphyry copper deposits are formed by the secondary enrichment of lean primary sulfides brought about by weathering and subsequent leaching and depositing of copper at lower levels from descending surface waters. This action usually develops an upper leached zone containing oxide minerals and underlain by an enriched section of higher grade sulfide ores. The major porphyry copper deposits of the world are in southwestern and western United States, Chile, Peru, and the U.S.S.R., with smaller deposits in Mexico and Canada.

Sedimentary copper deposits are underlain by metamorphic and igneous rocks and overlain by a thick series of younger sediments. The sedimentary beds have been strongly folded into a series of complex anticlines and synclines. Most of the ore bodies consist of sulfide ore, but considerable oxidized ores occur in certain sections. The better known occurrences in the Congo and Northern Rhodesia consist of oxidized ore near the surface, and large sulfide deposits at great depth.

Cupriferous pyrite deposits are usually lenticular or podshaped, with chalcopyrite and are found in crystalline schists or slates lying parallel with the foliation. Noted deposits of pyritic lenses are in Spain, Cyprus, Turkey, Sweden, and the United States.

Vein deposits are the result of filling open fissures or of replacing wall rock along cracks, thus forming workable ore bodies. The vein system at Butte, Montana is characteristic of this type of deposit.

In the United States the ores containing pure copper, the so-called "Lake ores" found in the upper Michigan peninsula, were the first to be exploited on a large scale. They dominated the country's production from 1845 to 1895. From then until about 1910, oxidized ores generally mined in vein deposits, provided the bulk of copper; and since 1910, sulfides occurring as vast porphyries have been the main source of the metal. Recently sulfide ores have accounted for about 90 percent of the United States production, with most of the remainder being oxide ores. Generally speaking, the copper oxide ores are a higher grade than the sulfides.

Mining

Differences in depth and in the geological formations have brought about two entirely different types of mining—open pit and underground.

Open pit mining is the most profitable method of exploiting thin flat beds of ore with shallow cover. Large bed-like masses and ore bodies with widely disseminated porphyry mineralization are mined by the open pit power shovel method, if they lie close enough to the surface so the cost of removing the overburden is not excessive. If the overburden-to-ore ratio is too high, these deposits usually are mined by underground caving systems designed for low-cost mass production. An open pit copper mine is shown in Figure 10.1.

In the development of the open pit, immense quantities of material must be removed, more than half of which is waste rock. Good management in open pit mining is thus essential. The shape and position of the ore body must be determined to allow planning of stripping disposal, approaches, benching design, pit slope, transportation, equipment, and other necessities to promote handling a maximum amount of ore and waste.

The advantages of open pit mining are: (1) the ease with which mine production can be increased or decreased, (2) the ease with which the

Figure 10.1: World's Largest Open Pit Copper Mine, Bingham Canyon, Utah.

SOURCE: Utah Copper Division, Kennecott Copper Corporation.

mine can be shut down or started up, (3) more selectivity in mining, and (4) complete extraction of the ore.

Various underground mining methods must be used when the ore is buried deep underground, perhaps half a mile. Where ore bodies are scattered far below the surface, access to the ore is gained by drifting out from the shaft in different directions and on many levels. The ore is first broken by drilling and blasting. Gravity helps speed the ore through shoots into cars at a lower level, and skips hoist the ore up the shaft to the surface for treatment. Ore handling systems at large mines are almost completely mechanized, and great tonnages of ore are moved at low cost with a minimum of labor. Although a substantial portion of the world's copper production is mined from deep deposits by underground methods, this type of mining is the exception rather than the rule in the United States.

About half of Chilean copper is produced from underground mines, while much of the Rhodesian output is recovered by block caving. However in the United States in 1963, 71 percent of the copper produced came from open pit mines compared with 70 percent in 1949, and 41 percent in 1939. Clearly, with some few exceptions, the trend in the United States is toward the production of copper from advantageous open pit mines.

Total world production of copper in 1963 scattered among 35 countries was 4,944,384 tons. But this production is highly concentrated as shown in Table 10.1 within six countries.

TABLE 10.1

Copper Production in the Major Producing Countries

Country	Tons
United States	1,209,800
Chile	662,126
Northern Rhodesia	648,238
Russia (estimated)	600,000
Canada	461,823
Congo	297,537
Total	3,879,514

Source: U.S. Bureau of Mines, *Minerals Yearbook*, Washington, D.C., 1964.

Figure 10.2: Copper Trends—Production and Consumption.

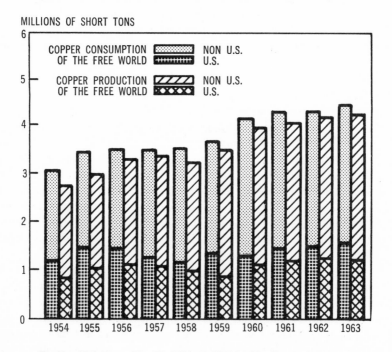

Source: *The New York Times*, May 17, 1964, © 1964 by The New York Times Company. Reprinted by permission.

TABLE 10.2

U. S. Mine Production of Recoverable Copper, by Selected States

(In thousands of short tons)

Year	Arizona	California	Colorado	Idaho	Michigan	Missouri	Montana	Nevada	New Mexico	Pennsylvania	Tennessee	Utah	Vermont	Washington	Grand Total
1952	395.7	.8	3.6	3.2	21.7	2.6	61.9	57.5	76.1	3.5	7.6	282.9	3.8	4.4	925.4
1953	393.5	.4	2.9	3.1	24.1	2.4	77.6	61.9	72.5	3.0	7.8	269.5	3.9	3.7	926.5
1954	377.9	.4	4.5	4.8	23.6	1.9	59.3	70.2	60.6	3.3	9.1	211.8	4.4	3.6	835.5
1955	454.1	.6	4.3	5.6	50.1	1.7	81.5	78.9	66.4	4.1	9.9	232.9	4.3	4.0	998.6
1956	505.9	.9	4.2	6.7	61.5	1.9	96.4	80.8	74.3	4.1	10.4	250.6	3.4	2.9	1,104.2
1957	515.9	.9	5.1	7.9	58.4	1.6	91.5	77.8	67.5	7.5	9.8	237.9	3.4	1.7	1,086.9
1958	485.8	.7	4.2	9.8	58.0	1.4	90.7	66.1	55.5	8.1	9.1	189.2	.5	.1	979.3
1959	430.3	.7	2.9	8.7	55.3	1.1	65.9	57.4	39.7	6.6	11.5	144.7		.1	824.8
1960	538.6	1.1	3.2	4.2	56.4	1.1	92.0	77.5	67.3	7.9	12.7	218.0		.1	1,080.2
1961	587.1	1.4	4.1	4.3	70.2	1.5	104.0	78.0	79.6	8.9	12.3	213.5		.1	1,165.2
1962	644.2	1.2	4.5	3.9	74.1	2.8	94.0	82.6	82.7	6.1	14.3	218.0			1,228.4
1963	661.0	.9	4.2	4.2	75.3	1.8	79.8	81.7	83.0	4.4	13.7	203.1		.1	1,213.2
1964[1]	687.4	.9	4.7	4.5	69.0	2.0	104.6	69.8	88.7	3.7	13.6	201.9		.1	1,250.8

1 Preliminary.
2 Includes North Carolina.
SOURCE: Data from U.S. Bureau of Mines, *Commodity Year Book*, New York, Commodity Research Bureau, Inc., 1965.

The trend of copper production in the Free World over a ten-year period is shown in Figure 10.2 on page 386. Most noteworthy is the fact that when one compares copper production with consumption in both the United States and the Free World, copper consumption exceeded production in each of the ten years.

Within the United States, as seen from Table 10.2, located on page 387, mine production of copper is most highly concentrated with over 50 percent mined in Arizona. The next most important producer is Utah, followed by a sharp drop to the states of New Mexico, Montana, and Nevada which in more recent years have been closely aligned for third-place position.

Finally, it should be noted that about 98 percent of the U.S. mine production of copper is recovered from copper ore; and the remainder from complex ores. In addition to copper, important quantities of by-products such as gold, silver, sulfuric acid, molybdenum, selenium, arsenic, and platinum-group metals are recovered. These by-products or co-products may be recovered at one or more of the various steps of concentration, smelting, and refining.

Once copper is mined, it is ready to be processed through the other functions of the industry.

COPPER PROCESSING

The manner in which copper is processed depends upon the ore: native copper, oxides, or sulfides.

Since processing sulfide ores of copper now provides and, in the foreseeable future, will continue to provide the bulk of the copper produced in the United States, the following processes will describe the typical operations for sulfide ores with brief comments on the processes used for oxide and native copper ores as shown in Figure 10.3.

The copper content of the copper ores mined in the United States is less than one percent. The three major steps in extracting this copper are concentration, smelting, and refining. The final step in copper processing is fabrication.

Concentration

Concentration is accomplished by floating the copper-bearing minerals away from the rest of the material. The typical flow sheet is made up of crushing, grinding, thickening, and filtering. First the ore is crushed and ground in water, and mixed with oils and reagents which adhere to the copper sulfide particles. Then in the flotation cells, air bubbles collect the coated mineral particles and float them to the surface forming the

Figure 10.3: Copper Processing.

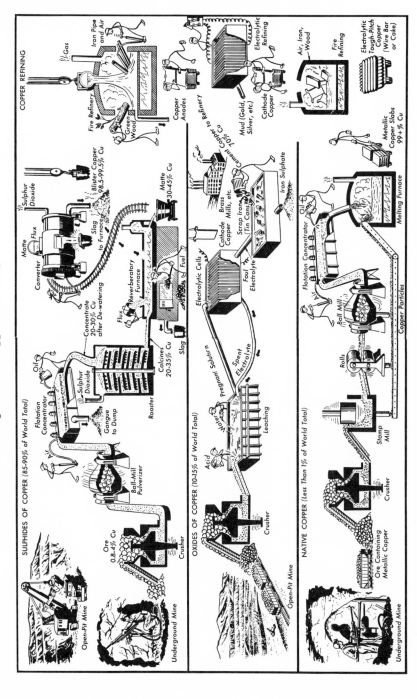

SOURCE: *Westinghouse Engineer.*

concentrate. The dried concentrate contains about 30 percent copper and significant quantities of gold, silver, and minor metals like selenium. Ore is first passed through a series of crushers in order to be prepared for flotation; then ball mills pulverize it. Classifiers pass the properly sized materials on to the flotation cells. In the flotation cells the rock particles, called tailings, remain in suspension, while the copper particles are floated to the top. The tailings from the flotation cells are sent to thickeners to recover most of the water, and they are then deposited on vast tailings dams. From every 100 tons of ore treated, 96 tons of material are discarded as tailings.

The concentrate is next upgraded by further grinding and flotation. After most of the water is removed on filter drums the concentrate is ready for smelting. Flotation has been the principal method of treatment for thirty years. There are many exceptions—leaching, for example, is used for oxide ores. However, leaching is not competitive with flotation for sulfide ores.

Smelting

The smelting of sulfide copper ores involves three major steps—roasting, reverberatory furnacing, and converting. The 30 percent copper concentrate, in addition to copper, contains iron and sulfur in combination.

Roasting. Roasting removes a portion of the sulfur, as well as some of the volatile components like arsenic, antimony, and bismuth, and oxidizes some of the iron to ferrous oxide.

Reverberatory Furnacing. Reverberatory smelting of the roasted material to copper matte is based on the strong affinity of copper and sulfur to each other, as compared with other metals and sulfur, and the relatively weaker affinity of copper for oxygen. The concentrate is charged into the reverberatory where at nearly 3,000 degrees it is reduced to molten fluid. Some of the iron floats to the top as slag, the matte containing copper, sulfur, and the remaining iron settles to the bottom. Periodically the slag is withrawn from the reverberatory furnace and discarded. The copper-bearing matte which has settled to the bottom of the furnace is withdrawn and transferred to converters.

Converting. The converter is a refractory lined vessel where thin streams of air are forced through the molten mass of the copper matte. The purpose of the air is to oxidize and burn off the sulfur. In the converter the remaining iron in the matte reacts with silica rock to form converter slag. Since the slag still contains some copper it is skimmed and returned to the reverberatory furnace. The copper from the converter still contains oxygen. This is removed by further treatment in the anode furnace. Here the oxygen reacting with reformed natural gas goes off as carbon dioxide and steam. Next the almost pure copper is poured into the molds of the casting wheel to make anode forms used in refining. However, even this so-called "blister copper" which contains 99.6 percent copper, is still too impure to be used for electrical purposes. There remain impurities, including gold and silver, which amount to about $\frac{4}{10}$ of one percent of the blister copper.

Refining

Refined copper is produced from the blister copper matte, which serves as an anode. Refining is necessary to remove the remaining impurities. This is accomplished by electrolysis. In the refining process the copper anodes are submerged with cathodes of pure copper in a solution containing copper sulfate and sulfuric acid. As electric current passes through the cell containing the solution, the anode is gradually etched away and pure copper flows with the current and is deposited on the cathode. In a refinery, acres of such cells accomplish the final electrolytic purification. The anodes are gradually lowered into the tanks and carefully placed to avoid short-circuits. The starting sheets, or cathodes of pure copper, are made in the refinery. It takes about fourteen days for the copper to be deposited on the cathode.

Most of the usual impurities such as gold, silver, and platinum precipitate out of solution and form anode mud which accumulates at the bottom of the electrolytic cell; others dissolve and become concentrated in the electrolyte and may be deposited or occluded on the cathode. Cathode copper has a minimum purity of 99.90 percent. Thus the process of producing pure copper is complete, and the cathodes are then melted down and recast into shapes required for fabrication.

Alternative Processes for Oxide and Native Ores

Oxide Ores. After crushing, oxide ores are treated by leaching. Approximately 9 percent of the United States production is by hydrometallurgical methods. Leaching followed by cementation or electrolysis is the process used to recover copper from ore containing oxide minerals. Oxidized copper minerals, such as carbonate and silicates are readily attacked and the copper is dissolved by a number of the more common acids and alkalies; the copper is precipitated from solution by electrolysis or by iron replacement of the copper, and in the case of ammonia leaching by simply boiling off the ammonia. The usual practice is to leach the ore with diluted sulfuric acid, followed by recovery of the copper by cementation on scrap iron.

When oxide ores are treated by electrolysis, cathode copper is the end-product. Cement copper is about 70 percent copper content, and it must be processed into copper anodes before electrolytic refining.

Native Copper. Native copper, which constitutes only about 1 percent of the world total, must be crushed, stamped, rolled, and run through a ball mill and a flotation concentrator. The native copper, or "Lake" in the United States, is fire-refined in a melting furnace into over 99 percent metallic copper slabs. Any copper particles resulting from the stamp mill, the rolls, and the ball mill go directly to the melting furnace. Then the final recovery of copper is made through flotation concentration, and this copper in turn is sent to the melting furnace for fire-refining.

Fabrication

Fabrication is the last function of copper processing. Refined copper in the form of cathodes, ingots, cakes, billets, and wire bars is used for processing at brass mills, wire mills, and foundries. This copper is processed into brass, bronze, and other alloys and pure copper products. Brass, bronze, and other alloys are first processed into cakes, slabs, bars, shells, billets, and wire bars; and are then made into the following shapes and products: plates, sheets, bars, and strip; pipe and tube; rod; wire; and finished castings. Pure copper in the form of cakes, billets, and wire bars is made into similar shapes and products. These shapes and products then go to fabricators and assemblers who distribute their products through the various trade channels to consumers.

COPPER USES

The uses to which copper is put are in large measure a result of its properties. The properties of major significance are high electrical and thermal conductivity, ductility, malleability, formability, strength, and corrosion resistance. When it is desirable to improve certain of these basic properties, and when such improvement can be effected without sacrificing any of the required qualities for a particular application, alloying often solves the problem. As a consequence, the popular commercial brasses, bronzes, copper-nickel alloys, and nickel-silvers have been developed. The chief use of copper is as a pure metal, for in this form its conductivity is best; it is weather resistant; it is easily rolled and drawn; and it is strong enough for minor structural purposes. However, alloys are also important, particularly when fused with zinc to form brass, which is easily worked, very resistant to corrosion, and stronger than pure copper.

Bronze, an alloy of copper and tin, is suitable for springs and is used in machine parts. Copper-nickel alloys have a wide range of mechanical and electrical applications. Copper is used with precious metals for jewelry and coins. The major non-metallic form is copper sulfate, which has important agricultural and industrial applications.

The relative importance of copper in various end-uses has to be approximated as there are no comprehensive figures on consumption available, but the distributions shown in Table 10.3 are working estimates of the market distribution of copper.

TABLE 10.3
End-Uses of Copper
(In percent of total)

	%
Electrical products	28
Machinery and industrial equipment	20
Miscellaneous	20
Building and construction	19
Transportation	13
	100

NOTE: Author's estimates.

Electrical applications of copper cut across many of these end-use categories. The estimate has been made that close to half of total copper consumption is for electrical purposes. Major applications include electric power transmission and distribution lines, components of electrical motors and generators, power control and switching apparatus, telephone and telegraph equipment, fine wiring for precision electronic components, and wiring for housing and commercial buildings.

In building and construction the noncorrosive quality of copper and its alloys have brought about many uses such as roofing products, plumbing goods, builder's hardware, and functional decorative applications.

In transportation copper is used by automobiles, aircraft, missiles, railroads, and ships. Automobiles alone account for at least 8 percent of the total U.S. consumption of copper. Volume uses are in radiators, heaters, air-conditioning units, bearings, bushings, carburetors, generators, oil lines, strainers, wiring, switches, and plating. In total, the average automobile consumes between 40 and 50 pounds of copper. For aircraft the maze of wiring is the major use, and the larger planes use from 600 to 3,000 pounds of copper in the electrical systems and mechanical components. In the missile program copper is an essential part of the wiring system. Railroads use large quantities of copper in diesel locomotives, passenger cars, and in switching and signaling devices. The average Pullman car uses about 2,000 pounds of copper. In tankers and other vessels large quantities of copper are also required.

One of the major uses, falling within the miscellaneous end-uses, is in appliances. In this field manufacturers of washing machines, air-conditioning units, refrigerators, TV sets, and other units specify copper and its alloys for many components requiring materials that are electrically or thermally conductive, corrosion resistant, and durable.

There are many other varied and specialized uses of copper, but principal mention should be made that in wartime, huge supplies of copper are used for ammunition and also in aircraft, naval ships, and military vehicles. It might be well to point out that a 37 mm. antiaircraft gun in action uses a ton of copper every twenty minutes, and a fighter-bomber squadron of fifty planes expels 7 tons of copper every sixty seconds in combat.

In spite of all these many uses of copper, consumption has not kept pace with the growth in the economy. During the 50-year period 1900–1950 copper did show tremendous growth and increased ten times. But between 1925 and 1950 copper consumption grew only about two-thirds as fast as GNP. The President's Materials Policy Commission in 1952 projected a doubling in the level of economic activity in the 25 years from 1950 to 1975 with only a 45 percent advance in the domestic consumption of copper. Thus U.S. copper requirements in 1975 were estimated at 2.5 million tons compared with an average of about 1.5 million tons in 1959–1963.

The accuracy of the projections will hinge mainly on price because, if copper prices are too high, substitutes will increase their share of the market and thus reduce the demand for copper. Copper's sharpest competition comes from aluminum. Aluminum has been most successfully used in overhead lines carrying high voltages due to its lighter weight requiring less support structures and related equipment. Aluminum has replaced copper as a conductor in many other uses, and the major reason has been the sharply higher copper prices since the end of World War II. Prior to the war copper generally sold for about half the price of aluminum, but this cost advantage was reversed in the postwar period. Aluminum has also reduced some of the uses for copper in the building industry. The conclusion is that the price of copper is important and that substitutes are being found for copper.

What this conclusion points up is that copper prices must be studied as a special problem, and that substitutes for copper may make it easier for the United States to improve its deficiency between copper production and consumption.

SOURCE AND DISTRIBUTION OF COPPER IN THE UNITED STATES

Total apparent consumption of copper in 1964 was 1,947,000 tons. This was made up of 1,638,000 tons of domestically produced new copper

Figure 10.4: Sources and Distribution of Copper in the United States.

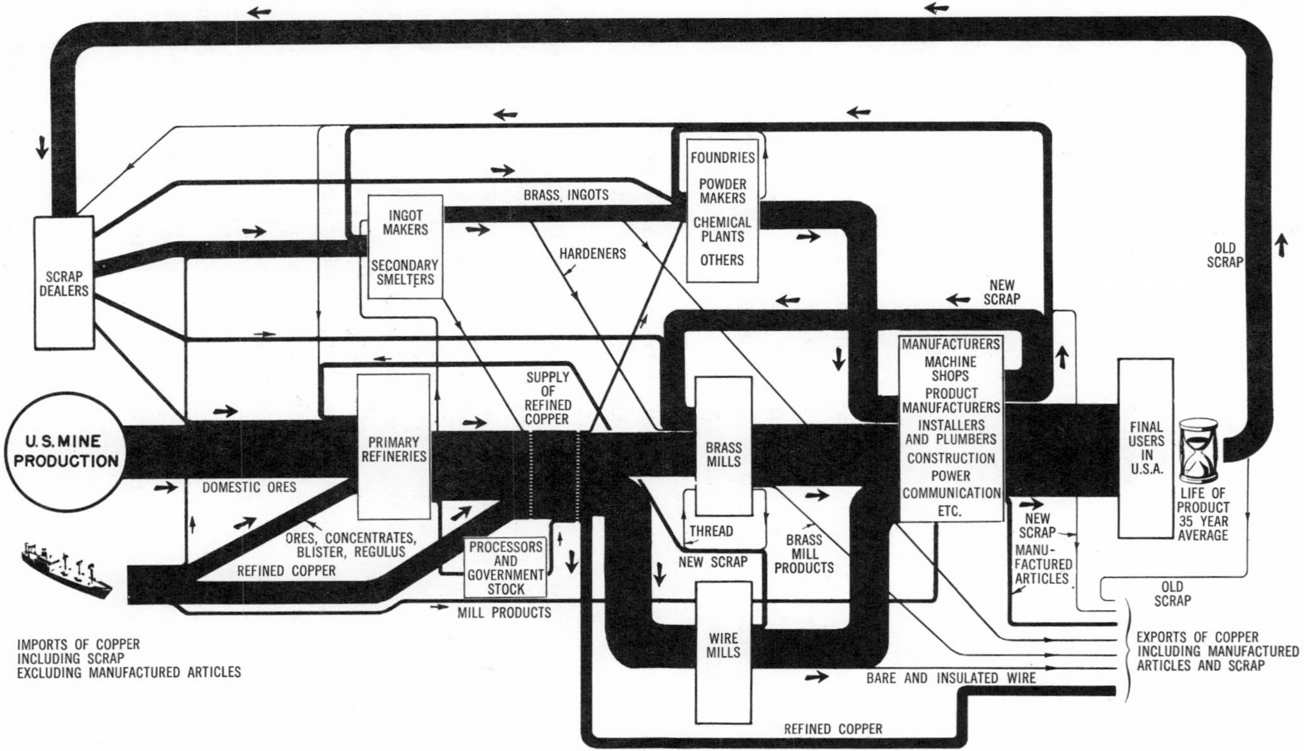

SOURCE: Copper and Brass Research Association.

from 1,251,000 tons of domestic ore and 393,000 tons of foreign, imported ore. Also imported was 695,000 tons of unmanufactured and refined copper. Secondary, or scrap copper, accounted for 460,000 tons. The complete balance sheet of United States production, consumption, and imports and exports for the years 1952 through 1964 is given in Table 10.4 of salient statistics. Also the flow chart Figure 10.4 deserves considerable study as a complete diagrammatic presentation of the source and distribution of copper in the United States. Basically one can see that the United States supply of copper must come from domestic ore, scrap, and imports. We have already examined the domestic ore position, but the nation's sources of scrap and imports need to be examined.

Scrap

Secondary copper is recovered from new and old scrap, the two general classes of scrap copper. New scrap in part is generated in the manufacture of articles from primary or refined metal and consumed at a plant of different location from the plant of generation. Typical types of new scrap are defectively finished or semifinished articles, clippings, punchings, turnings, skimmings, and slag. New scrap consumed at the plant of generation is called runaround or home scrap. New scrap should not be considered a net addition to overall supply since much of the copper obtained from new scrap never reaches the market but is just runaround material in manufacturing operations.

Old scrap consists of articles that have been discarded after serving a useful purpose. Such articles may be worn out, obsolete, or damaged, and include discarded wire, radiators, cartridge cases, used pipe, and lithograph plates. Old scrap is largely collected by several thousand scrap dealers, who for the most part are unaffiliated with the primary copper producers. Quite a bit of the secondary material is obtained from brass and bronze. For the five-year period ending in 1963, metal recovered from old scrap averaged 40 percent of total domestic mine production.

The flow chart (Figure 10.4) shows that the life of the copper product has a 35-year average, and it is estimated that about two-thirds of the copper consumed comes back to the market as scrap. The United States has a reserve of recoverable copper in use estimated to be about 30 million tons. This amount, one will remember, is of the same order of magnitude as the measured and indicated ore in the United States.

Imports

Before World War II U.S. imports and exports of copper constituted a well-balanced trade through which the smelting, refining, and fabricating facilities of this country were used to treat foreign crude materials

TABLE 10.4
Salient Statistics of Copper in the United States
(In thousands of short tons)

Year	New copper produced from domestic ores			From foreign ores[2]	Total new	Secondary recovered[7]	Imports[3]		Exports		Stocks Dec. 31			Appar. Consumption[9]	
	Mines	Smelters	Refineries				Un-mfg.	Re-fined	Metallic[4]	Re-fined[5]	At producers	Re-fined	Blister & materials in solution	Total new	Total new & old[8]
1952	925	927	923	255	1,178	415	619	347	212	174	211	26	185	1,360	1,775
1953	926	943	932	361	1,293	429	676	274	171	110	272	49	223	1,435	1,864
1954	835	834	842	370	1,212	407	595	215	312	216	214	25	189	1,235	1,642
1955	999	1,007	997	345	1,342	515	594	202	260	200	235	34	201	1,336	1,851
1956	1,104	1,118	1,080	362	1,443	468	596	192	281	223	339	78	261	1,367	1,835
1957	1,087	1,081	1,050	404	1,454	444	594	162	430	346	383	109	274	1,239	1,683
1958	979	993	1,002	351	1,353	411	496	128	428	385	305	48	257	1,156	1,568
1959	825	799	796	302	1,098	471	571	214	196	159	271	18	253	1,183	1,654
1960	1,080	1,143	1,121	398	1,519	429	524	143	510	434	359	98	261	1,148	1,577
1961	1,165	1,162	1,181	369	1,550	411	458	67	483	429	285	49	236	1,237	1,648
1962	1,228	1,282	1,214	398	1,612	416	479	99	367	337	317	71	246	1,352	1,768
1963	1,213	1,258	1,219	377	1,596	422	541	119	345	311	304	52	252	1,423	1,845
1964[1]	1,251	1,296	1,245	393	1,638	462	560	135	365	305	275	34	241	1,485	1,947

1 Preliminary.
2 Also from matte, etc., refinery reports.
3 Data are general imports; that is, they include copper imported for immediate consumption plus material entering country under bond.
4 Total exports of copper, exclusive of ore, concentrates, composition metal and unrefined copper. Exclusive also of "other manufactures of copper."
5 Ingots, bars, etc.
6 Withdrawals from total supply on domestic account.
7 From old scrap only.
8 Old scrap only
SOURCE: Data from U.S. Bureau of Mines, *Commodity Year Book*, New York, Commodity Research Bureau, Inc., 1965.

and to return refined copper and manufactures of copper abroad. After the beginning of the war the United States needed all the copper that entered this country to supply the growing wartime needs. In the postwar period demand continued above prewar levels to fill postponed civilian requirements; as a result the United States became partially dependent on imported material as this country shifted from a net exporter of copper to a net importer.

Most of the copper exported from the United States is refined copper and in advanced forms of manufacture, in which copper content is not calculable. Because supplies of copper in the United States have been inadequate to fill requirements since the end of World War II, copper has been subject to export controls. During 1949–1953 exports of refined copper averaged 140,000 tons annually, and ranged from 110,000 to 174,000 tons. In the 5-year period, 1954–1958, inclusive, exports of refined copper rose to an average of 274,000 tons annually and ranged from 200,000 tons to a high of 385,000 tons in 1958 after all restriction on exports of refined copper were removed in September, 1956. Exports declined sharply in 1959, only to rise to 428,700 tons in 1960, the highest since 1929. After 1960 exports declined.

Since World War II imports of copper into the United States have exceeded exports. The all-time record receipts of foreign materials was made in 1945 when 853,000 tons of copper in all forms were received. During the 13-year period ending in 1964 U.S. imports of copper ranged roughly between 500,000 and 600,000 tons. Overall, since the end of World War II about one-fourth of domestic needs have come from foreign sources. During the period from the end of the Korean War to 1960 domestic mine production provided about 50 percent of the supply and old scrap and imports furnished 22 and 29 percent respectively.

The United States obtains its copper imports principally from Western Hemisphere sources which have accounted for about 80 percent of the total. These figures vary from year to year as can be seen from Table 10.5. However, the chief sources in recent years have been Chile, 42 percent; Peru, 19 percent and Canada, 17 percent; plus 7 percent from South Africa. Peru has increased in importance as a source of our copper imports in recent years, while Mexico has declined both in relative importance and quantity.

Western Hemisphere production of copper is more than adequate to take care of Western Hemisphere consumption. Overall, the Western Hemisphere uses about 85 percent of its mine output; the balance mainly goes to Europe. Chile, the world's third largest producer, uses less than 10 percent of its copper; of the remainder, about half is shipped to the United States and half to Europe. Canada, which ranks fifth in production, exports about 60 percent of its supply.

The U.S. import position in copper is characteristic of the interna-

TABLE 10.5

U. S. Imports (General) of Copper (Unmanufactured), by Sources and Types
(In thousands of short tons)

Year	Ore & matte	Un-refined blister & black	Re-fined	Scrap	Australia	Canada	Mexico	Cuba	Chile	Peru	Philippines	Congo Rep.	Rhodesia	Rep. of So. Afr.	Total U.S. imports
1951	102.7	141.9	239.0	5.6	1.1	54.6	47.9	22.3	268.4	10.1	12.6		43.7	7.4	489.1
1952	105.3	162.2	347.0	4.5	.7	82.0	51.0	19.9	362.3	11.3	14.8		28.2	8.6	618.9
1953	120.6	273.6	274.1	7.8	13.0	107.4	65.8	18.2	281.1	26.5	13.8	5.8	88.0	8.2	676.1
1954	118.6	256.5	215.1	4.7	16.7	89.9	51.2	18.3	266.9	22.5	19.4	15.5	61.9	13.5	594.8
1955	125.5	253.7	202.3	12.6	11.8	107.1	49.6	21.1	226.1	31.1	18.3	14.2	73.5	13.1	594.1
1956	122.2	276.1	191.7	5.7	19.5	120.5	52.8	16.3	236.6	42.8	10.9	12.8	27.6	21.3	595.7
1957	124.8	301.1	162.3	5.8	15.1	120.2	47.7	17.4	236.0	41.6	13.1	10.2	45.4	19.9	594.0
1958	92.6	268.2	128.5	7.1	5.1	74.8	50.0	14.5	200.1	30.4	14.6	15.5	35.2	29.2	496.3
1959	81.5	269.0	214.1	6.2	7.5	112.3	29.5	10.8	241.4	28.7	13.8	4.3	32.6	31.0	570.9
1960	80.5	298.4	142.7	2.7	1.8	117.6	22.7	6.6	208.2	91.6	17.6	.2	5.8	28.2	524.3
1961	47.4	339.2	66.9	4.2	.8	78.4	21.0		227.0	90.4	13.9			23.5	457.7
1962	43.5	331.7	98.8	4.8	.8	98.8	23.8		225.4	72.1	10.1		19.0	24.5	478.9
1963	49.4	369.1	119.2	2.9	1.1	90.8	22.3		227.9	99.7	14.9		22.1	36.4	540.5
1964¹	52.0	389.6	137.8	4.8	1.2	98.4	22.7		259.4	111.5	11.6		24.4	38.9	584.1

NOTE: Includes refined; black, blister, and converter; scrap; and copper content of ore, matte, and regulus.
1 Preliminary.
SOURCE: Data from U.S. Department of Commerce, *Commodity Year Book*, New York, Commodity Research Bureau, Inc., 1965.

tional nature of the metal in regard both to production and consumption. Actually the only major producing area in the Free World using the bulk of its mine output is the United States. Europe is the chief importing area and receives over 90 percent of its copper requirement from abroad, mainly from Chile and Africa. African producers export over 95 percent of total tonnage; about 85 percent goes to Europe.

This interdependence of the Free World affects price relationships and the United States supply position for copper.

The interdependence adds volatility (over and above cyclical changes) to supply-demand relationships in copper and consequently to prices. For example, an interruption of Chilean production from a strike or other cause would affect the supply in the United States and Europe, and users wishing to insure adequate tonnage (as well as speculators) might increase purchases and cause an increase in prices, especially in the sensitive London and custom smelter's markets. Conversely, an easing in economic activity in one large consuming area might exert downward pressure on prices in a different area, despite no change in demand there. Thus international interdependence is a part of the copper price problem which must be studied in detail in the problems and policy section of this chapter.

The United States dependence on imports of copper has important consequences for self-sufficiency and strategic considerations. Not only has the United States been a net importer of copper since World War II, but the U.S. Bureau of Mines has concluded in *Mineral Facts and Problems:* "Projecting the future demand in relation to population increase and per capita consumption and mine production capacities, the United States will continue to be dependent on foreign sources for a sizable portion of its domestic requirements."

The United States has attempted to improve its supply position by encouraging domestic production, establishing a National Stockpile, reducing import restrictions, and through the part played by nationals in developing accessible foreign sources.

Under the Defense Production Act of 1950, as amended, various types of production expansion assistance were developed for copper—production loans, government floor-price purchase contracts with escalation provisions, certificates of necessity permitting accelerated amortization of capital investment for income tax purposes, and exploration loans amounting to 50 percent of total costs repayable from eventual production. Copper reserves have been developed in several areas as a result of programs sponsored by the Defense Minerals Exploration Administration.

A National Stockpile for copper is part of the overall defense program. The Office of Emergency Planning is the policy-making agency for the stockpile which at the beginning of 1965 had an objective of 775,000 tons for conventional war. Inventory at that time was 1,016,219, thus leaving 341,219 surplus if it were not for nuclear war considerations. Up to that time the Office of Emergency Planning, except for transfer of minor quantities to the Mint, had not authorized disposal of any of the stockpiled copper, lest studies of nuclear war requirements showed the United States needed all the stockpile inventory. Studies underway at that time indicated the need for massive increases above stockpile objectives established for conventional wars. This stockpile and domestic production, plus smelting and refining capacities to produce copper in the United States, are expected to be the first line of defense in an emergency.

Since imports of copper are likely to be a major source of supply in the future, United States policy toward imports has been modified in part to accommodate the nation's changed position. An excise tax of 4¢ a pound was imposed on copper on June 21, 1932. During World War II the U.S. government was virtually the only importer of copper, and the position was taken that the tax was not applicable. The tax was reinstated for a brief period, following which it was suspended by Acts of Congress from April 30, 1947, to June 30, 1950. The suspended tax, meanwhile, was reduced as a result of the Trade Agreement negotiations at Geneva in 1947, to 2¢ a pound effective March 16, 1949. The 2¢ tax came into effect on July 1, 1950, but was suspended again on April 1, 1951. The law provided that the Tariff Commission must notify the President within fifteen days after the end of any calendar month in which the average price dropped below 24¢ a pound, delivered Connecticut Valley, and within twenty days thereafter the President would revoke the suspension. The suspension was extended each year until 1955 when it was extended to June 30, 1958. Meanwhile, at the June 1956 meetings in Geneva on General Agreements Tariffs and Trade (GATT), copper was subjected to certain concessions. The excise tax on copper metal, ores, and concentrates would drop 15 percent (5 percent for each of three years) if the tariff were reimposed and the price of copper were not below 24¢. If the price fell below 24¢, the tariff was to be 2¢ a pound. Under the series of reductions a tax of 1.7¢ became effective July 1, 1958 and will remain at that rate as long as the price is above 24¢. This reduction in the tariff and its prior suspensions are steps in the right direction, but they give rise to the question: should the tariff be abolished?

In the final analysis, accessible foreign sources of copper appear to be necessary to supplement domestic ore and scrap. Therefore development of new deposits and planned expansion in existing mines on the part of United States companies should help to insure reliable sources of copper. United States companies have had dominant interests in Chile and Peru, and a U.S. company has 46.1 percent interest in Rhodesian Selection Trust, Limited. Yet economic and political instability in these countries does not insure reliable sources of copper. As a result, many companies are stressing Canada as a source of supply. Exploration there has been accelerated sharply, and considerable reserves have been located. In spite of this, industry officials warn that Canada probably will not be able to satisfy the growing requirements for copper; especially is this true in view of the fact that Canada's consumption of copper is rising at a fast rate.

The search for sources of copper for distribution in the United States is going to remain a challenge to the industry. The industry must find domestic resources, utilize domestic scrap, and pursue the ever-challenging search for a development of foreign sources. This search must be carried on despite the fact that there are few available sources of copper and most of these sources, with the exception of Canada, cannot be described as reliable. This problem of the United States dependence on international sources of copper will be reviewed briefly in the problems and policy section.

STRUCTURE OF THE INDUSTRY

The copper industry is characterized by geographic and company concentration.

Geographic Concentration

The point has already been made that five areas are believed to contain 93 percent of the world's measured and indicated reserves of copper. These are: (1) Chile and Peru; (2) Western United States; (3) Northern Rhodesia and the Republic of the Congo; (4) Kazakhstan, U.S.S.R.; and (5) Eastern Canada. Most of the copper produced in the United States comes from five western states. Chile's production comes principally from three American owned mines; Northern Rhodesia's output from four large mines; the Congo's production from the properties of one company; and three mines supply about 75 percent of Canada's output.

Concentration mills and smelters are usually near the principal mines, and some process custom ores for smaller producers. There are eight smelters in Arizona; one each in Utah, Montana, Nevada, New Mexico, and Tennessee, one in Texas, and one each at seaports in Washington, New York and New Jersey.

About 55 percent of the electrolytic refining capacity is accounted for by five refineries on the Atlantic coast in New York City, Carteret and Perth Amboy, New Jersey, and Baltimore, Maryland; five electrolytic refineries in Arizona, Washington, Montana, Utah, and Texas provide the remainder. Three Michigan plants fire-refine Lake copper, and fire-refined copper is also produced in New Mexico, Texas, and New Jersey.

Most of the major copper-fabricating plants (brass and wire mills) are in the Connecticut Valley area. Two California plants were placed in operation in 1957. Secondary smelters are far less concentrated, and about

3,000 foundries and miscellaneous users of copper materials are scattered throughout the United States.

Before World War II, the United States smelting and refining capacity was excessive for treating domestic materials, and the excess capacity was used to treat substantial quantities of foreign crude materials. Since the war, foreign producers have been building their own processing facilities, and by 1960 there were approximately 95 primary smelters and refineries in foreign countries.

Company Concentration

Ten companies or groups control about 70 percent of Free World output of copper. In order of importance they are: Anaconda, Kennecott, the Anglo-American group in Rhodesia, American Smelting and Refining and its affiliated companies, Union Miniere du Haut-Katanga in the Congo, Phelps Dodge, Rhodesian Selection Trust, Newmont Mining's affiliates (mainly in Africa), Noranda Mines and its subsidiaries and affiliates in Canada, and International Nickel of Canada.

In the United States the primary copper industry is composed of approximately 200 companies engaged in the production and sale of copper. The principal segments of the industry—mining, smelting, refining, fabricating, and marketing—are dominated in varying degrees by a few large, vertically integrated companies.

Mining. Twenty-five mines produce about 97 percent of the domestic copper output; the five largest produce 52 percent, and the ten leading mines supply 76 percent. The balance is supplied by small copper mines and producers of other ores, which contain recoverable by-product copper. Three companies, Kennecott, Phelps Dodge, and Anaconda usually account for three-fourths of total annual domestic copper production. Kennecott and Phelps Dodge are by far the largest producers and supply about 35 percent and 25 percent, respectively of the total each year.

Smelting. Four companies control about 90 percent of the smelting capacity in the United States (exclusive of the Lake smelters in Michigan). Copper smelting companies and their approximate percentage of the total U.S. smelting capacity are given in Table 10.6.

Refining. Electrolytic copper refining capacity in the United States is dominated by four companies which control over 80 percent of the capacity as shown in Table 10.7.

Thus Kennecott, Phelps Dodge, and Anaconda usually mine 75 percent of the total U.S. output, and with American Smelting and Refining smelt and refine a substantial part of the primary copper materials in the United States.

Fabricating. There are about 30 large fabricating companies in the United States making sheet, strip, wire, rods, pipe, and extruded and

TABLE 10.6
Control of Copper Smelting Capacity

Company	Percent of total capacity (charge)
Phelps Dodge Corp. and Phelps Dodge Refining Corp.	31
Kennecott Copper Corp.	28
American Smelting & Refining Co.	15
The Anaconda Co.	12
International Smelting & Refining Co.[1]	4
San Manuel Copper Corp.	4
American Metal Climax, Inc.	3
Magma Copper Co.	2
Tennessee Copper Co.	1
Total	100

1 A subsidiary of The Anaconda Co.
SOURCE: U.S. Bureau of Mines, *Mineral Facts and Problems,* Washington, D.C., 1960.

rolled shapes. Twelve of these companies handle over 50 percent of the total volume of business and are owned or controlled by the large copper producers, giving them completely integrated operations from the mines to finished copper and brass products. Anaconda is the most integrated of the major producers. Practically all of its output from domestic mines goes

TABLE 10.7
Control of Copper Refining Capacity

Company	Percent of total U.S. capacity
American Smelting & Refining Co.	27
Phelps Dodge Corp.	27
International Smelting & Refining Co.[1]	14
Kennecott Copper Corp.	12
American Metal Climax, Inc.	8
The Anaconda Co.	8
Inspiration Consolidated Copper Co.[2]	3
Cerro de Pasco Corp.	1
Total	100

1 A subsidiary of The Anaconda Co.
2 28 percent controlled by The Anaconda Co.
SOURCE: U.S. Bureau of Mines, *Mineral Facts and Problems,* Washington, D.C., 1960.

to its two fabricating facilities. Anaconda, the world's second largest miner of copper, is the largest fabricator, accounting for over 10 percent of the total U.S. volume in fabricated products.

Phelps Dodge and Kennecott are also leading fabricators, although the bulk of the latter's mine output is sold to others. These and other producing companies' interests in fabricating give some measure of control in the final market as well as captive outlets for mines.

American Smelting and Refining has sizable stockholdings in two of the largest "independent" fabricators, General Cable and Revere Copper and Brass. American Smelting and Refining produces copper as a custom smelter from ores of small mines and scrap, and from ore processed for toll for others; hence this company furnishes only relatively small amounts of copper to its associated companies. Fabricators must rely on the large producers to furnish most of the copper requirements.

Causes of Concentration

From the beginning of the copper industry there have been relatively few companies engaged in mining and processing copper. Unquestionably, one of the major reasons for this concentration of ownership has been the scarcity of commercial deposits and their geographical concentration. The shift to open pit mining of low-grade deposits did not help matters because of the tremendous capital requirements in such undertakings. A similar situation existed outside the United States, except that the investment required is sometimes greater coupled with the complexities and uncertainty of foreign investment.

The size, nature, and capital requirements of copper processing have also worked against the entry of small firms. Entry into fabrication always has to be made with the knowledge that sources of supply of copper are going to be limited to a few producers who are also directly or indirectly in the fabricating business.

A further limiting factor of entry has been the uncertainty of the copper market—supply, demand, and price.

Conclusion

As a result of these factors contributing to concentration, the U.S. industry tends to be dominated by the Big Three—Kennecott, Anaconda, and Phelps Dodge. American Smelting and Refining continues its role in the functions found in its corporate title. The most significant changes, as noted briefly below, are in the further vertical integration of these companies.

Kennecott remains the world's largest producer of copper. Its open pit mine in Bingham, Utah is the world's largest; and the Braden, Chile operation is the largest underground mine in the world. About one-fourth of Kennecott's output comes from foreign sources, and Kennecott supplies about 40 percent of the total annual production of domestically produced ore. Kennecott until recently did no refining and very little smelting and much of the copper mined by Kennecott was processed by American Smelting and Refining; but in the 1950's Kennecott built a refinery in Utah, and acquired the world's largest smelter from American Smelting and Refining at Garfield, Utah. Thus Kennecott became fully integrated.

Anaconda, the world's second largest producer of copper, secures more than three-fourths of its production from foreign areas. It is the owner of two mines in Chile, Chuquicamata and El Salvador, and a third, Poterillos, is now closed down. The Chuquicamata open pit rivals Kennecott's Bingham operations, and besides its enormous quantity, contains ore twice as rich as Bingham's. Pressure being put on Anaconda by the government of Chile is designed to increase the output in that country and to erect refining facilities so that less of the Chilean production will be refined in the United States. Thus Anaconda which smelts, refines, and fabricates all the copper it mines will find itself with integrated facilities in Chile as well as the United States.

Phelps Dodge, the second largest producer in the United States (Anaconda ranks third in this country) also smelts, refines, and fabricates all the copper it mines and is an important purchaser of copper. Unlike Kennecott and Anaconda, Phelps Dodge believes in staying in the United States and Canada. Since 1957 Phelps Dodge has increased its exploratory efforts in order to strengthen its ore and integrated position in this country.

American Smelting and Refining's position has been, in addition to processing a portion of Kennecott's output, to handle the output of most of the independent mines, which cannot afford to make the huge investment in capital equipment needed for smelting and refining. However, American Smelting and Refining which has traditionally restricted its activities to processing ore entered into the mining field in the 1950's. It has a 57.5 percent interest in Southern Peru Copper Corporation. This Peruvian concern has extensive holdings of proven reserves of low-grade ores. Thus American Smelting and Refining is beginning to integrate backward and further the concentrated control of the U.S. Big Four copper companies.

One would think that this high degree of concentration of ownership in the copper industry would lead to administered prices and a high degree of price stability. But as we shall see, this is far from the case.

PROBLEMS AND POLICY

Contrary to normal expectations, the copper industry has a long history of price instability. In addition, the domestic industry has a new worry in that it has a post-World War II history of increased dependence on foreign sources of supply. These two problems will be the subject matter of this special problems and policy section.

Instability of Prices

The copper industry is plagued by the problem of price instability. A glance at Figure 10.5 is enough to prove the existence of this century-old problem. But if one will take just the period from 1956 to 1962 for study it can be seen that producer's prices ranged from 46¢ to 25¢ a

Figure 10.5: Spot Copper Prices at New York.

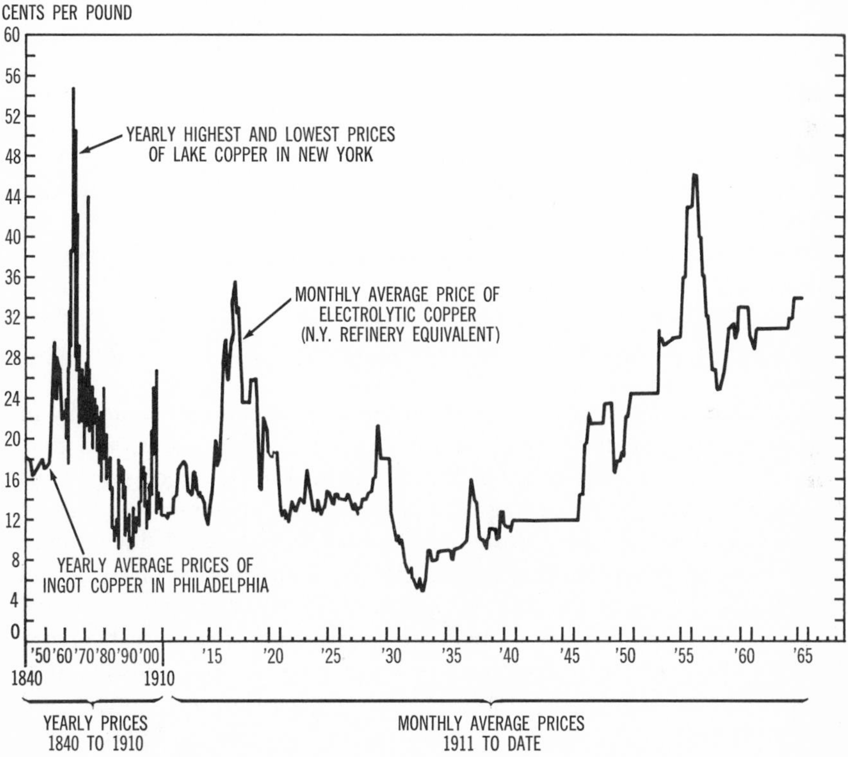
CENTS PER POUND
60
56
52
48
44
40
36
32
28
24
20
16
12
8
4
0
YEARLY HIGHEST AND LOWEST PRICES OF LAKE COPPER IN NEW YORK
MONTHLY AVERAGE PRICE OF ELECTROLYTIC COPPER (N.Y. REFINERY EQUIVALENT)
YEARLY AVERAGE PRICES OF INGOT COPPER IN PHILADELPHIA
'50 '60 '70 '80 '90 '00
1840
1910
'15
'20
'25
'30
'35
'40
'45
'50
'55
'60
'65
YEARLY PRICES 1840 TO 1910
MONTHLY AVERAGE PRICES 1911 TO DATE

SOURCE: From *Commodity Yearbook,* 1965.

pound, and during this period twenty price changes were made by producers; but a study of smelters' prices showed that over 100 price changes were made. During this same time, in the London market the price range was from 19¢ to 54½¢. Most remarkable is the flat part of Figure 10.5

during the early 1960's, for the U.S. price remained unchanged at 31¢ from May, 1961 to March, 1964. One might conclude that during this unprecedented record (except for wartime when price controls were in effect) the industry had found a solution to its perennial problem if it were not for the jump in price to 34¢ in 1964, and a prior knowledge of some of the causes of price instability in copper.

Facts Bearing on the Causes of Price Instability. The causes of price instability are many, including markets, demand and supply conditions, inventory policies, the role of the custom smelter, international interdependence, and foreign and domestic policies of government.

Markets for copper are multiple, thus facilitating wide fluctuations in prices. In the United States producers' prices are usually set by quotations of Kennecott, Phelps Dodge, and Anaconda. Custom smelters in the United States, which generally smelt and refine ore and concentrates purchased from small mines and heat scrap, are the second source of prices. The London Metal Exchange on which foreign-produced copper is sold and which is most volatile is the third source of prices. This market is of particular importance to Anaconda and Kennecott which sell their Chilean output on the basis of the London price. A foreign producer market may be dominated by two different sets of prices set by Rhodesian Selection Trust, Limited, and Union Miniere du Haut-Katanga. Still another source of prices is a kind of "quasi black market" in which copper is sold above regular quoted prices when copper is short, and fabricators cannot obtain required supplies. And finally there is a market for scrap copper based on prices paid by custom smelters and asked by metal dealers.

Demand for copper is cyclical. Consumption of copper is primarily in the production of capital goods and consumer durable goods, and purchase of both types of these goods is postponable during a recession. Thus demand is sensitive to business investment and consumer purchasing power. Consequently the industry is susceptible to cyclical fluctuations. Demand may drop as a result of the gradual accumulation of copper in many fabricated items, and scrap copper may become an important source of copper for reuse. At such a time, highly mechanized, large-scale operators must find an outlet by lowering prices. Thus primary producers, particularly during depressed periods, assume the position of marginal producers. During periods of high level of economic activity, and particularly during wartime, the primary producers must operate at peak capacity and prices will be bid up in response to the increased demand for producer and consumer durable goods. Hence fluctuating cyclical demand is a major causative factor in copper price fluctuations.

Supply of copper affects price instability through the nature and occurrence of the ore and the costs of producers. The limited occurrence of the ore in major producing areas means that anything affecting the production in any one area is going to have an impact on the world price of copper. This is in contrast to a situation where widely distributed supplies with a large number of producers, and changes in the supply in any one area have little or no effect on the total supply and resulting prices.

In addition, on the supply side the nature of copper production and the value of the end-product coupled with variations in demand bring about price instability. Copper wire, ingot bars, billets, or cathodes are too expensive to be held in inventory for a considerable period of time in anticipation of orders. However, copper can be stored in the ground. When orders for copper slow down, the policy is to restrict operations or to close the mine. Reopening the mine is expensive and will be done only when market conditions justify it. In the interim, there is a time lag of fifteen to twenty weeks between starting operations and delivery of finished copper to the purchaser. In the meantime a shortage may develop; to overcome it the mine is run at capacity operations and inventories may build up while prices weaken. Then the cycle may begin to repeat itself.

Finally, on the supply side the cost structure of mining has had important effects on industry operations, prices, and structure. It has been conclusively proven that large-scale, mechanized mining by both strip and block-caving techniques is most efficient in the copper industry. But this type of mining requires tremendous capital investment. Mining tends to be carried on and copper produced in order to reduce fixed charges. When labor as a variable cost was more important it was easier to shut down a mine during depressed periods by laying off excess manpower with no financial obligations. However, the mechanized mine continues to incur depreciation charges even when equipment is idle. Thus, higher fixed costs give an added incentive to continue production and to lower unit fixed costs; and as a result price cutting is used to increase sales. An important corollary of the industry's instability and the cost structure following mechanization, has been the gradual elimination of small-scale enterprise and thus further concentration of ownership.

Inventory policies of consumers effect short-term fluctuations in copper prices in addition to the basic demand and supply factors mentioned above. Consumers tend to accumulate stocks in periods of expected shortages and deplete them when industry supplies are adequate. This tendency to over-buy and underbuy intensifies price movements.

The *custom smelter* which processes virgin and scrap copper is another contributing factor to price instability. The nature of the smelting operation is that continuous operations are required twenty-four hours a day and seven days a week. Thus to insure a constant supply of copper to feed its furnaces, the smelting company buys at prevailing price for resale after three months, the time required to run a batch through. As a hedge the smelter balances inflow with outflow by selling each day as much copper as it buys. At the first sign of decline in sales, the smelter cuts the selling price to attract buyers. This is looked upon as evidence of a decline in the level of copper prices; so the buyers withhold orders, accelerating the downward spiral.

Interdependence of the Free World, as previously noted, adds volatility, over and above cyclical changes, to supply-demand relationships and price. For example, any factor interrupting Chilean production would affect the supply of copper in both the United States and Europe and cause an increase in price in London and an upward push on U.S. prices. Political unrest in Africa, resulting in a temporary closing of copper mines would have a similar effect in the European markets. Conversely, a decrease in economic activity in one large consuming area might exert downward pressure on prices in a different area, despite no change in demand there.

Government policies, both foreign and domestic, are likely to lead to a final cause of price instability. A case in point is a Chilean government that insists that Anaconda and Kennecott raise copper prices since copper is responsible for more than 60 percent of Chile's foreign exchange reserves; and under local law, Chile, if it so decided, could dictate the price for its domestic copper. Or the Chilean government could back the demands of labor (contracts expire every fifteen months), which had submitted demands for wage increases as high as 100 percent, but generally had to accept much less.

Domestic policies in the United States may also contribute to copper price instability. The United States as a buyer of copper for defense and stockpile needs, has often jumped into the market at times of a high level of demand and causing a rapid increase in prices when a more orderly buying program would have interfered less with the market. Similarly, the mere suggestion that the United States might sell part of the stockpile has led to a fall in prices. Late in 1964 *The Wall Street Journal* carried the headline: "Copper Prices Fall After Mansfield Urges U.S. Release 50,000 Tons From Stockpile." The *Journal* followed this with a story that Senate Majority Leader Mike Mansfield had proposed the move to help stabilize prices. In the London Market, after the announcement of Senator Mansfield's proposal had been made, the price of copper dropped in unofficial dealings to 53⅛¢ a pound, off 3⅛¢. This was said by traders to be the largest drop that they could recall for one day's market.

Thus both foreign and domestic governments bring about price instability when it should be in their best interest to promote stability, and further, they do it sometimes even in the name of stability.

Policy and Programs to Promote Price Stability. Many attempts have been made to stabilize prices, and the whole history of the copper industry is replete with illustrations of how the leading copper producers have entered into cartels for the alleged purpose of stabilizing the price of copper. However, in the discussion which follows only the more recent attempts at price stabilization will be discussed. Many attempts have been made to stabilize the price, but except during wartime no cartel or government has been successful in its attempt for a period of more than two or three years.

The United States Copper Export Association was organized in 1918 immediately after the passage of the Webb-Pomerene Export Act. This act exempted the export activities of U.S. business interests from certain limitations of the antitrust laws provided that their activities abroad did not *artificially* or *willfully* enhance or depress domestic (United States) prices.

World War I greatly stimulated copper production. When the armistice suddenly cut off the war demand, huge supplies accumulated for which there was no market in sight at prices the industry was willing to accept. Even though very low prices might have stimulated consumption and would have certainly discouraged production, the industry did not choose to follow this plan. Therefore, the U.S. Copper Export Association was organized under the Webb-Pomerene law to reduce competition in the export business.

The plan was for the association to purchase copper from members on the basis of "export capacity" which was in turn used for the purpose of assigning quotas to fill export orders taken by the association. The association determined the price to be paid to members and fixed the price for export. The announced purpose of the association was to dispose of stocks held by members, by participating nonmembers, who agreed to sell for export through the association, and by the United States Government. An attempt was made to obtain participation of the British and French Governments in disposing of their wartime stocks, but they preferred to hold their stocks and consume them gradually.[1]

After operating for some time with rather indifferent results, the Association, which controlled about 85 percent of production in 1921, organized a large export pool to purchase stocks of copper from its members and sell them abroad at higher prices. The last copper was sold by the pool in 1923, and while the stocks were disposed of at some profit the experiment was costly, for it was bought at the expense of output and reduced control over export trade. Outside interests managed to raise their share of exports to almost half the total. In addition, the association failed in its attempt to stabilize world copper prices because higher prices stimulated production from new mines discovered in Northern Rhodesia and Canada. Africa, Canada, and South America were all forging ahead in copper and the United States began to lose its grip on the world market. In 1924 the U.S. Copper Export Association met its demise, and U.S. companies led a concerted drive into foreign producing areas.

[1] Federal Trade Commission, *Report on the Copper Industry*, Washington, D.C., 1947, p. 12.

Copper Exporters, Incorporated was formed in 1926. Immediately after the Copper Export Association became inactive, negotiations looking toward the resumption of price control efforts on a broader international basis began. This organization included foreign as well as U.S. companies, and as a result the amount of world copper controlled by the cartel reached 86 percent as compared with 68 percent under the old association. Whereas the old association acted as a sales agency for members and participating nonmembers on a quota basis, the new corporation merely fixed prices and quotas, leaving the actual selling to the individual firms.

Prices rose rapidly as a result of the cartel during the business boom, and they were maintained after the 1929 crash. Again U.S. producers came out on the short end, for they had to curtail production while both foreign associate producers and domestic nonmember producers gained from a larger output at pegged prices.

The Federal Trade Commission investigated the activities of the cartel and the Copper Institute, a trade association and statistical clearing house, to determine whether the cartel had "artificially or willfully" affected the domestic copper market. Before the formal recommendation was handed down, the depression brought on a collapse of the copper market.

With the depression, U.S. firms could not sell their copper at high prices, and this, together with scrap that was thrown on the market, broke the domestic market. In the meantime, foreign producers continued to benefit for a short period from increased production and higher prices. Of particular importance were the accelerated deliveries from the discovery of an immense copper-bearing district in Northern Rhodesia in 1927, and the development at about the same time of the Noranda, Frood (International Nickel), and Hudson Bay mines in Canada. For nearly eighty years prior to this time the United States had dominated the world copper industry, but these new mines radically changed the position of the United States and the world copper industry. Not only were these mines large but they were also low-cost producers because of their relatively high-grade ores. In the case of the three Canadian mines, which have complex ores, the development of the selective flotation process made possible the recovery of important quantities of other metals.

The International Copper Cartel was entered into in 1936 by foreign producers in order to restrict their supplies, which were in excess of what could be sold outside the U.S. market. Foreign subsidiaries of Anaconda, Phelps Dodge, and Kennecott participated. The cartel set up an elaborate regulation scheme, including a set of variable production quotas, rules for common trade practices, and a bureau for the exchange of information. Thus, although U.S. firms were not direct participants, a definite *esprit de corps* bound most of the copper producers of the world.

This cartel, like the previous one, was too ambitious; it drove the price too high, and finding that the market would bear it, threw aside their production quotas. Demand was rapidly satisfied, and the price collapsed. Before the cartel could recoup, World War II started, and the cartel was dissolved after prices fell to 10.10¢ a pound in 1939.

World War II brought the copper industry in the United States under complete control. Prices were stabilized under wartime controls at 11.87¢ from 1941 until price controls were removed on November 10, 1946. All copper production was allocated to priority defense uses under the Controlled Materials Plan. Since the 11.87¢ represented a ceiling on prices that would retard the discovery and development of additional domestic mining sources, the two price or premium price plan referred to in Chapter 8 was put into effect. Premiums above ceiling prices were paid for output in excess of quotas based on "normal" production. During the program, premiums were paid on 20 percent of the copper produced domestically. This two price plan was a reasonably successful program for wartime use, but its use is most effective in stimulating production from known reserves when it is desirable in an emergency period to retain ceiling prices and to avoid the general increase in the price of the commodity that would be necessary to induce the additional production.

Once the ceiling prices were removed on copper, the price jumped from 11.87¢ on November 10, 1946 to 19.37¢ by the end of the year. By once again observing Figure 10.5, one will note the instability of copper prices returned to the prewar pattern with a continued rise to about 24¢, then a fall to 17¢ during the recession of 1949 and then a rise again at the beginning of the Korean War.

The Korean War in the middle of 1950 caused a sudden increase in the demand for copper and an increase in copper prices. The manner in which controls were administered during the Korean emergency is described as follows by the U.S. Bureau of Mines.

Ceiling prices for copper were established by the General Ceiling Price Regulation issued by the Economic Stabilization Agency and effective January 26, 1951. This order set maximum prices at not to exceed the highest prices received by individual producers between December 19, 1950, and January 25, 1951, inclusive. Most primary producers were selling electrolytic copper, delivered Connecticut Valley, at 24½ cents a pound, and that price became the ceiling for those producers. Some other companies, representing a relatively small aggregate tonnage, sold for substantially higher prices during the period selected, and these higher prices became their ceilings.

Foreign countries, like the United States, had mobilization plans calling for increased quantities of copper, and world consumption in 1951 was rising. Efforts of all countries to obtain supplies of metal led to increasing world prices and to speculation, causing further price increases. Rumors had it that prices up to 60 cents a pound were paid for copper on the European continent, while United States prices were frozen substantially at 24½ cents.

The situation led to an agreement between the United States and the Chilean Government in May 1951 providing for payment of an additional 3 cents over the United States ceiling for Chilean copper sold in the United States. A little later the Office of Price Stabilization permitted all copper refined in the United States from imported materials to be paid for on the basis of 27½ cents a pound.

Another factor that tended to confuse the price situation was action of the Defense Materials Production Agency to avoid loss of production from mines that faced closing because of rising costs. Maintenance-of-production contracts based on production costs of the mines involved were entered into with these companies; thus additional sets of prices were established.

Prices in foreign countries continued above those for foreign copper sold in the United States (27½ cents), and Chile became dissatisfied with the foregoing arrangement. The outcome was abrogation, in May 1952, of its agreement with the United States.

On May 21, 1952, the Office of Defense Mobilization authorized importers to pay higher prices for imported copper and to pass 80 percent of increased costs on to users. Early in June it was decided that the increases were to be calculated using 24½ instead of 27½ cents as a base. In an effort to distribute the effects of these price ceilings fairly among consumers, the National Production Administration began to allocate domestic copper production and foreign entitlements to all users on an approximate 60–40 percent basis instead of just allocating copper. As a result of this move, some domestic consumers whose domestic copper-producing affiliates usually supplied ample copper had to sell some of their production to competing companies and to buy some foreign metal or to decrease consumption. Domestic fabricating affiliates of American mining companies producing in Chile, on the other hand, since May 1951 had been absorbing the 3-cent differential in costs between 24½ and 27½ cents but during that time were not receiving the higher prices permitted for their Chilean-produced metal. They continued to receive only 24½ cents for their output until July 1952 when they, with all other fabricators, were permitted to pass on to consumers 80 percent of increased costs over 24½ cents.

The improved supply-requirements relationship resulted in abandonment of price controls on copper and copper products in February 1953; and by the end of April domestic and foreign prices, except Chilean, were close together at about 30 cents a pound; the price for the Chilean outputs of the three large American mines was held, under Chilean Government direction, at 35½ cents a pound in Chile (about 36½ cents in the United States) until December 1953.[2]

In addition and supplementary to these price controls, in 1951 the Defense Production Administration reinstituted the Controlled Material Plan, used effectively in World War II, for distributing fabricated products made from copper. Copper raw materials were placed under complete allocation control, effective August 1, 1951. Copper was placed under international allocation; and quotas for the Free World were established

[2] Helena Meyers, "Copper," in *Mineral Facts and Problems,* Bureau of Mines Bulletin 556, Washington, D.C., 1956, p. 242.

by the International Materials Conference beginning with the fourth quarter of 1951. The member countries voluntarily accepted restrictions upon quantities to be consumed and agreed not to dispose of copper to countries in the Soviet bloc.

With the abandonment of price controls on copper and copper products in February, 1953, the stage was set for the return to normalcy of price instability in the copper industry. The post-Korean period was followed by the period of dramatic fluctuations of prices, which was described in the opening paragraph of this section on instability of prices, and which lasted until May, 1961.

From May, 1961 to March, 1964 the price of copper in the United States remained unchanged at 31¢ without the aid of a formal cartel agreement or wartime emergency controls. Similarly through the end of 1963, the price of copper on the London Metal Exchange held steady at 29¼¢ a pound (which due to the United States duty of 1.7¢ per pound is equal to 31¢ in New York). This long-term stability of copper prices was brought about by an exercise of so-called "business statesmanship." Most remarkable about this period was that it was characterized by a protracted period of excess capacity, and consumption that was not rising as fast as the industry desired.

Business statesmanship to achieve price stability was begun in mid-1961 when African producers started curtailing production and holding supplies off the market; they continued this process and later persuaded the major U.S. producers to do the same. In addition, the African producers became heavy buyers on the London Metal Exchange and in the process acquired as much as 300,000 tons of surplus stock. The process led to a firming-up of the highly volatile London Metal Exchange, and was of immediate importance to Anaconda and Kennecott which sell the Chilean output on the basis of the London price. Additional stability was achieved as foreign producers sold copper overseas at a fixed price instead of basing prices on the volatile London Metal Exchange quotation, which in turn helped firm up the Exchange.

The principal motive on the part of producers to stabilize copper prices was purely self-interest; stable prices tend to make any commodity more attractive to consumers, and to discourage the use of substitutes. Prior to the period of stabilization, fluctuating copper prices had had the opposite effect. For example, a study comparing the pre-Korean and post-Korean War use of copper and aluminum showed some of the following changes in major groups: Power transmission equipment, copper rose 92 percent and aluminum 310 percent; radio and radio products, copper rose 74 percent and aluminum 261 percent; engine electrical equipment, copper rose 32 percent and aluminum 556 percent; metal stampings, copper dropped 27 percent while aluminum rose 25 percent; telephone and telegraph equipment, copper dropped 11 percent while aluminum rose 170 percent; and in the grand total for all industrial groups copper dropped 14 percent as aluminum rose 103 percent.

The change to stable prices for copper was constructive so far as markets were concerned. During the period, copper companies began showing more marketing vigor, and the International Copper Development Association was begun with the major objective of developing new markets for the metal. As a result, by the beginning of 1964 inventories had melted away, copper for future delivery was selling way above the spot price, and demand clearly exceeded supply. Stabilization came under mounting pressure.

The upside pressures on prices became so great that in March, 1964, the New York price quotation was grudgingly increased by a penny to 32¢ where it held until the first week in August when Anaconda and Kennecott raised the price at which they sold abroad to 34¢. Meanwhile the lid was off the London Metal Exchange where prices had spiraled to over 47¢. In addition, on the domestic scene custom smelters had increased their price to attract scrap to the market, and some metal dealers had sold copper at 41½¢ as early as May, 1964 compared with the 32¢ producer price. Thus came to the end the period of long price stability under business statesmanship.

Barron's National Business and Financial Weekly felt that the stabilization program had been a failure both from the foreign and the domestic point of view.[3] This may be too harsh a judgment, but the program did ultimately result in certain unfortunate developments.

On the foreign side the thought was expressed that a ceiling on prices had served to deprive the hard-pressed Chilean government of badly needed revenue. As a result, Chile had lost millions in foreign exchange (each cent a pound brings in an additional 7 million dollars annually), and thus Chile had "been handed still another stick with which to beat the damn Yanquis." It is true that the Minister of Mines in Chile had been asking for an increase of 3¢ a pound for Chilean copper. But it is also true that African producers were making a determined effort to hold the price, and a delegation from the Rhodesian Selection Trust and the Anglo-American Corporation of South Africa, both of Northern Rhodesia, and from Union-Miniere went to Santiago, Chile to try to impress upon the government the continued need for a policy of business statesmanship in copper price stability.

On the domestic front there were important consequences of the policy of stabilization which developed during the latter phases of the period.

The reassuring presence of the huge African stockpile encouraged copper users to keep their inventories low. With price held down, demand began to increase at unanticipated rates. (In 1964 forecasts, producers

[3] "Bad Week for Tinkers, The Artificial Lid on the Copper Price," *Barron's National Business and Financial Weekly*, August 17, 1946, p. 1.

had estimated a modest 3 to 4 percent advance in consumption which turned out to be only one-third of the gain in the first six months). With supply of copper limited, producers were compelled to ration output to strike an even rough balance between supply and demand. Rationing of copper was made only to old customers on the basis of prior business done in 1963.

As a result of the lack of availability of copper, a black or free market was created. Any new customers for copper, and any old customers whose demands were rising, had to find supplies in this unofficial market. Hence the industries whose needs for raw materials were expanding were forced to pay 10 to 15¢ a pound above producers' prices. This system gave unearned profits to some and penalized others. In fact it very well may have strangled the growth in copper consumption, and growth was what the business statesmanship price policy was trying to create.

Conclusions. The conclusion can be drawn that attempts at price stabilization have been remarkably unsuccessful, with certain exceptions during war periods. *Barron's* concluded that the last attempt at stabilization while masquerading as a piece of business statesmanship had undermined the prestige of a relatively friendly government of Chile and instead of yielding precious stability, it had disrupted the customary channels of trade, encouraged hoarding and profiteering, and led to price chaos. The point was made that a decade before nobody knew the score better than the industry. "Free operation of the laws of supply and demand," two leading Rhodesian producers were quoted as saying at the time, "is the safest, surest and most effective means of determining the price of copper." *Barron's* concluded that the last few years had shown they were right.[4]

Even though one agrees with the statement about the laws of supply and demand, it may be that *Barron's* conclusions about the policy of business statesmanship are much too harsh. Perhaps we are about to throw out the baby with the bath water that became fouled in the latter phases of the stabilization program. The baby was the realization that copper had to be competitively priced. This realization has been impressed upon African and U.S. producers and it may be in time that the Chilean government will see the wisdom of having copper competitively priced and not insist on unwarranted price increases. And it also may be that the U.S. government and officials can be persuaded that in the cause of copper price stability our policy statements and actions should be such that they will help generate stability rather than create instability.

International Interdependence for Copper

The President's Materials Policy Commission concluded its study of copper by stating: "It is clear that the principal future problem in copper

[4] *Ibid.*

will be maintaining production in the United States and increasing production abroad. Maintenance of domestic production is geared almost entirely to successful discovery of new deposits to replace the old as they are depleted."[5]

Facts Bearing on the Problem. Sufficient data have been presented within the body of this chapter to show the international interdependence on copper. We know that the United States in the 1960's was both the world's largest producing and consuming nation, accounting for about 29 percent of Free World mine output and about 33 percent of consumption. We know further that the United States is a net importer of copper and that the U.S. Bureau of Mines has concluded that: "Projecting the future demand in relation to population increase and per capita consumption and mine production capacities the United States will continue to be dependent on foreign sources for a sizable portion of its domestic requirements." The President's Material Policy Commission tried to project our dependence on copper and relationship to the Free World as shown in Figure 10.6. This chart obviously underestimates U.S. production at present and may underestimate demand, especially outside the United States; nevertheless it is presented so as to give an idea of the order of magnitude of the problem. Further it is interesting to note that the Commission, and other studies since then, have concluded that there are adequate reserves outside the United States to meet the demands that will be put upon them.

The facts lead us to conclude then that the United States problem of interdependence falls into: (1) increasing domestic discoveries and production, and (2) insuring an adequate supply of copper imports from increased foreign production.

The domestic problem of finding new sources of ore is a difficult one since virtually all the known occurrences of copper mineralization in this country have been explored. It appears that any significant expansion of productive capacity in this country will have to depend on entirely new discoveries; not discoveries of just single deposits or mines but of whole new districts. Such discoveries will entail the geological mapping of large areas of the country, intensive prospecting of those areas, testing the indicated deposits to determine whether they are commercial, and developing those that prove to be commercial. The success of such endeavors depends largely on the development of geological techniques which can be used economically to find and prove ore bodies buried without surface indications. For this reason the Materials Policy Commission recommended that the U.S. government strengthen its program for gathering and analyzing basic facts about minerals, that industry groups undertake an integrated and complementary program, and that a complete census of mineral industries be taken every five years. To encourage replacement of depleted

[5] *Resources for Freedom, Vol. II, The Outlook for Key Commodities,* Washington, D.C., June, 1952, p. 37.

copper reserves, the United States offers a depletion allowance of 15 percent on domestic and foreign production.

Figure 10.6: Copper Position of the United States and the Free World.

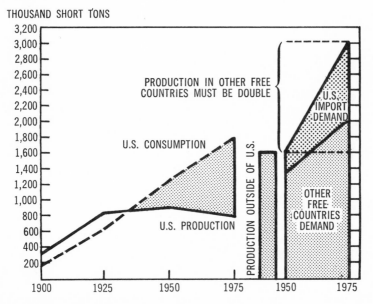

Source: President's Materials Policy Commission.

During the Korean War, as previously noted, under the Defense Production Act of 1950 the United States granted exploration loans; underwrote the government output of certain mines through government contracts at 22 to 25½¢ a pound, plus escalation for certain increases in cost; and gave fast tax write-offs. The effect of this policy on expanded capacity after 1955 is shown in Table 10.8 in summary, and in detailed enumeration of the mines. Due to the length of the development period of the mines, the result of the domestic expansion of capacity was not felt until 1956. The Office of Defense Mobilization "closed" the expansion goal for copper in September, 1956.

The reasonable success of this program in the light of pessimistic opinions about copper reserves in this country suggests that it might be used again in a national emergency. But the delay in achieving the expansion of output also indicates the necessity of maintaining an adequate National Stockpile of copper for conventional and nuclear war in the event that imports of copper are shut off. It also suggests the importance of copper scrap as a secondary source of supply.

Price stabilization policies of copper producers also affect the avail-

TABLE 10.8
Estimated Free World Copper Capacity, 1955 to 1962

(thousands of short tons)

	U.S.A.		Outside U.S.A.		Total	
	Tons	Increase Over 1955	Tons	Increase Over 1955	Tons	Increase Over 1955
1955	1,014	—	1,997	—	3,011	—
1956	1,130	116	2,183	186	3,313	302
1957	1,190	176	2,315	318	3,505	494
1958	1,226	212	2,391	394	3,617	606
1959	1,237	223	2,444	447	3,681	670
1960	1,244	230	2,578	581	3,822	811
1961	1,278	264	2,652	655	3,930	919
1962	1,278	264	2,666	669	3,944	933

Copper Mine Expansion

	Expansion	Annual full capacity		Expansion	Annual full capacity
United States:			1960		
			Anaconda (Mont.)	7	1,244
1955		1,014			
			1961		
1956		1,130	Anaconda (Mont.)	34	1,278
			1962		1,278
1957	60	1,190			
San Manuel			Outside United States:		
(pre-1957 equaled 50)	20				
Berkeley	17		1955		1,968
Pima (pre-1957–3)	15				
White Pine	5		1956		2,183
Inspiration	3				
			1957	132	2,315
1958	36	1,226	Canada:		
Berkeley (1958–29)	4		Gaspe (pre-1957–30)	6	
White Pine	5		Geco (start)	10	
Ray	20		Heath Steele	3	
Inspiration	7		Tilt Cove		
			(start)	7	
1959	11	1,237	Chile:		
Inspiration	8		Chuquicamata		
Anaconda (Mont.)	3		(pre-1957–25)	25	

TABLE 10.8 (Continued)

Copper Mine Expansion

	Expansion	Annual full capacity		Expansion	Annual full capacity
La Africana	4		Canada:	6	
Ireland: Avoco			Gullbridge	3	
(start)	4		Brunswick		
Israel: King			No. Rhodesia:		
Solomon	7		Bancroft	24	
Nicaragua:			Fr. W. Africa:		
Rosita (start)	1		Mauritania		
Philippines:			(completed, 22)	11	
Atlas (pre-			So. Rhodesia:		
1957–18)	12		Molly	9	
Sipalay	9		1960	134	2,578
Cobapa	1		Chile:		
No. Rhodesia:			El Salvador		
Chibuluma			(completed, 100)	100	
(pre-1957–12)	6		Potrerillos		
Bancroft (start)	24		(minus)	–50	
Kansanshi	5		Peru: Toquepala		
Kenya, Ma-			(start)	60	
calder, Nyanza	2		No. Rhodesia:		
Uganda: Kilembe			Bancroft		
(pre-1957–4)	6		(completed, 96)	24	
1958	76	2,391	1961	74	2,652
Canada:			Peru: Toquepala		
Greco	8		(completed, 120)	60	
Tilt Cove	10		Yugoslavia:		
Others	10		Majdenpek	14	
Ireland: Avoca			1962	14	2,666
(completed at 13)	9		Yugoslavia:		
Nicaragua: Rosita			Majdenpek		
(completed, 5)	4		(completed, 28)	14	
No. Rhodesia:					
Bancroft	24				
Fr. W. Africa			Note: Cuajone and Quellaveco		
Mauritania			are scheduled to come into produc-		
(start)	11		tion after 1962.		
1959	53	2,444			

SOURCES: American Bureau of Metal Statistics; Copper & Brass Research Association estimates, based on first 10 months ABMS reports; *Mining Congress Journal*, Annual Review, 1957; *Engineering and Mining Journal*, February, 1957. Olin T. Mouzon, *International Resources and National Policies*, New York, Harper & Row, 1959.

ability of domestic supplies. At the very time when major producers were attempting to hold the line on price increases, some domestic producers were complaining that the then current prices they were receiving provided an inadequate return on their investment, particularly in view of the depleting nature of the industry. The answer here is that stabilization moves by major producers should not attempt to preclude price movements altogether, and that a gradual rising price to offset increases in wages and other costs will be necessary. Of course, copper prices cannot advance much faster than do those of competing materials, but prices must be sufficient to allow medium and high-cost mines to operate profitably, and thus provide needed supplies. Copper pricing as related to domestic production poses something of a dilemma because consumption must be sufficient to insure a high rate of production. Copper costs are somewhat different from other minerals because most of the cost is incurred in mining rather than processing. Thus a high rate of production is needed in the low-grade ore mines to spread fixed costs over sufficient units. Thus prices must be low enough to encourage an increasing consumption with its implications for capacity production, lower costs, and profit margins equivalent to those in a price increase.

The hope is that high profit margins will generate sufficient funds to permit aggressive search and development of domestic copper reserves without need for a renewal of government subsidies to the industry.

Foreign sources of copper, as we have already concluded, are going to be necessary to supplement domestic ore and scrap. In addition, we have noted that development of new deposits and planned expansion in existing mines on the part of U.S. companies will be required to help insure reliable sources of copper. Since there appear to be adequate reserves in the areas which interest U.S. companies, the obstacles to large-scale expansion in these countries fall into two categories. First, there are physical obstacles such as shortages of fuel, power, transportation, and labor. Second, there are man-made obstacles such as governmental policies on taxes, exchange rates, foreign investment, capital transfers, labor, and expropriation. The physical obstacles raise the costs chargeable to increased production and thereby increase the capital risk involved. The man-made obstacles, which are much more serious, lower the expected profits or increase the capital risk.

Although there are limits to what U.S. policy can do, it certainly should be designed to help overcome the man-made obstacles which in large measure are the result of the policy of foreign governments. As a minimum the following three are recommended: price stabilization, investment protection, and the removal of the U.S. tariff on copper.

A flexible price stabilization policy of the type recommended would certainly help both foreign and domestic producers. There are dangers in such arrangements, but there are definite advantages. However, there is no danger in the repetition of the recommendation that the U.S. government should give greater attention to long-term price stabilization whenever it enters into a copper transaction. In addition, there is no danger in a concerted effort, such as was undertaken by the African producers, to convince the Chilean government that price stabilization can, if properly achieved, benefit all concerned.

Problems of investment protection and the development of a more favorable framework for expansion abroad, and policy recommendations were covered in detail in Chapter 8 in the section on private investment.

The nature of the tariff on copper has been studied in detail. The United States reductions in this tariff have been moves in the right direction. However, it does appear in view of our sustained and future import needs for copper that this tariff should be abolished and that the domestic industry should be protected when necessary by more direct methods. These might be less costly to the consumer, improve copper's competitive position, and prove beneficial to both domestic and foreign producers.

Conclusions. A continuing problem of the domestic copper industry is the finding and developing of new reserves, but it is certain that this effort will have to be supplemented by a continued reliance on imports to sustain the United States consumption. To overcome the obstacles of depletion of resources and substitution, the domestic copper producers must strive constantly to devise lower-cost and more efficient methods of finding and evaluating copper deposits, methods and equipment for the economical mining of low grade materials, and improved extraction processes that will reduce costs and increase recovery of copper and any by-products. Our national policies should be directed to facilitate the importation of copper and to assure sources of production from a variety of sources in the Free World outside the United States, with special emphasis on the Western Hemisphere.

SUMMARY

Copper is the most important nonferrous metal. The reserves are highly concentrated in geographic location and ownership. Increased U.S. consumption of copper has been brought about because of its use for electrical purposes and in recent years has been made possible by the increased use of scrap and imported copper. The consumption patterns for the future are that copper will be put to those uses for which it is best suited and aluminum and other substitutes will continue to take over many markets formerly supplied by copper. The United States will become increasingly dependent on domestic scrap and imported copper. Recommended policy measures are those which will assure foreign sources of production and facilitate imports of copper. At the same time it must be remembered that copper is a vital necessity for peacetime strength and military security. Therefore, security measures necessary to protect the domestic industry and provide for a stockpile are absolutely essential as a part of our national policy.

SELECTED REFERENCES

"Bad Week for Tinkers, The Artificial Lid on the Copper Price," *Barron's National Business and Financial Weekly*, August 17, 1964, p. 1.

Federal Trade Commission, *Report on the Copper Industry*, Washington, D.C., 1947.

Harris, Herbert, "Copper; Less Pinch in 56," *Nation's Business*, July, 1955, pp. 58–61.

McMahon, A. D., "Copper," in *Mineral Facts and Problems*, Bureau of Mines Bulletin 585, Washington, D.C., 1960, pp. 235–259.

Metals—Copper—Basic Analysis, Standard & Poor's Industry Surveys, New York, Standard & Poor, pp. m98–m115, 1963, and later issues.

Meyer, Helena, "Copper," in *Mineral Facts and Problems*, Bureau of Mines Bulletin 556, Washington, D.C., 1956, pp. 219–245.

"Price Stability Sought in Copper," *The New York Times*, May 17, 1964, Section 3, pp. 1 ff.

Stocking, George W., and Myron W. Watkins, *Cartels in Action*, New York, Twentieth Century Fund, 1946.

U.S. Congress, Temporary National Economic Committee, *Investigation of Concentration of Economic Power*, Hearings; Part 25, *Cartels*, Washington, D.C., 1940, pp. 13,037–33,583.

U.S. Department of Commerce, "Copper," *Quarterly Industry Report*, Washington, D.C., January, 1965, and later issues.

Wideman, F. L., "Copper," Preprint for U.S. Bureau of Mines *Minerals Yearbook 1963*, Washington, D.C., 1964.

11

ALUMINUM

Students of energy and material predicted in the 1930's that the phase of history of the harnessing of fossil fuels by heavy metals was rapidly drawing to a close, and was being replaced by a new stage which would be characterized by continuous energy sources harnessed by light metals. As this predicted stage was dawning a new energy era exploded. The forecast was correct for the light metals. Copper has been described as "the oldest modern metal." Aluminum is not the newest modern metal, but its history is relatively short, beginning with the discovery of the electrolytic process for production of the metal in 1886 by Charles Martin Hall in the United States and independently by Paul L. T. Heroult in France. Its success has been dramatic. Today, aluminum is the leading nonferrous metal in terms of tonnage and second only to copper in value.

Aluminum's tremendous growth of 10 percent per year in capacity, production, and consumption has stemmed from the metal's virtues of lightness, and its resistance to corrosion, high heat, and electric conductivity. Another virtue is its continuing favorable price relationship to competitive, nonferrous metals. As early as 1955 the United States was producing aluminum at a rate of more than 1,500,000 tons a year. This was almost ten times the level of 1939 and about double the actual output either at the World War II peak or as recently as five years earlier in 1950. One would expect this rate of growth to slow down, and it has; but by 1965 production was about 2,500,000 tons.

PRODUCTION OF ALUMINUM

The major steps involved in the production of aluminum are three-fold: (1) mining of bauxite, the principal ore; (2) removal of nonaluminous materials from the ore, and consequent production of alumina (aluminum oxide), a whitish powder; and (3) electrolytic reduction of alumina to metallic aluminum. In addition, there are two other functions of the aluminum industry: (4) fabricating aluminum pig and ingot into semifinished and finished aluminum; and (5) manufacturing end products.

Aluminum is the most abundant metallic element in the crust of the earth. Nevertheless it is relatively scarce because of its affinity for oxygen, and the silica content of the reserves. Thus its use as a resource depends on technology and economic feasibility. At present the principal reserves of aluminum are bauxite. Bauxite, a claylike mineral low in silica and high in alumina, was discovered in 1821 near the village of Les Baux in southern France. The word *bauxite* does not designate a specific mineral, but is a general term for a rock or a mixture of minerals with sufficient high alumina content to be useful as an ore of aluminum. Bauxite, an ore containing hydrated aluminum oxide minerals such as gibbsite, boehmite, or diaspore, is formed by weathering processes acting on alumina-bearing rocks. The largest deposits occur in tropical or subtropical climates and are at or near the surface.

There are three types of bauxite. The Surinam or trihydrate type is mainly gibbsite and usually contains 50 percent or more alumina, 2 to 15 percent silica, and 15 percent iron oxide. The European type is composed of boehmite or disaspore. A typical European type ore analyzes 55 percent alumina, 4 percent silica, and 10 to 20 percent iron oxide. The Jamaica, or mixed type, is a mixture of monohydrate and trihydrate minerals. It contains about 50 percent alumina, 1 to 2 percent silica, and 20 to 30 percent iron oxide.

Reserves and Mining

Reserves. The world's reserves of bauxite are estimated at 5.2 billion tons. The reserve is sufficient to last over 160 years at the 1963 rate of production. The U.S. bauxite reserve totalling 50 million tons and averaging 50 percent alumina and 10 percent silica, is 97 percent in Arkansas and 3 percent in Georgia and Alabama. The U.S. Bureau of Mines estimates that there are potential bauxite reserves in the United States in the order of 350 million tons. These potential reserves are essentially bauxite and bauxitic clays that typically analyze 32 to 45 percent alumina. Included in these reserves are bauxitic clays and bauxitic laterites. The resource of bauxitic clays, associated with the bauxite reserves in Arkansas, is estimated at 140 million tons with an average analysis of more than 35 percent alumina. Large deposits of bauxitic laterite in Oregon contain 35 percent alumina, less than 10 percent silica, and about 30 percent iron oxide. The estimated world reserves of bauxite are given in Table 11.1 together with the 1963 rate of production.

In spite of these potential reserves, the fact remains that the United

States contains less than one percent of the world reserves of bauxite. In addition, the only known bauxite deposits occur in two districts in the United States: (1) central Arkansas, and (2) the southeastern part of the country in two areas: (a) the coastal plain in Georgia, Alabama, and Mississippi and (b) the Appalachian Valley in Georgia, Alabama, Tennessee, and Virginia. The Arkansas deposits, which as previously noted, contain 97 percent of the U.S. total are contained in about 275 square miles in Saline and Pulaski counties extending about twenty-five miles southwestward from Little Rock.

TABLE 11.1
World Reserves and Mine Production of Bauxite
(Thousands of long tons)

	Reserves		Production
	Quantity	Grade, % A1203	1963
United States	50,000	50	1,525
Australia	2,000,000	50	100
British Guiana	80,000	58	2,800
France	70,000	58	2,200
Jamaica	550,000	50	7,730
Surinam	200,000	58	3,330
Other Free World	1,850,000	55	7,460
Sino-Soviet Bloc	420,000	50	6,180
World Total	5,220,000		31,345

SOURCE: Data from U.S. Bureau of Mines.

Mining. Most bauxite in the United States, about 80 percent, is mined in open pits, and the remainder is mined by underground methods, in which variations of the room-and-pillar technique are employed. Open pit mining may require stripping an overburden several times the thickness of the ore body; but mining recovery is greater than from underground mines. In Arkansas, stripping is done by means of draglines, shovels, and carry-alls. Stripping ratios as much as 10 feet of overburden to 1 foot of ore are used and a ratio of 15 to 1 is considered feasible. Several pits in Arkansas have been mined to depths of more than 100 feet, and about 200 feet is estimated to be the present economic limit for large ore bodies. Bauxite deposits in Jamaica lie at the surface, and stripping is limited to vegetation and topsoil. In Surinam, as much as 80 feet is stripped by draglines, hydraulic giants, or dredges.

The ore as mined is called crude, green, wet, or undried bauxite. The bauxite ore comes out of the mine in chunks of various sizes mixed with gangue (worthless matter). As large a portion as possible of the valueless materials is removed by washing and screening. The ore is crushed and treated by drying in cylindrical kilns at 200° to 250°F to drive off moisture and reduce the shipping weight. The percentage by weight of free moisture in undried bauxite varies from 5 percent to 25 percent and averages 15 percent for domestic ores. Only in Arkansas where it is processed directly into alumina is bauxite used in the crude form. The removal of excess weight is absolutely necessary where bauxite is to be shipped to an alumina plant. Since much of the ore, especially in the Western Hemisphere, is located in underdeveloped mining countries, the ores have traditionally moved to alumina plants in industrial countries that process them into alumina and aluminum.

United States production of baxuite began in Georgia in 1889. A decade later the deposits of central Arkansas were opened up, and these soon became the chief source of domestic ore. Alabama and Georgia have consistently produced small quantities, and for several years bauxite was mined in Tennessee and Virginia. However, over 85 percent of the domestic production has come from Arkansas every year since 1914. Until the early 1920's, domestic production far exceeded imports—in fact in many of those years the United States was a net exporter. In 1923 this pattern began to change significantly as imports from the large Surinam and British Guiana deposits began to flow into the United States.

In 1940-1941 it became apparent that the aluminum and bauxite industries required a large expansion to meet wartime needs. At that time the federal government through the U.S. Bureau of Mines and the Geological Survey launched an extensive exploration program that resulted in a substantial increase in known reserves of ore in Arkansas. In addition, the government began to stockpile Arkansas bauxite. These activities resulted in an expansion of mining operations, and Arkansas production increased to over 6 million tons in 1943, which was almost four times as much as total U.S. production was in 1963 as shown in Table 11.1

Since the end of World War II U.S. production of bauxite has remained rather stable, ranging approximately between 1.2 and 2.0 million tons annually as shown in Figure 11.1. On the other hand, consumption of bauxite has steadily increased which has called for increased imports that reached a high of 10.6 million tons in 1962. At this same time, foreign sources supplied 85 percent of total consumption. Jamaican-type ore (from Jamaica, Haiti, and the Dominican Republic) comprised 49 percent of the total consumption; Surinam-type ore (from Surinam and British Guiana) made up 36 percent. Domestic sources supplied the remainder.

Figure 11.1: United States Supply and World Production of Bauxite.

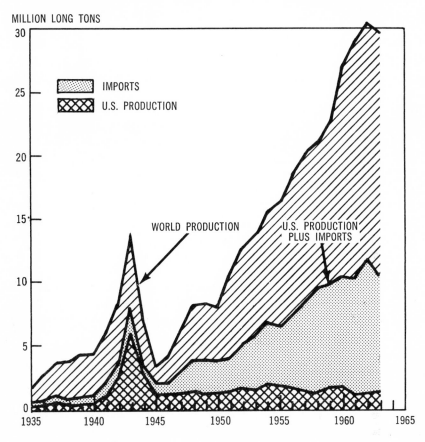

MILLION LONG TONS

WORLD PRODUCTION

U.S. PRODUCTION PLUS IMPORTS

IMPORTS
U.S. PRODUCTION

Source: U.S. Bureau of Mines.

World production of baxuite by countries is given in Table 11.2. Most significant for the United States is the dramatic increase in production in Jamaica. Only since 1952, when Jamaican deposits began to be mined, did production in North America become really significant. Jamaica has surpassed Surinam as the world's leading source of baxuite and the chief supplier of U.S. imports. This development of Jamaican bauxite is largely the result of U.S. companies' investment. Of the total Jamaican production in 1962 shown in Table 11.2 a high of almost 6.0 million tons was imported into the United States.

Bauxite used in the United States soared to 11.4 million tons in 1963. Although most of the bauxite goes into the production of alumina, it is also used for abrasive, refractory, or chemical applications in which a high

TABLE 11.2
World Production of Bauxite
(Thousands of long tons)

Year	British Guiana	France	Ghana[4]	Hungary	Indonesia	Italy	Malaya	Greece	Surinam	U.S.S.R.[2]	Jamaica[3]	United States[3]	Yugoslavia	World total
1951	2,003	1,127	129	741	388	171	–	161	2,657	837	–	1,849	490	10,700
1952	2,388	1,101	74	1,188	338	261	22	280	3,173	886	340	1,667	604	12,600
1953	2,275	1,138	115	1,372	147	267	152	323	3,223	890	1,154	1,580	470	13,600
1954	2,310	1,267	164	1,240	171	289	166	348	3,309	1,390	2,044	1,995	676	15,900
1955	2,435	1,470	116	1,221	260	322	222	492	3,074	2,030	2,645	1,788	779	17,500
1956	2,481	1,439	138	879	299	271	264	687	3,430	2,190	3,141	1,744	868	18,450
1957	2,202	1,663	185	893	238	257	326	820	3,324	2,410	4,643	1,416	874	20,150
1958	1,586	1,801	207	1,082	338	294	262	843	2,941	2,750	5,722	1,311	721	21,075
1959	1,674	1,729	148	923	381	290	382	904	3,376	3,000	5,125	1,700	802	22,690
1960	2,471	2,035	224	1,171	389	310	452	870	3,400	3,500	5,745	1,998	1,009	27,020
1961	2,374	2,190	196	1,344	413	318	410	1,100	3,351	4,000	6,663	1,228	1,213	28,890
1962[1]	2,690	2,124	287	1,450	484	304	349	1,300	3,202	4,200	7,495	1,369	1,311	30,535
1963[1]	2,210	1,971	207	1,340	485	265	444	1,280	3,427	4,300	6,903	1,525	1,265	29,835
1964[2]	3,500	2,000							3,500	4,500	7,500	1,600		33,000

1 Preliminary.
2 Estimate.
3 Dried equivalent of crude ore.
4 Exports.
SOURCE: Data from U.S. Bureau of Mines, *Commodity Year Book*, New York, Commodity Research Bureau, Inc., 1965.

degree of purity is desirable. Its minor uses as aluminum oxide or corundum include production of the nose cones of missiles, artificial sapphires, and thread guides for textile plants. This increased use of bauxite has steadily led to a decline in U.S. self-sufficiency as already seen in Figure 11.1, which leads the U.S. Bureau of Mines to conclude: "The domestic reserve of bauxite is sufficient to maintain an annual production of approximately 1.5 million tons for several decades; and increase in demand must be supplied by imports."

Alumina

Approximately 4 long dry tons of bauxite are required to produce 2 short tons of alumina. Although research on the extraction of alumina has continued for many years, virtually all of the commercially produced alumina is obtained by a process patented by Karl Bayer (German Patent 43,997) for use on bauxite. The materials required in the Bayer process other than bauxite are soda ash; lime for causticizing the soda ash; and fuel oil, gas, or coal. The function of the Bayer process is the removal of the nonaluminous materials in the ore and the concentration of aluminum by chemical processes. Bauxite must contain less than 8 percent silica for economic treatment by the Bayer process.

In the Bayer process the crushed, washed, and dried bauxite from the mines is reduced further in size in crushers and hammer mills. Finally, it is ground into a powder, mixed with a hot solution of sodium hydroxide, or caustic soda, and pumped into large pressure tanks or digesters. In these digesters, the caustic soda dissolves the aluminum hydroxide out of the bauxite to form a sodium aluminate solution.

The impurities in the ore, not affected by the caustic, remain solid in form and are removed from the sodium aluminate solution when it is pumped from the digesters into filter presses. The solution, being liquid, passes through the filters, while the impurities remain behind as residue. This residue is commonly called "red mud."

The reason that the Bayer process precludes the use of much silica-bearing clay is apparent when it is realized that the clay is attacked by the caustic soda solution, forming sodium silicate, which in turn reacts with sodium aluminate to produce an insoluble sodium aluminum silicate. Thus the silica in the clay not only decreases the amount of alumina recovered from the bauxite, but also robs the purifying solution of caustic soda, thereby increasing the cost of purification.

After passing through the filter presses, the sodium aluminate solution is pumped into precipitating tanks as high as a five- or six-story building. As the solution slowly cools in these tanks, fine crystals of aluminum hydroxide begin to settle out of the solution; thus the term *precipitating tanks.*

The solution is allowed to remain in the precipitating tanks until the precipitating process has been completed, after which the aluminum hydroxide is transferred to other tanks in which it is washed to remove the caustic. The caustic soda solution is then pumped back into the digesters to treat a new batch of bauxite; while the aluminum hydroxide, which is nothing more than aluminum oxide chemically combined with water, is heated white-hot in large, rotating kilns to drive off the chemically combined water and change the character of the material so that it will not reabsorb moisture from the air (See Figure 11.2).

Figure 11.2: From Bauxite to Alumina (Bayer Process) and from Alumina to Aluminum.

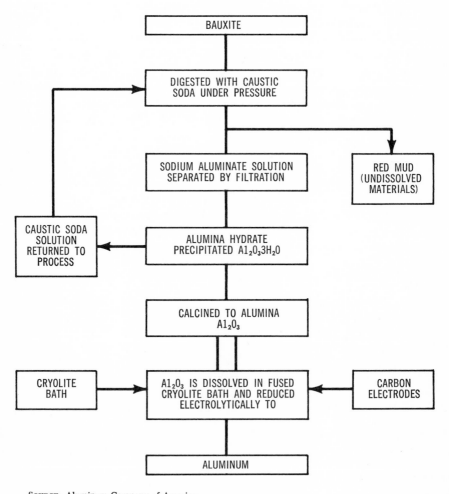

SOURCE: Aluminum Company of America.

During World War II the Bayer process was supplemented by a newly-developed combination process. Under this process, bauxite with more than 8 percent silica in the range of 12 to 15 percent silica is first subjected to a Bayer leach. The resulting red mud, which contains the complex sodium silicate compound, is sintered with limestone and soda ash, and then leached with water to recover alumina and soda. The brown mud residue has a composition, on a dry basis, somewhat similar to that of Portland cement.

The additional cost required in capital investment, raw materials, and processing by the combination method is partly offset by higher recoveries of alumina and soda, and partly by lower mining costs. A major advantage of the combination process is the decreased need for selective mining, as high-silica bauxite, previously regarded as unsuitable for alumina production, can be used. The upper limit for silica in this process is 15 percent; however in practice bauxite containing as high as 25 percent silica is mined and blended with low-silica ore in proportions that will give a feed

TABLE 11.3

Capacities of United States Alumina Plants

(Short tons per year)

Company and plant	Capacity
Aluminum Company of America	
Mobile, Ala.	985,500
Bauxite, Ark.	420,000
Point Comfort, Tex.	750,000
Total	2,155,500
Reynolds Metals Co.	
Hurricane Creek, Ark.	803,000
La Quinta, Tex.	876,000
Total	1,679,000
Kaiser Aluminum & Chemical Corp.	
Baton Rouge, La.	850,000
Gramercy, La.	430,000
Total	1,280,000
Ormet Corp., Burnside, La.	345,000
Grand Total	5,459,500

SOURCE: Data from U.S. Bureau of Mines, *Minerals Yearbook*, Washington, D.C., 1964.

material of approximately 12 to 13 percent silica. This process is an excellent example of the functional concept of resources, where technology has expanded the resource base.

Prior to 1940 there was only one alumina plant located in the United States at East St. Louis, Illinois. This was followed by the erection of one at Mobile, Alabama. There are now eight alumina plants in the United States at the locations and with the capacities shown in Table 11.3. The plants at Bauxite, Arkansas and Hurricane Creek, Arkansas use the combination process, and are obviously located to take advantage of nearness to the raw material bauxite. This is a reversal of the former trend of location which caused alumina plants to be located where water transportation was available for the bauxite and fuel supplies were readily available.

Aluminum

Aluminum is obtained from alumina by an electrolytic reduction process which separates the metal from oxygen. The reduction takes place in a "pot" and a series of pots is referred to as a "potline." These pots are rectangular electric furnaces or cells, which consist of steel shells lined with carbon. The carbon lining serves as the cathode, and the current is led into each cell through carbon anodes suspended from above the cells on overhead busbars. In each reduction plant there are long rows of electrolytic cells (the potline), and each cell is capable of turning out approximately 750 pounds of aluminum a day.

The successful operation of the Hall-Heroult process is based on the fact that alumina, when dissolved in molten cryolite, can be decomposed by the passage of electric current without any change in the solvent. The cryolite bath material is first introduced into the electrolytic cell. When it has been fused by the electric current, the alumina is added and dissolved in the cryolite; and as the current passes through, the alumina is separated into its component parts of aluminum and oxygen. The oxygen, liberated at the anodes, combines with the carbon and escapes through the crust of the bath. The aluminum is deposited on the bottom of the cell (the cathode) where it remains as a molten layer. It is tapped from the cell into large mixing ladles and cast into pigs, each of which weighs approximately 50 pounds. The cryolite bath material is not affected by the decomposition of the alumina; hence the process is continuous, alumina being added to the bath from time to time.

When the metal comes from the electrolytic cells it contains some dross and bath material. For this reason, pig aluminum undergoes a remelting operation to remove these nonmetallic impurities. If alloys rather than commercially pure aluminum are desired, the alloying can take place during this remelting. The principal alloying elements are copper, silicon, magnesium, manganese, zinc, nickel, iron, and more recently, chromium. After remelting, the metal is cast into ingots for use by industry. Alumi-

TABLE 11.4
Aluminum Production Capacity in the United States
(Short tons per year)

Company and plant	Capacity
Aluminum Company of America	
Alcoa, Tenn.	157,100
Badin, N.C.	52,000
Evansville, Ind.	175,000
Massena, N.Y.	150,000
Point Comfort, Tex.	140,000
Rockdale, Tex.	150,000
Vancouver, Wash.	97,500
Wenatchee, Wash.	108,500
Total	1,030,100
Reynolds Metals Company	
Arkadelphia, Ark.	55,000
Jones Mills, Ark.	109,000
Listerhill, Ala.	190,000
Longview, Wash.	60,500
Massena, N.Y.	100,000
San Patricio Tex.	95,000
Troutdale, Ore.	91,500
Total	701,000
Kaiser Aluminum and Chemical Corp.	
Chalmette, La.	247,500
Mead, Wash.	176,000
Ravenswood, W. Va.	145,000
Tacoma, Wash.	41,000
Total	609,500
Anaconda Aluminum Co., Columbia Falls, Mont.	100,000
Consolidated Aluminum Corp., New Johnsonville, Tenn.	62,000
Harvey Aluminum, Inc., The Dalles, Oreg.	80,000
Ormet Corp., Hannibal, Ohio	180,000
Grand Total	2,762,600

SOURCE: Data from U.S. Bureau of Mines, *Minerals Yearbook*, Washington, D.C., 1964.

num reduction must be a continuous operation; otherwise the mixture in the pot will freeze, and the initial expense of starting up the process is considerable.

Raw materials used per ton of aluminum pig, include 2 tons of alumina, about 1,200 pounds of carbon paste for electrodes, and smaller quantities of cryolite and aluminum fluoride. The main factor in converting alumina to aluminum is electric power as from 15,000 to 17,000 kwh are required for one ton of aluminum. To produce this amount of electric power would require 6 to 7 tons of coal. No other electrometallurgical operation consumes so much power.

The large quantities of electric power required to produce aluminum led the U.S. industry to locate plants near sources of low-cost hydroelectric power. As late as 1950, practically all the electric power needs were obtained from hydroelectric power stations, principally operated by government agencies, except for a portion of the power purchased from the TVA which was generated by steam. Since then the trend has been away from hydroelectric power as dependable supplies of low-cost hydropower have been harder to find. In addition, important factors contributing to this trend have been the rising costs of transporting finished products to market from remote hydropowered reduction plants and the higher shipping charges on raw materials. Increasing efficiency of fuel-generated electric power coupled with the lessening availability of hydroelectric power sources have also been factors.

As a result, by the mid-1960's only about 50 percent of the aluminum was produced by hydroelectric power and the balance was based 25 percent on coal and 25 percent on natural gas. The coal-powered plants, except for the Aluminum Company's lignite-fueled plant in Texas, are all in the Ohio Valley, where abundant supplies of low-cost coal are available; 70 percent of the nation's aluminum-consuming industries are within a 500-mile radius, and raw materials can be transported cheaply on inland waterways. Table 11.4 gives the location and capacity of the aluminum plants in the United States.

Finally, it should be noted that direct reduction processes, wherein the alumina stage is eliminated, are being tried experimentally and might be used if verified in larger-scale tests because the processes might greatly reduce costs.

Fabrication

Fabrication converts aluminum ingot into wrought products, also called mill and fabricated products, and castings.

The most important wrought mill products are sheet, plate, and strip; rolled structural shapes; extruded shapes; and powder, flake, and paste. These wrought products account for about 75 percent of total aluminum consumption.

Aluminum castings differ from mill products in the raw materials used and the processing methods. In castings both primary aluminum and secondary scrap are used; and aluminum is melted and not just heated as is the case in processing mill products. The molten metal is then poured into molds to form the finished casting. The principal types of casting are die, permanent mold, and sand castings. Die castings are made by forcing molten metal under high pressure into a steel die cavity which forms the finished product. Die castings are especially suited for automobiles and machinery where long production runs and exactness in sizes are required. Permanent mold castings are also chiefly used in automobiles. Sand castings are made by pouring metal into cavities formed in sand, and their applications are limited to uses which can use rougher casts such as airplane frames and gun bases. Total casting volume is equal to about 15 percent of total aluminum tonnage.

A third major use of aluminum, in addition to wrought and cast products, is in dissipative or destructive uses in which the metal loses its identity. This happens when it serves as an alloying element in other metal base alloys, as a metallurgical reducing agent, or as a source of aluminum for aluminum chemicals.

Manufacturing End Products

The fifth and final function in the production of aluminum is the manufacturing of end products which converts sheet, forgings, extrusions, and castings into finished products such as foil, pots and pans, automobile parts, Venetian blinds, window frames, and approximately 4,000 other end uses. Only a small portion of manufacturing is done by the integrated producers who are dominant in the other four functions in the production of aluminum.

ALUMINUM MARKETS

Reference has already been made to the dramatic growth in the aluminum industry. Further evidence of this sustained growth can be seen from Table 11.5. Aluminum production reached 2.3 million tons in the United States in 1963, which made this country by far the world's leading producer with almost 40 percent of the total and much over double the production of the U.S.S.R., the second-ranked nation. Further this production was 2.7 times greater than it was in 1951, the first year shown in the table. At the same time consumption of primary aluminum rose by the same order of magnitude to about 2.6 million tons. This should be compared with a .25 million tons in pre-World War II 1940—more than a tenfold increase.

This dramatic growth was largely made possible by the industry's aggressive bid for an ever-increasing share of existing markets and its

TABLE 11.5

Salient Statistics of Aluminum in the United States
(In thousands of short tons)

| | Production | | Apparent consumption | | | Secondary | | | Net shipments[5] | | | | | Im-ports[6] | Ex-ports[6] |
| | | | Primary | | | Domestic recovery | | | Wrought products | | | | | | |
Year	Pri-mary	Sec-ond-ary	Sold[2]	Net im-ports[3]	Ap-parent con-sumption	From old scrap	From new scrap	Net im-ports[4]	Plate, sheet, & strip	Oth-ers	Total	Cast-ings	Total ship-ments		
1951	837	293	845	128	973	77	216	17	537	341	878	258	1,136	162	15
1952	937	305	938	134	1,072	71	233	5	543	420	963	259	1,222	151	11
1953	1,252	369	1,220	322	1,542	79	290	20	684	459	1,143	329	1,472	359	15
1954	1,461	292	1,479	227	1,706	60	232	–22	583	461	1,044	312	1,355	244	50
1955	1,566	336	1,572	183	1,755	76	260	20	771	625	1,396	410	1,806	239	34
1956	1,679	340	1,591	190	1,781	72	268	6	784	659	1,443	397	1,840	265	68
1957	1,648	362	1,579	197	1,776	72	289	–2	698	641	1,339	376	1,715	258	63
1958	1,566	290	1,591	220	1,811	64	225	–8	677	622	1,299	321	1,619	293	82
1959	1,954	360	1,989	159	2,146	78	282	–19	884	809	1,693	393	2,086	302	164
1960	2,014	329	1,866	113	1,753	63	267	–67	819	706	1,525	376	1,901	196	384
1961	1,904	340	1,956	92	2,048	102	238	–68	882	791	1,673	381	2,053	255	238
1962	2,118	400	2,185	174	2,359	109	291	–53	1,004	902	1,906	463	2,369	373	259
1963[1]	2,313	501	2,354	237	2,591	115	386	–56						466	292

1 Preliminary.
2 Or used by producers.
3 Crude and semifabricated, excluding scrap. May include some secondary.
3 Ingot equivalent of net imports. Imports are largely scrap pig.
4 Consists of total shipments less shipments to other metal mills for further fabrication.
5 Crude and semicrude products.
Source: U. S. Bureau of Mines, *Commodity Year Book*, New York, Commodity Research Bureau, Inc., 1965.

outstanding effectiveness in creating and developing new markets. Much of this success is due to aluminum's properties which make it preferable to other materials. These properties are lightness, strength in alloy form, ductility which allows it to be shaped, resistance to atmospheric corrosion and attack by many chemicals, excellent conductivity for heat and electrical energy, and reflection of light and radiant heat. It is nonsparking, nonmagnetic, and nontoxic.

Major aluminum markets include the industries of building, transportation, consumer durables, and electrical applications. The percentage shared by these and other markets is shown in Table 11.6, which compares these data for 1964 and 1952 to show the percentage changes and offers some indication of the shift in relative importance of different markets during the period covered.

TABLE 11.6
Estimated Major Aluminum Markets
(Millions of pounds)

Industry	1952		1964	
	Total	Percentage	Total	Percentage
Building	382	21.7	1,682	25.5
Transportation	227	12.9	1,598	24.3
Electrical	347	19.7	838	12.7
Consumer Durables	281	16.0	766	11.6
Containers–Packaging	91	5.2	574	8.7
Machinery–Equipment	171	9.7	505	7.7
All Other	260	14.8	626	9.5
Total	1,759	100.0%	6,589	100.0%

SOURCE: Aluminum Association.

Building

Building products and transportation each account for about 25 percent of the aluminum market. In the building category, the uses are manifold, since aluminum has been replacing other metals and materials in industrial, commercial, and residential building. Aluminum is used for roofing and siding, doors and frames, store fronts, awnings, curtain walls, builder's hardware, insect screening, foil insulation, wiring, plumbing and heating equipment, and prefabricated buildings. Increased usage of aluminum in the construction industry is anticipated, particularly in commercial building and also in housing, where aluminum is used for windows, doors, and sidings.

Commercial construction currently absorbs the bulk of the tonnage consumed by the building industry, but aluminum producers are continuing their efforts to promote the "all aluminum" house and are succeeding in making inroads into markets previously dominated by other metals. Major advantages of the metal in home construction are its ease of handling and virtually maintenance-free nature.

Transportation

The transportation market has showed the most rapid growth. Automobiles account for the major share of this growth, but trailers and railroad equipment are also important. The average 1965 car contained about 74 pounds of aluminum as compared with 30 pounds in 1955. Automatic transmissions account for the largest share of the aluminum used by the motor industry; motor components, principally pistons, are second. The metal is also used in power brakes and steering, and usage in decorative trim is growing. The aluminum engine block, which once offered great potential for the market, has not proved entirely satisfactory because of the disadvantage of higher raw material and casting costs over iron. However, the delivery of aluminum to automotive plants has been an important factor in establishing the metal's position in this market.

The most spectacular growth in the transportation field has come in truck trailers, mobile homes, and railroad cars. It is estimated that some 75 percent of all trailer truck bodies are made of aluminum as compared with 2 to 3 percent around 1950. Similarly, about 95 percent of all mobile homes built today are made of aluminum. The first order for all-aluminum railroad cars was booked only as recently as 1959, and by four years later several thousand cars had been ordered.

Aircraft, once aluminum's major market, will require additional supplies of the metal, particularly with improvement in high-temperature alloys. However, growth in this market will be limited by the use in supersonic planes and missiles of other materials with greater heat and fatigue resistance.

Electrical

Electrical applications of aluminum continue to rank slightly above consumer durables. Here aluminum's advantage is that aluminum conductors can carry about twice as much current as those made of equivalent-weight, higher-cost copper. Aluminum cables reinforced with steel have already captured 90 percent of the new transmission lines of electric utilities. Further gains are likely by both this product and all-aluminum cable and wire in other electrical applications. As a conductor, aluminum's major advantages are the relatively low price and lightness which result in reduced costs of supporting structures.

With the growth of the electric power industry, aluminum is sure to find increasing markets. The aluminum product for high-tension lines is ACSR (aluminum conductor, steel reinforced). Aluminum wires are stranded around a steel core which gives the cable steel added strength and the lightness of aluminum. All-aluminum cable (EC) is used for distribution lines. However, aluminum loses much of its cost advantage in underground power cables and in other conductors which require insulation. The thicker aluminum cable needs a greater amount of insulating material and these costs, including additional labor costs, offset the lower metal costs. In addition, aluminum cables would not fit into conduits laid for thinner copper conductors.

Consumer Durables

Consumer durables, while declining in the share of the market, continue to grow in volume. Major appliances, such as refrigerators and the like and the myriad of kitchen utensils, offer a continuously growing demand as population increases and new family formations take place. These items still account for about 12 percent of aluminum's market.

Containers—Packaging

The containers and packaging market is particularly attractive to aluminum producers as it represents a more stable consumer's market. However, competition in this field is very severe, especially with steel in the "tin" can market; and most importantly, since steel has introduced a new lightweight tin plate for cans. Aluminum's potential in the can market would seem to lie more in high-priced commodities where the packaging cost is smaller relative to the overall cost of packaged product to the ultimate consumer. In this and some other applications, aluminum's cost disadvantage is offset by the metal's attractiveness for display purposes and savings in shipping costs.

The fiber-foil can (paperboard laminated to aluminum foil) is a new development that has found a market in packaging frozen citrus fruits and in the packaging of motor oil for gasoline service stations. Foil demand for home use and commercial packaging is a continuing and developing market, and together with the increased use of foil laminations, is one of the bright spots in the container and packaging market.

Machinery—Equipment

Finally, it should be noted that even though the use of aluminum in machinery and equipment has slipped to last place for the uses which are classified separately, this group of uses still accounts for almost 8 percent of the total. Machine parts account for a large share of this market, which is particularly important for castings.

Markets and Prices

The aluminum industry's price policy probably has been an important factor in the rapidly increasing usage of the metal by many consuming industries. A U.S. Bureau of Mines' study showed that while prices of other nonferrous metals had increased between 100 to 150 percent from 1939 to 1959 the price of aluminum ingot increased only 34 percent during the same period. In addition, the study showed that historically a 1 percent decrease in the ratio of the price of aluminum to the composite price of copper, lead, and zinc has increased aluminum consumption by 1.4 percent.

The average price of aluminum ingot in 1925 was 28.2¢ a pound and gradually decreased to the World War II price of 15¢ a pound. The first increase was in 1948, but the 1925 price was not approached until August, 1957 when a postwar high of 28.1¢ a pound was reached. Subsequently the price dropped to a low of 22.5¢ a pound at the beginning of 1963. Compared with copper, aluminum prices are relatively stable, and to date the industry has followed a policy of administered prices. Both the downward trend and stability of price have been a function of the pricing policy of the industry and have been related in part to the structure of the industry.

Conclusion

The inherent advantages of aluminum, plus the research, development, sales, and pricing policy of the industry have been responsible for the growth in consumption of the metal and the displacement of many materials from their historical market. As a result, per capita consumption has risen in the United States to 27.7 pounds, while that in the Common Market nations averages only 11 pounds, Japan somewhat over 4 pounds, and the newly emerging nations a negligible quantity per capita.

The future market for aluminum in the United States is expected to continue to grow but at a somewhat lower rate, perhaps 7 percent. However, the lower per capita consumption outside the United States points to a rapid growth in the market in other areas in the Free World. This, in turn, may lead to a change in the structure of the industry.

STRUCTURE OF THE INDUSTRY

The Aluminum Company of America (Alcoa), owning bauxite, alumina and aluminum producing facilities was the only domestic producer from 1886 to 1940. The history of the production of aluminum up to World War II in the United States is the story of Alcoa and its search for electric power. From its first establishment at Pittsburgh, reduction moved to Kensington, a few miles to the north, where natural gas was available and then to Niagara Falls, the first major hydroelectrical development. When power supplies there were outgrown, expansion was to Massena, New York, where power from the Canadian Cedar Rapids development was used. Then a move south was made to build reduction plants on the Yadkin at Badin, North Carolina and on the Little Tennessee River at Alcoa, Tennessee. To these plants alumina was shipped exclusively from East St. Louis based on bauxite from Arkansas, and from Surinam and British Guiana which was unloaded at New Orleans and transshipped up the Mississippi by barge. In 1938 a second alumina plant was put in operation at Mobile, Alabama. Thus up until World War II, Alcoa had a complete monopoly of aluminum production in the United States.

But Alcoa was also international. In 1926 Alcoa began to manufacture aluminum at Arvida on the Saguenay River in Eastern Canada, and in 1928 alumina works were added and Arvida became the first integrated plant in North America. Bauxite is brought up to Port Alfred from British Guiana and then moved twenty miles by rail to Arvida. Power for Arvida was provided from Chûte-a-Carron farther up the Saguenay until World War II. A gigantic expansion in reduction capacity at Arvida was powered by the erection of the Shipshaw power project down the river from the existing site and closer to Arvida. In addition to the plant at Arvida, Alcoa built reduction plants in Canada at Shawinigan Falls, Beuharnais, and La Tuque. Canada and the United States had thus set the stage to replace Germany, which before World War II, had been the leading producer of aluminum.

While Alcoa was expanding in the United States and Canada, its international interests had become widespread. Aluminium Limited (Alted) was organized in 1928 to take over all of Alcoa's foreign holdings except bauxite deposits and mining properties in Surinam. These holdings included: (1) bauxite deposits in France, Istria, Yugoslavia, Rumania and other parts of Europe (the holdings were later expanded to include Africa, India, and the West Indies); and (2) stock interests in such producing companies as the Norway Aluminum and the Norwegian Nitrit companies. The Canadian holdings were placed under a single subsidiary of Alted, called Alcan (Aluminum Company of Canada). By World War II, outside of Russia and Japan, the world aluminum industry was largely controlled by Alcoa, Alted, and Germany's government-controlled in· dustry.

In the United States with the possibility of World War II, and an obvious need for aluminum, the U.S. government, long eager to break the Alcoa monopoly, assisted the Reynolds Metals Company, by means of substantial loans, to build a reduction plant at Longview, Washington, and a combined alumina-aluminum plant at Listerhill, Alabama. Reynolds also entered the bauxite mining business in the United States and later acquired bauxite reserves in the Caribbean, especially in Haiti, the Dominican Republic, and Jamaica. As a result, due to this new entry in the business, and the addition of a reduction plant opened by Alcoa in Vancouver, Washington in 1940, there were in 1941, just prior to this country's entry into the war, three alumina and seven aluminum plants in the United States. They are listed in Table 11.7.

TABLE 11.7

Aluminum Plants in the United States Prior to World War II

Alumina

Aluminum Company of America
East St. Louis, Ill.
Mobile, Alabama

Reynolds Metals Company
Listerhill, Alabama

Aluminum

Aluminum Company of America
Niagara Falls, New York
Massena, New York
Alcoa, Tennessee
Badin, North Carolina
Vancouver, Washington

Reynolds Metals Company
Listerhill, Alabama
Longview, Washington

Source: U.S. Bureau of Mines.

The aggregate capacity of these U.S. plants was 426,000 tons of aluminum, of which Alcoa controlled 345,000 and Reynolds 81,000. It soon became apparent that this capacity would be totally inadequate for wartime demands, and the question of how expansion of capacity could be brought about was raised. What complicated this problem was that private enterprise was not anxious to undertake the job for fear that the capacity would not be needed at the close of the war. How this problem was resolved, how the plants were disposed of after the war, and how growth in capacity was encouraged during the Korean War will be studied in the problems and policy section.

For the present we will note that out of World War II there came a third producer of alumina and aluminum—Kaiser Aluminum and Chemical Corporation. After the Korean War expansion, three additional producers began operation: Anaconda Aluminum Company, Harvey Aluminum, and Ormet Corporation (a subsidiary of Olin Mathieson Chemical Corporation and Revere Copper and Brass, Incorporated). Anaconda Aluminum began production of primary aluminum at Columbia Falls, Montana in 1955; and Harvey Aluminum and Ormet produced primary metal for the first time in 1958. In 1963, a seventh firm, Consolidated Aluminum Corporation (Conalco) began producing primary aluminum at a new facility at New Johnsonville, Tennessee. Thus, the structure of the aluminum industry in the United States can be diagrammed as shown in Figure 11.3.

The organization as depicted shows four fully integrated producers of aluminum—Ormet, Alcoa, Kaiser, and Reynolds. The three other firms produce aluminum from alumina either supplied by another company or from outside the United States. Anaconda buys alumina from Reynolds, and Harvey and Conalco obtain alumina from Japan and Surinam respectively. Of the total aluminum capacity of 2,762,600 tons shown in Figure 11.3 and Table 11.4, Alcoa had 37.3 percent; Reynolds 25.4 percent; Kaiser 22.1 percent; Ormet 6.5 percent; Anaconda 3.4 percent; Harvey 2.9 percent; and Conalco 2.2 percent.

A noteworthy aspect of the changed structure of the U.S. aluminum industry is the entrance of foreign firms—Conalco and Pechiney. Conalco, a fully owned subsidiary of Swiss Aluminum of Zurich, Switzerland, began production of primary aluminum at a plant with a capacity of 20,000 tons per year at New Johnsonville, Tennessee. Conalco is also a producer of superfine aluminum and has facilities for producing foil, sheet, and other aluminum products. The company's planned expansion of the reduction plant called for 31,000 tons by 1964 and 62,000 tons by mid-1965 as shown in Figure 11.3. Future plans called for an annual capacity of 250,000 tons.

Not shown on the organization chart, but now of major significance is the aluminum plant of Intalco Aluminum Corporation at Bellingham, Washington. Intalco is a new company organized in 1964 and owned 50 percent by American Metal Climax, 25 percent by Pechiney, Compagnie de Produits Chimiques et Electrometallurgiques, and 25 percent by Howe Sound Aluminum Company, which in turn is controlled by Pechiney. The Bellingham operation called for a capacity of 76,000 tons of aluminum by 1967, and an ultimate expansion to 152,000 tons. Pechiney, with an annual output of 285,000 tons of aluminum ranks fifth in world production of aluminum behind Alcoa, Reynolds Metals, Alted, and Kaiser. Pechiney's

Figure 11.3: Structure of the Aluminum Industry.

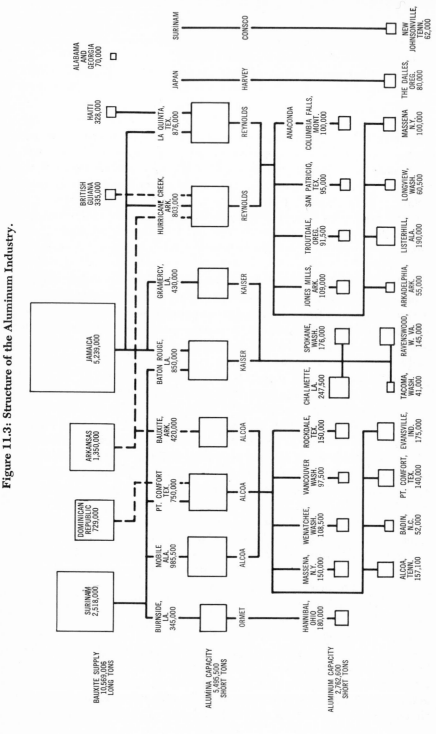

SOURCE: U.S. Bureau of Mines.

principal market for aluminum is Europe, but it has worldwide bauxite, alumina, aluminum, and fabricating facilities. Of interest as a developing source of bauxite and alumina are the deposits of the French African colony of Guinea which were developed in 1960 by an international consortium called FRIA in which Pechiney participates. Howe Sound will handle the fabrication and sales of aluminum in the United States and thus give Pechiney an integrated operation. Pechiney's main interest in the United States is in aluminum flat products the consumption of which it estimates is growing by 15 percent per year. Pechiney's further interest in the United States in indicated by the fact that it has set up a subsidiary in New York, called Pechiney Enterprises, whose function is to keep watch for other possibilities.

The integration of the major producers includes all five functions of the industry: mining, production of alumina, reduction of aluminum, fabricating aluminum pig and ingot into semifinished and finished aluminum, and manufacturing end products. Although there are many manufacturers of end products, the aluminum producers have found it necessary to engage in this total process of fabrication in order to successfully market aluminum. In aluminum, the leading companies have a much greater degree of integration from "mine to consumer" than in copper. This has been true of Alcoa, Reynolds, and Kaiser, and during the 1950's they bought primary aluminum on balance from Alted in Canada to supply requirements for the fabricating plants. Other primary producers, Ormet, Anaconda, and Harvey now fabricate much of their output.

Thus domestically the structure of the aluminum industry is quite different from the one-firm monopoly that existed in 1939.

In addition, on the international front the scene has been marked by a change in structure. As can be seen from Table 11.5, the United States has been an importer of primary, crude, and semifabricated aluminum. But as the United States industry expanded capacity during the 1950's domestic producers went into export markets to utilize some of their overexpanded facilities. Since this move, the U.S. industry has made and is making substantial investments in foreign bauxite mining, alumina processing facilities, smelters, and fabricating plants.

Alcoa, in addition to extensive overseas bauxite supplies, has an integrated aluminum complex in Australia, smelters in Norway, Mexico, and Surinam, and fabricating plants in the United Kingdom, Japan, Mexico, and Venezuela.

Kaiser has bauxite in Jamaica; a 50 percent interest in bauxite in Australia; 50 percent ownership in Comalco, an integrated aluminum complex in Oceania with extensive bauxite reserves, a 660,000 ton alumina plant, a smelter and fabricating facilities; a 90 percent participation in a 100,000 ton smelter in Ghana; and fabricating plants in England, West Germany, and Argentina.

Reynolds owns bauxite reserves in Jamaica, British Guiana, and Haiti; 47 percent interest in British Aluminum, a leading fabricator that also produces primary metal; fabricating plants in Canada, Latin America, Europe, Japan, and the Philippines; and is a participant in proposed smelters in Ghana, Greece, and Venezuela.

These foreign investments were fostered by competition and enable U.S. companies to participate in the faster rate of growth anticipated in overseas aluminum consumption; give control over low-cost export smelters; and provide alternate raw material supplies, particularly in Australia. These alternate supplies serve as a hedge against political uncertainties in the Caribbean and South America, which, as we have seen, supply the bulk of the U.S. bauxite requirements.

Meanwhile, Alted, which through its subsidiaries, is the leading primary aluminum producer in the world with 18 percent of production, was making moves both in Canada and in this country which were of interest to domestic producers.

In Canada, Alcan, a subsidiary of Alted, has three large aluminum plants in Quebec—Arvida, 380,000 tons; Shawinigan Falls, 70,000 tons; and Isle Mailgne, 115,000 tons. These plants were especially suitable for exporting products to the East Coast and to Europe. But a most significant development is that Alcan is developing at Kitamat, British Columbia what will become the world's largest reduction plant, designed for an ultimate output of 555,000 tons of metal per year from Jamaican alumina. Here a tremendous engineering feat was accomplished to achieve low-cost hydropower. The water for the power is procured by damming the Nechako River, which makes a reservoir storage basin 150 miles long. A 10-mile tunnel was made to penetrate the Coast Mountains so that water from the lakes can fall 2,600 feet to the hydroelectric plant located at Kemano in a cavern at sea level. The power is then delivered over high-tension lines some 50 miles to Kitimat, at the head of a deep-water fiord. The plant is well located not only to supply our Pacific Coast markets, but the Far East as well. But most important, as well, it is an excellent example of the pull of low-cost power. For as noted, the reduction plant is drawing alumina from Jamaica 5,600 miles away and is presently shipping aluminum ingots 2,500 to 3,000 miles to manufacturers in eastern Canada and the United States.

Alted's moves in the United States were to provide fabricating facilities. Some of the more recent moves were to purchase the sheet mills and extrusion facilities of Bridgeport Brass, the sheet mills operation of Cerro Corporation, and the remaining 49.9 percent interest in Alroll, Incorporated. Thus Alted along with Conalco and Intalco put further outside pressure on aluminum production and competition in the United States.

Elsewhere throughout the world Alted and other producers were expanding overseas facilities just as U.S. producers had been doing. The major increases were in France, Norway, and Japan. The result of this expansion outside of North America was that whereas in 1950 overseas smelters produced only 23 percent of Free World aluminum tonnage, and whereas the percentage had increased in 1956 to just 25 percent, by 1963 overseas producers were turning out 34 percent of Free World output.

The net effect of these expanded facilities was to increase competition for markets. Alted's Canadian smelters of Alcan, which export the bulk of their metal were the hardest hit by the new competition abroad and increased U.S. exports. But Alted's expansion into fabricating facilities increased competition in this country.

The changed structure of the alumnium industry has made the metal a growing object of international trade and subject to world supply-demand relations. With this changed structure there is the possibility that the price of aluminum will become more susceptible to world conditions and thus subject to greater fluctuations. This is not to say that aluminum is expected to show the price volatility of copper, but it is obvious that the possibility of administered prices has been lessened.

Another effect of the increased competition is to reduce profits in the aluminum industry and this in turn may limit new entrants into the primary and fabricating segments of the industry. Indeed the industry will probably attempt to retain the structure by restricting new entrants by means of lower prices, increased control over new raw material deposits, and further aggressive expansion in foreign markets. The hope is that lower prices would also enhance market expansion, and if existing producers obtain a greater share of future growth of demand, they would, in turn, receive larger profits from spreading the heavy burden of fixed costs over an increased tonnage, from greater reliance in fabricating on mass production rather than relatively short runs, and from further gains in smelter efficiency.

PROBLEMS AND POLICY

The central national aluminum problem and policy issues have been concerned with: (1) the structure of the industry which has resulted in market control, and (2) the growth of the industry, especially in times of national emergencies.

Market Control in Aluminum

Until World War II the Aluminum Company of America (Alcoa) represented the classical example of a complete manufacturing monopoly in the United States. Yet the courts of the United States did not find an effective way to deal with this problem until more firms had entered the aluminum industry and the monopoly had ceased to exist.

Facts Bearing on the Problem. Alcoa's market control was accomplished through a combination of patent control, vertical and horizontal integration, and cartel arrangements.

As noted in the introduction to this chapter the electrolytic process for the production of aluminum was developed independently in 1866 by Charles Martin Hall and by Paul L. T. Heroult in France. The Pittsburgh Reduction Company was formed in 1888 by Hall and associates to produce aluminum with the Hall process which was patented in 1889. Pittsburgh Reduction became the Aluminum Company of America in 1907. A second company, Cowles Electric Smelting and Aluminum Company had been producing aluminum alloys since 1885 using a patent of Charles S. Bradley, but had failed to produce commercially pure aluminum by a carbon reduction process. From 1891 to 1893 the Cowles Company produced aluminum using an electrolytic process almost the same as the Hall process, but Cowles shifted to aluminum fabrication after losing a patent infringement suit to Pittsburgh Reduction. However, the Cowles Company had secured a broad process patent issued to Charles S. Bradley in 1892, and in 1903 Cowles won a countersuit on alleged patent infringement by Pittsburgh Reduction. With this deadlock over patents, Pittsburgh Reduction bought the Bradley patents; and the Cowles Company withdrew with a lump-sum payment and annual royalties, and promised not to enter the aluminum business again. Thus with the protection of the Hall patent until 1906 and the Bradley patents until 1909, the Pittsburgh Reduction Company had an assured monopoly on the production of primary aluminum in the United States.

Patent control was followed by vertical integration, both backward and forward. As early as 1895 Pittsburgh Reduction initiated an active policy of backward integration with the acquisition of bauxite deposits, and the development of ore processing, alumina, and hydroelectric plants. It bought bauxite deposits in Georgia, Alabama, and Arkansas. By 1910 Pittsburgh Reduction, then Alcoa, was integrated backward by processing this ore through crushing, grinding, and drying, converting it into alumina at East St. Louis, and then sending it to be reduced to aluminum at its first plant in Kensington, Pennsylvania and its other plants at Niagara Falls and Massena, New York, and Shawinigan Falls, Quebec. Almost all of the electricity was generated by Alcoa, and it manufactured most of its process materials. One problem that Pittsburgh Reduction had had was in marketing. As a result the conclusion was drawn that fabrication of aluminum products was necessary to prove the many advantages of the metal. This led to forward integration, which again by 1910 led Alcoa to the manufacture of many semi-finished and finished aluminum products. A large part of its ingot production was used for rolling sheet, rods, tubes, shapes, cooking utensils, wire, and other articles. Undoubtedly substantial reduction in costs resulted from this vertical integration.[1]

Horizontal integration during the period 1905–1929 followed as vertical integration was completed. This included the purchase of foreign bauxite reserves, power sites, and reduction plants, and the extension of fabricating facilities. Bauxite holdings were acquired in British and Dutch Guiana (Surinam), France, Yugoslavia, and Istria, which together with previous holdings were estimated to bring Alcoa's bauxite to about 90 percent of the total known world reserves. Alcoa expanded electric power generating facilities in New York, Quebec, and on the Little Tennessee River, and purchased power sites in Norway, Italy, the Pyrenees, and Southern France. In aluminum reduction, Alcoa acquired stock interests in Norway Aluminum Company and Norwegian Nitrit Company. It also acquired a majority interest in a European company which held important electrode patents. In fabricating, Alcoa gained an interest in a French plant through the Norwegian acquisition and expanded into South America and many facilities in the United States. All of these acquisitions and purchases served to extend the market control of Alcoa in the United States after the patent monopoly expired in 1909. This was achieved through control of bauxite reserves, power sites, the market position of the acquired companies and their patent rights. The entry into the European market served as a counterthreat to foreign companies that might attempt to enter the U.S. aluminum market.

An example of how this market position was maintained in the United States was in the unsuccessful attempt of the Southern Aluminum Company to enter the market just before World War I. A U.S. group had purchased control of a hydroelectric company on the Yadkin River in North Carolina. This property was purchased by Southern Aluminum which was composed of a number of experienced French producers who owned bauxite deposits and who had financial help from several large French and Swiss banks. Just before the outbreak of the war, Southern Aluminum was in need of further financing but was unable to secure funds from Europe because of the uncertainties. Then the company attempted to borrow from financial interests in the United States but could find no source of funds. The suggestion is that since Alcoa was backed by the Mellon banking interests, other members of the financial community had no desire to foster competition in aluminum. But also paramount was the fact that no U.S. group could have gotten bauxite or alumina. There is further evidence that the syndicate of seven French firms was entering the U.S. market with the passive permission of Alcoa as at one time Northern Aluminum (a Canadian subsidiary of Alcoa) was mentioned as a possible member of the syndicate, and at another time Alcoa was offering to swap

[1] Donald W. Wallace, *Market Control in the Aluminum Industry,* Cambridge, Harvard University Press, 1937, p. 27.

alumina to Southern Aluminum for supplies delivered to Alcoa elsewhere. In any event, the upshot was that Alcoa purchased all the assets of Southern Aluminum for $6,990,627.02—the exact amount expended by the European interests in the venture. Thus with one stroke Alcoa eliminated this domestic threat and maintained the goodwill of foreign interests.

Two other threats to Alcoa's position were also eliminated about ten years later. Both of these ventures were related to the James B. Duke interests in a magnificent undeveloped waterpower site on the Saguenay River which were later acquired by Alcoa from the Duke interests in 1925. The first threat was a venture promoted by the Uihleins, a Milwaukee family of brewers who by 1924 after six years of prospecting, negotiating, and extensive litigation with Alcoa had obtained enough bauxite in South America to supply an aluminum reduction plant of economical size. They had also built a carbon plant at an expense of about 2.5 million dollars and, in a search of a source of electric power had approached James B. Duke with respect to the Saguenay site. These negotiations fell through and the Uihleins were forced to sell out to Alcoa.

A second, and much more formidable threat was that of the Duke interests who had financed George D. Haskell in an extensive survey for the prospects of an integrated aluminum enterprise, but abandoned the project to merge the prospective venture with Alcoa's going concern. In exchange for a substantial block of stock in Alcoa, the Dukes gave up their independent aluminum project and turned over to Alcoa their huge undeveloped waterpower site. This acquisition eliminated the most powerful competitor that Alcoa had encountered in its entire history, and after this no competitive threat in the form of an integrated aluminum enterprise again confronted Alcoa on the domestic front until Reynolds Metals' entry at the outbreak of World War II.

Additional steps to further secure market control in the United States were taken by Alcoa. The company set out to secure international market control through cartel agreements with foreign producers and to consolidate its international holdings. Reference has already been made to the formation of Aluminium, Limited (Alted) in which Alcoa incorporated in 1928 all its foreign holdings except bauxite deposits and mining facilities in Surinam. Actually Alted was a separate company only for organizational and operational and control purposes as four of its stockholders who owned 55 percent of the common voting stock also owned 41 percent interest in Alcoa. One purpose Alted did serve was to permit Alcoa interests to enter into cartel arrangements with foreign producers without technically violating the U.S. antitrust laws. But cartels had been a part of Alcoa's market control strategy since before 1900.

By 1900 there were four European producers of aluminum using the Heroult process. These were the Swiss Company Aluminum Industries, A.G. (AIAG), 1888; the French companies Societe Electro-Metallurgique

Francaise, 1889; and Societe Industrielle d'Aluminum, 1894, taken over by the Compagnie des Produits Chimiques d'Alais et de las Camargue, 1896 (Pechiney); and the British Aluminum Company.

The first cartel was a bilateral agreement between AIAG and Alcoa in 1896 which safeguarded each of the parties from the export of the aluminum of the other to its own domestic and tributary market areas.

The second cartel was formed five years later, on November 2, 1901, just before the Heroult patents expired. Just before the cartel was signed Alcoa incorporated its wholly owned Canadian subsidiary the Northern Aluminum Company to participate along with AIAG and the three other previously listed European producers. This second and more comprehensive cartel: (1) reserved home markets for domestic producers, (2) divided foreign markets by assigning shares to the cartel members, and (3) set domestic as well as international prices. During the 5-year period 1901–1906, which was the specific term of the cartel, prices advanced in Europe, but Alcoa did not change its scheduled domestic price of 33¢ a pound until 1905. Since Alcoa did not have any competition in the U.S. market, it is not quite clear why the price was maintained unless it was the price calculated to receive the maximum net revenue. Finally in 1906, Alcoa raised the price to 36¢ in compliance with obligations assumed under the agreement.

The third cartel was a renewal of the second in 1906 with the four European companies and Alcoa's wholly owned Canadian subsidiary, Northern Aluminum, participating. It was apparent that the participants had deemed the first agreement a success; and the revised agreement incorporated similar provisions for dividing the market and fixing prices. Alcoa's price was advanced to 38¢ in 1907; but a general depression in 1908 led to an internal dispute over the "high price" policy which led to the dissolution of the third cartel on September 30, 1908.

The fourth cartel was a contract negotiated between Alcoa and AIAG in October, 1908, immediately after the dissolution of the third cartel. In the agreement Alcoa and AIAG mutually pledged not to invade the other's market. This agreement delayed the impact of competitive prices on the U.S. market. But soon imported aluminum was competitively offered in the U.S. market, and Alcoa was forced to reduce the price of aluminum to 29.3¢ in 1908, 24¢ in 1909, and 22¢ in 1910. This latter price was the lowest at which aluminum had been offered in the United States. Most interesting for the economist was the elasticity of demand in response to this lower price, which upset Alcoa's previous judgments as to the price which would yield the maximum net revenue. Domestic consumption increased from 31 million pounds in 1909 to 47 million in 1910; and Alcoa's earnings in 1909 were more than double those in the peak year of 1907 at a rate of 41 percent on stockholders equity. In spite of still lower prices in 1910, net profits were again higher than those realized at the peak of the boom; this time they reached 50 percent of equity.

With the expiration of the basic Heroult patents in 1903, seven new aluminum enterprises were started in Europe, and this intensified competition abroad and for the ever-growing U.S. market. Thus even though Alcoa had undergone financial success during the interim of competition, the ever-present threat of expanded capacity abroad led Alcoa to undertake negotiations with European producers in late 1911 to organize a new cartel. These negotiations through Northern Aluminum resulted in the formation of the fifth international cartel on June 12, 1912. This particular date is of significance because just five days earlier on June 7, 1912, Alcoa had accepted a consent decree which terminated antitrust proceedings against it. One provision of the decree was the cancellation of the October, 1908 cartel agreement with AIAG, which already had expired; and the enjoining of Alcoa itself from taking part in similar agreements in the future. The provisions of this fifth cartel, which was for a ten-year period, followed the general pattern of the 1906 cartel; but the agreement specifically provided that restrictions applied solely to "sales of aluminum outside the United States." Alcoa was not a member of the new cartel, but its wholly owned Canadian subsidiary Northern Aluminum was. Alcoa apparently felt that it did not need specific restrictions to sales in the United States, and preferred to enter into a policy of price stabilization which would hold prices down as well as keep them from falling too low. This was the policy Alcoa continued to follow in order to improve its position in the market and with the United States government.

Actually United States imports of aluminum continued at a high level until the outbreak of World War I and the price fell to a new low of 18.8¢ a pound in 1914 after having risen briefly in 1913. Nevertheless the fifth international cartel was considered effective because it brought about a "firm alliance" of the participating aluminum producers. The cartel voluntarily suspended operations on January 23, 1915.

The outstanding developments during World War I were that Alcoa doubled its capacity from 1914 to 1920; and Alcoa's prewar price policy seemed to have changed, as between 1914 and 1917 the domestic price of aluminum also doubled from 18.8¢ to 37.5¢ a pound in 1917. At this point, late in 1917, the War Industries Board made arrangements with Alcoa which stabilized the price for the duration of the war at 33.5¢ a pound. The outstanding developments in Europe during the war were the rapid expansion of productive capacity in Norway and Germany. French and British interests financed the Norwegian growth. Most important the German government organized a state monopoly Vereinigte Aluminiumwerke A.G. (VAW), and financed a huge construction program which later developed into the world's leading producer of aluminum.

After the war European producers found the price of 33.5¢ a pound in the United States with an import duty of only 2¢ a pound an attractive market for disposing of their excess production, and forced the U.S. price back down to the prewar level of 19¢ by the end of 1921. In 1921 U.S. imports were equivalent to about 50 percent of Alcoa's domestic production, and for the first time since 1897 Alcoa suffered an operating deficit. The response on the part of Alcoa, as we have noted, was an expansion into the European market in order to have a counterweapon. This was a policy that Alcoa followed vigorously for a 5-year period and its aggressiveness abroad was aided at home by the Fordney-McCumber Tariff of 1922 which raised the duty on aluminum to 5¢ a pound.

By 1923 European producers found it desirable to organize the sixth international aluminum cartel. This was a rather loose agreement which did not establish quotas or reserve home markets, but simply was a gentlemen's agreeement on prices. Alcoa did not join in this agreement, although after 1923 it did enter into an arrangement with major European aluminum producers regulating exports to the U.S. market. This cartel resulted in a rapid rise in the U.S. price by roughly 50 percent to 27¢ a pound in 1924. European prices rose only moderately so that by 1925 the growing price differential had wiped out the additional tariff protection given to Alcoa in 1922. This led to additional imports into the United States, but this gentlemen's agreement was apparently not satisfactory in Europe.

Accordingly, in 1926 the European producers established a seventh and full-fledged international cartel. Quota restrictions were placed on both domestic and export sales, and the association's executive committee periodically fixed standard delivered prices. Members were penalized for exceeding their assigned quotas; and they received compensation for underselling. The original term of the cartel was for two years, but on December 31, 1928 it was extended for three years. Alcoa was not formerly a member of either the 1926 or 1928 agreement. However, Alcoa cooperated with the cartel by not exporting aluminum, and followed exactly the cartel-fixed export prices through its Canadian affiliate Northern Aluminum. Actually this seventh cartel appeared to function very smoothly without Alcoa's formal participation, but since Alcoa was growing in importance to where it controlled over 50 percent of the world's aluminum productive capacity, it appeared that a more formal agreement would be desirable. Since the company was under a restraining order not to participate in a cartel, it devised the spin-off of its foreign properties under Alted as a means of setting up another corporation to be able to participate in nondomestic affairs. This incorporation took place on May 31, 1928; but one can surmise that Alcoa did not want Alted to participate in the 1928 cartel because it was yet too soon to test so "patent" an arrangement where the majority of the stock of both companies was held by the same stockholders, and two brothers headed the two concerns—Arthur V. Davis, Alcoa; E. K. Davis, Alted.

Three years after the formation of Alted, the effects of the great depression had hit the aluminum business with full force; and it appears that Arthur V. Davis, then chairman of Alcoa's Board of Directors, decided that the time was ripe to hold a conference with M. Louis Marilio, chairman of the existing cartel. The outgrowth was the eighth international aluminum cartel—the Alliance Aluminium Campagnie, which was incorporated in Switzerland in October, 1931. The company issued shares of stock based on the annual rated capacity of the participants which determined both voting and the allowable quota as regulated by the Alliance. Quotas of the members were as follows: Alted, 28.58 percent; French, 21.36 percent; German, 19.65 percent; Swiss, 15.42 percent; and British, 15 percent. In the beginning the Alliance removed excess stocks of the participants by purchasing them. The directors periodically fixed minimum prices on both ingot and fabricated aluminum. If a member was unable to sell the full quota the Alliance stood ready to buy the unsold portion at the minimum price. Unlike some of the previous agreements, this cartel made no express exception of the U.S. market. Indeed it was clear that the restriction by any producer anywhere would necessarily affect the producer's ability to sell, and therefore, to export to the United States.

The net effect of the Alliance on prices was that prices outside the United States began a steady rise, while Alcoa's prices in the United States fell steadily from 22.9¢ in 1931 to 19¢ in 1936. Part of this resulted from the fact that the demand for aluminum was stronger outside the United States as rearmament took place, while domestically this country was still suffering from the aftereffects of the depression.

The Alliance was established for a period of 99 years, but its powers began to be weakened when Germany started its rearmament program and insisted on expansion of production. At first, the members attempted to supply the demands of the German rearmament program, but the Germans insisted on self-sufficiency; and thus, finally, all restrictions were removed from VAW with the understanding that none of the German production would be exported. During the three years from 1933 to 1936, VAW increased capacity by 200 percent while Alcoa's and Alted's capacity remained constant. By the end of 1937 Germany's aluminum capacity exceeded that in the United States, and a year later Germany became the world's leading producer of aluminum. What this meant to the United States is now understood by all, but it is doubtful that the Alcoa executives understood even though through Alted they knew what was going on, for they, like most other citizens of this country, were unaware of the grave threat to this nation's security.

A revision of the 1931 agreement became effective January 1, 1936 after the Germans had been released from production restrictions; but the worldwide boom in armament soon made production restrictions commercially inexpedient, as well as impolitic. After 1938 the Alliance remained comparatively inactive although it was not dissolved.

Meanwhile, the United States remained asleep at the switch until finally the U.S. government in 1940, recognizing the need for increased aluminum production, and long eager to break Alcoa's monopoly, assisted Reynolds Metals in entering the field. How the wartime expansion was accomplished will be the subject of our second problem study. For the moment it is most interesting to note that while Alcoa had been able to raise the domestic price of aluminum from 19¢ to 20¢ in 1939, it suddenly reduced the price to an all-time low in 1940 of 18.7¢ a pound at a time when world demand was pushing prices up in all foreign markets.

The conclusion is that the Aluminum Company of America effectively exercised market control in aluminum in the United States from the time of its organization to the beginning of World War II by a combination of patent control, vertical and horizontal integration, and a series of cartel arrangements.

United States Policy. The Sherman Antitrust Act of 1890 outlawed restraints of trade, monopoly, and attempts to monopolize, as follows:

Section 1. Every contract, combination in the form of a trust or otherwise, or conspiracy, in restraint of trade or commerce among the several states, or with foreign nations, is hereby declared to be illegal . . .

Section 2. Every person who shall monopolize, or attempt to monopolize, or combine or conspire with any other person or persons to monopolize any part of the trade or commerce among the several states, or with foreign nations, shall be deemed guilty of a misdemeanor . . .

During the early stages of its integration, Alcoa's general practice was to exact from sellers of properties, which it acquired, covenants not to compete afterward directly or indirectly with Alcoa. This and other charges resulted in the Justice Department filing a complaint against Alcoa on May 11, 1912 which was settled when Alcoa accepted a consent decree on June 7, 1912 which called for: (1) dropping the restrictive agreements which kept two firms, whose bauxite Alcoa had purchased, from producing aluminum, (2) discontinuing price and other discriminations against competitors including refusal or threat of refusal to deliver raw materials for aluminum production, (3) cancelling the 1908 cartel agreement, and (4) enjoining Alcoa from taking part directly in agreements which had the effect of controlling output or price. We have seen just how effective this latter provision was since five days later Alcoa, through Northern Aluminum Company, signed the 1912 cartel agreement.

In 1914 the Federal Trade Commission Act created a commission to act as a watchdog against unfair trade practices aimed at creating a monopoly and injuring competitors. Also in 1914 the Clayton Act was passed which listed specific unfair and illegal practices, one of which was contained in Section 7 prohibiting the acquisition of stock in competing companies to obtain monopoly powers. The Federal Trade Commission (FTC) brought suit against Alcoa under this provision charging that Alcoa's purchase of controlling stock in Cleveland Products was in violation of the law. The FTC was successful in this action, and Alcoa was ordered to sell its holdings. Nevertheless, Alcoa reacquired Cleveland Products at a sheriff's sale, held to settle the indebtedness of the company which arose in large part out of a supply contract with Alcoa for ingots in quantities and at prices that were ruinous under the World War I price-fixing of aluminum products. The FTC objected to the sale, but strangely enough was overruled by the same judges who had sustained the FTC in the first instance.

Again in 1924, the FTC issued a complaint against Alcoa charging violations of the 1912 consent decree such as discrimination in prices, interfering with competitors' attempt to enlarge operations, delaying shipments to competitors, and other discriminatory practices. However, the Department of Justice cleared Alcoa of the alleged charges in 1926, and the FTC dismissed its complaint in 1930 admitting the charges could not be sustained by the available evidence.

The landmark case against Alcoa was action begun by the Department of Justice in the District Court for the Southern District of New York in 1937. The Justice Department charged violation of both Section 1 and Section 2 of the Sherman Act, to wit:

1. conspiracy with foreign producers to restrain importation of aluminum into the United States, to fix prices, limit production, and to allocate customers of alumina and aluminum; and
2. monopolizing the production and sale of aluminum and aluminum products (including castings, cooking utensils, pistons, extrusions, structural shapes, sheet, cable, foil, and miscellaneous other products), by (a) acquiring bauxite deposits, waterpower sites and plants in excess of its needs, and entering into restrictive agreements designed to prevent potential competitors from obtaining waterpower; and (b) "squeezing" independent fabricators (e.g., Baush) by fixing and maintaining the price differential between ingot and fabricated products at such levels as to suppress and exclude others from the production of aluminum products.

In 1941 District Judge Francis G. Caffey ruled in favor of Alcoa on all charges. Part of Judge Caffey's ruling was based on a calculation that Alcoa's control of the aluminum market was only 33 percent by excluding that part of Alcoa's total production which it fabricated and all secondary aluminum. Another basis was to balance Alcoa's total production fabricated and sold against the sum of imported "virgin" and "secondary" aluminum, in which case Alcoa's share of the market was 64 percent for the period 1929–1938, inclusive. There was no argument about the fact that Alcoa had been the sole producer of primary aluminum ingots; but Alcoa did argue that it had expanded capacity when necessary, had produced aluminum efficiently, had passed these benefits on to consumers in terms of lower prices, and had not profited unduly from these operations. These positions perhaps led to the heart of Judge Caffey's ruling: that mere size, unaccompanied by abuses of power did not violate the Sherman Act. The Judge had a good precedent for such a ruling, for this had been the dictum laid down by the Supreme Court in the U.S. Steel case of 1920 and in the International Harvester case of 1927.

The Justice Department appealed Judge Caffey's decision to the Supreme Court, but no disinterested quorum in the Supreme Court was available as four of the Justices disqualified themselves because of earlier participation in the case before appointment to the court. As a result in June, 1944, Congress passed a law providing that the Supreme Court certify the case to the three senior judges of the appropriate Circuit Court of Appeals as final authority. The court chosen was that of the Second District (New York, Judges Learned Hand, Swan and Augustus Hand).

In 1945, Judge Learned Hand, speaking for the three judges, sustained Judge Caffey on almost all the charges, but held that Alcoa had in fact monopolized the market for primary aluminum. The arguments pertinent to this decision and that with respect to the charge that Alcoa had conspired with foreign producers are most important.

Judge Learned Hand rejected the argument that secondary aluminum should be considered in determining Alcoa's share of the market, and concluded that Alcoa's control over the ingot market must be reckoned at over 90 percent, that being the proportion which its production bears to imported "virgin" ingot; and that percentage was enough to constitute a monopoly. The Judge further concluded that the whole issue as to a fair profit was irrelevant, "for it is no excuse for 'monopolizing' a market that a monopoly has not been used to extract from the consumer more than a 'fair' profit." This act was meant to be interpreted more broadly.

Throughout the history of these antitrust statutes, it has been constantly assumed that one of their purposes was to perpetuate and preserve, for its own sake and in spite of all cost, an organization of industry in small units which can effectively compete with each other. We hold that "Alcoa's" monopoly was the kind covered by Section 2.

What makes Judge Hand's decision a landmark case is the following conclusion with respect to monopoly:

We disregard any question of intent . . . In order to fall within Section 2, the monopolist must have both the power to monopolize and the intent to monopolize. To read the passage as demanding any specific intent makes nonsense out of it, for no monopolist monopolizes unconscious of what he is doing. So here, Alcoa meant to keep, and did keep, that complete and exclusive hold upon the ingot market with which it started. That was to monopolize that market, however innocently it otherwise proceeded. So far as the judgement held that it was not within Section 2, it must be reversed.

Thus, this opinion was a milestone in antitrust history in reversing the established dictum that size must be accompanied by an offense to be a violation. According to Judge Hand, size—meaning market control—was not only evidence of violation, or of potential offense under the Sherman Act, but was also the essence of the offense.

With respect to the charge that Alcoa had conspired with foreign producers, the court found that the cartel arrangements of Aluminium Limited and foreign producers affected imports into the United States and therefore violated the Sherman Act. It was held, however, that Alcoa had not participated in the cartel, and therefore could not be held responsible for the import restrictions; however, interestingly enough Judge Hand enjoined Alted, even though it was a foreign corporation, from further participation in cartels.

The U.S. government had originally requested that Alcoa, if found guilty as charged, be dissolved; but the court referred to the fact that additional aluminum facilities had been built during the war which in part were under government ownership and that the Surplus Property Act of 1944 provided that such property should be disposed of in such a manner as "to discourage monopolistic practices and strengthen the competitive position of small business concerns in an economy of free enterprise . . ." Thus the case was turned back to the District Court with instruction to withhold remedial measures until after the disposal of the government's surplus aluminum plants.

In 1947, Alcoa petitioned the District Court for a decree that the company had ceased to monopolize primary aluminum production on the grounds that competitive conditions prevailed. The government opposed this move in a petition filed in 1948, and requested the court to divest Alcoa of enough plants to create effective competition. Judge Knox ruled in 1950 that Alcoa still had the power to expand and exclude competitors; but he denied the government's petition for divesture on the grounds that effective competition depended upon countervailing power in the market, and reducing the power of Alcoa through dissolution would hamper rather than promote competition. The only punitive measure that Judge Knox called for was to deal with the fiction that existed in the separate existence of Alcoa and Alted. To get at this problem the court required certain large stockholders of Alcoa to divest themselves of either their Alcoa stock or their Aluminium Limited stock. However, the court did extend jurisdiction in the case for five years.

In June 1957, the government petitioned for another 5-year extension, but was refused by District Court Judge Cashin, who ruled that the new entrants into aluminum production in the United States could effectively compete with Alcoa, whose relative share of the market had declined appreciably.

Conclusion. The case of Alcoa is a classic example of market control by a monopoly, and of the United States progressively unsuccessful attempts to deal with this problem through legal means until the stage had

been set for the entrance of other firms which existed because the government aided additional firms to enter the market during World War II and
the postwar period. One question worthy of discussion is whether, in view
of the court's ringing denunciation of the monopoly, the punishment fit
the crime. One argument is that divesture of some of Alcoa's facilities
would have led to a loss of technical efficiency. On the other hand, a student of the structure of American industry has concluded: "It is altogether
surprising that a company which had monopolized the aluminum industry
for almost fifty years was allowed to remain intact, the restructuring of the
industry to be accomplished by 'indirection.' "[2] How this restructuring
took place is the subject of our next problem.

Growth

In 1940 the writer was present at a conference of the National Defense Advisory Commission when a question was put to industry officials:
Do we have enough aluminum to provide for wartime requirements? The
answer was "Yes!" How wrong it was. Even though at that time the figure
of 50,000 required military aircraft per year was being tossed about, no
one took time before that quick answer of "Yes" to multiply an estimated
number of pounds of aluminum by 50,000 and then to compare the result
with aluminum capacity. Even with only that one requirement the answer
would have been "NO." Aluminum's accelerated growth began with World
War II, and national policies related to growth have been closely associated with military requirements.

Facts Bearing on the Problem. Before World War II, U.S. national
policy in aluminum was directed unsuccessfully toward breaking up the
monopolistic position of the Aluminum Company of America. In 1940–
1941 it became apparent that the bauxite and aluminum industries required a large expansion to meet wartime needs.

In bauxite, the U.S. Bureau of Mines and the Federal Geological
Survey launched an extensive exploration program that resulted in a
substantial increase in known reserves of ore in Arkansas. In addition, the
government began to stockpile Arkansas bauxite. These activities resulted
in expansion of mining operations, and Arkansas production increased to
over 6 million tons in 1943.

In aluminum, the government embarked on a program that resulted
in greatly increased imports from Canada, and in a program of expansion
of domestic productive capacity that incorporated decentralization of
ownership as part of its policy. The initial step on the part of the government was to make substantial loans through the Reconstruction Finance
Corporation to the Reynolds Metals Company, which had been a producer

[2] Walter Adams, *The Structure of American Industry,* New York, Macmillan,
1961, p. 197.

of aluminum foil. This assistance, as we have previously noted, enabled Reynolds to build a combined alumina-aluminum plant at Listerhill, Alabama and a reduction plant at Longview, Washington. Reynolds also entered the bauxite mining business in the United States, and later acquired bauxite reserves in Haiti, the Dominican Republic, and Jamaica. As a result, there were in 1941, just prior to this country's entry into the war, three alumina and seven aluminum plants in the United States as previously listed in Table 11.7. The aggregate capacity of these plants was 426,000 tons of aluminum, of which Alcoa controlled 345,000 tons and Reynolds 81,000.

Thus a start had been made, but it soon became apparent that this capacity would be totally inadequate for wartime needs. Since private interests were reluctant to expand capacity that might not be needed at the end of the war, it was decided that the government would undertake the risk of ownership while relying on private enterprise to build and operate the required capacity. As a result, the government constructed two commercial and four experimental alumina plants and nine commercial-sized aluminum plants. The commercial alumina plants were located at Hurricane Creek, Arkansas and Baton Rouge, Louisiana; and the nine aluminum plants were located as shown in Table 11.8.

In initiating this program the government's policy to encourage a more competitive industry ran into the overriding policy of the need to have the plants built quickly and operated efficiently by experienced producers. As a result, Alcoa became the operator of all the new government plants built during the war, except for one small plant that was operated by the Olin Corporation at Tacoma, Washington. On the other hand, Reynolds Metals owned and operated during the war the alumina and two aluminum plants which were constructed with government financial aid.

The net effect of the wartime expansion program was that the total U.S. aluminum capacity in 1944, as shown in Table 11.8, reached 1,163,-500 tons, or over three times what it was in 1941. This pre-war capacity of 345,000 tons, one will remember, also included Reynolds' 81,000 tons. A most significant fact about this aggregate 1944 capacity was that over half of it was government-owned; that is, the capacity of the government-owned plants exceeded the total capacity of the plants owned by Alcoa and Reynolds.

This successful threefold expansion of aluminum capacity and production during World War II and an overestimation of the aluminum requirements for military aircraft during 1945 created a problem during the early post-war years of disposal of surplus government-owned plants. The Surplus Property Act of 1944 established the ground rules of national policy for the aluminum plants, for all government-owned plants were to be disposed of in order to: (1) give maximum aid in the reestablishment of a peacetime economy of free independent enterprise, (2) foster the development of the maximum of independent operators, (3) discourage monopolistic practices, and (4) strengthen the position of small business concerns.

TABLE 11.8

United States Aluminum Reduction Plants, Operator and Capacity, 1944

Ownership and location of plant	Operator	Capacity (short tons)
Alcoa-owned		
Niagara Falls, N.Y.	Alcoa	21,000
Massena, N.Y.	Alcoa	82,000
Alcoa, Tenn.	Alcoa	170,500
Badin, N.C.	Alcoa	55,500
Vancouver, Wash.	Alcoa	86,000
Total Alcoa-owned		415,000
Reynolds-owned		
Longview, Wash.	Reynolds	31,000
Listerhill, Ala.	Reynolds	50,000
Total Reynolds-owned		81,000
Government-owned		
Jones Mill, Ark.	Alcoa	70,500
Los Angeles, Calif.	Alcoa	89,000
Modesto (Riverbank), Calif.	Alcoa	54,000
Troutdale, Ore.	Alcoa	70,500
Burlington, N.J.	Alcoa	53,000
Maspeth (Queens, L.I.), N.Y.	Alcoa	149,500
Massena (St. Lawrence), N.Y.	Alcoa	52,500
Meade (Spokane), Wash.	Alcoa	108,000
Total Alcoa-operated		647,000
Tacoma, Wash.	Olin Corp.	20,500
Total Government-owned		667,500
Grand total		1,163,500

Source: United States Tariff Commission, Olin T. Mouzon, _International Resources and National Policy_, New York, Harper & Row, 1959.

There were several factors which complicated the disposal of the aluminum plants in line with the recommended policy:

1. All but one of the plants had been operated by Alcoa, and the Surplus Property Board could not sell the plants to many independent firms in-

capable of competing with Alcoa. Thus, the Board had to create new producers.

2. Bauxite reserves were under the control of Alcoa and Alted, although Reynolds had gotten a foot in the door.
3. The government-built alumina plant at Hurricane Creek, Arkansas was based on the use of the newly-developed combination process which made possible the use of low-grade domestic bauxite reserves. Alcoa held the patent to the combination process which was the key to the use of the plant.
4. Some of the plants were so poorly located and had such high power costs as to make them uneconomical.
5. An assured supply of electric power at rates which did not place new producers at a disadvantage with Alcoa's generated power was necessary.
6. Leases held by Alcoa on government plants were not due to expire until 1947 and 1948; which meant that the entire disposal program would be delayed unless Alcoa gave up the leases.

The solution to this many-sided problem began to unravel with the continued interest of Reynolds Metals in the aluminum industry, and with the appearance of the Henry J. Kaiser enterprises, which had effectively and aggressively worked on many industrial fronts for government contracts during World War II. Kaiser formed Permanete Metals Corporation, later renamed Kaiser Aluminum and Chemical Corporation.

This was followed by the promise of access on the part of the new entrants to the government's bauxite reserves. With the dissolution suit hanging over the head of Alcoa, the government succeeded in inducing Alcoa to license its patents covering combination process to the government free of charge and unencumbered. Flexible power contracts were made available on public power through the TVA and the Bonneville Power Administration; and finally, Alcoa's leases were cancelled on technical grounds.

With these problems resolved, the government-owned plants were disposed of as shown in Table 11.9.

The net effect of the disposal of the plants on the distribution of aluminum capacity can be tabulated from Tables 11.8 and 11.9. Alcoa's capacity was 415,000 tons, but when the Niagara Falls and other uneconomic portions were closed it stood at 325,000 tons. To Reynolds' capacity of 81,000 tons should be added 141,000 tons for a total of 222,000 tons and Kaiser acquired a total of 128,500 tons. The total immediate post-war aluminum capacity was 675,500 tons in 1946. The alumina plant at Hurricane Creek, Arkansas gave Reynolds additional integrated facilities along with the two aluminum plants at Jones Mills, Arkansas and Troutdale, Oregon. In addition, Reynolds acquired three government-built fabricating plants at Listerhill, Alabama, Chicago, Illinois, and Grand Rapids, Michigan. Kaiser's integrated facilities began with the alumina plant at

Baton Rouge, Louisiana, included the aluminum plants at Spokane and Tacoma, Washington, and were extended to include a government-owned fabricating plant at Spokane, Washington.

TABLE 11.9
Disposition of Government Alumina and Aluminum Plants
(Short tons)

Type of plant and location	Capacity (Short tons)	Wartime operator	Sold or leased to
Alumina plants			
Hurricane Creek, Ark.	777,500	Alcoa	Reynolds
Baton Rouge, La.	500,000	Alcoa	Kaiser
Aluminum reduction plants			
Jones Mill, Ark.	70,500	Alcoa	Reynolds
Los Angeles, Calif.	89,000	Alcoa	Cannibalized
Modesto (Riverbank), Calif.	54,000	Alcoa	Cannibalized
Troutdale, Ore.	70,500	Alcoa	Reynolds
Burlington, N.J.	53,000	Alcoa	Cannibalized
Maspeth (Queens, L.I.), N.Y.	149,500	Alcoa	Cannibalized
Massena (St. Lawrence), N.Y.	52,500	Alcoa	Standby
Meade (Spokane), Wash.	108,000	Alcoa	Kaiser
Tacoma, Wash.	20,500	Olin	Kaiser

SOURCE: Data from U.S. Bureau of Mines.

In summary, it can be said that the disposition of the aluminum plants left the aluminum reduction capacity distributed as follows: Alcoa, 48 percent; Reynolds, 33 percent; and Kaiser, 19 percent. Thus, the goals of redistribution had been accomplished and the market control power of Alcoa had been substantially weakened.

The market conditions for entry of the new firms turned out to be better than had been expected. Actually the haunting fear of an inadequate postwar demand, due to expanded capacity and the loss of the military aircraft market, probably turned out to the advantage of the industry. During 1945 and 1946, other nonferrous metals were in short supply so that aluminum at that time began to capture old markets for copper and to develop new markets and consumer acceptance. Thus what appeared to be a disadvantage for the industry, probably resulted in stimulating postwar growth. The peak production of 920,000 tons in 1943 was down to 410,000 in 1945, but by 1948 the growth was underway, with a production of 622,000 tons.

The pattern of the aluminum industry was unchanged from 1946 to the beginning of the Korean War.

Policy for Growth During the Korean War. The outbreak of the Korean War and the decision of the government to establish a defense economy resulted in passage of the Defense Production Act of 1950. The need for large expansion of the U.S. aluminum industry and increased supplies of bauxite became evident. An expansion program was planned to create enough new processing capacity to meet essential civilian and military requirements, and to leave a surplus for stockpiling. At the start of the program, the capacity of new facilities required to meet these demands was variously estimated at 500,000 to 1,000,000 tons of primary aluminum a year. The policy agreed upon in advance was that expansion during this period would differ from that in World War II in that none of the facilities would be owned by the government and in that all facilities would be located near electric power sources which would permit economic operation of the plants in peacetime.

The Office of Defense Mobilization (ODM) started in 1950 what has been designated as round one of the expansion program. In 1950, production was about 800,000 tons of aluminum, and the expansion goal for the first round, in 1951, was 446,000 tons; for the second round, in 1952, the goal was 231,000 tons. To achieve this expansion the government offered the following incentives: (1) "certificates of necessity" that allowed fast tax write-offs for depreciation; (2) government-guaranteed loans to insure and speed the companies' expansions; and (3) guaranteed markets, under which all aluminum that the companies could not sell would be bought by the government for the strategic stockpile. Again, in an attempt to break up Alcoa's position, these incentives were given only to Reynolds and Kaiser.

Part one of this program involved increased alumina production and bauxite. Table 11.10 shows that as a result of this program the alumina capacity of the United States was nearly doubled. This increased the need for bauxite. In July, 1951 the government agreed to contribute funds for approved bauxite-exploration projects. Probably, as a result of the search for bauxite during World War II, requests for such assistance were few. This led to increased dependence on foreign sources of bauxite. Both Kaiser and Reynolds met most of their increased bauxite requirements with Jamaican ore. Part of the funds to develop this great reserve of ore were supplied to Reynolds by the government before enactment of the Defense Production Act (DPA). Alcoa increased shipments from Surinam to meet its expanded needs.

Part two of the program was aimed at the major objectives of increasing aluminum capacity as spelled out in the objectives for round one and round two. How well these goals were translated into plans and expansion can be seen clearly from Table 11.11 on page 469. Total aluminum capacity in 1949 was 727,075, only slightly in excess of what it was in 1946. The capacity goal for round one and round two called for an increase of

677,000 tons. Actual planned expansion was only 663,000 tons, but when the previous expansion under way in 1950 is taken into consideration, the actual total capacity achieved in 1955 was 1,523,000 tons—795,000 tons greater than 1949 capacity. Thus capacity was more than doubled.

TABLE 11.10

Estimated Annual Alumina Capacity of the United States
(Short tons)

	End of 1950	Increase, 1951-1953	Total
Aluminum Co. of America:			
Mobile, Ala.	602,250	273,750	876,000
East St. Louis, Ill.	182,500	146,000	328,500
Bauxite, Ark.		401,500	401,500
Total Alcoa	784,750	821,250	1,606,000
Reynolds Metals Co.:			
Hurricane Creek, Ark.	521,000	209,000	730,000
La Quinta, Tex.		365,000	365,000
Total Reynolds	521,000	574,000	1,095,000
Kaiser Aluminum & Chemical Corp.:			
Baton Rouge, La.	440,000	360,000	800,000
Total	1,745,750	1,755,250	3,501,000

SOURCE: U.S. Bureau of Mines, *Mineral Facts and Problems*, Washington, D.C., 1956.

Rounds one and two were hardly under way when in 1952 the ODM promoted a third round. In this round ODM wanted to bring smaller firms into the industry. Actually, as noted in Table 11.11, Anaconda Aluminum Company had already entered as a fourth producer. *Business Week* of August 13, 1955 described the progress of the third round as follows:

This time it wanted to bring smaller outfits into the industry. But this time there were complications; some of the smaller companies lost interest, were caught up in squabbles, or were stricken by financing troubles.

Week after week through this summer [1955], ODM has been trying to decide whether to offer more incentives. It's likely to make up its mind soon.

WIDE MOVES—Meanwhile, the whole face of the industry is changing. The big three are finding that other companies are getting deeper and deeper into aluminum.

Anaconda has moved in. Next week it dedicates its $65-million primary aluminum plant at Columbia Falls, Mont., adding 60,000 tons of new capacity. This expansion is part of the government-sponsored second round.

And Aluminum Co. of Canada, which must be figured as a big factor in the U.S. market, has 91,000 tons of new capacity coming in between now and the end of 1956 from its Kitimat plant. (By the end of 1959, Alcan reckons to have Kitimat's capacity stepped up to 331,000 tons.)

DELAYS—So it's clear that the market is there for the expansion that's now under way. The question that's holding up ODM's decision probably is: How far should government incentives for expansion go?

It's a question that has produced explosive arguments with ODM. One side—backed by Treasury Secy. George M. Humphrey—argues that the government has done enough, that most companies applying for fast tax write-off are big enough to handle expansion on their own. The other side argues that aluminum must be urged to expand because of the great demand for it.

Beyond this row there's the noisy bitter tussle between the independent fabricators and the big producers. The independent's cry is that the big producers have been giving them short shrift on supplies.

But out of all the strong words shot back and forth only one thing has come clear: There just isn't enough aluminum this year for everybody.

Secretary Humphrey won his argument, and in September, 1955 new "certificates" for rapid amortization were halted.

At the beginning of 1956, a continued shortage of aluminum, due to the growth of demand, set off the third round of expansion which promised at the outset to add 850,000 tons to U.S. capacity. This would mean not only another increase in U.S. capacity but also physically more tonnage than was added in 1951–1955.

The predictions were for the following additions by the big three:

Alcoa	240,000 tons—up 34 percent
Reynolds	145,000 tons—up 34 percent
Kaiser	226,000 tons—up 52 percent
Total	611,000 tons

This round would include four new companies:

Olin-Mathieson	60,000 tons
Harvey Machine	54,000 tons
Revere Copper and Brass	60,000 tons
St. Joseph Lead and Pittsburgh Consolidation	66,000 tons [abandoned]
Total	240,000 tons

Olin-Mathieson and Harvey Machine had holdover "certificates," but only Olin-Mathieson of the new companies had made arrangements for raw materials. In late 1956 Olin-Mathieson and Revere Copper and Brass

TABLE 11.11

Estimated Annual Primary Aluminum Capacity of the United States
(Short tons)

	End of 1949[a]	End of 1950[b]	Expansion planned in 1950-1951[c]	Total
Aluminum Co. of America:				
Alcoa, Tenn.	145,300	145,500		145,500
Badin, N.C.	33,850	43,500		43,500
Massena, N.Y.	57,500	127,000		127,000
St. Lawrence, N.Y.				
Vancouver, Wash.	76,100	76,000		76,000
Point Comfort, Tex.	57,000	57,000	35,000	92,000
Wenatchee, Wash.			85,000	85,000
Rockdale, Tex.			85,000	85,000
Total Alcoa	369,750	449,000	205,000	654,000
Reynolds Metals Co.:				
Jones Mills, Ark.	73,850	74,000[d]	23,000	97,000
Troutdale, Oreg.	72,000	76,000[d]	2,000	78,000
Listerhill, Ala.	48,600	50,000		50,000
Longview, Wash.	30,500	31,000	20,000	51,000
San Patricio, Tex.			80,000	80,000
Arkadelphia, Ark.			55,000	55,000
Total Reynolds	224,950	231,000	180,000	411,000
Kaiser Aluminum & Chemical Co.:				
Spokane, Wash.	108,125	155,000	20,000	175,000
Tacoma, Wash.	24,250	25,000	8,000	33,000
Chalmette, La.			200,000	200,000
Total Kaiser	132,375	180,000	228,000	408,000
Anaconda Aluminum Co.: Columbia Falls, Mont.			50,000	50,000
Total	727,075	860,000	663,000	1,523,000

a Represents economic capacity, having reference to the availability and price of electrical energy.
b Economic capacity plus capacity requiring high-cost power.
  c Data represent capacities as "scheduled" in the expansion program and may differ from "actual" capacities as determined by production. All of this new capacity was installed between 1951 and 1955.
  d Does not include capacity available from programmed expansion.
Source: U.S. Bureau of Mines, *Mineral Facts and Problems*, Washington, D.C., 1956.

formed Olin-Revere Metals (Ormet) after they found that, by pooling, the same investment capacity could be increased by 50 percent from 120,000 to 180,000. Olin was to get 120,000 tons and Revere 60,000 tons of this production.

What were the results of round three? The plans were not followed as closely as in rounds one and two because some of the initial plans described above were altered, but the results were explosive. Once the snowball of expansion got rolling, there were indeed four new companies added to the number of aluminum producers which resulted in the structure of the aluminum industry previously shown in Figure 11.3, with a total installed capacity of 2,762,600 tons—over 1,225,000 tons greater than at the end of round two, and more than a 50 percent greater increase than was anticipated at the start of the round.

Thus the aluminum industry accepted the challenge of growth. The Korean War incentives were a tremendous energizing force for expansion; but growth continued even after the incentives were removed.

Conclusions. One net effect of the government's participation in the Korean expansion program was the accumulation of a large stockpile of aluminum which reached a total of 1,508,087 tons on June 1, 1964, and stood as shown in Table 11.12 on September 30, 1965.

TABLE 11.12
Stockpiles of Aluminum and Indicated Surplus
(Short tons)

	As of Sept. 30, 1965
National Stockpile	1,127,197
Supplemental Stockpile	0
DPA Inventory	764,168
Total	1,891,365
Stockpile goal[1]	450,000
Surplus	1,441,365

1 Revised in 1963 from 1,200,000 tons.
SOURCE: U.S. Office of Emergency Planning.

The excess of aluminum was acquired under the Korean War purchase program, principally through purchase contracts which resulted in total deliveries over the duration of the program of 875,651 tons. The last of the shipments was made by Harvey in 1963 under a supply contract negotiated in 1950–1952. Alcoa, Kaiser, and Reynolds also made deliveries under the guaranteed program. The 1,508,000 tons of excess aluminum was equivalent to approximately a seven-month supply, and thus loomed as a potential threat to the market.

Another net effect of the expansion program was that it galloped ahead at a faster rate than growth in consumption; and the industry found itself in a position it had long tried to avoid—overexpansion of capacity. As a result, the new as well as the major companies had hard-sledding under increasingly competitive conditions—the price of aluminum fell from a high of 28.1¢ a pound in 1958 to a low of 22.5¢ a pound at the end of 1962. Not until 1964 did consumption begin to catch up with capacity, and only then did the aluminum industry begin to draft cautious plans for further growth.

Two interesting facets of the post-Korean growth experience deserve careful observation in the future. In view of the changed structure of the industry: Can overexpansion of capacity be avoided? What will be the price policy followed?

First, in any industry where the capital inputs are extremely large due to the size of the plant, overinvestment is likely to take place because the marginal doses of input and resultant production must exceed the marginal increase in consumption. With one or two firms in a monopolistic or oligopolistic position, the problem of avoiding overinvestment is likely to be difficult enough. With more firms in the industry trying to share in growth and each firm building a huge new facility to capture the increase in consumption, the question is whether the industry can expand in an orderly fashion. The conclusion is not at hand; but the opinion of the industry appears to be that the "overcapacity wringer" of the 1950's has to be avoided, and that the growth policy of the future should be "to expand gradually, in step with the market."

Second, what price policy will be followed as a result of the growth and changed industry structure is another unknown. Early indications were that Alcoa would attempt to continue its price leadership, if not its market control. Ample evidence was at hand in 1964 and 1965 when consumption began to catch up with capacity and there was an upward pressure on price. Alcoa resisted price advances in aluminum ingot which had eased up to 23¢ at the beginning of 1964, but at the same time it was aggressively raising mill product prices. What were the motives? Two are worthy of suggestion since they are related both to the market control and growth problems.

1. Holding ingot price down and advancing mill product prices is good economic strategy for Alcoa since it sells only a small portion of aluminum as ingot and a very large portion of mill products. But most important such a policy is also good political strategy in reversing its often charged antitrust violation of a "squeeze" on independent fabricators.

2. Holding ingot price down might also be good strategy to restrict

new entrants into the aluminum industry, and thus help control growth in capacity and structure. Indeed, as previously indicated, the industry as a whole may attempt to limit new entrants by lower prices with the hope that such a price policy will also enhance market expansion and resultant economies to established integrated producers.

Finally, the U.S. government made it crystal clear in November, 1965, that the policy was to maintain a very watchful eye on aluminum prices. The major weapon of control was the stockpile which at that time had a surplus of 1,441,365 tons of which 500,000 tons could be disposed of without Congressional approval. The new policy was dramatically initiated, for when industry members all announced a ½¢ per pound increase in the price of aluminum ingots to 25¢, the government announced a sale of 300,000 tons of aluminum from the stockpile. One by one the companies rescinded the price increase. Whether this is an appropriate government action is highly debatable, especially in view of the new element of competition that existed in the industry and the real need of the industry to maintain prices as low as possible consistent with a reasonable return on equity. In 1964 the aluminum industry's return on capital was 4.9 percent and for other industries 11.2 percent. The government's position was that the price increase *was not necessary* and that the proposed government action *was necessary* to counter inflationary tendencies. *The Wall Street Journal's* position was that at best this was a case of the pot calling the kettle black in view of the government's own inflationary monetary and fiscal policies (low interest rates and deficit spending), and at worst the move was "disruptive of the economic process, since under control prices cannot perform their function in the market economy."

In aluminum, as in the case of steel three years earlier, the U.S. government again demonstrated a policy of pressure to interfere with prices established in the market place. What the long-range implications of this type of government intervention are for business and private investment can only be conjectural. But if private enterprise, which is the keystone of this nation's industrial capacity and potential, is to continue to flourish, management must have a measure of freedom of control over its actions, to insure a return on investment sufficient to attract continued investment which is so necessary for sustained growth in the U.S. economy.

SUMMARY

The aluminum industry is representative of the light metal age. Aluminum's advantageous properties have brought about a sustained growth in consumption of the metal. Except for a few years immediately before World War II, the United States has been the world's leading producer of aluminum. The capacity of the industry expanded sharply under the impetus of World War II and the Korean hostilities with significant aid from government funds and incentives. From 1888 to 1940 Alcoa was the only domestic producer of primary aluminum. At the end of World War II there were three producers, and by 1965 there were eight producers. Up until the end of World War II the government's policy had been directed toward breaking up the market control of Alcoa. Unable to do this through antitrust measures, the government successfully combined a policy of promoting growth of this strategic metal with one of restructuring the industry by actively aiding new entrants. This restructured industry is likely to be more competitive, and resultant price policies should lead to further growth in the use of the metal. Finally, it should be noted that aluminum is still a strategic metal for the production of which this country is highly dependent on the importation of the basic raw material—bauxite. A recommended strategic policy is an adequate stockpile, diversified sources of foreign bauxite, and further intensive research in the use of lower grade reserves with the knowledge that aluminum is the most abundant metallic element in the crust of the earth.

Resources are functional and relative to man's wants and technology. Surely in the case of aluminum with its absolute abundance and relative scarcity, we need have fewer worries about the inadequacies of the United States resource position than with certain other minerals. The development of the combination process during World War II is a classic illustration of the functional resource concept whereby man's increasing wants developed a new technology to overcome the resistances of high silica content and push back the frontier of available aluminum resources.

In the future man must look to technology as the indispensable finder, developer, and multiplier of natural resources to meet the expanding needs of industry in a growing economy.

SELECTED REFERENCES

"Aluminum," *Resources for Freedom*, Vol. II, *The Outlook for Key Commodities*, Washington, D.C., June, 1952, pp. 65–73.

"Aluminum Demand Up 100% by 1965 . . . Where All the Metal Is Going," *Business Week*, March 30, 1957, pp. 190 ff.

"Aluminum's Paradox in Prices," *Business Week*, February 1, 1964, p. 21.

"Aluminum's Third Round Is On," *Business Week*, August 13, 1955, pp. 32 ff.

Bart, Peter, "Aluminum Industry Enters '61 Burdened With Overcapacity," *The New York Times*, January 15, 1961, Section 3, p. 1 ff.

Heindl, R. A., "Aluminum," in *Mineral Facts and Problems*, Bureau of Mines Bulletin 585, Washington, D.C., 1960, pp. 27–41.

Lanzillotti, Robert F., "The Aluminum Industry," in Walter Adams, *The Structure of American Industry*, New York, Macmillan, 1961, pp. 185–232.

Metals—Aluminum—Basic Analysis, Standard & Poor's Industry Surveys, New York, Standard & Poor, 1964, and later editions.

A Special Study on the Aluminum Industry, New York, Merrill Lynch, Pierce, Fenner & Smith, February, 1964.

Stamper, John K., "Aluminum," Preprint for U.S. Bureau of Mines *Minerals Yearbook 1963*, Washington, D.C., 1964.

Stocking, George W., and Myron W. Watkins, "The Aluminum Alliance," in *Cartels in Action*, New York, The Twentieth Century Fund, 1964, pp. 216–273.

United States v. Aluminum Company of America (44 F Supp. 97), opinion of Judge Caffey, March 12, 1941.

United States v. Aluminum Company of America (148 F 2d 416), opinion of Judge Hand, March 12, 1945.

United States v. Aluminum Company of America (91 F Supp. 333), opinion of Judge Knox, June 2, 1950.

United States v. Aluminum Company of America (153 F Supp. 132), opinion of Judge Cashin, June 28, 1957.

Wallace, Donald W., *Market Control in the Aluminum Industry*, Cambridge, Harvard University Press, 1937.

Williams, Lloyd R., and John W. Stamper, "Bauxite," Preprint for U.S. Bureau of Mines *Minerals Yearbook 1963*, Washington, D.C., 1964.

Wilmont, R. C., "Alumina and Bauxite," in *Mineral Facts and Problems*, Bureau of Mines Bulletin 585, Washington, D.C., 1960, pp. 15–26.

INDEX